OCR BIOLOGY 2

A-Level Year 2   Student Workbook

OCR BIOLOGY 2

A-Level Year 2 **Student Workbook**

Meet the Writing Team

Tracey
Senior Author

Tracey Greenwood
I have been writing resources for students since 1993. I have a Ph.D in biology, specialising in lake ecology and I have taught both graduate and undergraduate biology.

Lissa
Author

Lissa Bainbridge-Smith
I worked in industry in a research and development capacity for 8 years before joining BIOZONE in 2006. I have an M.Sc from Waikato University.

Kent
Author

Kent Pryor
I have a BSc from Massey University majoring in zoology and ecology and taught secondary school biology and chemistry for 9 years before joining BIOZONE as an author in 2009.

Richard
Founder & CEO

Richard Allan
I have had 11 years experience teaching senior secondary school biology. I have a Masters degree in biology and founded BIOZONE in the 1980s after developing resources for my own students.

Thanks to:

The staff at BIOZONE, including Gemma Conn and Julie Fairless for design and graphics support, Paolo Curray for IT support, Debbie Antoniadis and Tim Lind for office handling and logistics, and the BIOZONE sales team.

Cover Photograph

White-backed vulture *Gyps africanus* in Kenya's Maasai Mara. This species is the most widespread vulture in Africa although populations are rapidly declining and it is now absent from much of its former range. A major threat to survival is the widespread use of the anti-inflammatory drug diclofenac, which is used to treat livestock. It is toxic to the birds, which ingest it to lethal levels when they scavenge carcasses.

PHOTO: Aurora Photos/Offset

First edition 2015

ISBN 978-1-927309-14-8

Copyright © 2015 Richard Allan
Published by BIOZONE International Ltd

Printed by REPLIKA PRESS PVT LTD using paper produced from renewable and waste materials

Purchases of this workbook may be made direct from the publisher:

BIOZONE Learning Media (UK) Ltd.

Telephone local:	01283 530 366
Telephone international:	+44 1283 530 366
Fax local:	01283 831 900
Fax international:	+44 1283 831 900
Email:	sales@biozone.co.uk

www.**BIOZONE**.co.uk

Contents

Activity is marked: • to be done;   ☑ when completed

Contents

Activity is marked: ● to be done; ✓ when completed

Contents

Activity is marked: • to be done; ✓ when completed

Using This Workbook

This first edition of OCR Biology 2 has been specifically written to meet the content and skills requirements of A Level OCR Biology. Learning outcomes in the introduction to each chapter provide you with a concise guide to the knowledge and skills requirements for each module. Each learning outcome is matched to the activity or activities addressing it. Practical Activity Groups are identified in the chapter introductions by a code (PAG) and supported by activities designed to provide background and familiarity with apparatus, techniques, experimental design, and interpretation of results. A wide range of activities will help you to build on what you already know, explore new topics, work collaboratively, and practise your skills in data handling and interpretation. We hope that you find the workbook valuable and that you make full use of its features.

▶ The outline of the chapter structure below will help you to navigate through the material in each chapter.

Introduction
- A check list of the knowledge and skills requirements for the chapter.
- A list of key terms.

Activities
- The KEY IDEA provides your focus for the activity.
- Annotated diagrams help you understand the content.
- Questions review the content of the page.

Review
- Create your own summary for review.
- Hints help you to focus on what is important.
- Your summary will consolidate your understanding of the content in the chapter.

Literacy
- Activities are based on, but not restricted to, the introductory key terms list.
- Several types of activities test your understanding of the concepts and biological terms in the chapter.

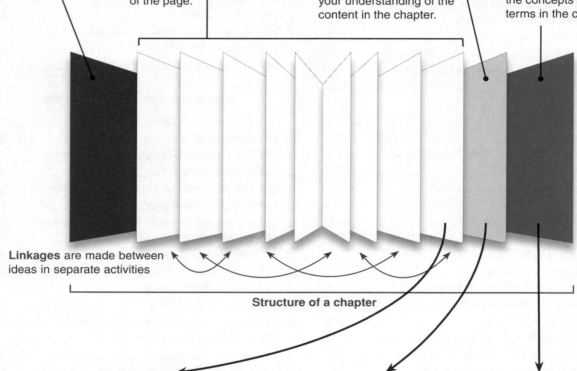

Linkages are made between ideas in separate activities

Structure of a chapter

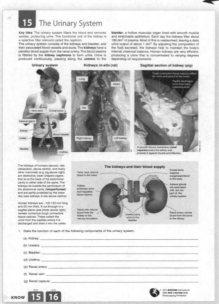

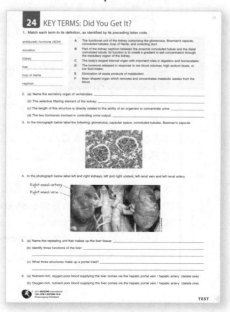

▶ Understanding the activity coding system and making use of the online material identified will enable you to get the most out of this resource. The chapter content is structured to build knowledge and skills but this structure does not necessarily represent a strict order of treatment. Be guided by your teacher, who will assign activities as part of a wider programme of independent and group-based work.

Look out for these features and know how to use them:

The **chapter introduction** provides you with a summary of the knowledge and skills requirements for the topic, phrased as a set of learning outcomes. Use the check boxes to identify and mark off the points as you complete them. The chapter introduction also provides you with a list of key terms for the chapter, from which you can construct your own glossary as you work through the activities.

The **activities** form most of this workbook. They are numbered sequentially and each has a task code identifying the skill emphasised. Each activity has a short introduction with a key idea identifying the main message of the page. Most of the information is associated with pictures and diagrams, and your understanding of the content is reviewed through the questions. Some of the activities involve modelling and group work.

Free response questions allow you to use the information provided to answer questions about the content of the activity, either directly or by applying the same principles to a new situation. In some cases, an activity will assume understanding of prior content.

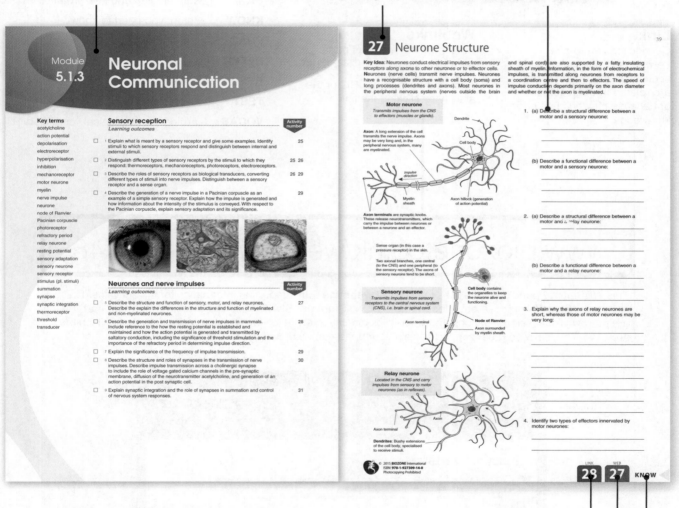

LINK tabs at the bottom of the activity page identify activities that are related in that they build on content or apply the same principles to a new situation.

WEB tabs at the bottom of the activity page alert the reader to the **Weblinks** resource, which provides external, online support material for the activity, usually in the form of an animation, video clip, photo library, or quiz. Bookmark the Weblinks page (see next page) and visit it frequently as you progress through the workbook.

A **TASK CODE** on the page tab identifies the type of activity. For example, is it primarily information-based (KNOW), or does it involve modelling (PRAC) or data handling (DATA)? A full list of codes is given on the following page but the codes themselves are relatively self explanatory.

Using the Tab System

The tab system is a useful system for quickly identifying related content and online support. Links generally refer to activities that build on the information in the activity in depth or extent. In the example below, the weblink 38 describes the key stages in insulin signalling. Activity 3 reviews cell signalling by hormones and 40 describes the effects of a lack of insulin (diabetes type 1). Sometimes, a link will reflect on material that has been covered earlier as a reminder for important terms that have already been defined or for a formula that may be required to answer a question. The weblinks code is always the same as the activity number on which it is cited. On visiting the weblink page (below), find the number and it will correspond to one or more external websites providing a video or animation of some aspect of the activity's content. Occasionally, the weblink may provide a bank of photographs where images are provided in colour, e.g. for plant and animal histology.

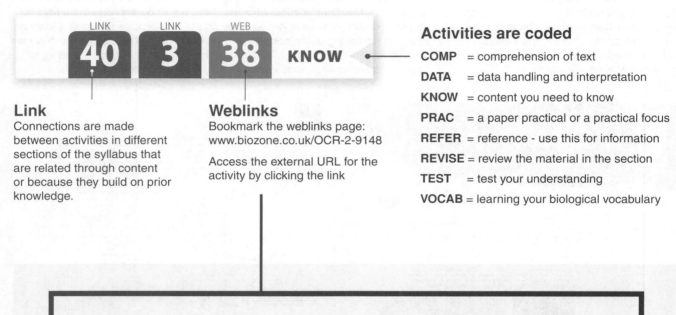

Link
Connections are made between activities in different sections of the syllabus that are related through content or because they build on prior knowledge.

Weblinks
Bookmark the weblinks page:
www.biozone.co.uk/OCR-2-9148

Access the external URL for the activity by clicking the link

Activities are coded

COMP	= comprehension of text
DATA	= data handling and interpretation
KNOW	= content you need to know
PRAC	= a paper practical or a practical focus
REFER	= reference - use this for information
REVISE	= review the material in the section
TEST	= test your understanding
VOCAB	= learning your biological vocabulary

www.biozone.co.uk/weblink/OCR-2-9148

This WEBLINKS page provides links to **external websites** with supporting information for the activities. These sites are distinct from those provided in the BIOLINKS area of BIOZONE's web site. For the most part, they are narrowly focussed animations and video clips directly relevant to some aspect of the activity on which they are cited. They provide great support to help your understanding of basic concepts.

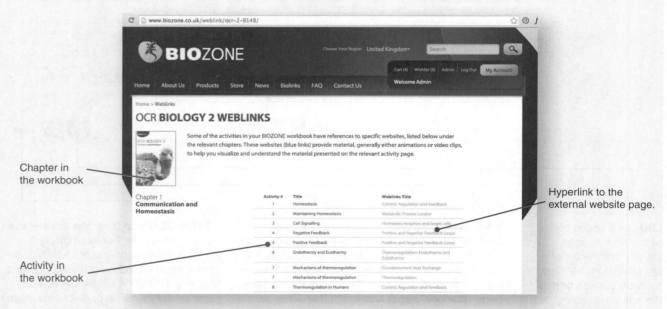

Chapter in the workbook

Hyperlink to the external website page.

Activity in the workbook

Bookmark weblinks by typing in the address: it is not accessible directly from BIOZONE's website
Corrections and clarifications to current editions are always posted on the weblinks page

Summary of Practical Skills for OCR 2

▶ The practical and mathematical skills for OCR A Level are outlined below and supported in the activities indicated.

1.2   Practical skills assessed in the practical endorsement
Learning outcomes (PAGs and exemplars throughout OCR Biology 1 & 2)

		Activity number
☐	1 Solve problems in a practical context using investigative approaches and methods.	83 92 94 238
☐	2 Use a range of apparatus, materials, and techniques correctly, following written instructions and making and recording observations and measurements.	83 92 94 238
☐	3 Record experimental work and present information and data in a scientific way.	70 232
☐	4 Process data, carry out research and report findings using appropriate tools.	54 83 94
☐	5 Use appropriate apparatus to record a range of quantitative data.	69 92 94
☐	6 Use appropriate instrumentation to record quantitative data.	240 241
☐	7 Use laboratory glassware for a range of techniques, including serial dilution.	203
☐	8 Use a light microscope (including graticule) at high and low power.	16 36
☐	9 Make annotated scientific drawings from observations.	12 16 36
☐	10 Use qualitative reagents to identify biological molecules.	OCR 1
☐	11 Separate biological compounds using thin layer chromatography or electrophoresis.	77 164 165
☐	12 Record physiological functions and plant or animal responses safely and ethically.	50 62 70
☐	13 Use aseptic techniques in microbiological investigations.	201 202
☐	14 Use dissection equipment safely.	OCR 1
☐	15 Use sampling techniques e.g. quadrats, transects, in fieldwork.	232 237 238
☐	16 Use ICT, e.g in computer modelling or to collect or process data.	126 235 236

Mathematical skills
Supported as noted but also throughout OCR Biology 1 & 2

			Activity number
☐	M0	1 Recognise and use appropriate units in calculations.	94 203 219
☐		2 Recognise and use expressions in both decimal and standard form.	203
☐		3 Carry out calculations involving fractions, percentages, and ratios.	115 121 148
☐		4 Estimate results to assess if calculated values are appropriate.	OCR 1
☐		5 Use calculator to find and use power, exponential, and logarithmic functions.	206
☐	M1	1 Use an appropriate number of significant figures in reporting calculations.	54 62
☐		2 Find arithmetic means for a range of data.	54 62
☐		3 Represent and interpret frequency data in the form of bar graphs and histograms.	139 142
☐		4 Demonstrate an understanding of simple probability, e.g. as in genetic inheritance.	114 121
☐		5 Understand sampling and analyse data collected by an appropriate method.	233 236 237
☐		6 Calculate or compare mean, mode, and median for sample data.	130 233
☐		7 Plot and interpret scatter graphs to identify correlation between two variables.	141
☐		8 Make order of magnitude calculations, e.g. in calculating magnification.	OCR 1
☐		9 Select and apply appropriate statistical tests to analyse and interpret data.	54 62 126 236
☐		10 Understand and use measures of dispersion, e.g. standard deviation and range.	54
☐		11 Identify and determine uncertainties in measurements.	OCR 1
☐	M2	1 Demonstrate understanding of the symbols =, <, <<, >>, >, ∝, ~	136
☐		2 Manipulate equations to change the subject.	136
☐		3 Substitute numerical values into algebraic equations using appropriate units.	136
☐		4 Use logarithms in relation to quantities ranging over several orders of magnitude.	206
☐	M3	1 Translate information between graphical, numerical, and algebraic forms.	92 94 233
☐		2 Select an appropriate format to plot two variables from experimental or other data.	92 94 233
☐		3 Predict or sketch the shape of a graph with a linear relationship ($y = mx + c$).	OCR 1
☐		4 Determine the intercept of a graph.	OCR 1
☐		5 Calculate rate of change from a graph showing a linear relationship.	OCR 1
☐		6 Draw and use the slope of a tangent to a curve as a measure of rate of change.	OCR 1
☐	M4	1 Calculate the circumferences, surface areas, and volumes of regular shapes.	OCR 1

Communication and Homeostasis

Key terms

autocrine signalling

cell signalling

ectotherm

effector

endocrine signalling

endotherm

homeostasis

homeotherm

hypothalamus

ligand

negative feedback

paracrine signalling

poikilotherm

positive feedback

receptor

stimulus (pl. stimuli)

thermoregulation

Cell signalling

Learning outcomes

Activity number

☐ 1 Explain why organisms need to respond to stimuli in their environment and coordinate the activities of their different organs.

1 2

☐ 2 Describe how cells communicate by cell signalling. Include reference to signalling between neighbouring cells (paracrine signalling) and signalling between distant cells (endocrine signalling).

3

☐ 3 Explain what is meant by a signalling molecule (ligand) and identify examples in plants and animals, e.g. plant growth regulators such as auxin, hormones, pheromones, neurohormones, neurotransmitters, and clotting factors. Using examples, outline the role of receptors in responding to specific ligands.

3

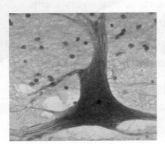  

Principles of homeostasis

Learning outcomes

Activity number

☐ 4 Explain what is meant by homeostasis and describe why it is important. Distinguish between receptors and effectors in physiological systems and explain their roles in receiving and responding to stimuli.

1 2

☐ 5 Explain what is meant by negative feedback and outline its role in maintaining homeostasis. Use examples to demonstrate your understanding of how negative feedback mechanisms stabilise systems against excessive change.

4

☐ 6 Explain positive feedback as a destabilising mechanism with a specific role in certain physiological processes. Describe an example of positive feedback and explain what brings the positive feedback loop to a close.

5

Temperature regulation

Learning outcomes

Activity number

☐ 7 Explain what is meant by thermoregulation and explain why it is important.

1 6

☐ 8 Distinguish between sources of body heat in endotherms and ectotherms. Recognise that most ectotherms allow their body temperature to fluctuate to varying extents with the environment (poikilothermic) and most endotherms maintain a constant body temperature (homeothermic).

6

☐ 9 Describe the physiological and behavioural responses involved in thermoregulation in ectotherms and endotherms. For endotherms, e.g. mammals, include the role of peripheral temperature receptors in the skin, the hypothalmaus, and effectors in the skin and muscles. For ectotherms, e.g. lizards, include reference to the role of behaviours such as basking and stilting.

6 7 8

1 Homeostasis

Key Idea: Homeostasis refers to the (relatively) constant physiological state of the body despite fluctuations in the external environment.

Organisms maintain a relatively constant physiological state, called **homeostasis**, despite changes in their environment. Any change in the environment to which an organism responds is called a **stimulus** and, because environmental stimuli are not static, organisms must also adjust their behaviour and physiology constantly to maintain homeostasis. This requires the coordinated activity of the body's organ systems. Homeostatic mechanisms prevent deviations from the steady state and keep the body's internal conditions within strict limits. Deviations from these limits can be harmful.

An example of homeostasis occurs when you exercise (right). Your body must keep your body temperature constant at about 37.0°C despite the increased heat generated by activity. Similarly, you must regulate blood sugar levels and blood pH, water and electrolyte balance, and blood pressure. Your body's organ systems carry out these tasks.

To maintain homeostasis, the body must detect stimuli through receptors, process this sensory information, and respond to it appropriately via effectors. The responses provide new feedback to the receptor. These three components are illustrated below.

How homeostasis is maintained

Muscles and glands

Sense organ (e.g. eye)

Receptor
Detects change and sends a message to the control centre.

Effector
Responds to the output from the control centre.

Brain and spinal cord

Control centre
Receives the message and coordinates a response. Sends an output message to an effector.

The analogy of a thermostat on a heater is a good way to understand how homeostasis is maintained. A heater has sensors (a receptor) to monitor room temperature. It also has a control centre to receive and process the data from the sensors. Depending on the data it receives, the control centre activates the effector (heating unit), switching it on or off. When the room is too cold, the heater switches on. When it is too hot, the heater switches off. This maintains a constant temperature.

1. What is homeostasis? _____

_____

2. What is the role of the following components in maintaining homeostasis:

(a) Receptor: _____

_____

(b) Control centre: _____

_____

(c) Effector: _____

_____

LINK LINK WEB

3 **2** **1** **KNOW**

2 Maintaining Homeostasis

Key Idea: The body's organ systems work together to maintain homeostasis.

Homeostasis relies on monitoring all the information received from the internal and external environment and coordinating appropriate responses. This often involves many different organ systems working together to ensure proper functioning of the whole organism. Most of the time an organism's body systems are responding to changes at the subconscious level, but sometimes homeostasis is achieved by changing a behaviour (e.g. finding shade if the temperature is too high).

Regulating respiratory gases

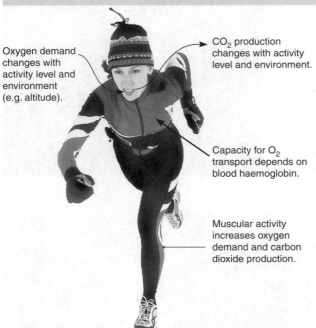

Oxygen demand changes with activity level and environment (e.g. altitude).

CO_2 production changes with activity level and environment.

Capacity for O_2 transport depends on blood haemoglobin.

Muscular activity increases oxygen demand and carbon dioxide production.

Oxygen must be delivered to all cells and carbon dioxide (a waste product of cellular respiration) must be removed. Breathing brings in oxygen and expels CO_2, and the cardiovascular and lymphatic systems circulate these respiratory gases (the oxygen mostly bound to haemoglobin). The rate of breathing is varied according to oxygen demands (as detected by CO_2 levels in the blood).

Coping with pathogens

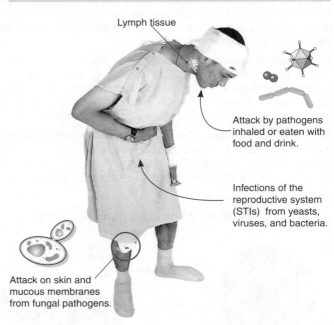

Lymph tissue

Attack by pathogens inhaled or eaten with food and drink.

Infections of the reproductive system (STIs) from yeasts, viruses, and bacteria.

Attack on skin and mucous membranes from fungal pathogens.

All of us are under constant attack from pathogens (disease causing organisms). The body has a number of mechanisms that help to prevent the entry of pathogens and limit the damage they cause if they do enter the body. The skin, the digestive system, and the immune system are all involved in the body's defence, while the cardiovascular and lymphatic systems circulate the cells and antimicrobial substances involved.

Maintaining nutrient supply and removing wastes

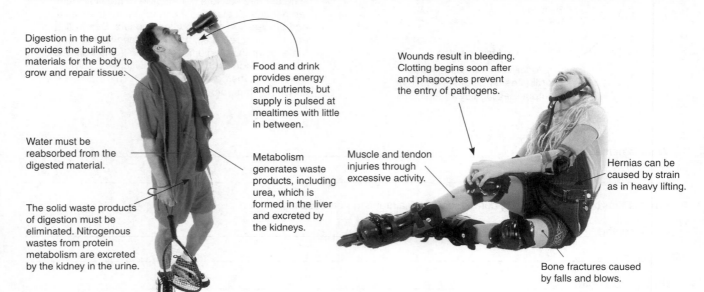

Digestion in the gut provides the building materials for the body to grow and repair tissue.

Food and drink provides energy and nutrients, but supply is pulsed at mealtimes with little in between.

Water must be reabsorbed from the digested material.

Metabolism generates waste products, including urea, which is formed in the liver and excreted by the kidneys.

The solid waste products of digestion must be eliminated. Nitrogenous wastes from protein metabolism are excreted by the kidney in the urine.

Food and drink is taken in to maintain energy supplies. The digestive system makes these nutrients available, and the cardiovascular system distributes them throughout the body. Food intake is regulated largely through nervous mechanisms, while hormones control the cellular uptake of glucose. The liver metabolises proteins to form urea, which is excreted by the kidneys.

Repairing injuries

Wounds result in bleeding. Clotting begins soon after and phagocytes prevent the entry of pathogens.

Muscle and tendon injuries through excessive activity.

Hernias can be caused by strain as in heavy lifting.

Bone fractures caused by falls and blows.

Damage to body tissues triggers the inflammatory response and white blood cells move to the injury site. The inflammatory response is started (and ended) by chemical signals (e.g. from histamine and prostaglandins) released when tissue is damaged. The cardiovascular and lymphatic systems distribute the cells and molecules involved.

© 2015 **BIOZONE** International
ISBN: 978-1-927309-14-8
Photocopying Prohibited

Regulating temperature, fluid and electrolytes

Water loss through breathing.

Water and ions taken in with food and drink.

Metabolism generates heat

Loss of water and ions via sweat.

Changes in heat losses and gains

Loss of urea, water, and ions via urine. Loss of water and ions via faeces.

Coordinating responses

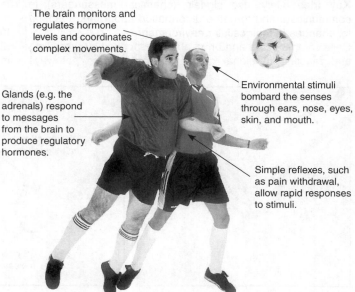

The brain monitors and regulates hormone levels and coordinates complex movements.

Glands (e.g. the adrenals) respond to messages from the brain to produce regulatory hormones.

Environmental stimuli bombard the senses through ears, nose, eyes, skin, and mouth.

Simple reflexes, such as pain withdrawal, allow rapid responses to stimuli.

The balance of fluid and electrolytes (and excretion of wastes) is the job of the kidneys. Osmoreceptors monitor blood volume and bring about the release of the hormones ADH and aldosterone, which regulate reabsorption of water and sodium from blood via the kidneys. The cardiovascular and lymphatic systems distribute fluids around the body. The circulatory system and skin both help to maintain body temperature.

The body is constantly bombarded by stimuli from the environment. The brain sorts these stimuli into those that require a response and those that do not. Responses are coordinated via nervous or hormonal controls. Simple nervous responses (reflexes) act quickly. Hormones, which are distributed by the cardiovascular and lymphatic systems, take longer to produce a response and the response is more prolonged.

1. Describe two mechanisms that operate to restore homeostasis after infection by a pathogen:

   (a) _____

   _____

   (b) _____

   _____

2. Describe two mechanisms by which responses to stimuli are brought about and coordinated:

   (a) _____

   _____

   (b) _____

   _____

3. Explain two ways in which water and ion balance are maintained. Name the organ(s) and any hormones involved:

   (a) _____

   _____

   (b) _____

   _____

4. Explain two ways in which the body regulates its respiratory gases during exercise:

   (a) _____

   _____

   (b) _____

© 2015 **BIOZONE** International
ISBN: 978-1-927309-14-8
Photocopying Prohibited

3 Cell Signalling

Key Idea: Cells use signals (chemical messengers) to communicate and to gather information about, and respond to, changes in their cellular environment.

Cells communicate and bring about responses by producing and reacting to signal molecules. Three main pathways for cell signalling exist. The endocrine pathway involves the transport of hormones in the blood or haemolymph. In paracrine signalling, the signal travels an intermediate distance to act upon neighbouring cells. Autocrine signalling involves a cell producing and reacting to its own signal.

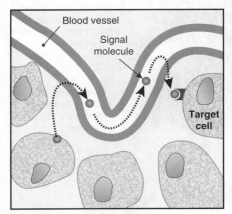

Endocrine signalling: Hormone signals are released by ductless endocrine glands and are carried by the circulatory system through the body to the target cells. Examples include sex hormones, growth factors and neurohormones such as dopamine.

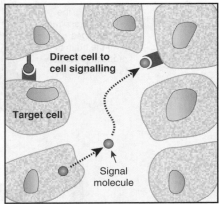

Paracrine signalling: Signals released from a cell act on target cells close by. The messenger can be transferred through the extracellular fluid (e.g. at synapses) or directly between cells. Examples include histamine and prostaglandins.

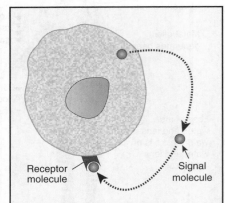

Autocrine signalling: Cells produce and react to their own signals. In vertebrates, when a foreign antibody enters the body, some T-cells produce a growth factor to stimulate their own production. The increased number of T-cells helps to fight the infection.

Signalling receptors and signalling molecules

Histamine is a paracrine signal molecule involved in local immune responses.

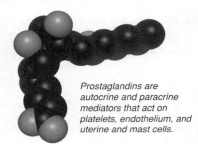

Prostaglandins are autocrine and paracrine mediators that act on platelets, endothelium, and uterine and mast cells.

Examples of cell signalling molecules

The binding sites of cell receptors are specific only to certain **ligands** (signal molecules). This stops them reacting to every signal the cell encounters. Receptors generally fall into two main categories:

▸ **Cytoplasmic receptors**

Cytoplasmic receptors, located within the cell cytoplasm, bind ligands which are able to cross the plasma membrane unaided.

▸ **Transmembrane receptors**

These span the cell membrane and bind ligands which cannot cross the plasma membrane on their own. They have an extra-cellular domain outside the cell, and an intracellular domain within the cell cytosol.

Ion channels, protein kinases and G-protein linked receptors are examples of transmembrane receptors (see diagram on right).

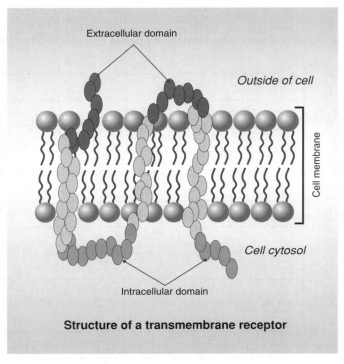

Structure of a transmembrane receptor

1. Briefly describe the three types of cell signalling:

   (a) _____

   (b) _____

   (c) _____

2. Identify the components that all three cell signalling types have in common: _____

_____

_____

© 2015 **BIOZONE** International
ISBN: 978-1-927309-14-8
Photocopying Prohibited

4 Negative Feedback

Key Idea: Negative feedback mechanisms detect departures from a set point norm and act to restore the steady state. Most physiological systems achieve homeostasis through negative feedback. In negative feedback systems, movement away from a steady state is detected and triggers a mechanism to counteract that change. **Negative feedback** has a stabilising effect, dampening variations from a set point and returning internal conditions to a steady state.

Negative feedback and control systems

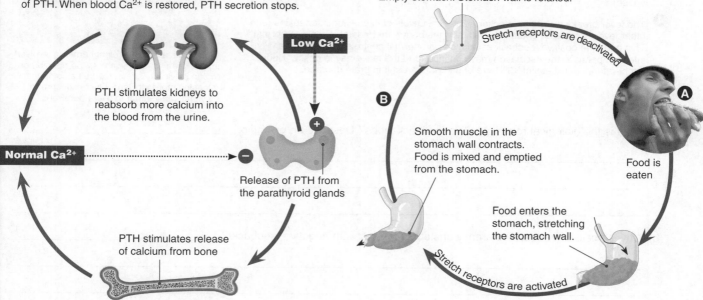

2 Corrective mechanisms activated, e.g. sweating

3 Return to optimum

Stress, e.g. exercise generates excessive body heat

Stress, e.g. cold weather causes excessive heat loss

Normal body temperature

Corrective mechanisms activated, e.g. shivering

1 A **stressor**, e.g. exercise, takes the internal environment away from optimum.

2 Stress is detected by receptors and corrective mechanisms (e.g. sweating or shivering) are activated.

3 Corrective mechanisms act to restore optimum conditions.

Negative feedback acts to counteract departures from steady state. The diagram shows how stress is counteracted in the case of body temperature.

Negative feedback in calcium homeostasis

Blood calcium is regulated by several hormones, including parathyroid hormone (PTH). Low blood Ca^{2+} stimulates release of PTH. When blood Ca^{2+} is restored, PTH secretion stops.

Low Ca^{2+}

PTH stimulates kidneys to reabsorb more calcium into the blood from the urine.

Normal Ca^{2+}

Release of PTH from the parathyroid glands

PTH stimulates release of calcium from bone

Negative feedback in stomach emptying

Empty stomach. Stomach wall is relaxed.

Stretch receptors are deactivated

B

A

Smooth muscle in the stomach wall contracts. Food is mixed and emptied from the stomach.

Food is eaten

Food enters the stomach, stretching the stomach wall.

Stretch receptors are activated

1. How do negative feedback mechanisms maintain homeostasis in a variable environment? _____

_____

_____

2. On the diagram of stomach emptying:

   (a) State the stimulus at A: _____ State the response at B: _____

   (b) Name the effector in this system: _____

   (c) What is the steady state for this example? _____

LINK **8** LINK **5** WEB **4** **KNOW**

5 Positive Feedback

Key Idea: Positive feedback results in the escalation of a response to a stimulus. It causes system instability and occurs when a particular outcome or resolution is required. Positive feedback mechanisms amplify a physiological response in order to achieve a particular result. Labour, fever, blood clotting, and fruit ripening all involve positive feedback. Normally, a positive feedback loop is ended when the natural resolution is reached (e.g. baby is born, pathogen is destroyed). Positive feedback is relatively rare because such mechanisms are unstable and potentially damaging.

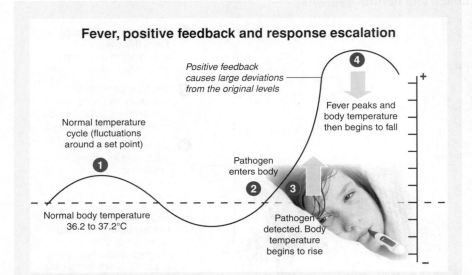

Fever, positive feedback and response escalation

Positive feedback causes large deviations from the original levels

Fever peaks and body temperature then begins to fall

Normal temperature cycle (fluctuations around a set point)

1

Pathogen enters body

2

3

Pathogen detected. Body temperature begins to rise

Normal body temperature 36.2 to 37.2°C

4

1 Body temperature fluctuates on a normal, regular basis around a narrow set point.

2 Pathogen enters the body.

3 The body detects the pathogen and macrophages attack it. Macrophages release interleukins which stimulate the hypothalamus to increase prostaglandin production and reset the body's thermostat to a higher 'fever' level by shivering (the chill phase).

4 The fever breaks when the infection subsides. Levels of circulating interleukins (and other fever-associated chemicals) fall, and the body's thermostat is reset to normal. This ends the positive feedback escalation and normal controls resume. If the infection persists, the escalation may continue, and the fever may intensify. Body temperatures in excess of 43°C are often fatal or result in brain damage.

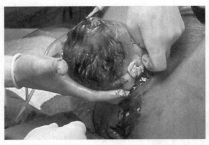

Labour and lactation: During childbirth (above), the release of oxytocin intensifies the contractions of the uterus so that labour proceeds to its conclusion. The birth itself restores the system by removing the initiating stimulus. After birth, levels of the milk-production hormone prolactin increase. Suckling maintains prolactin secretion and causes the release of oxytocin, resulting in milk release. The more an infant suckles, the more these hormones are produced.

Ethylene is a gaseous plant hormone involved in fruit ripening. It accelerates the ripening of fruit in its vicinity so nearby fruit also ripens, releasing more ethylene. Over-exposure to ethylene causes fruit to over-ripen (rot).

1. (a) What is the biological role of positive feedback loops? Describe an example: _____

_____

_____

_____

(b) Why is positive feedback inherently unstable (contrast with negative feedback)? _____

_____

_____

_____

(c) How is a positive feedback loop normally stopped? _____

_____

(d) Describe a situation in which this might not happen. What would be the result? _____

_____

_____

_____

© 2015 **BIOZONE** International
ISBN: 978-1-927309-14-8
Photocopying Prohibited

6 Endothermy vs Ectothermy

Key Idea: Ectotherms depend on heat from the environment whereas endotherms generate heat through metabolic activity. Both endotherms and ectotherms may thermoregulate to maintain an optimum temperature for functioning.

Animals are classified into two broad groups based on the source of their body heat. **Ectotherms** depend on the environment for their heat energy (e.g. heat from the sun)

whereas **endotherms** generate most of their body heat from internal metabolic processes. All endotherms and many ectotherms **thermoregulate** (control body temperature) in order to maintain an optimum temperature for the functioning of their metabolic pathways. Ectotherms rely on behavioural mechanisms to do this, whereas in endotherms both behavioural and physiological responses are involved.

Most fish and all amphibians are ectothermic. Unlike many reptiles, they do not thermoregulate, so their body temperature fluctuates with the environment (they are poikilothermic) and they are usually restricted to thermally stable environments.

Reptiles, such as snakes, lizards, and crocodiles, depend on environmental sources of heat energy and regulate body temperature using behaviour. They bask and use body positioning to raise their body temperature for activity. Some larger reptiles maintain a relatively elevated body temperature for a lot of the time.

Birds and mammals achieve a high body temperature through metabolic activity and reduction of heat exchanges. They can function independently of the environmental temperature (within the species-specific tolerance range) and maintain high metabolic rates. Their body temperature remains stable (they are homeothermic).

Daily temperature variations in ectotherms and endotherms

Ectotherm: Diurnal lizard
Body temperature is regulated by behaviour so that it does not rise above 40°C. Basking increases heat uptake from the sun. Activity occurs when body temperature is high. Underground burrows are used for retreat.

Endotherm: Human
Body temperature fluctuates within narrow limits over a 24 hour period. Exercise and eating increase body temperature for a short time. Body temperature falls during rest and is partly controlled by an internal rhythm.

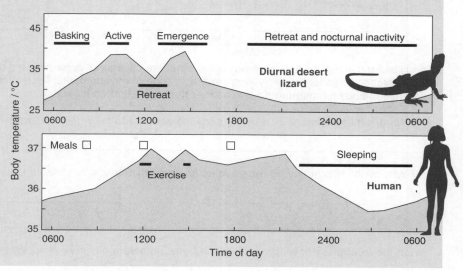

1. Distinguish between ectotherms and endotherms in terms of their sources of body heat: _____

_____

_____

2. The diagrams above show daily temperature variations in an ectotherm and an endotherm.

    (a) Which animal has the largest temperature variation? _____

    (b) How does the lizard regulate its body temperature? _____

    _____

    _____

    (c) Describe the effect of eating and exercise on the temperature in humans: _____

    _____

    (d) What effect does sleeping have on human body temperature? _____

    _____

Liolaemus

Sauromalus

The Peruvian mountain lizard (Liolaemus) emerges in the morning when the air temperature is below freezing. By exposing itself to the sun, it rapidly heats up to a body temperature that enables it to be fully active. Once warm, the lizard maintains its preferred body temperature of around 35°C by changing posture and orientation to the sun and thereby controlling the amount of heat energy absorbed.

When the desert lizard, the chuckawalla (Sauromalus) is moved from 15°C to 45°C, cloacal and brain temperatures increase rapidly. At ~41°C, these temperatures diverge and the brain stays at ~2°C below the cloacal temperature* and 3°C below air temperature. The chuckawalla achieves this by panting. Its carotid arteries supplying the brain run close to the surface of the pharynx and heat is lost there by evaporative cooling.

*Cloacal temperature measures deep body temperature through the cloaca (equivalent to rectal temperature in mammals)

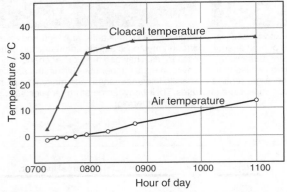

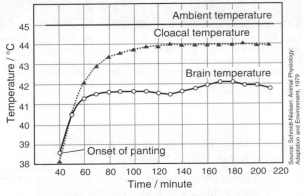

Source: Schmidt-Nielsen: Animal Physiology: Adaptation and Environment, 1979

3. As illustrated in the examples above, ectotherms are capable of achieving and maintaining high, relatively constant body temperatures for relatively long periods in spite of environmental fluctuations. However, they also tolerate marked declines in body temperature to levels lower than are tolerated by endotherms.

(a) What is the advantage of allowing body temperature to fall when ambient temperature drops? _____

_____

(b) Why might ectothermy be regarded as an adaptation to low or variable food supplies?_____

_____

_____

4. (a) In the examples above, the increase in body temperature is very rapid. Why is this important for an ectotherm?

_____

(b) What is the purpose of 'panting' in the chuckawalla? _____

_____

5. (a) In the generalised graph right, identify the optimum temperature range for an endotherm:

_____

(b) Describe the energetic costs of thermoregulation (as measured by oxygen consumption) in an endotherm:

_____

_____

(c) Explain why this is the case: _____

_____

_____

_____

Body temperature and oxygen consumption in an endotherm at different ambient temperatures

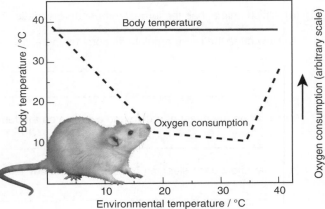

7 Mechanisms of Thermoregulation

Key Idea: Animals thermoregulate by regulating exchanges with the environment and by generating heat from metabolism. To maintain a constant temperature, animals must balance heat losses and gains. Heat exchanges with the environment occur via **conduction** (direct heat transfer), **radiation** (indirect heat transfer), and **evaporation**. Animals employ a range of structural, behavioural, and physiological mechanisms to maintain a body temperature that is optimum for functioning.

Water has a much greater capacity than air to transfer heat away from organisms, so aquatic mammals have heavily insulated surfaces of vascularised fat called blubber (up to 60% of body thickness). Blood is diverted to the outside of the blubber if heat needs to be lost.

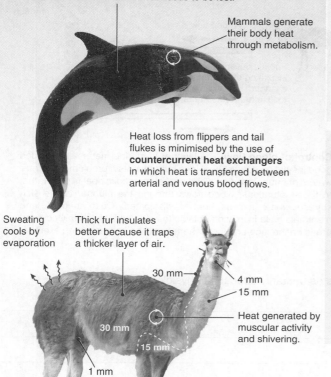

Mammals generate their body heat through metabolism.

Heat loss from flippers and tail flukes is minimised by the use of **countercurrent heat exchangers** in which heat is transferred between arterial and venous blood flows.

Temperature regulation mechanisms in water

▸ Heat generation from metabolic activity
▸ Insulation layer of blubber
▸ Changes in circulation patterns when swimming
▸ Large body size
▸ Heat exchange systems in limbs or high activity muscle

In fast swimming fish, such as tuna, heat exchangers are used to maintain muscle temperatures up to 14°C above the water temperature.

Temperature regulation mechanisms in air

▸ Behaviour or habitat choice
▸ Heat generation from metabolic activity, including shivering.
▸ Insulation (fat, fur, feathers)
▸ Circulatory changes including constriction and dilation of blood vessels
▸ Large body size
▸ Sweating and panting
▸ Tolerance of fluctuation in body temperature

Sweating cools by evaporation

Thick fur insulates better because it traps a thicker layer of air.

30 mm

4 mm
15 mm

30 mm

15 mm

1 mm

4 mm

Heat generated by muscular activity and shivering.

Hair loss (moulting) in warmer months assists cooling.

For most mammals, the thickness of the fur or hair varies around the body (as indicated above). Thermoregulation is assisted by adopting body positions that expose or cover areas of thin fur (the figures above are for the llama-like guanaco).

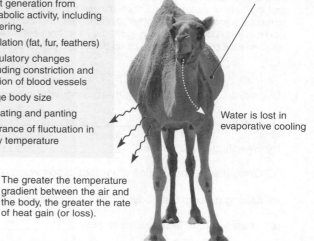

Large body size reduces heat loss by lowering the surface area to volume ratio.

Water is lost in evaporative cooling

The greater the temperature gradient between the air and the body, the greater the rate of heat gain (or loss).

Animals adapted to temperature extremes (hot or cold) often tolerate large fluctuations in their body temperature. In well watered camels, body temperature fluctuates less than 2°C, but when they are deprived of water, the body temperature may fluctuate up to 7°C (34°C to 41°C) over a 24 hour period. By allowing their body temperature to rise, heat gain is reduced and the animal conserves water and energy.

Dog
Panting to lose accumulated heat is important in dogs, which have sweat glands only on the pads of their feet.

Marine iguana
Circulation changes slow heat loss in water and speed heat gain when basking on land in marine iguanas.

Elephant seal
Thick blubber and large body size in seals and other marine mammals provide an effective insulation.

Musk oxen
Mammals and birds in cold climates, like the musk oxen above, cluster together to retain body heat.

Namib lizard
Behaviours to reduce heat uptake via conduction, e.g. standing on two legs, are important in desert lizards.

Crocodile
Gaping is a behavioural mechanism in large ectotherms to protect the brain from overheating.

Brown bear
Hair, fur, wool, or feathers trap air next to the skin. The air layer slows the loss and gain of heat.

Sweat in human
Most mammals can sweat to cool down. Heat is lost when sweat evaporates from the body surface.

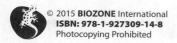
LINK 8   LINK 6   WEB 7   KNOW

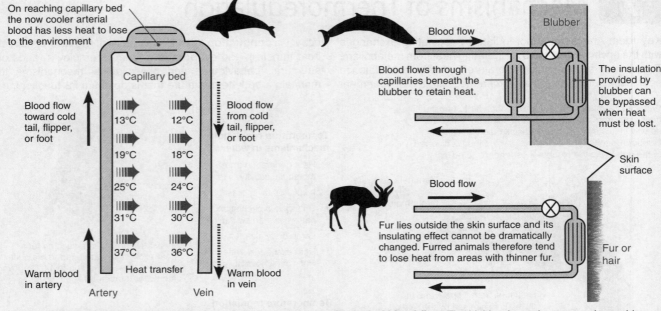

Countercurrent heat exchange systems occur in both aquatic and terrestrial animals as an adaptation to maintaining a stable core temperature. In the flippers and fins of whales and dolphins, and the legs of aquatic birds, they minimise heat loss. In some terrestrial animals adapted to hot climates, the heat exchangers works in the opposite way to prevent the brain from overheating: venous blood cools the arterial blood before it supplies the brain.

Control of blood flow: The blubber in marine mammals provides good insulation against heat loss but presents a problem in warmer waters or during exertion when a lot of metabolic heat is generated. In these situations, blood flows through the blubber to the skin surface where excess heat is dissipated. Cold adapted land mammals have insulation outside the skin and have thinly covered areas on the face and feet, where heat can be lost during exertion.

1. Classify each of the following thermoregulatory mechanisms as primarily structural, physiological, or behavioural:

   (a) Panting in mammals: _____

   (b) Sweating in mammals: _____

   (c) Constriction and dilation of surface blood vessels: _____

   (d) Stilting (raising the body up off the surface) in lizards: _____

   (e) Thick fur, hair, feathers, or blubber: _____

2. (a) How does thick hair or fur assist in thermoregulation in mammals? _____

   _____

   _____

   (b) Why is fur/hair thickness variable over different regions of a mammal's body? _____

   _____

   (c) How would you expect fur thickness to vary between related mammal species at high and low altitude?

   _____

   _____

   (d) How do marine mammals compensate for lack of thick hair or fur? _____

3. Explain how a marine mammal regulates its body temperature when moving from colder to warmer waters:

   _____

4. Explain how countercurrent heat exchangers help retain body heat in marine mammals: _____

   _____

   _____

   _____

© 2015 **BIOZONE** International
ISBN: 978-1-927309-14-8
Photocopying Prohibited

8 Thermoregulation in Humans

Key Idea: In humans, the temperature regulation centre is in the hypothalamus. Thermoregulation relies on negative feedback mechanisms and involves several body systems.

In humans, the temperature regulation centre of the body is in the hypothalamus. It has a 'set point' temperature of 36.7°C. The hypothalamus responds directly to changes in core temperature and to nerve impulses from peripheral temperature receptors in the skin. It then coordinates nervous and hormonal responses to counteract the changes and restore normal body temperature. Like a thermostat, the hypothalamus detects a return to normal temperature and the corrective mechanisms are switched off (negative feedback).

Counteracting heat loss

Heat promoting centre in the hypothalamus monitors fall in skin or core temperature below 35.8°C and coordinates responses that generate and conserve heat. These responses are mediated primarily through the **sympathetic nerves** of the autonomic nervous system.

Thyroxine increases metabolic rate.

Erector muscles of hairs contract, raising the hairs and increasing the insulating air layer.

Under conditions of <u>extreme</u> cold, the hormones adrenaline and thyroxine increase the energy releasing (exergonic) activity of the liver.

Muscular activity, including **shivering** produces internal heat.

Vasoconstriction: Blood vessels to the skin constrict and blood flow to skin decreases keeping warm blood near the core.

Factors causing heat loss
▶ Wind chill factor accelerates heat loss through conduction.
▶ Heat loss due to temperature difference between the body and the environment.
▶ The rate of heat loss from the body is increased by being wet, by inactivity, dehydration, inadequate clothing, or shock.

Receptors

Factors causing heat gain
▶ Gain of heat directly from the environment through radiation and conduction.
▶ Excessive fat deposits make it harder to lose the heat that is generated through activity.
▶ Heavy exercise, especially with excessive clothing.

Counteracting heat gain

Heat losing centre in the hypothalamus monitors any rise in skin or core temperature above 37.5°C and coordinates responses that increase heat loss. These responses are mediated primarily through the **parasympathetic nerves** of the autonomic nervous system.

Receptors

Sweating increases, cooling by evaporation.

Muscle tone and metabolic rate decrease, reducing the body's heat output.

Vasodilation: Blood vessels to the skin dilate. Warm blood from the body core is transported to the skin, and heat is lost from the skin surface.

Erector muscles of hairs relax, flattening the hairs to decrease the insulating air layer.

---

1. Describe two mechanisms by which body temperature could be reduced after intensive activity (e.g. hard exercise):

(a) _____

_____

(b) _____

_____

2. Describe the role of the following in regulating internal body temperature:

(a) The hypothalamus: _____

_____

(b) The skin: _____

_____

(c) Nervous input to effectors: _____

_____

(d) Hormones: _____

_____

© 2015 **BIOZONE** International
ISBN: 978-1-927309-14-8
Photocopying Prohibited

LINK **7**   WEB **8**   **KNOW**

Skin section

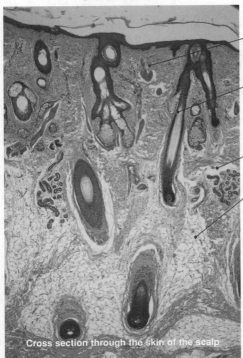

Cross section through the skin of the scalp

Blood vessels in the dermis dilate or constrict to promote or restrict heat loss.

Hairs raised or lowered to increase or decrease the thickness of the insulating air layer between the skin and the environment.

Sweat glands produce sweat, which cools through evaporation.

Fat in the sub-dermal layers insulates the organs against heat loss.

Thermoreceptors in the dermis are free nerve endings, which respond to changes in skin temperature and send that information to the hypothalamus. Hot thermoreceptors detect an increase in skin temperature above 37.5°C and cold thermoreceptors detect a fall below 35.8°C.

Regulating blood flow to the skin

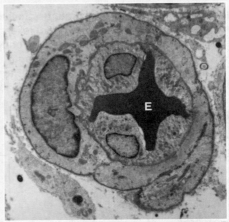

Constriction of a small blood vessel. An erythrocyte (E) (red blood cell) is in the centre of the vessel.

To regulate heat loss or gain from the skin, the blood vessels beneath the surface constrict (**vasoconstriction**) to reduce blood flow or dilate (**vasodilation**) to increase blood flow. When blood vessels are fully constricted there may be as much as a 10°C temperature gradient from the outer to inner layers of the skin. Extremities such the hands and feet have additional vascular controls which can reduce blood flow to them in times of severe cooling.

The hair erector muscles, sweat glands, and blood vessels are the effectors for mediating a response to information from thermoreceptors. Temperature regulation by the skin involves **negative feedback** because the output is fed back to the skin receptors and becomes part of a new stimulus-response cycle.

Left photograph shows vasodilation and sweating in response high temperature or exertion.
Right photograph shows vasoconstriction and goosebumps in response low temperature or inactivity.

3. (a) What is the purpose of sweating and how does it achieve its effect?_____

_____

(b) Why does a dab of methanol or ethanol on the skin feels cold, even if the liquid is at room temperature? _____

_____

_____

4. Describe the feedback system that regulates body temperature: _____

_____

_____

_____

_____

5. How do the blood vessels help to regulate the amount of heat lost from the skin and body? _____

_____

_____

6. (a) What is the role of subcutaneous fat in temperature regulation in humans: _____

_____

(b) Why do excessive deposits of fat tend to lead to overheating during exercise?_____

_____

© 2015 **BIOZONE** International
ISBN: 978-1-927309-14-8
Photocopying Prohibited

9 Chapter Review

Summarise what you know about this topic under the headings and sub-headings provided. You can draw diagrams or mind maps, or write short notes to organise your thoughts. Use the images and hints to help you and refer back to the introduction to check the points covered:

Principles of homeostasis
HINT: Using examples, explain how homeostasis is maintained through feedback mechanisms.

Thermoregulation in endotherms and ectotherms
HINT: Include sources of body heat and reference to structural, physiological, and behavioural mechanisms and their relative importance.

Thermoregulation in humans
HINT: Include reference to the role of the skin, blood vessels, and hypothalamus.

REVISE

10 KEY TERMS: Did You Get It?

1. Test your vocabulary by matching each term to its definition, as identified by its preceding letter code.

ectotherm	**A** Regulation of the internal environment to maintain a stable, constant condition.
effector	**B** The behaviour occurring as a result of an external or internal stimulus.
endocrine signalling	**C** Signalling that involves hormones released by ductless endocrine glands and carried through the body by the circulatory system to target cells.
endotherm	**D** A muscle, gland, or organ capable of responding to a stimulus (e.g. nerve impulse).
homeostasis	**E** Signalling involving a chemical messenger whose effect is only exerted at short range on neighbouring cells.
negative feedback	**F** A mechanism in which the output of a system acts to oppose changes to the input of the system. The net effect is to stabilise the system and dampen fluctuations.
paracrine signalling	**G** The regulation of body temperature.
positive feedback	**H** In cell signalling, a molecule (usually) on the cell surface, which receives chemical signals originating from outside the cell. In a neural pathway, a sensory structure that responds to a stimulus in the internal or external environment of an organism.
receptor	**I** An animal that relies on the external environment for its body heat.
response	**J** A destabilising mechanism in which the output of the system causes an escalation in the initial response.
stimulus	**K** Any change in the environment that is capable of generating a response in an organisms.
thermoregulation	**L** An animal that generates its body heat through metabolic activity.

2. Test your knowledge about feedback mechanisms by studying the two graphs below, and answering the questions about them. In your answers, use biological terms appropriately to show your understanding.

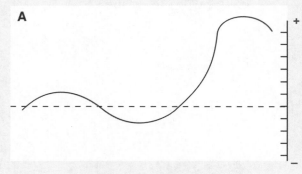

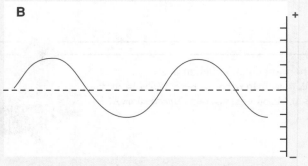

Type of feedback mechanism: _____

Type of feedback mechanism: _____

_____

_____

Mode of action: _____

Mode of action: _____

_____

_____

_____

_____

Biological examples of this mechanism: _____

Biological examples of this mechanism: _____

_____

_____

_____

_____

© 2015 **BIOZONE** International
ISBN: 978-1-927309-14-8
Photocopying Prohibited

TEST

Module 5.1.2

Excretion

Key terms

ADH (anti-diuretic hormone)

bile

Bowman's capsule

collecting duct

distal convoluted tubule

excretion

glomerular filtration rate

glomerulus

hepatocyte

kidney

kidney (renal) failure

kidney transplant

liver

loop of Henle

nephron

osmoreceptor

portal triad

posterior pituitary

proximal convoluted tubule

renal dialysis

sinusoid

ureter

urinalysis

urine

Excretion and homeostasis

Learning outcomes

Activity number

☐ 1 Explain what is meant by excretion and outline its role in maintaining metabolism and homeostasis. List the waste products of metabolism and their origin, including reference to carbon dioxide and nitrogenous wastes. — 11

☐ 2 Describe the gross structure of the mammalian (e.g. human) liver to include the lobes, falciform ligament, and the significance of the liver's double blood supply. — 12

☐ 3 Describe the histology of the liver to include cords of hepatocytes, sinusoids, Kupffer cells, liver lobules, bile canaliculi, central veins, and the portal triads. — 12 13

☐ 4 Describe the many homeostatic functions of the mammalian liver, including in carbohydrate and protein metabolism, bile production, and detoxification. — 12 14 39

☐ 5 **PAG1** Examine and draw stained sections to show the histology of liver tissue. — 12

 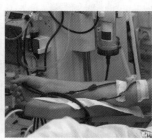 

The structure and function of the kidney

Learning aims and skills

Activity number

☐ 6 Describe the gross structure and roles of the mammalian kidney to include the renal capsule, medulla, cortex, renal pelvis, ureter, and renal artery and vein. — 15

☐ 7 Describe the histology of the mammalian kidney to include the structure of a nephron and its associated blood vessels. Include reference to the roles of the main regions of the nephron: glomerulus and Bowman's capsule, proximal and distal convoluted tubules, loop of Henle, and collecting duct. — 15 17

☐ 8 **PAG1** Dissect, examine, and draw the external and internal structure of the mammalian kidney. — 16

☐ 9 **PAG2** Examine and draw stained sections to show the histology of the kidney nephron (glomerulus, Bowman's capsule, and convoluted tubules). — 16

☐ 10 Explain how the water potential of the blood is regulated. Include reference to the role of hypothalamic osmoreceptors and ADH from the posterior pituitary gland. — 17 18

☐ 11 Describe the effects of kidney (renal) failure, including the effect on glomerular filtration rate (GFR) and electrolyte balance. — 19

☐ 12 Describe how renal dialysis and kidney transplants are used to treat renal failure. — 19 20

☐ 13 **PAG9** Describe how excretory products are used in medical diagnosis, including the use of urine analysis to test for steroids and drugs. — 21

☐ 14 Describe the use of monoclonal antibodies in pregnancy testing. — 22

11 Waste Products in Humans

Key Idea: Metabolism produces a number of waste products that must be excreted from the body. Excretion is primarily the job of the kidneys although other organs also play a role. **Excretion** refers to the elimination from the body of the waste products of metabolism. It should not be confused with the elimination or egestion of undigested and unabsorbed food material from the gut. In mammals, a number of organs are involved in excretion, primarily the kidneys, which produce urine, but also the liver, lungs, and skin. The liver is particularly important in processing wastes, particularly in detoxifying poisons, breakdown of haemoglobin, and forming **urea** from ammonia. Note that the breakdown products of haemoglobin are excreted in bile and pass out with the faeces, but they are not the result of digestion.

CO_2
Water

Lungs
Excretion of carbon dioxide (CO_2) with some loss of water.

Skin
Excretion of water, CO_2, hormones, salts and ions, and small amounts of urea as sweat.

Liver
Produces urea from ammonia in the urea cycle. Breakdown of haemoglobin in the liver produces the bile pigments e.g. bilirubin. These pass out with the faeces, but are not the result of digestion.

Gut
Excretion of bile pigments in the faeces. Also loses water, salts, and carbon dioxide.

Bladder
Storage of urine before it is expelled to the outside.

All cells
All the cells that make up the body carry out cellular respiration, breaking down glucose to release energy and produce the waste products carbon dioxide and water.

Excretion in humans

In mammals, the kidneys are the main organs of excretion, although the liver, skin, and lungs are also important. As well as ridding the body of nitrogenous wastes, the kidneys also regulate pH and excrete many toxins that are taken in from the environment. Many toxic substances, such as alcohol, are rendered harmless by detoxification in the liver, but the kidneys can also eliminate some by actively secreting them into the urine.

Kidney
Filtration of the blood to remove urea. Unwanted ions, particularly hydrogen (H^+) and potassium (K^+), and some hormones are also excreted by the kidneys. Some poisons and drugs (e.g. penicillin) are excreted by active secretion into the urine. Water is lost in excreting these substances and extra water may be voided if necessary.

Substance	Origin*	Organ(s) of excretion
Carbon dioxide		
Water		
Bile pigments		
Urea		
Ions (K^+, HCO_3^-, H^+)		
Hormones		
Poisons		
Drugs		

*Origin refers to from where in the body each substance originates

1. Explain the need for excretion: _____

_____

2. Complete the table above summarising the origin of excretory products and the main organ(s) of excretion for each.

3. What is the role of the liver in excretion, even though it is not primarily an excretory organ? _____

_____

_____

4. Based on the information on this page, predict the effects of kidney failure:_____

_____

_____

_____

_____

© 2015 **BIOZONE** International
ISBN: **978-1-927309-14-8**
Photocopying Prohibited

12 The Structure and Role of the Liver

Key Idea: The liver has both homeostatic and digestive functions. It receives a double blood supply and has a simple internal structure, made up of repeating units called lobules. The liver the largest homeostatic organ. It is located just below the diaphragm and makes up 3-5% of body weight. It performs a vast number of functions including production of bile, storage and processing of nutrients, and detoxification of poisons and metabolic wastes. The liver receives a dual blood supply from the hepatic portal vein and hepatic arteries, and up to 20% of the total blood volume flows through it at any one time. This rich vascularisation makes it the central organ for regulating activities associated with the blood and circulatory system. In spite of its many functions, the liver tissue and the hepatocytes (liver cells) themselves are structurally relatively simple. Features of liver structure and function are outlined below.

The gross structure of the liver

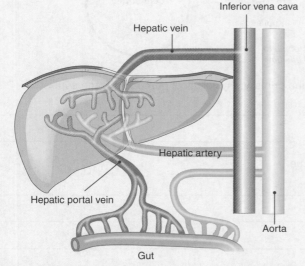

The liver is made up of several lobes and is surrounded by a two layered supportive capsule.

Falciform ligament attaches the liver to the diaphragm and anterior abdominal wall.

Right lobe

Left lobe

Branches of the hepatic duct (bile ductules)

Common hepatic duct drains bile from the liver

Cystic duct

Common bile duct drains bile into small intestine

Gall bladder stores and releases bile

Inferior vena cava

Hepatic vein

Hepatic artery

Aorta

Hepatic portal vein

Gut

The liver has a double blood supply. The hepatic portal vein brings nutrient-rich blood from the gut, and the hepatic artery branches from the aorta to supply the liver with oxygen-rich blood. The hepatic vein drains the liver to return blood to heart via the vena cava. Branches of the hepatic artery, hepatic portal vein, and hepatic duct form the portal triads surrounding each functional unit (lobule) of the liver (right).

Homeostatic roles of the liver

► Hepatocytes secrete bile, which emulsifies fats in digestion.
► Metabolises amino acids, fats, and carbohydrates.
► Synthesises glucose from non-carbohydrate sources.
► Stores iron, copper, and some vitamins (A, D, E, K, B_{12}).
► Synthesises cholesterol from acetyl coenzyme A.
► Converts unwanted amino acids to urea (ornithine cycle).
► Manufactures heparin and plasma proteins (e.g. albumin).
► Detoxifies poisons or turns them into less harmful forms.
► Some liver cells phagocytose worn-out blood cells.

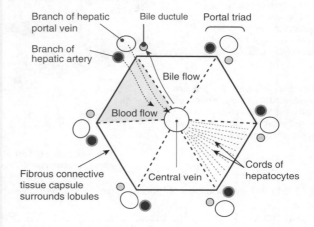

Branch of hepatic portal vein

Bile ductule

Portal triad

Branch of hepatic artery

Bile flow

Blood flow

Fibrous connective tissue capsule surrounds lobules

Central vein

Cords of hepatocytes

Liver tissue comprises many roughly hexagonal units called **lobules**. Cords of hepatocytes radiate from a central vein. Portal triads are arranged around the lobule boundary. Blood flows in sinusoids between the cords of hepatocytes towards the central vein. Bile flows in the opposite direction to the bile ductules.

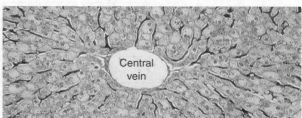

Central vein

This photo shows part of a lobule. The sinusoids (specialised capillaries) are the dark spaces between the rows of hepatocytes.

1. What cells produce bile? _____

2. (a) State one vascular function of the liver: _____

   (b) State one metabolic function of the liver: _____

   (c) State one digestive function of the liver: _____

   (d) State one excretory function of the liver: _____

   (e) State one storage function of the liver: _____

3. What is the basic functional unit of the liver? _____

13 The Histology of the Liver

Key Idea: Liver lobules are made up of mostly of hepatocytes. These receive blood via sinusoids, which transport blood from the hepatic portal vein and hepatic artery to the central vein. The functional repeating unit of the liver is the **lobule**, which is made up of tightly packed rows (cords) of liver cells radiating from a central vein and surrounded by small blood vessels called sinusoids. Branches of the hepatic artery and the hepatic portal vein supply the lobules. This highly vascular structure is a reflection of the liver's important role as dynamic blood reservoir, able to both store and release blood as required. More than half of the 10-20% of the total blood volume normally in the liver resides in the sinusoids. Sinusoids are similar to capillaries but have a more porous endothelium. The increased permeability of the sinusoids allows small and medium-sized proteins, such as albumin, to readily enter and leave the bloodstream.

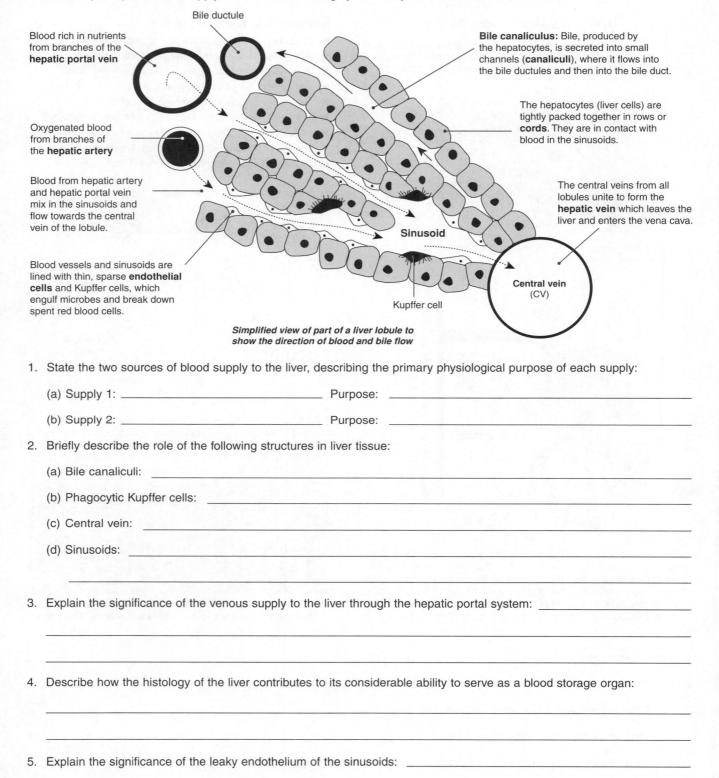

Bile ductule

Blood rich in nutrients from branches of the **hepatic portal vein**

Bile canaliculus: Bile, produced by the hepatocytes, is secreted into small channels (**canaliculi**), where it flows into the bile ductules and then into the bile duct.

Oxygenated blood from branches of the **hepatic artery**

The hepatocytes (liver cells) are tightly packed together in rows or **cords**. They are in contact with blood in the sinusoids.

Blood from hepatic artery and hepatic portal vein mix in the sinusoids and flow towards the central vein of the lobule.

The central veins from all lobules unite to form the **hepatic vein** which leaves the liver and enters the vena cava.

Blood vessels and sinusoids are lined with thin, sparse **endothelial cells** and Kupffer cells, which engulf microbes and break down spent red blood cells.

Sinusoid

Central vein (CV)

Kupffer cell

Simplified view of part of a liver lobule to show the direction of blood and bile flow

1. State the two sources of blood supply to the liver, describing the primary physiological purpose of each supply:

    (a) Supply 1: _____ Purpose: _____

    (b) Supply 2: _____ Purpose: _____

2. Briefly describe the role of the following structures in liver tissue:

    (a) Bile canaliculi: _____

    (b) Phagocytic Kupffer cells: _____

    (c) Central vein: _____

    (d) Sinusoids: _____

    _____

3. Explain the significance of the venous supply to the liver through the hepatic portal system: _____

    _____

    _____

4. Describe how the histology of the liver contributes to its considerable ability to serve as a blood storage organ:

    _____

    _____

5. Explain the significance of the leaky endothelium of the sinusoids: _____

    _____

    _____

© 2015 **BIOZONE** International
ISBN: **978-1-927309-14-8**
Photocopying Prohibited

14 The Liver's Role in Protein Metabolism

Key Idea: The liver has a crucial role in the metabolism of proteins and the storage and detoxification of hormones and ingested or absorbed poisons (including alcohol).

The most critical aspects of protein metabolism occurring in the liver are deamination and transamination of amino acids, removal of ammonia from the body by synthesis of urea, and synthesis of non-essential amino acids. Hepatocytes

are responsible for synthesis of most of the plasma proteins, including albumins, globulins, and blood clotting proteins. Urea formation via the ornithine cycle occurs primarily in the liver. The urea is formed from ammonia and carbon dioxide by condensation with the amino acid ornithine, which is recycled through a series of enzyme-controlled steps. Urea is transported in the blood to the kidneys and excreted.

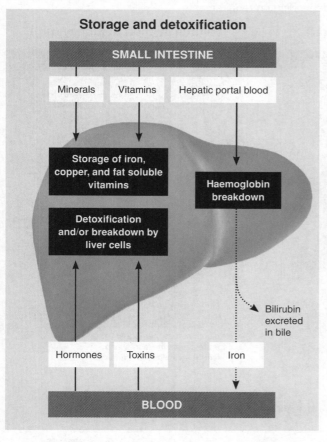

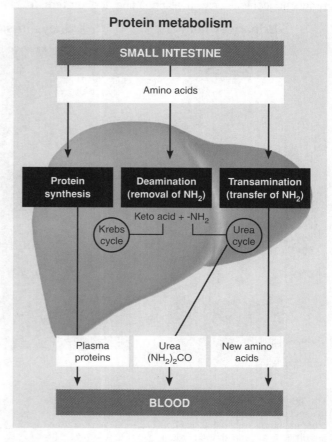

1. Describe three aspects of protein metabolism in the liver:

   (a) _____

   _____

   (b) _____

   _____

   (c) _____

   _____

2. Identify the waste products arising from deamination of amino acids and describe their fate:

   _____

   _____

   _____

3. An X-linked disorder of the ornithine cycle results in sufferers lacking the enzyme to convert ornithine to citrulline. Suggest what the symptoms and the prognosis might be:

   _____

   _____

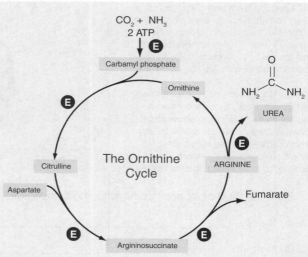

Ammonia (NH_3), the product of protein metabolism, is toxic in even small amounts and must be removed. It is converted to the less toxic urea via the ornithine cycle and is excreted from the body by the kidneys. The liver contains a system of carrier molecules and enzymes (**E**) which quickly convert the ammonia (and CO_2) into urea. One turn of the cycle consumes two molecules of ammonia (one comes from aspartate) and one molecule of CO_2, creates one molecule of urea, and regenerates a molecule of ornithine.

LINK
39

KNOW

15 The Urinary System

Key Idea: The urinary system filters the blood and removes wastes, producing urine. The functional unit of the kidney is a selective filter element called the nephron.

The urinary system consists of the kidneys and bladder, and their associated blood vessels and ducts. The **kidneys** have a plentiful blood supply from the renal artery. The blood plasma is filtered by the **kidney nephrons** to form urine. Urine is produced continuously, passing along the **ureters** to the **bladder**, a hollow muscular organ lined with smooth muscle and stretchable epithelium. Each day the kidneys filter about 180 dm³ of plasma. Most of this is reabsorbed, leaving a daily urine output of about 1 dm³. By adjusting the composition of the fluid excreted, the kidneys help to maintain the body's internal chemical balance. Human kidneys are very efficient, producing a urine that is concentrated to varying degrees depending on requirements.

Urinary system

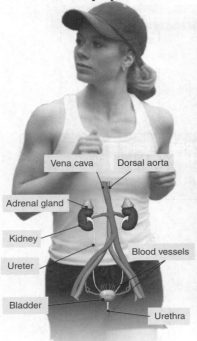

Vena cava
Dorsal aorta
Adrenal gland
Kidney
Ureter
Blood vessels
Bladder
Urethra

Kidneys *in-situ* (rat)

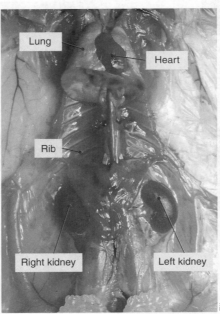

Lung
Heart
Rib
Right kidney
Left kidney

Ell

Sagittal section of kidney (pig)

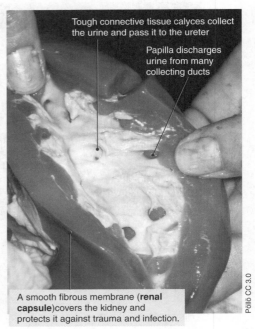

Tough connective tissue calyces collect the urine and pass it to the ureter

Papilla discharges urine from many collecting ducts

A smooth fibrous membrane (**renal capsule**) covers the kidney and protects it against trauma and infection.

Pöllö CC 3.0

The kidneys of humans (above), rats (dissection, above centre), and many other mammals (e.g. pig above right) are distinctive, bean shaped organs that lie at the back of the abdominal cavity to either side of the spine. The kidneys lie outside the peritoneum of the abdominal cavity (**retoperitoneal**) and are partly protected by the lower ribs (see kidneys *in-situ* above centre).

Human kidneys are ~100-120 mm long and 25 mm thick. A cut through in a sagittal plane (see photo above right), reveals numerous tough connective tissue calyces. These collect the urine from the papillae where it is discharged and drain it into the ureter.

The kidneys and their blood supply

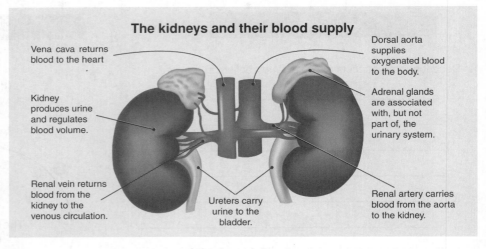

Vena cava returns blood to the heart

Kidney produces urine and regulates blood volume.

Renal vein returns blood from the kidney to the venous circulation.

Ureters carry urine to the bladder.

Dorsal aorta supplies oxygenated blood to the body.

Adrenal glands are associated with, but not part of, the urinary system.

Renal artery carries blood from the aorta to the kidney.

1. State the function of each of the following components of the urinary system:

   (a) Kidney: _____

   (b) Ureters: _____

   (c) Bladder: _____

   (d) Urethra: _____

   (e) Renal artery: _____

   (f) Renal vein: _____

   (g) Renal capsule: _____

© 2015 **BIOZONE** International
ISBN: **978-1-927309-14-8**
Photocopying Prohibited

Internal structure of the human kidney

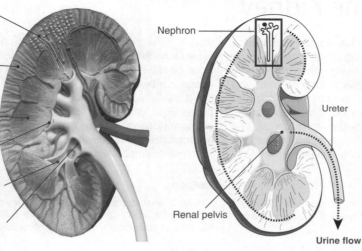

Nephrons are arranged with all the collecting ducts pointing towards the renal pelvis.

Outer cortex contains the renal corpuscles and convoluted tubules.

Inner medulla is organised into pyramids.

Each pyramid ends in a papilla or opening.

Urine enters the **calyces**

Urine collects in a space near the ureter called the renal pelvis, before leaving the kidney via the ureter.

Nephron

Ureter

Renal pelvis

Urine flow

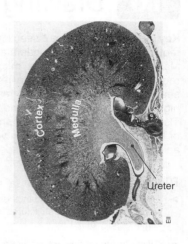

The functional units of the kidney are selective filter elements called **nephrons**. Each kidney contains more than 1 million nephrons and they are precisely aligned so that urine is concentrated as it flows towards the ureter (model and diagram above). The alignment gives the kidney tissue a striated (striped) appearance and makes it possible to accommodate all the filtering units needed.

The outer cortex and inner medulla can be seen in a low power LM of the kidney. The ureter is seen extending into the fat and connective tissue surrounding and protecting the kidney.

The bladder

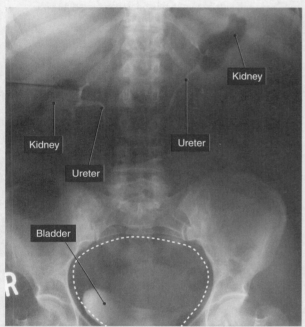

Kidney

Kidney

Ureter

Ureter

Bladder

R

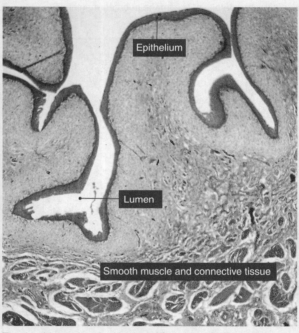

Epithelium

Lumen

Smooth muscle and connective tissue

The bladder is a hollow stretchable organ, which stores the urine before it leaves the body via the urethra. In this X-ray, it is empty and resembles a deflated balloon. The dotted line shows where it would sit if full.

The bladder is lined with **transitional epithelium**. This type of epithelium is layered, or **stratified**, so it can be stretched without the outer cells breaking apart from each other. This image shows the bladder in a deflated state.

2. Calculate the percentage of the plasma reabsorbed by the kidneys: _____

3. (a) What is a nephron? _____

   (b) What is its role in excretion? _____

   _____

4. (a) Where would you find transitional epithelium in the urinary system: _____

   (b) Why do you find this type of epithelium here? _____

5. In adults, the opening of the urethra is regulated by a voluntary sphincter muscle. What is the purpose of this sphincter?

   _____

16 Drawing the Kidney

Key Idea: Drawing from a dissection or histological preparation requires practise and an understanding of structure.

Many observational studies made using microscopes will require you to make accurate representations of what you see. Observations need to be made at both low (X40) and high magnifications to identify the finer structure of the tissue. Tissue sections will usually be provided as longitudinal (LS) or traverse sections (TS). When you have access to both TS and LS images from the same specimen, it is also possible to visualise the three dimensional shape of the structure under view. Observational drawing from a microscope is a skill that must be developed. It requires relaxed viewing in which the image is viewed with one eye, while the other eye attends to the drawing. Attention should be given to the symmetry and proportions of the structure, accurate labelling, statement of magnification and sectioning, and stain used, if this is appropriate. In this activity, you will practise the skills required to translate what is viewed into a good biological drawing.

Biological drawings

▶ Biological drawings should include as much detail as you need to distinguish different structures and types of tissue, but avoid unnecessary detail.

▶ Tissue preparations are rarely neat and tidy and there may be areas where it is difficult to distinguish detail. In these cases you will need to infer detail where possible from adjacent cells.

▶ Avoid shading as this can obscure detail.

▶ Labelling involves interpretation based on your knowledge. Labels should be away from the drawing with label lines pointing to the structures identified.

▶ Add a title and details of the image such as magnification.

TASK 1

Complete a biological drawing of the kidney shown below left including the labels on the photo. At this level, the layers of the kidney can be seen while the detail of each layer cannot.

TASK 2

Complete an annotated drawing of a TS through the cortical region (cortex) of a kidney nephron (below). The ovoid glomerular cluster of capillaries can be seen in the upper centre of the photograph, separated from the Bowman's capsule by a space. The capsule is lined with squamous epithelium and surrounded by tubules formed by cuboidal epithelial cells. You can infer this from the position and spacing of the cell nuclei. To assist you with the level of detail required, one kidney tubule has been completed for you.

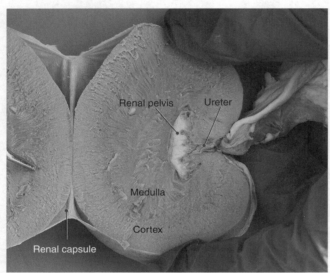

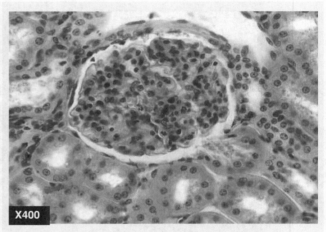

Light micrograph of a transverse section through a kidney nephron to show glomerulus and convoluted tubules.

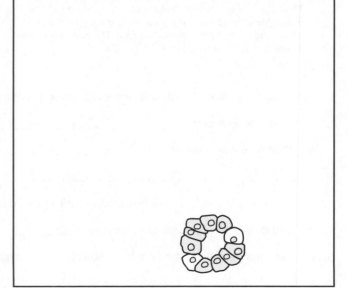

17 The Physiology of the Kidney

Key Idea: Each nephron comprises a renal corpuscle and its associated tubules and ducts. It produces the urine by ultrafiltration, selective reabsorption, and secretion.

Ultrafiltration, i.e. forcing fluid and dissolved substances through a membrane by pressure, occurs in the first part of the nephron, across the membranes of the capillaries and the glomerular capsule. The passage of water and solutes into the nephron and the formation of the glomerular filtrate

depends on the pressure of the blood entering the afferent arteriole (below). If it increases, filtration rate increases. When it falls, glomerular filtration rate also falls. This process is so precisely regulated that, in spite of fluctuations in arteriolar pressure, glomerular filtration rate per day stays constant. After formation of the initial filtrate, the **urine** is modified through secretion and tubular reabsorption according to physiological needs at the time.

Nephron structure and function

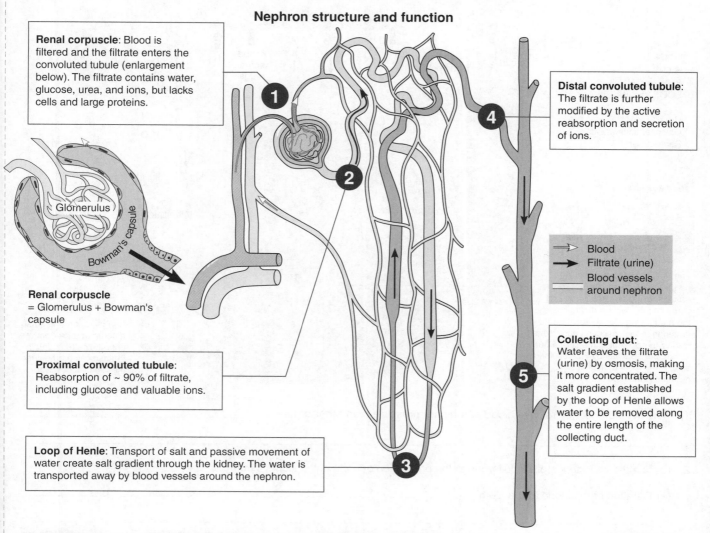

Renal corpuscle: Blood is filtered and the filtrate enters the convoluted tubule (enlargement below). The filtrate contains water, glucose, urea, and ions, but lacks cells and large proteins.

Glomerulus

Bowman's capsule

Renal corpuscle = Glomerulus + Bowman's capsule

Proximal convoluted tubule: Reabsorption of ~ 90% of filtrate, including glucose and valuable ions.

Loop of Henle: Transport of salt and passive movement of water create salt gradient through the kidney. The water is transported away by blood vessels around the nephron.

Distal convoluted tubule: The filtrate is further modified by the active reabsorption and secretion of ions.

→ Blood
→ Filtrate (urine)
Blood vessels around nephron

Collecting duct: Water leaves the filtrate (urine) by osmosis, making it more concentrated. The salt gradient established by the loop of Henle allows water to be removed along the entire length of the collecting duct.

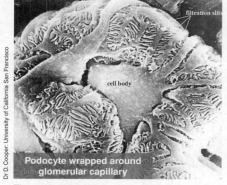

filtration slits

cell body

Podocyte wrapped around glomerular capillary

Dr D. Cooper: University of California San Francisco

The epithelium of Bowman's capsule is made up of specialised cells called **podocytes**. The finger-like cellular processes of the podocytes wrap around the capillaries of the glomerulus, and the plasma filtrate passes through the filtration slits between them.

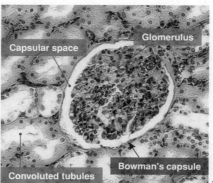

Capsular space

Glomerulus

Convoluted tubules

Bowman's capsule

Bowman's capsule is a double walled cup, lying in the cortex of the kidney. It encloses a dense capillary network called the **glomerulus**. The capsule and its enclosed glomerulus form a **renal corpuscle**. In this section, the convoluted tubules can be seen surrounding the renal corpuscle.

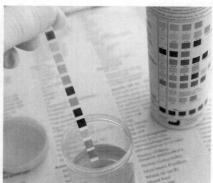

Normal, fresh urine is clear and pale to dark yellow or amber in colour. A urine dipstick test is a fast and convenient way to make a qualitative analysis of urine to diagnose a medical problem. The presence of specific molecules in the urine (e.g. glucose) are indicated by a colour change on the dipstick.

LINK 21   LINK 18   WEB 17   KNOW

Summary of activities in the kidney nephron

Urine formation begins by **ultrafiltration** of the blood, as fluid is forced through the capillaries of the glomerulus, forming a filtrate similar to blood but lacking cells and proteins. The filtrate is then modified by **secretion** and **reabsorption** to add or remove substances (e.g. ions). The processes involved in urine formation are summarised below for each region of the nephron: glomerulus, proximal convoluted tubule, loop of Henle, distal convoluted tubule, and collecting duct.

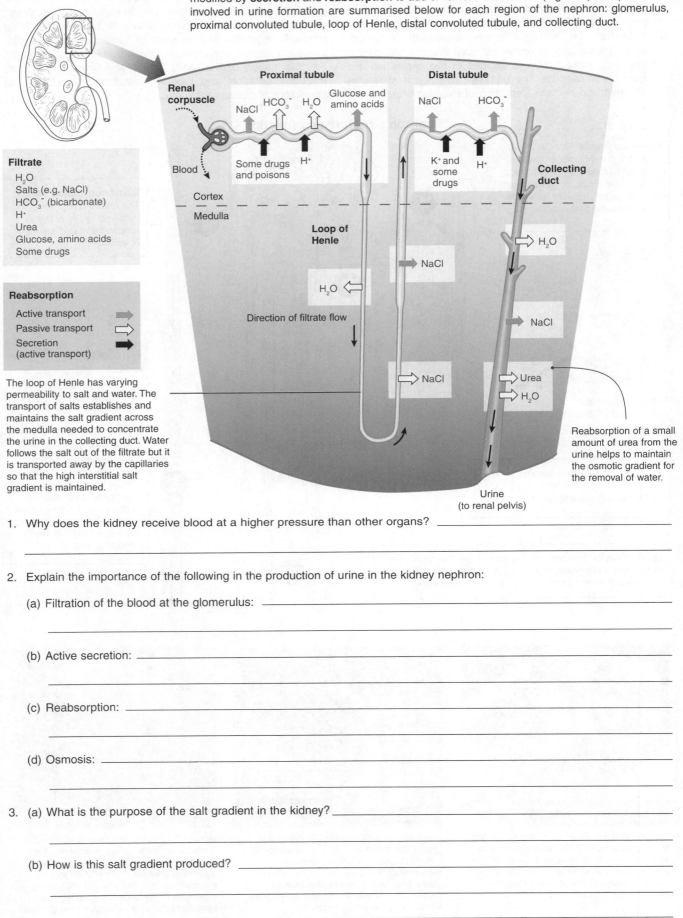

Filtrate

H_2O
Salts (e.g. NaCl)
HCO_3^- (bicarbonate)
H^+
Urea
Glucose, amino acids
Some drugs

Reabsorption

Active transport
Passive transport
Secretion (active transport)

The loop of Henle has varying permeability to salt and water. The transport of salts establishes and maintains the salt gradient across the medulla needed to concentrate the urine in the collecting duct. Water follows the salt out of the filtrate but it is transported away by the capillaries so that the high interstitial salt gradient is maintained.

Reabsorption of a small amount of urea from the urine helps to maintain the osmotic gradient for the removal of water.

1. Why does the kidney receive blood at a higher pressure than other organs? _____

_____

2. Explain the importance of the following in the production of urine in the kidney nephron:

   (a) Filtration of the blood at the glomerulus: _____

   _____

   (b) Active secretion: _____

   _____

   (c) Reabsorption: _____

   _____

   (d) Osmosis: _____

   _____

3. (a) What is the purpose of the salt gradient in the kidney? _____

   _____

   (b) How is this salt gradient produced? _____

   _____

   _____

© 2015 **BIOZONE** International
ISBN: **978-1-927309-14-8**
Photocopying Prohibited

18 Control of Urine Output

Key Idea: The body's fluid and electrolyte balance is regulated by varying the composition and volume of urine. This is achieved through the action of the hormones antidiuretic hormone (ADH) and aldosterone.

The body regulates the composition and volume of the blood to maintain homeostasis to compensate for variations in salt and water intake, and environmental conditions. This is achieved by varying the volume and composition of the urine and is under hormonal control. Antidiuretic hormone (ADH), from the posterior pituitary, regulates water reabsorption from the kidney collecting duct. Aldosterone, from the adrenal cortex, regulates sodium absorption from the kidney tubules.

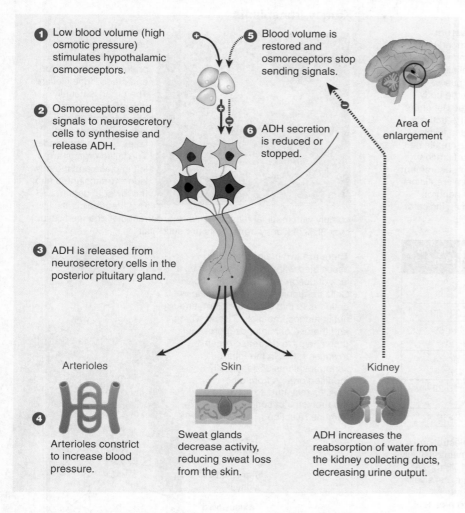

1. Low blood volume (high osmotic pressure) stimulates hypothalamic osmoreceptors.

2. Osmoreceptors send signals to neurosecretory cells to synthesise and release ADH.

3. ADH is released from neurosecretory cells in the posterior pituitary gland.

5. Blood volume is restored and osmoreceptors stop sending signals.

6. ADH secretion is reduced or stopped.

Area of enlargement

Arterioles

4. Arterioles constrict to increase blood pressure.

Skin

Sweat glands decrease activity, reducing sweat loss from the skin.

Kidney

ADH increases the reabsorption of water from the kidney collecting ducts, decreasing urine output.

Osmoreceptors in the **hypothalamus** of the brain respond to changes in blood volume. A blood volume stimulates the synthesis and secretion of the hormone ADH (antidiuretic hormone), which is released from the posterior pituitary into the blood. ADH increases the permeability of the kidney collecting duct to water so that more water is reabsorbed and urine volume decreases. A second hormone, aldosterone, helps by increasing sodium reabsorption.

Factors causing ADH release
▸ Low blood volume
   = More negative water potential
   = High blood sodium levels
   = Low fluid intake
▸ Nicotine and morphine

Factors inhibiting ADH release
▸ High blood volume
   = Less negative water potential
   = Low blood sodium levels
▸ High fluid intake
▸ Alcohol consumption

Factors causing the release of aldosterone
Low blood volumes also stimulate secretion of aldosterone from the adrenal cortex. This is mediated through a complex pathway involving osmoreceptors near the kidney glomeruli and the hormone renin from the kidney.

1. State what happens to urine volume and blood volume when:

   (a) ADH secretion increases: _____

   (b) ADH secretion decreases: _____

2. Diabetes insipidus is caused by a lack of ADH. From what you know about ADH, describe the symptoms of this disease:

   _____

   _____

3. Explain why alcohol consumption (especially to excess) causes dehydration and thirst: _____

   _____

4. (a) State the effect of aldosterone on the kidney nephron: _____

   (b) What would be the net result of this effect: _____

5. Explain the role of negative feedback in the regulation of blood volume and urine output: _____

   _____

   _____

LINK
17
WEB
18
KNOW

19 Kidney Transplants

Key Idea: A kidney transplant, where a healthy kidney from one person is transplanted into another, is a procedure used to treat people with complete kidney failure.

Kidney failure may come on suddenly (acute) or develop over a long period of time (chronic). Recovery from acute kidney failure is possible, but chronic kidney damage can not be reversed. If kidney deterioration is ignored, the kidneys will fail completely. In some cases diet and medication can be used to treat kidney failure, but when the damage is extensive, a kidney transplant is required.

Renal failure

Kidney (renal) failure is indicated by levels of **serum creatinine**, as well as by kidney size on ultrasound and the presence of anaemia (chronic kidney disease generally leads to anaemia and small kidney size). Creatinine is a break-down product of creatine phosphate in muscle, and is usually produced at a fairly constant rate by the body (depending on muscle mass). It is chiefly filtered out of the blood by the kidneys, although a small amount is actively secreted by the kidneys into the urine. Creatinine levels in both blood and urine is used to calculate the creatinine clearance (CrCl), which reflects the glomerular filtration rate (GFR). The GFR is a clinically important measurement of renal function and more accurate than serum creatinine alone, since serum creatinine only rises when nephron function is very impaired. Reduction in GFR in an indicator of kidney disease.

Disease stage	Description	GFR / mL min^{-1} 1.73 m^{-2}
1	Kidney damage but normal kidney function	>90
2	Mild loss of kidney function	60 - 89
3a	Mild to moderate loss of kidney function	44-59
3b	Moderate to sever loss of kidney function	30-44
4	Severe loss of kidney function	15-29
5	Kidney disease	<15

Problems arising from kidney failure include electrolyte imbalances. Sodium and potassium levels remain relatively normal until the GFR falls below 15 mLmin^{-1} 1.73 m^{-2}. At this point fluid may be excessively retained or excessively lost. The acid buffering ability of the kidneys reduces with the progression of kidney disease, leaving a patient vulnerable to metabolic acidosis and muscle protein breakdown.

Kidney transplants

Transplantation of a healthy kidney from an organ donor is the preferred treatment for end-stage kidney failure. The organ is usually taken from a person who has just died, although kidneys can also be taken from living donors. The failed organs are left in place and the new kidney transplanted into the lower abdomen. Provided recipients comply with medical requirements (e.g. correct diet and medication) over 85% of kidney transplants are successful.

There are two major problems associated with kidney transplants: a lack of donors and tissue rejection. Cells from donor tissue have different antigens to that of the recipient, and are not immunocompatible. Tissue-typing and the use of immunosuppressant drugs helps to decrease organ rejection rates. In the future, xenotransplants of genetically modified organs from other species may help to solve both the problems of supply and immune rejection.

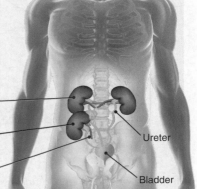

Diseased kidney

Transplanted kidney

Transplanted ureter

Ureter

Bladder

1. Distinguish between acute and chronic kidney failure: _____

_____

_____

2. Why would a rise in blood levels of creatinine indicate kidney failure? _____

_____

_____

3. Describe some of the advantages and disadvantages of kidney transplantation: _____

_____

_____

_____

_____

© 2015 **BIOZONE** International
ISBN: **978-1-927309-14-8**
Photocopying Prohibited

20 | Renal Dialysis

Key Idea: A kidney dialysis machine acts as an artificial kidney, removing waste from the blood when the kidneys fail. When the kidneys do not function properly, waste products build up in the body, and medical intervention is required to correct the problem. A dialysis machine removes wastes from the blood. It is used when the kidneys fail, or when blood acidity, urea, or potassium levels increase above normal. Blood flows through a system of tubes composed of partially permeable membranes. Dialysis fluid (dialysate) has a composition similar to blood except that the concentration of wastes is low. It flows in the opposite direction to the blood on the outside of the dialysis tubes. Consequently, waste products like urea diffuse from the blood into the dialysis fluid, which is constantly replaced. Dialysis can be ongoing, or can be used to allow the kidneys to rest and recover from injury, the effects of drugs or other metabolic disturbance.

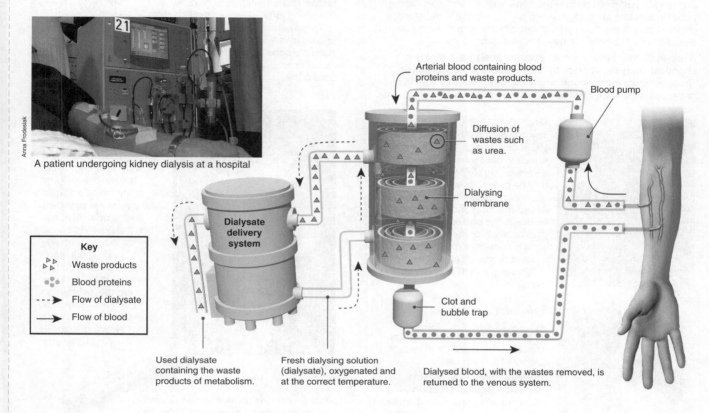

A patient undergoing kidney dialysis at a hospital

Arterial blood containing blood proteins and waste products.

Blood pump

Diffusion of wastes such as urea.

Dialysing membrane

Dialysate delivery system

Clot and bubble trap

Key
- ▷▷▷ Waste products
- •°•° Blood proteins
- - - ▶ Flow of dialysate
- ──▶ Flow of blood

Used dialysate containing the waste products of metabolism.

Fresh dialysing solution (dialysate), oxygenated and at the correct temperature.

Dialysed blood, with the wastes removed, is returned to the venous system.

1. In kidney dialysis, explain why the dialysing solution is constantly replaced rather than being recirculated:

_____

_____

2. Explain why ions such as potassium and sodium, and small molecules like glucose do not diffuse rapidly from the blood into the dialysing solution along with the urea:

_____

_____

3. Explain why the urea passes from the blood into the dialysing solution: _____

_____

4. Describe the general transport process involved in dialysis: _____

_____

5. Explain why the dialysing solution flows in the opposite direction to the blood: _____

_____

_____

_____

© 2015 **BIOZONE** International
ISBN: **978-1-927309-14-8**
Photocopying Prohibited

LINK 19 | WEB 20 | **KNOW** ▶

21 Urine Analysis

Key Idea: Urine analysis can be used to detect medical disorders, pregnancy, and the use of illegal drugs.

Urine analysis (**urinalysis**) is used as a medical diagnostic tool for a wide range of metabolic disorders. In addition, urine analysis can be used to detect the presence of illicit (non-prescription) drugs and for diagnosing pregnancy.

Diagnostic urinalysis

A urinalysis is an array of tests performed on urine. It is one of the most common methods of medical diagnosis, as most tests are quick and easy to perform, and they are non-invasive. Urinalysis can be used to detect for the presence of blood cells in the urine, glucose, proteins, and drugs. Special dipsticks, which use immunological detection of a hormone are used to detect pregnancy.

A urinalysis may include a **macroscopic analysis**, a **dipstick chemical analysis**, in which the test results are read as colour changes, and a **microscopic analysis**, which involves centrifugation of the sample and examination for crystals, blood cells, or microbes.

MACROSCOPIC URINALYSIS

The first part of a urinalysis is direct visual observation. Normal, fresh urine is pale to dark yellow or amber in colour and clear. **Turbidity** or cloudiness may be caused by excessive cellular material or protein in the urine. A **red or red-brown** (abnormal) colour may be due to the presence of proteins (haemoglobin or myoglobin). If the sample contained many red blood cells, it would be cloudy as well as red, as in this sample (left) indicating blood in the urine.

DIPSTICK URINALYSIS

A urine dipstick is a narrow band of paper saturated with chemical indicators for specific substances. Dipstick tests include:

Protein: Normal total protein excretion does not exceed 10 mg 100 cm^{-3} in a single specimen. More than 150 mg per day can indicate kidney malfunction.

Glucose: Less than 0.1% of glucose filtered by the glomerulus normally appears in urine. Excess sugar in urine is usually due to untreated diabetes mellitus, which is characterised by high blood glucose levels (the cells cannot take up glucose so it is excreted).

Ketones: Ketones in the urine result from diabetic ketosis or some other form of starvation.

Testing for anabolic steroids

Anabolic steroids are synthetic steroids related to the male sex hormone **testosterone** (right). They work by increasing protein synthesis within cells, causing tissue, especially skeletal muscle, to build mass. They are used in medicine to stimulate bone growth and appetite, induce male puberty, and treat chronic wasting conditions.

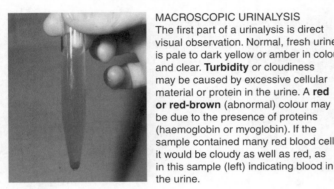

Steroids increase muscle mass and physical strength, and are used illegally by some athletes to gain an advantage over their competitors. Anabolic steroid use is banned by most major sporting bodies, but many athletes continue to use them illegally. Athletes are routinely tested for the presence of performance enhancing drugs, including anabolic steroids.

Anabolic steroids break down into known metabolites which are excreted in the urine. The presence of specific metabolites indicates which substance has been used by the athlete. Some steroid metabolites stay in the urine for weeks or months after being taken, while others are eliminated quite rapidly.

Athletes using anabolic steroids can escape detection by stopping use of the drugs prior to competition. This allows the body time to break down and eliminate the components, and the drug use goes undetected.

1. Why is **urinalysis** a frequently used diagnostic technique for many common disorders? _____

_____

_____

2. What might the following abnormal results in a urine test suggest to a doctor?

(a) Excess glucose: _____

(b) A red-brown colour: _____

3. Why might an athlete who is using illegal drugs withhold them for a period of time before competition? _____

_____

_____

© 2015 **BIOZONE** International
ISBN: **978-1-927309-14-8**
Photocopying Prohibited

22 Urine Analysis for Pregnancy Testing

Key Idea: The reaction of enzyme-linked monoclonal antibodies with the hormone HCG in the urine can be used to detect pregnancy.

Monoclonal antibodies (mAb) are artificially produced antibodies, which are all clones of a single cell and are specific to a particular antigen. Their ability to bind a specific molecule enables them to be used to detect that molecule (and only that molecule) in a biological sample, e.g. of urine, blood, or milk. Assays using monoclonal antibodies are fast and very sensitive and are now widely used in diagnostic tests. The example below describes the use of monoclonal antibodies to detect and bind the hormone HCG, which is present in the urine of women early in pregnancy. This type of pregnancy test also involves the use of polyclonal antibodies, which recognise a range of different antigenic markers and act to trap HCG molecules in a test zone.

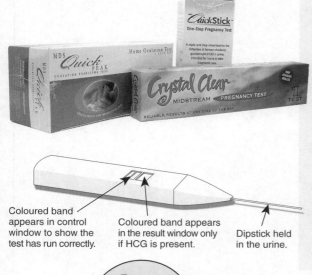

Coloured band appears in control window to show the test has run correctly.

Coloured band appears in the result window only if HCG is present.

Dipstick held in the urine.

Pregnancy testing using monoclonal antibodies

Enzyme-linked monoclonal antibodies are used to detect and quantify specific antigens (e.g. peptides, proteins, or hormones). Prepared monoclonal antibodies specific to the antigen are used to bind to the antigen in a controlled way. The antibody has an enzyme attached and the enzyme's reaction with a substrate is used to produce an observable colour change. Pregnancy testing (below) relies on the presence or absence of the hormone, human chorionic gonadotropin (**HCG**), which is produced by women early in pregnancy. HCG accumulates in the blood and is excreted in the urine. Antibodies (**Ab**) are artificially produced against the HCG molecule and used to detect pregnancy.

The method described here is an ELISA-based pregnancy test. ELISA stands for **E**nzyme-**L**inked **I**mmuno**s**orbent **A**ssay and simply refers to the use of an immunological (antibody) reaction that is linked to a detectable enzyme reaction. This method uses three different antibody (Ab) preparations (below). The centre test zone contains polyclonal antibodies (Ab from different lines), which detect different antigenic regions of the HCG molecule and can therefore trap HCG in the test zone.

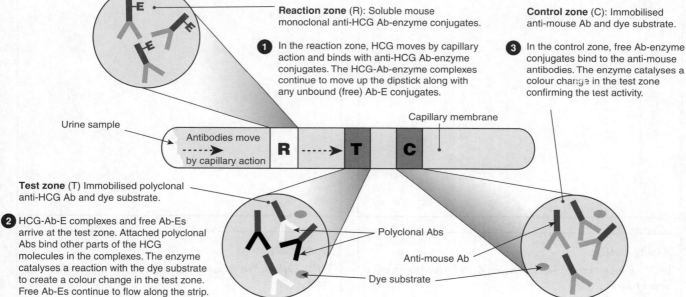

Reaction zone (R): Soluble mouse monoclonal anti-HCG Ab-enzyme conjugates.

1 In the reaction zone, HCG moves by capillary action and binds with anti-HCG Ab-enzyme conjugates. The HCG-Ab-enzyme complexes continue to move up the dipstick along with any unbound (free) Ab-E conjugates.

Control zone (C): Immobilised anti-mouse Ab and dye substrate.

3 In the control zone, free Ab-enzyme conjugates bind to the anti-mouse antibodies. The enzyme catalyses a colour change in the test zone confirming the test activity.

Urine sample

Antibodies move by capillary action

Capillary membrane

Test zone (T) Immobilised polyclonal anti-HCG Ab and dye substrate.

2 HCG-Ab-E complexes and free Ab-Es arrive at the test zone. Attached polyclonal Abs bind other parts of the HCG molecules in the complexes. The enzyme catalyses a reaction with the dye substrate to create a colour change in the test zone. Free Ab-Es continue to flow along the strip.

Polyclonal Abs

Anti-mouse Ab

Dye substrate

1. In the ELISA-based pregnancy test kit described above, what is the nature and purpose of each of the three zones:

   (a) The reaction zone: _____

   _____

   (b) The test zone: _____

   _____

   (c) The control zone: _____

   _____

2. What would you expect to see in the windows if a woman was not pregnant? _____

23 Chapter Review

Summarise what you know about this topic under the headings and sub-headings provided. You can draw diagrams or mind maps, or write short notes to organise your thoughts. Use the images and hints to help you and refer back to the introduction to check the points covered:

Structure and function of the liver
HINT: Include the gross structure and histology of the liver and its roles in homeostasis.

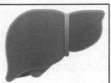

Structure and function of the urinary system
HINT: Include the structure of the kidney, the histology and function of the nephron.

Kidney disease
HINT: Include the effects, diagnosis, and treatment of renal failure.

Urine analysis
HINT: Explain the diagnostic applications of urine analysis.

© 2015 **BIOZONE** International
ISBN: **978-1-927309-14-8**
Photocopying Prohibited

REVISE

24 KEY TERMS: Did You Get It?

1. Match each term to its definition, as identified by its preceding letter code.

antidiuretic hormone (ADH)

excretion

kidney

liver

loop of Henle

nephron

A The functional unit of the kidney comprising the glomerulus, Bowman's capsule, convoluted tubules, loop of Henle, and collecting duct.

B Part of the kidney nephron between the proximal convoluted tubule and the distal convoluted tubule. Its function is to create a gradient in salt concentration through the medullary region of the kidney.

C The body's largest internal organ with important roles in digestion and homeostasis.

D The hormone released in response to low blood volumes, high sodium levels, or low fluid intake.

E Elimination of the waste products of metabolism.

F Bean shaped organ which removes and concentrates metabolic wastes from the blood.

2. (a) Name the excretory organ of vertebrates: _____

   (b) Name the selective filtering element of the kidney: _____

   (c) The length of this structure is directly related to the ability of an organism to concentrate urine: _____

   (d) Name the two hormones involved in controlling urine output: _____

3. In the micrograph below label the following: glomerulus, capsular space, convoluted tubules, Bowman's capsule.

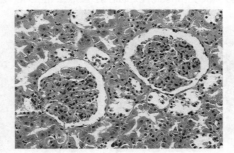

4. In the photograph below label left and right kidneys, left and right ureters, left renal vein and left renal artery.

Right renal artery

Right renal vein

Anatomist90 CC 3.0

5. (a) Name the repeating unit that makes up the liver tissue: _____

   (b) Identify three functions of the liver: _____

   _____

   (c) What three structures make up a portal triad? _____

   _____

6. (a) Nutrient-rich, oxygen-poor blood supplying the liver comes via the hepatic portal vein / hepatic artery (delete one)

   (b) Oxygen-rich, nutrient poor blood supplying the liver comes via the hepatic portal vein / hepatic artery (delete one)

TEST

Neuronal Communication

Key terms

acetylcholine
action potential
depolarisation
electroreceptor
hyperpolarisation
inhibition
mechanoreceptor
motor neurone
myelin
nerve impulse
neurone
node of Ranvier
Pacinian corpuscle
photoreceptor
refractory period
relay neurone
resting potential
sensory adaptation
sensory neurone
sensory receptor
stimulus (pl. stimuli)
summation
synapse
synaptic integration
thermoreceptor
threshold
transducer

Sensory reception

Learning outcomes

Activity number

☐ 1 Explain what is meant by a sensory receptor and give some examples. Identify stimuli to which sensory receptors respond and distinguish between internal and external stimuli. — 25

☐ 2 Distinguish different types of sensory receptors by the stimuli to which they respond: thermoreceptors, mechanoreceptors, photoreceptors, electroreceptors. — 25 26

☐ 3 Describe the roles of sensory receptors as biological transducers, converting different types of stimuli into nerve impulses. Distinguish between a sensory receptor and a sense organ. — 26 29

☐ 4 Describe the generation of a nerve impulse in a Pacinian corpuscle as an example of a simple sensory receptor. Explain how the impulse is generated and how information about the intensity of the stimulus is conveyed. With respect to the Pacinian corpuscle, explain sensory adaptation and its significance. — 29

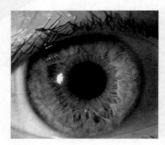 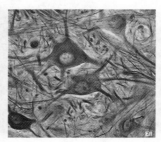 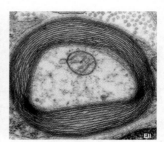

Neurones and nerve impulses

Learning outcomes

Activity number

☐ 5 Describe the structure and function of sensory, motor, and relay neurones. Describe and explain the differences in the structure and function of myelinated and non-myelinated neurones. — 27

☐ 6 Describe the generation and transmission of nerve impulses in mammals. Include reference to the how the resting potential is established and maintained and how the action potential is generated and transmitted by saltatory conduction, including the significance of threshold stimulation and the importance of the refractory period in determining impulse direction. — 28

☐ 7 Explain the significance of the frequency of impulse transmission. — 29

☐ 8 Describe the structure and roles of synapses in the transmission of nerve impulses. Describe impulse transmission across a cholinergic synapse to include the role of voltage gated calcium channels in the pre-synaptic membrane, diffusion of the neurotransmitter acetylcholine, and generation of an action potential in the post synaptic cell. — 30

☐ 9 Explain synaptic integration and the role of synapses in summation and control of nervous system responses. — 31

25 Detecting Changing States

Key Idea: Sensory receptors allow the body to respond to a range of stimuli in the internal and external environments. A **stimulus** is any physical or chemical change in the environment capable of provoking a response in an organism. Organisms respond to stimuli in order to survive. Stimuli may be either external (outside the organism) or internal (within its body). Some of the sensory receptors that animals (including humans) use to detect stimuli are shown below. Sensory receptors respond only to specific stimuli, so the sense organs an animal has determines how it perceives the world.

Hair cells in the vestibule of the inner ear respond to **gravity** by detecting the rate of change and direction of the head and body. Other hair cells in the cochlea of the inner ear detect **sound** waves. The sound is directed and amplified by specialised regions of the outer and middle ear (pinna, canal, middle ear bones).

Photoreceptor cells in the eyes detect colour, intensity, and movement of **light**.

Olfactory receptors in the nose detect airborne **chemicals**. The human nose has about 5 million of these receptors, a bloodhound nose has more than 200 million. The taste buds of the tongue detect dissolved chemicals (gustation). Tastes are combinations of five basic sensations: sweet, salt, sour, bitter, and savoury (umami receptor).

Chemoreceptors in certain blood vessels, e.g. carotid arteries, monitor carbon dioxide levels (and therefore pH) of the blood. Breathing and heart rate increase or decrease (as appropriate) to adjust blood composition.

Baroreceptors in the walls of some arteries, e.g. aorta, monitor blood pressure. Heart rate and blood vessel diameter are adjusted accordingly.

Proprioreceptors (stretch receptors) in the muscles, tendons, and joints monitor limb position, **stretch**, and **tension**. The muscle spindle is a stretch receptor that monitors the state of muscle contraction and enables muscle to maintain its length.

Pressure deforms the skin surface and stimulates sensory receptors in the dermis. These receptors are especially abundant on the lips and fingertips.

Simple nerve endings in the skin detect pain and temperature. Deep tissue injury is sometimes felt on the skin as referred pain.

Hearing is important to humans when learning to communicate; without it, speech and language development are more difficult.

The vibration receptors in the limbs of arthropods are sensitive to movement: either sound or vibration (as caused by struggling prey).

The chemosensory Jacobson's organ in the roof of the mouth of reptiles (e.g. snakes) enables them to detect chemical stimuli.

Breathing and heart rates are regulated in response to sensory input from chemoreceptors.

Baroreceptors and osmoreceptors act together to regulate blood pressure and volume.

Many insects, such as these ants, rely on chemical sense for location of food and communication.

Jacobson's organ is also present in mammals. It is used to detect sexual receptivity in potential mates.

1. What is a stimulus and how are stimuli perceived by an organism? _____

_____

2. (a) Name one external stimulus and its sensory receptor: _____

(b) Name one internal stimulus and its sensory receptor: _____

LINK 29   LINK 26   **KNOW**

26 The Basis of Sensory Reception

Key Idea: Sensory receptors act as transducers, detecting stimuli and converting them to an electrochemical signal.

Sensory receptors are specialised to detect stimuli and respond by producing an electrical (or chemical) discharge. In this way they act as **biological transducers**, converting the energy from a stimulus into an electrochemical signal. They can do this because the stimulus opens (or closes) ion channels and leads to localised changes in membrane potential called **receptor potentials**. Receptor potentials are graded and not self-propagating, but sense cells can amplify them, generating action potentials directly or inducing the release of a neurotransmitter. Whether or not the sensory cell itself fires action potentials, ultimately the stimulus is transduced into action potentials whose frequency is dependent on stimulus strength. The simplest sensory receptors consist of a single sensory neurone (e.g. nerve endings). More complex sense cells form synapses with their sensory neurones (e.g. taste buds). Sensory receptors are classified according to the stimuli to which they respond (e.g. photoreceptors respond to light).

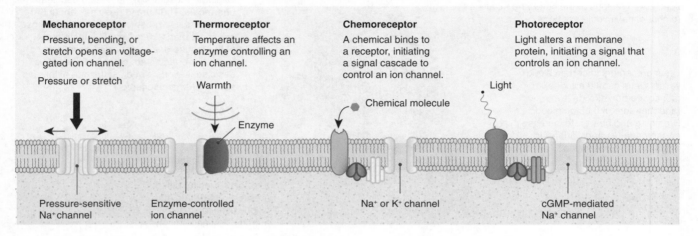

Mechanoreceptor
Pressure, bending, or stretch opens an voltage-gated ion channel.

Pressure or stretch

Pressure-sensitive Na⁺ channel

Thermoreceptor
Temperature affects an enzyme controlling an ion channel.

Warmth

Enzyme

Enzyme-controlled ion channel

Chemoreceptor
A chemical binds to a receptor, initiating a signal cascade to control an ion channel.

Chemical molecule

Na⁺ or K⁺ channel

Photoreceptor
Light alters a membrane protein, initiating a signal that controls an ion channel.

Light

cGMP-mediated Na⁺ channel

Signal transduction

Sensory cells convert one type of stimulus energy (e.g. pressure) into an electrical signal by altering the flow of ions across the plasma membrane and generating receptor potentials. In many cases (as in the Pacinian corpuscle), this leads directly to action potentials which are generated in the voltage-gated region of the sensory cell.

In some receptor cells, the receptor potential leads to neurotransmitter release, which then directly or indirectly leads to action potentials in a post-synaptic cell.

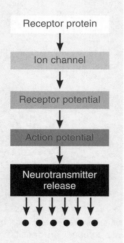

Receptor protein
↓
Ion channel
↓
Receptor potential
↓
Action potential
↓
Neurotransmitter release
↓↓↓↓↓↓
● ● ● ● ● ●

The Pacinian corpuscle

Pacinian corpuscles are pressure receptors in deep tissues of the body. They are relatively large but structurally simple, consisting of a sensory nerve ending (dendrite) surrounded by a capsule of connective tissue layers. Pressure deforms the capsule, stretching the nerve ending and leading to a localised depolarisation called a **receptor potential**. Receptor potentials are graded and do not spread far, although they may sum together and increase in amplitude.

The sense cell converts the receptor potentials to action potentials at the start of the axon (where there are voltage-gated channels). The action potential is then propagated along the axon.

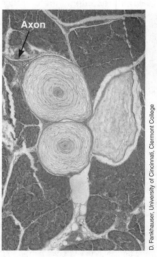

Axon

D. Fankhauser, University of Cincinnati, Clermont College

1. Explain why sensory receptors are termed 'biological transducers': _____

_____

_____

2. Identify one feature that all sensory receptors have in common: _____

_____

3. Explain how a stimulus received by a sensory receptor is converted into an electrical response: _____

_____

_____

4. Describe the properties of receptor potentials: _____

_____

_____

© 2015 **BIOZONE** International
ISBN: **978-1-927309-14-8**
Photocopying Prohibited

27 Neurone Structure

Key Idea: Neurones conduct electrical impulses from sensory receptors along axons to other neurones or to effector cells.

Neurones (nerve cells) transmit nerve impulses. Neurones have a recognisable structure with a cell body (soma) and long processes (dendrites and axons). Most neurones in the peripheral nervous system (nerves outside the brain and spinal cord) are also supported by a fatty insulating sheath of myelin. Information, in the form of electrochemical impulses, is transmitted along neurones from receptors to a coordination centre and then to effectors. The speed of impulse conduction depends primarily on the axon diameter and whether or not the axon is myelinated.

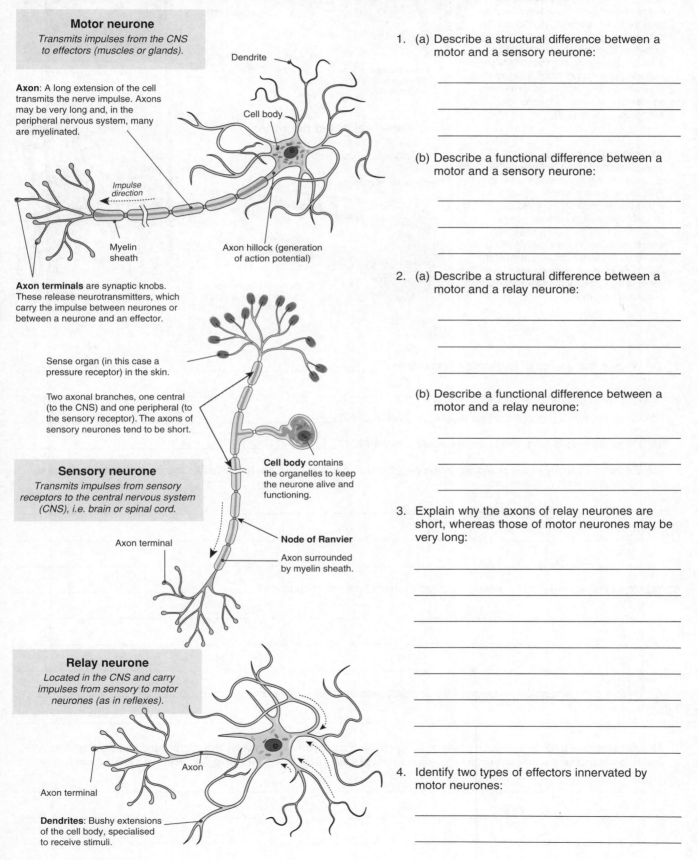

Motor neurone
Transmits impulses from the CNS to effectors (muscles or glands).

Dendrite

Cell body

Axon: A long extension of the cell transmits the nerve impulse. Axons may be very long and, in the peripheral nervous system, many are myelinated.

Impulse direction

Myelin sheath

Axon hillock (generation of action potential)

Axon terminals are synaptic knobs. These release neurotransmitters, which carry the impulse between neurones or between a neurone and an effector.

Sense organ (in this case a pressure receptor) in the skin.

Two axonal branches, one central (to the CNS) and one peripheral (to the sensory receptor). The axons of sensory neurones tend to be short.

Sensory neurone
Transmits impulses from sensory receptors to the central nervous system (CNS), i.e. brain or spinal cord.

Axon terminal

Cell body contains the organelles to keep the neurone alive and functioning.

Node of Ranvier

Axon surrounded by myelin sheath.

Relay neurone
Located in the CNS and carry impulses from sensory to motor neurones (as in reflexes).

Axon

Axon terminal

Dendrites: Bushy extensions of the cell body, specialised to receive stimuli.

1. (a) Describe a structural difference between a motor and a sensory neurone:

_____

_____

_____

(b) Describe a functional difference between a motor and a sensory neurone:

_____

_____

_____

2. (a) Describe a structural difference between a motor and a relay neurone:

_____

_____

_____

(b) Describe a functional difference between a motor and a relay neurone:

_____

_____

_____

3. Explain why the axons of relay neurones are short, whereas those of motor neurones may be very long:

_____

_____

_____

_____

_____

_____

_____

_____

_____

4. Identify two types of effectors innervated by motor neurones:

_____

_____

LINK
WEB

28 27 **KNOW**

Where conduction speed is important, the axons of neurones are sheathed within a lipid and protein rich substance called **myelin**. Myelin is produced by **oligodendrocytes** in the central nervous system (brain and spinal cord)) and by **Schwann cells** in the peripheral nervous system (PNS). At intervals along the axons of myelinated neurones, there are gaps between neighbouring Schwann cells and their sheaths. These are called **nodes of Ranvier**. Myelin acts as an insulator, increasing the speed at which nerve impulses travel because it prevents ion flow across the neurone membrane and forces the current to "jump" along the axon from node to node.

Myelinated neurones
Diameter: 1-25 μm
Conduction speed: 6-120 ms⁻¹

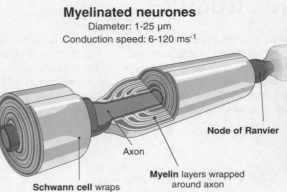

Node of Ranvier

Axon

Myelin layers wrapped around axon

Schwann cell wraps only one axon and produces myelin

Myelin

TEM cross section through a myelinated axon

Roadnottaken cc3.0

Non-myelinated axons are relatively more common in the CNS where the distances travelled are less than in the PNS. Here, the axons are encased within the cytoplasmic extensions of oligodendrocytes or Schwann cells, rather than within a myelin sheath. **Impulses travel more slowly** because the nerve impulse is propagated along the entire axon membrane, rather than jumping from node to node as occurs in myelinated neurones.

Non-myelinated neurones
Diameter: <1 μm
Conduction speed: 0.2-0.5 ms⁻¹

Cytoplasmic extensions

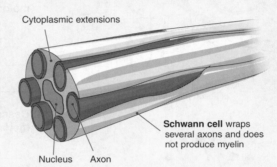

Schwann cell wraps several axons and does not produce myelin

Nucleus   Axon

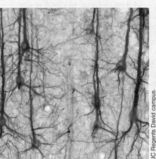

Unmyelinated pyramidal neurones of the cerebral cortex

UC Regents David campus

5. (a) What is the function of myelination in neurones? _____

_____

(b) What cell type is responsible for myelination in the CNS? _____

(c) What cell type is responsible for myelination in the PNS? _____

(d) Explain why many of the neurones in the peripheral nervous system are myelinated, whereas those in the central nervous system are often not:

_____

_____

_____

6. (a) How does myelination increase the speed of nerve impulse conduction? _____

_____

_____

_____

(b) Describe the adaptive advantage of faster conduction of nerve impulses: _____

_____

7. Multiple sclerosis (MS) is a disease involving progressive destruction of the myelin sheaths around axons. Why does MS impair nervous system function even though the axons are still intact (see *The Nerve Impulse* if you need more help)?

_____

_____

_____

© 2015 **BIOZONE** International
ISBN: **978-1-927309-14-8**
Photocopying Prohibited

28 The Nerve Impulse

Key Idea: A nerve impulse involves the movement of an action potential along a neurone as a series of electrical depolarisation events in response to a stimulus.

The plasma membranes of cells, including neurones, contain **sodium-potassium ion pumps** which actively pump sodium ions (Na^+) out of the cell and potassium ions (K^+) into the cell. The action of these ion pumps in neurones creates a separation of charge (a potential difference or voltage) either side of the membrane and makes the cells **electrically**

excitable. It is this property that enables neurones to transmit electrical impulses. The **resting state** of a neurone, with a net negative charge inside, is maintained by the sodium-potassium pumps, which actively move two K^+ into the neurone for every three Na^+ moved out (below left). When a nerve is stimulated, a brief increase in membrane permeability to Na^+ temporarily reverses the membrane polarity (a **depolarisation**). After the nerve impulse passes, the sodium-potassium pump restores the resting potential.

The resting neurone

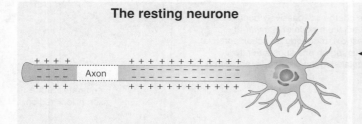

When a neurone is not transmitting an impulse, the inside of the cell is negatively charged relative to the outside and the cell is said to be electrically polarised. The potential difference (voltage) across the membrane is called the **resting potential**. For most nerve cells this is about -70 mV. Nerve transmission is possible because this membrane potential exists.

The nerve impulse

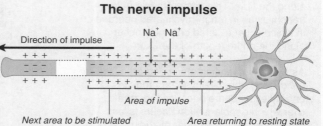

When a neurone is stimulated, the distribution of charges on each side of the membrane briefly reverses. This process of **depolarisation** causes a burst of electrical activity to pass along the axon of the neurone as an **action potential**. As the charge reversal reaches one region, local currents depolarise the next region and the impulse spreads along the axon.

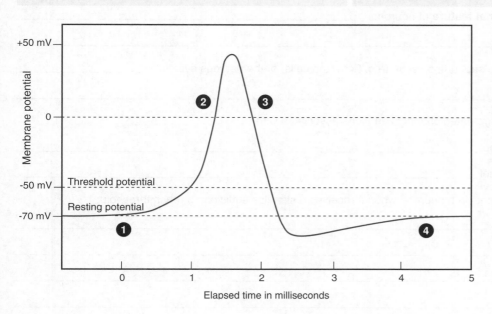

The depolarisation in an axon can be shown as a change in membrane potential (in millivolts). A stimulus must be strong enough to reach the **threshold potential** before an action potential is generated. This is the voltage at which the depolarisation of the membrane becomes unstoppable.

The action potential is **all or nothing** in its generation and because of this, impulses (once generated) always reach threshold and move along the axon without attenuation. The resting potential is restored by the movement of potassium ions (K^+) out of the cell. During this **refractory period**, the nerve cannot respond, so nerve impulses are discrete.

Voltage-gated ion channels and the course of an action potential

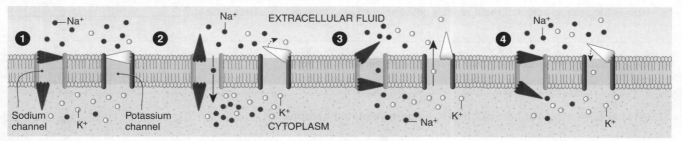

Resting state:

Voltage activated Na^+ and K^+ channels are closed.

Depolarisation:

Voltage activated Na^+ channels open and there is a rapid influx of Na^+ ions. The interior of the neurone becomes positive relative to the outside.

Repolarisation:

Voltage activated Na^+ channels close and the K^+ channels open; K^+ moves out of the cell, restoring the negative charge to the cell interior.

Returning to resting state:

Voltage activated Na^+ and K^+ channels close to return the neurone to the resting state.

Axon myelination is a feature of vertebrate nervous systems and it enables them to achieve very rapid speeds of nerve conduction. Myelinated neurones conduct impulses by **saltatory conduction**, a term that describes how the impulse jumps along the fibre. In a myelinated neurone, action potentials are generated only at the nodes, which is where the voltage gated channels occur. The axon is insulated so the action potential at one node is sufficient to trigger an action potential in the next node and the impulse jumps along the fibre. This differs from impulse transmission in a non-myelinated neurone in which voltage-gated channels occur along the entire length of the axon.

As well as increasing the speed of conduction, the myelin sheath reduces energy expenditure because the area over which depolarisation occurs is less (and therefore the number of sodium and potassium ions that need to be pumped to restore the resting potential is fewer).

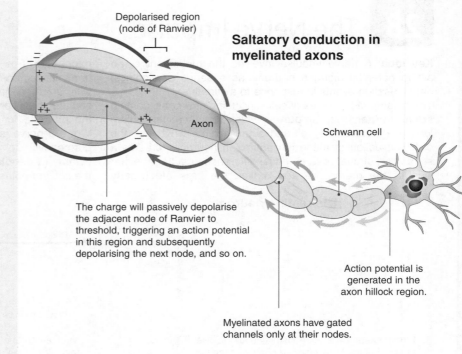

Depolarised region
(node of Ranvier)

Saltatory conduction in myelinated axons

Axon

Schwann cell

The charge will passively depolarise the adjacent node of Ranvier to threshold, triggering an action potential in this region and subsequently depolarising the next node, and so on.

Action potential is generated in the axon hillock region.

Myelinated axons have gated channels only at their nodes.

1. In your own words, define what an **action potential** is: _____

   _____

2. (a) Identify the defining **functional feature** of neurones: _____

   _____

   (b) How does this differ from the supporting tissue (e.g. Schwann cells) of the nervous system? _____

   _____

3. Describe the movement of voltage-gated channels and ions associated with:

   (a) Depolarisation of the neurone:_____

   (b) Repolarisation of the neurone: _____

4. Summarise the sequence of events in a neurone when it receives a stimulus sufficient to reach threshold:

   _____

   _____

   _____

   _____

   _____

5. How is the resting potential restored in a neurone after an action potential has passed? _____

   _____

6. (a) Explain how an action potential travels in a **myelinated neurone**: _____

   _____

   (b) How does this differ from its travel in a **non-myelinated neurone**? _____

   _____

7. Explain how the **refractory period** influences the direction in which an impulse will travel: _____

   _____

   _____

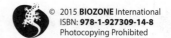
© 2015 **BIOZONE** International
ISBN: **978-1-927309-14-8**
Photocopying Prohibited

29 Encoding Information

Key Idea: Receptors use the frequency of a stimulus to encode information about the strength of a stimulus.

A receptor must do more than simply record a stimulus. It is important that it also provides information about the stimulus strength. Action potentials obey the 'all or none law' and are always the same size, so stimulus strength cannot be encoded by varying the amplitude of the action potentials. Instead, the frequency of impulses conveys information about the stimulus intensity; the higher the frequency of impulses,

the stronger the stimulus. This encoding method is termed **frequency modulation**, and it is the way that receptors inform the brain about stimulus strength. In the Pacinian corpuscle (below) frequency modulation is possible because a stronger pressure produces larger receptor potentials, which depolarise the first node of Ranvier to threshold more rapidly and results in a more rapid volley of action potentials. Sensory receptors also show **sensory adaptation** and will cease responding to a stimulus of the same intensity.

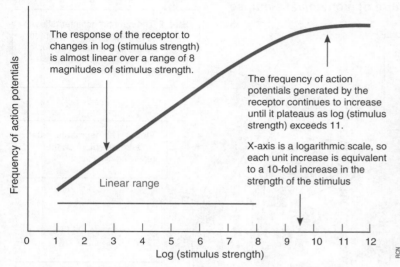

The response of the receptor to changes in log (stimulus strength) is almost linear over a range of 8 magnitudes of stimulus strength.

The frequency of action potentials generated by the receptor continues to increase until it plateaus as log (stimulus strength) exceeds 11.

X-axis is a logarithmic scale, so each unit increase is equivalent to a 10-fold increase in the strength of the stimulus

Receptors can use variation in action potential frequency to encode stimulus strengths that vary by nearly 11 orders of magnitude.

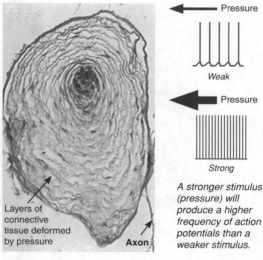

A stronger stimulus (pressure) will produce a higher frequency of action potentials than a weaker stimulus.

A Pacinian corpuscle (above), illustrating the many layers of connective tissue. Pacinian corpuscles are rapidly adapting receptors; they fire at the beginning and end of a stimulus, but do not respond to unchanging pressure.

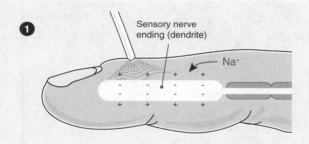

1 Deforming the corpuscle leads to an increase in the permeability of the nerve to sodium. Na⁺ diffuses into the nerve ending creating a localised depolarisation. This depolarisation is called a **receptor potential**.

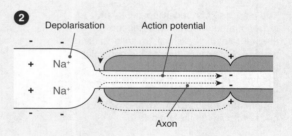

2 The receptor potential spreads to the first node of Ranvier, which is the first region with voltage-gated Na⁺ channels. It depolarises the node to threshold and generates an action potential, which propagates along the axon.

1. (a) Explain how the strength of a stimulus is encoded by the nervous system: _____

_____

(b) Explain the significance of encoding information in this way: _____

_____

_____

2. Using the example of the Pacinian corpuscle, explain how stimulus strength is linked to frequency of action potentials:

_____

_____

3. Why is sensory adaptation important? _____

_____

© 2015 **BIOZONE** International
ISBN: **978-1-927309-14-8**
Photocopying Prohibited

WEB
29 **KNOW**

30 The Cholinergic Synapse

Key Idea: Synapses are junctions between neurones or between neurones and effector (e.g. muscle) cells.

Action potentials are transmitted across junctions called **synapses**. Synapses can occur between two neurones, or between a neurone and an effector cell (e.g. muscle or gland). Chemical synapses are the most widespread type of synapse in nervous systems. In these, the axon terminal is a swollen knob, and a gap (the synaptic cleft) separates it from the receiving cell. The synaptic knobs are filled with tiny packets of a chemical called **neurotransmitter**. The neurotransmitter diffuses across the gap, where it interacts with the receiving (post-synaptic) membrane and causes an electrical response. In the example below, the neurotransmitter causes a depolarisation and the generation of an action potential. Some neurotransmitters have the opposite effect and cause inhibition (e.g. slowing heart rate).

The structure of a chemical synapse

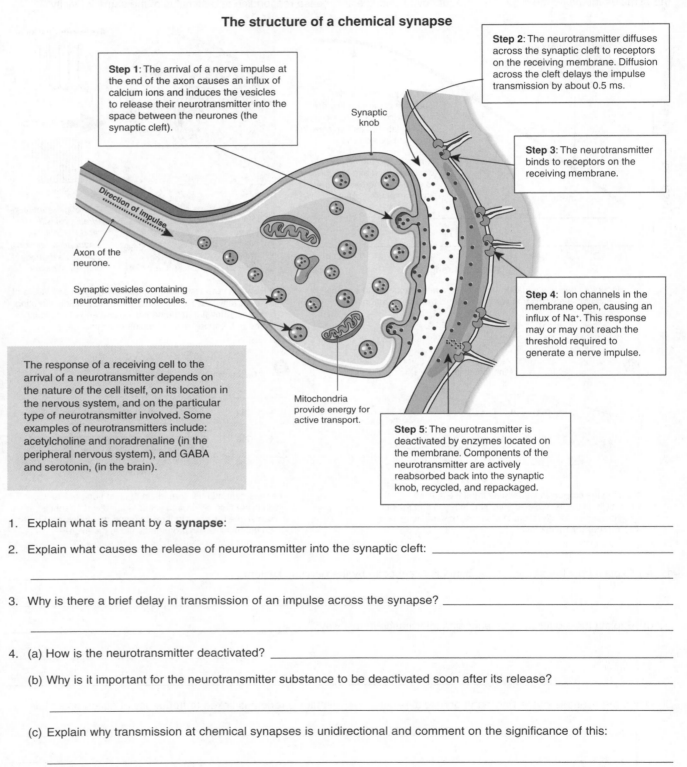

Step 1: The arrival of a nerve impulse at the end of the axon causes an influx of calcium ions and induces the vesicles to release their neurotransmitter into the space between the neurones (the synaptic cleft).

Step 2: The neurotransmitter diffuses across the synaptic cleft to receptors on the receiving membrane. Diffusion across the cleft delays the impulse transmission by about 0.5 ms.

Step 3: The neurotransmitter binds to receptors on the receiving membrane.

Step 4: Ion channels in the membrane open, causing an influx of Na^+. This response may or may not reach the threshold required to generate a nerve impulse.

Step 5: The neurotransmitter is deactivated by enzymes located on the membrane. Components of the neurotransmitter are actively reabsorbed back into the synaptic knob, recycled, and repackaged.

Synaptic knob

Axon of the neurone.

Synaptic vesicles containing neurotransmitter molecules.

Direction of impulse

Mitochondria provide energy for active transport.

The response of a receiving cell to the arrival of a neurotransmitter depends on the nature of the cell itself, on its location in the nervous system, and on the particular type of neurotransmitter involved. Some examples of neurotransmitters include: acetylcholine and noradrenaline (in the peripheral nervous system), and GABA and serotonin, (in the brain).

1. Explain what is meant by a **synapse**: _____

2. Explain what causes the release of neurotransmitter into the synaptic cleft: _____

_____

3. Why is there a brief delay in transmission of an impulse across the synapse? _____

_____

4. (a) How is the neurotransmitter deactivated? _____

   (b) Why is it important for the neurotransmitter substance to be deactivated soon after its release? _____

_____

   (c) Explain why transmission at chemical synapses is unidirectional and comment on the significance of this: _____

_____

5. Describe one factor that might influence the strength of the response in the receiving cell: _____

_____

© 2015 **BIOZONE** International
ISBN: **978-1-927309-14-8**
Photocopying Prohibited

31 Integration at Synapses

Key Idea: Synapses play a pivotal role in the ability of the nervous system to respond appropriately to stimulation and to adapt to change by integrating all inputs.

The nature of synaptic transmission in the nervous system allows the **integration** (interpretation and coordination) of inputs from many sources. These inputs need not be just excitatory (causing depolarisation). Inhibition results when the neurotransmitter released causes negative chloride ions (rather than sodium ions) to enter the postsynaptic neurone. The postsynaptic neurone then becomes more negative inside (hyperpolarised) and an action potential is less likely to be generated. At synapses, it is the sum of **all** inputs (excitatory and inhibitory) that leads to the final response in a postsynaptic cell. Integration at synapses makes possible the various responses we have to stimuli. It is also the most probable mechanism by which learning and memory are achieved.

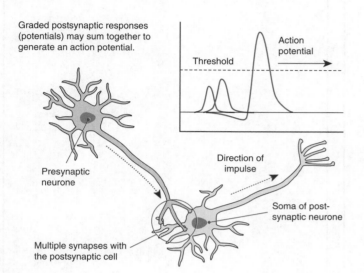

Graded postsynaptic responses (potentials) may sum together to generate an action potential.

Threshold

Action potential

Direction of impulse

Presynaptic neurone

Soma of post-synaptic neurone

Multiple synapses with the postsynaptic cell

Synapses and summation

Nerve transmission across chemical synapses has several advantages, despite the delay caused by neurotransmitter diffusion. Chemical synapses transmit impulses in one direction to a precise location and, because they rely on a limited supply of neurotransmitter, they are subject to fatigue (inability to respond to repeated stimulation). This protects the system against overstimulation.

Synapses also act as centres for the **integration** of inputs from many sources. The response of a postsynaptic cell is often graded; it is not strong enough on its own to generate an action potential. However, because the strength of the response is related to the amount of neurotransmitter released, subthreshold responses can sum to produce a response in the post-synaptic cell. This additive effect is termed **summation**. Summation can be **temporal** or **spatial** (below). A neuromuscular junction (photo below) is a specialised form of synapse between a motor neurone and a skeletal muscle fibre. Functionally, it is similar to any excitatory cholinergic synapse.

❶ Temporal summation

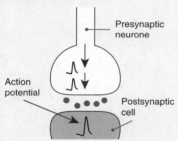

Presynaptic neurone

Action potential

Postsynaptic cell

Several impulses may arrive at the synapse in quick succession from a single axon. The individual responses are so close together in time that they sum to reach threshold and produce an action potential in the postsynaptic neurone.

❷ Spatial summation

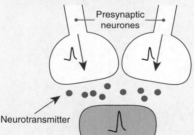

Presynaptic neurones

Neurotransmitter

Individual impulses from spatially separated axon terminals may arrive simultaneously at different regions of the same postsynaptic neurone. The responses from the different places sum to reach threshold and produce an action potential.

❸ Neuromuscular junction

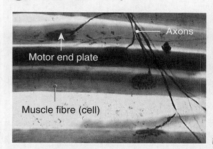

Axons

Motor end plate

Muscle fibre (cell)

The arrival of an impulse at the neuromuscular junction causes the release of acetylcholine from the synaptic knobs. This causes the muscle cell membrane (sarcolemma) to depolarise, and an action potential is generated in the muscle cell.

1. Explain the purpose of nervous system integration: _____

_____

2. (a) Explain what is meant by **summation**: _____

_____

(b) In simple terms, distinguish between temporal and spatial summation: _____

_____

_____

3. Describe two ways in which a neuromuscular junction is similar to any excitatory cholinergic synapse:

(a) _____

(b) _____

© 2015 **BIOZONE** International
ISBN: **978-1-927309-14-8**
Photocopying Prohibited

LINK **66**   LINK **30**   **KNOW**

32 Chapter Review

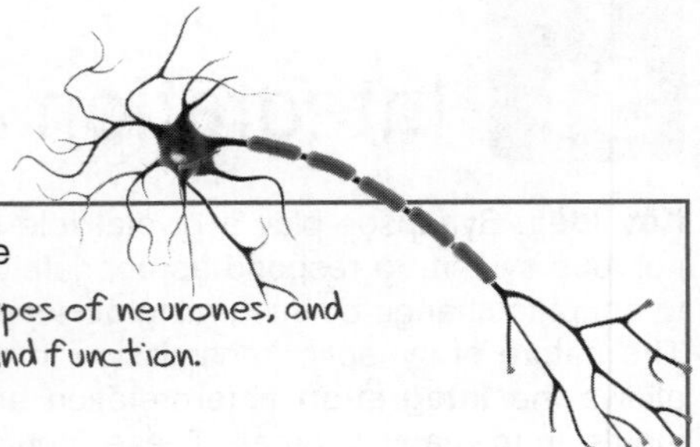

Summarise what you know about this topic under the headings and sub-headings provided. You can draw diagrams or mind maps, or write short notes to organise your thoughts. Use the images and hints to help you and refer back to the introduction to check the points covered:

Sensory reception
HINT: Describe types of receptors and their role as biological transducers.

Neurone structure
HINT: Describe types of neurones, and their structure and function.

The action potential and transmission across synapses
HINT: Explain the generation of the action potential, the structure and function of synapses, and the role of synaptic integration.

© 2015 BIOZONE International
ISBN: 978-1-927309-14-8
Photocopying Prohibited

REVISE

33 KEY TERMS: Did You Get?

1. Complete the crossword below:

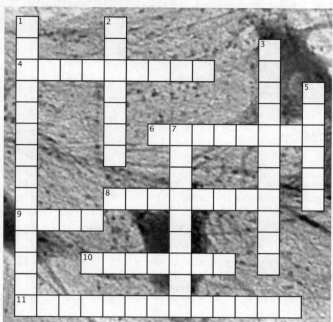

Across

4. A self propagating nerve impulse is called an action
   _ _ _ _ _ _ _ _ _ _ .
6. Extension of the nerve cell body specialised to receive stimuli.
8. A specialised cell that detects stimuli and responds by producing a nerve impulse.
9. Long extension of the nerve cell which transits the nerve impulse to another cell.
10. A cell specialised to transmit electrical impulses.
11. An organ system comprising a network of specialised cells or neurones, which coordinates responses and transmits signals between parts of the body (2 words).

Down

1. A temporary change in membrane potential caused by influx of sodium ions.
2. The gap between neighbouring neurones or between a neurone and an effector.
3. These synapses release acetylcholine.
5. This lipid-rich substance surrounds and insulates the axons of nerves in the peripheral nervous system.
7. Motor nerves carry impulses from the central nervous system to these.

2. (a) Label the components of this neurone (right) using the following word list: *cell body, axon, dendrites, node of Ranvier.*

   (b) Is this neurone myelinated or unmyelinated?(delete one)

   (c) Explain your answer: _____

   _____

   _____

   (d) In what form do electrical signals travel in this cell?

   _____

3. (a) The graph below shows a recording of the changes in membrane potential in an axon during transmission of an action potential. Match each stage (A-E) to the correct summary provided below.

Analysis of an action potential

Trace of a real recording of an action potential (rather than an idealised schematic). Recordings of action potentials are often distorted compared to the schematic view because of variations in the techniques used to make the recording.

Membrane potential

+50 mV

0 mV

-50 mV

-70 mV

Ⓐ Ⓑ Ⓒ Ⓓ Ⓔ

Elapsed time in milliseconds

☐ Membrane depolarisation (due to rapid Na⁺ entry across the axon membrane.

☐ Hyperpolarisation (an overshoot caused by the delay in closing of the K⁺ channels.

☐ Return to resting potential after the stimulus has passed.

☐ Repolarisation as the Na⁺ channels close and slower K⁺ channels begin to open.

☐ The membrane's resting potential.

(b) What is the resting potential of the axon? _____

(c) What is the maximum voltage reached by the action potential? _____

TEST

Hormonal Communication

Endocrine communication

Learning outcomes

		Activity number
☐	1 Define the terms endocrine gland, hormone, and target cell (tissue or organ). Appreciate that the body's two regulatory systems (hormonal and neuronal) in homeostasis are frequently interdependent.	34
☐	2 Describe endocrine communication by hormones to include secretion, transport, and effect on target cells or tissues.	34
☐	3 Describe the structure and function of the adrenal glands as an example of endocrine glands. Include reference to the cortex and medulla, the hormones secreted by each region and their functions, and how the secretion is regulated in each case.	35

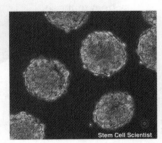
Stem Cell Scientist

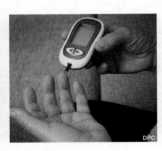
DPC

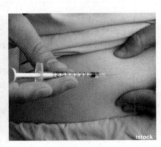
istock

The pancreas and blood glucose regulation

Learning outcomes

		Activity number
☐	4 Describe the histology of the pancreas to include the organisation of the endocrine tissues (islets of Langerhans).	36
☐	5 PAG1 Examine and draw stained sections of the pancreas to show the histology of the endocrine tissue.	36
☐	6 Explain how blood glucose level is regulated, including reference to the antagonistic actions of the hormones insulin and glucagon, negative feedback, and the role of the liver in glucose-glycogen conversions.	37 39
☐	7 Explain how insulin secretion is controlled, with reference to potassium and calcium channels in the islet beta cells and ATP.	38
☐	8 Distinguish between type 1 and type 2 diabetes mellitus, including reference to their different causes and treatments.	40 41
☐	9 Describe the treatment of diabetes mellitus with insulin produced using genetically modified organisms (e.g. *E. coli* bacteria or *Saccharomyces*). Describe the benefits of producing insulin this way.	40 199
☐	10 Describe the potential use of stem cells to treat diabetes mellitus. Discuss the advantages offered by stem cell therapy and possible technical and ethical considerations.	42

34 The Basis of Hormonal Control

Key Idea: The endocrine system regulates physiological processes by releasing blood borne chemical messengers (called hormones) which interact with target cells.

The endocrine system is made up of endocrine cells (organised into endocrine glands) and the hormones they produce. Hormones are potent chemical regulators. They are produced in very small quantities but can exert a very large effect on metabolism. Endocrine glands secrete hormones directly into the bloodstream rather than through a duct or tube. The basis of hormonal control and the role of negative feedback mechanisms in regulating hormone levels are described below.

How hormones work

Endocrine cells produce hormones and secrete them into the bloodstream where they are distributed throughout the body. Although hormones are sent throughout the body, they affect only specific target cells. These target cells have receptors on the plasma membrane which recognise and bind the hormone (see inset, below). The binding of hormone and receptor triggers the response in the target cell. Cells are unresponsive to a hormone if they do not have the appropriate receptors.

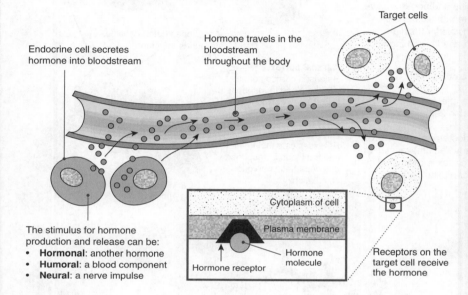

Target cells

Hormone travels in the bloodstream throughout the body

Endocrine cell secretes hormone into bloodstream

Cytoplasm of cell

Plasma membrane

Hormone molecule

Hormone receptor

Receptors on the target cell receive the hormone

The stimulus for hormone production and release can be:
- **Hormonal**: another hormone
- **Humoral**: a blood component
- **Neural**: a nerve impulse

Antagonistic hormones

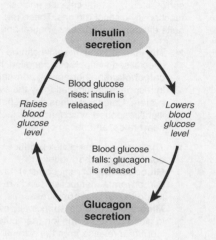

Insulin secretion

Blood glucose rises: insulin is released

Raises blood glucose level

Lowers blood glucose level

Blood glucose falls: glucagon is released

Glucagon secretion

The effects of one hormone are often counteracted by an opposing hormone. Feedback mechanisms adjust the balance of the two hormones to maintain a physiological function. Example: insulin acts to decrease blood glucose and glucagon acts to raise it.

1. (a) What are **antagonistic hormones**? Describe an example of how two such hormones operate:

_____

_____

_____

_____

(b) Describe the role of feedback mechanisms in adjusting hormone levels (explain using an example if this is helpful):

_____

_____

2. How can a hormone influence only the target cells even though all cells may receive the hormone?

_____

_____

3. Explain why hormonal control differs from nervous system control with respect to the following:

(a) The speed of hormonal responses is slower: _____

_____

(b) Hormonal responses are generally longer lasting: _____

_____

LINK 59   WEB 34   KNOW

35 The Adrenal Glands

Key Idea: The adrenal glands secrete hormones involved in the metabolism of carbohydrates, ion regulation, and the body's immediate and long term responses to stress.
The adrenal glands are endocrine glands that produce a variety of hormones with roles in carbohydrate metabolism, ion regulation, and response to stress. One adrenal sits above each kidney and each has two functionally and structurally distinct regions: an outer cortex and an inner medulla.

The adrenal glands

The adrenal glands sit above the kidneys. Each one is surrounded by a fatty capsule enclosing two structurally and functionally distinct regions. These regions are controlled by quite different mechanisms (neural and hormonal):

▶ The inner adrenal medulla can be regarded as a specialised sympathetic ganglion. It releases two **catecholamine** hormones, adrenaline and noradrenaline, in response to stimulation by the sympathetic nervous system. Catecholamines are responsible for the 'fight or flight' response, which includes increased breathing and heart rates, and paling of skin.

▶ The outer adrenal cortex produces a number of **corticosteroid** hormones.
Glucocorticoids (e.g. cortisol) have effects on carbohydrate metabolism, and are also secreted in response to long term stress.
Mineralocorticoids, (principally aldosterone) are involved in blood pressure and ion (particularly sodium) regulation. Hormone release from the adrenal cortex is controlled by the hormone ACTH from the anterior pituitary gland.

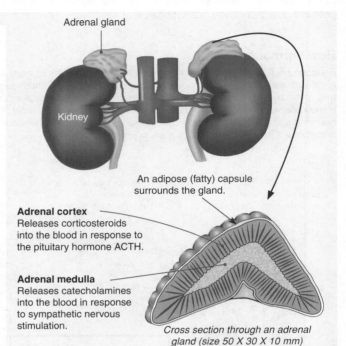

Adrenal gland

Kidney

An adipose (fatty) capsule surrounds the gland.

Adrenal cortex
Releases corticosteroids into the blood in response to the pituitary hormone ACTH.

Adrenal medulla
Releases catecholamines into the blood in response to sympathetic nervous stimulation.

Cross section through an adrenal gland (size 50 X 30 X 10 mm)

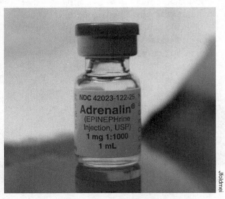

Adrenaline (epinephrine) is a stress related hormone involved in the fight or flight response. Medically, it is used as a treatment for heart attacks and anaphylaxis.

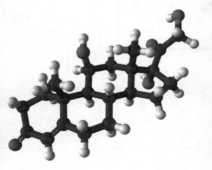

Cortisol is released by the adrenal cortex in response to stress and low blood glucose. It activates the formation of glucose in the liver, and suppresses the inflammatory response.

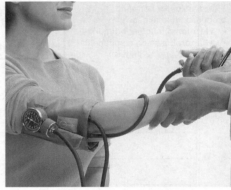

Aldosterone is involved in regulating blood pressure and ion balance. It acts on the distal convoluted tubule and collecting duct of the kidneys to stimulate reabsorption of sodium and secretion of potassium.

1. (a) Describe the structure of the adrenal glands: _____

   _____

   (b) Relate the structural differentiation of the adrenal glands to the functional role of each distinct region:

   _____

   _____

2. What two mechanisms regulate secretion from the adrenals? _____

3. (a) Name a catecholamine and briefly state its role: _____

   _____

   (b) Name a corticosteroid and briefly state its role: _____

   _____

© 2015 **BIOZONE** International
ISBN: **978-1-927309-14-8**
Photocopying Prohibited

36 Pancreatic Histology

Key Idea: The pancreas has dual exocrine and endocrine roles. The endocrine portion produces the hormones insulin and glucagon, which together regulate blood glucose levels. The **pancreas** is a diffuse organ, located alongside the stomach. It is both an exocrine gland, producing digestive secretions, and an endocrine gland, producing hormones from ductless cell clusters within the pancreatic tissue. This endocrine tissue is called the **islets of Langerhans**, after its discoverer and the two of the hormones produced, insulin and glucagon, regulate blood glucose levels. The histology of the pancreas, and the functions of its endocrine and exocrine regions are described below.

The pancreas

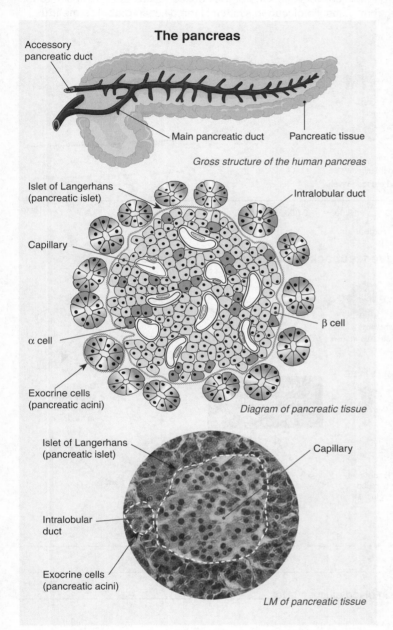

Gross structure of the human pancreas

Diagram of pancreatic tissue

LM of pancreatic tissue

Endocrine function

The islets of Langerhans are distinctive areas containing the endocrine cells of the pancreas. They make up 1-2% of the total mass of the pancreas. Islet cells are not readily distinguishable by routine staining techniques. Special stains are required to differentiate them. There are five types of endocrine cells. The alpha (α) cells and beta (β) cells make up the majority of the islet cell mass (15% and 65% of the total respectively). The main homeostatic role of the pancreas is to regulate blood sugar levels.

▶ The α cells secrete **glucagon**, which elevates blood glucose levels if they become too low.

▶ The β cells secrete **insulin**, which lowers blood glucose by promoting its cellular uptake. The two hormones work together to maintain blood glucose at a constant level.

The remaining endocrine cells have the following roles:

▶ Delta (δ) cells: produce the hormone **somatostatin** which affects neurotransmission and cell proliferation.

▶ PP-cells: control self regulation of pancreatic secretions.

▶ Epsilon (ε) cells: produce ghrelin, an appetite stimulant.

Exocrine function

The bulk of the pancreas is composed of pancreatic exocrine cells, which are arranged in clusters called **acini** (singular acinus). The cells contain **bicarbonate ions** and **precursor digestive enzymes** which are secreted into the duodenal region of the small intestine to aid digestion of food. Secretion from the acini is via a series of small intralobular ducts which drain into the major pancreatic duct, and from there into the duodenum.

The enzymes (in their active form) are as follows:

▶ Trypsin and chymotrypsin: digestion of protein

▶ Pancreatic lipase: digestion of lipid (fats)

▶ Pancreatic amylase: digestion of carbohydrates

The role of the bicarbonate ions is to neutralise the acidic **chyme** entering the small intestine from the stomach. The increase in pH allows the digestive enzymes of the small intestine to function.

1. (a) Which part of the pancreas has an endocrine function? _____

(b) What is the endocrine function of the pancreas? _____

_____

_____

2. How would you distinguish the endocrine from the exocrine tissue in a stained section of the pancreas?_____

_____

_____

3. Using a light microscope and relaxed viewing, examine and draw a stained section of pancreatic tissue. Use the information on the organisation of the tissues on this page to help you. Attach your finished drawing to this page.

 © 2015 **BIOZONE** International
ISBN: **978-1-927309-14-8**
Photocopying Prohibited

LINK **40** | LINK **39** | **KNOW**

37 Control of Blood Glucose

Key Idea: The endocrine part of the pancreas (the α and β cells of the islets of Langerhans) produces two hormones, glucagon and insulin, which maintain blood glucose homeostasis through negative feedback.

Insulin promotes a decrease in blood glucose by promoting cellular uptake of glucose and synthesis of glycogen. Glucagon promotes an increase in blood glucose through the breakdown of glycogen and the synthesis of glucose from amino acids. Negative feedback stops hormone secretion when normal blood glucose levels are restored. Blood glucose homeostasis allows energy to be available to cells as needed. Extra energy is stored as glycogen or fat. These storage molecules are converted to glucose when energy is needed. The liver has a central role in these carbohydrate conversions. One of the consequences of a disruption to the insulin-glucagon system is the disease **diabetes mellitus**.

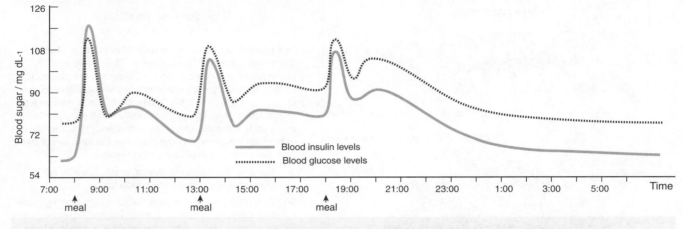

Blood sugar / mg dL^{-1} — Time (7:00, 9:00, 11:00, 13:00, 15:00, 17:00, 19:00, 21:00, 23:00, 1:00, 3:00, 5:00). Scale: 54, 72, 90, 108, 126. meal markers at ~8:00, 13:00, 18:00.

— Blood insulin levels
········· Blood glucose levels

Negative feedback in blood glucose regulation

In type 1 diabetes mellitus, the β cells of the pancreas are destroyed and insulin must be delivered to the bloodstream by injection. Type 2 diabetics produce insulin, but their cells do not respond to it.

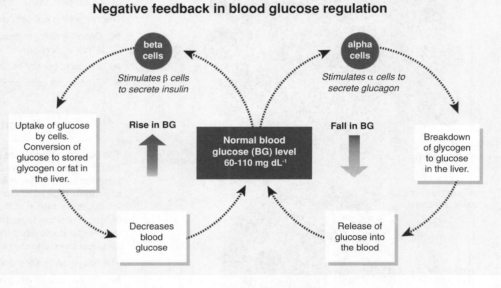

beta cells — Stimulates β cells to secrete insulin

alpha cells — Stimulates α cells to secrete glucagon

Uptake of glucose by cells. Conversion of glucose to stored glycogen or fat in the liver.

Rise in BG

Normal blood glucose (BG) level 60-110 mg dL^{-1}

Fall in BG

Breakdown of glycogen to glucose in the liver.

Decreases blood glucose

Release of glucose into the blood

1. (a) Identify the stimulus for the release of insulin: _____

    (b) Identify the stimulus for the release of glucagon: _____

    (c) Explain how glucagon brings about an increase in blood glucose level: _____

    _____

    (d) Explain how insulin brings about a decrease in blood glucose level: _____

    _____

2. Explain the pattern of fluctuations in blood glucose and blood insulin levels in the graph above:

    _____

    _____

    _____

    _____

3. The stimulus for the production and release of insulin and glucagon is: hormonal / humoral / neural (circle one):

© 2015 **BIOZONE** International
ISBN: **978-1-927309-14-8**
Photocopying Prohibited

38 Mechanism of Insulin Secretion

Key Idea: A rise in blood glucose initiates insulin secretion via a pathway involving an increase of intracellular K+ and Ca2+. The release of insulin from the pancreatic β cells is a complex multi-stage process involving selective entry of glucose into the cells and intracellular metabolism of the glucose to trigger the activation of voltage-gated calcium channels and export of insulin by exocytosis. The exported insulin then diffuses into the extensive network of blood vessels surrounding the pancreatic islets. Insulin release occurs in two phases. The insulin initially released when glucose is taken up into the cell depends on the amount in storage. Once this is depleted, a second phase of longer duration occurs, during which insulin must be synthesised, processed, and secreted for the period of time over which blood glucose levels are elevated.

The diagram below summarises the role of potassium and calcium channels in insulin secretion from a pancreatic islet β cell.

1 Glucose in the blood is transported into the β cells (of the pancreatic islets) by glucose transporter proteins.

2 Glucose is phosphorylated and used to generate ATP, increasing the intracellular ATP levels.

3 The ATP/ADP ratio increases, and ATP-sensitive potassium (K+) channels are closed.

4 Increased K+ levels lead to rise in positive charge inside the β cell, resulting in membrane depolarisation.

5 The depolarisation activates the voltage gated Ca2+ channels, and Ca2+ is transported into the β cell.

6 The increased Ca2+ levels within the β cell initiates insulin transportation across the cell membrane by exocytosis. The insulin is then transported around the body via the bloodstream.

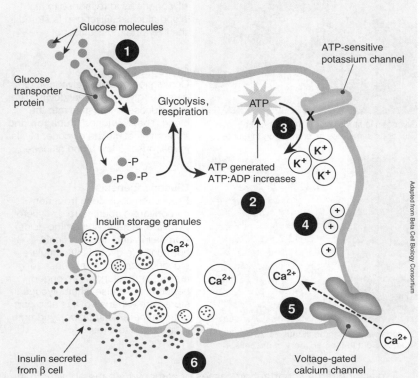

Adapted from Beta Cell Biology Consortium

1. Explain the role the following steps play in insulin secretion from a pancreatic beta cell:

   (a) The glucose transporter protein: _____

   _____

   (b) Increased intracellular ATP levels: _____

   _____

   (c) Membrane depolarisation: _____

   _____

   (d) Activation of the voltage-gated Ca2+ channels: _____

   _____

2. Explain the importance of the pancreatic islets being surrounded in an extensive network of blood vessels:

   _____

   _____

3. Explain the adaptive value of a two phase insulin release: an initial, large rapid release after eating, followed by a slower, longer lasting phase of insulin secretion:

   _____

   _____

LINK **40**   LINK **3**   WEB **38**   **KNOW**

39 Carbohydrate Metabolism in the Liver

Key Idea: Glycogen and glucose interconversions occur in the liver in response to hormones.

The liver has a central role in carbohydrate metabolism, specifically the production of glucose from non-carbohydrate sources (such as lipids and proteins) and the interconversion of glucose and glycogen. These dynamic processes are closely regulated by hormones, principally insulin and glucagon, but also adrenaline and glucocorticoids (e.g. cortisol). They ensure that carbohydrate is stored or made available to cells as required.

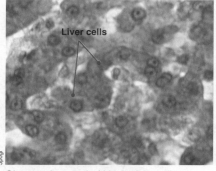

Glycogen is stored within the liver cells. Glucagon stimulates its conversion to glucose.

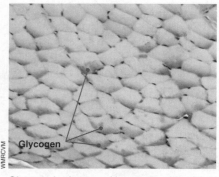

Glycogen is also stored in muscle, where it is squeezed out to the periphery of the cells.

▶ **Glycogenesis**

Excess glucose in the blood is converted to **glycogen** (a glucose polysaccharide). **Insulin** stimulates glycogenesis in response to high blood glucose. Glycogen is stored in the liver and muscle tissue.

▶ **Glycogenolysis**

Conversion of stored glycogen to glucose (glycogen breakdown). The free glucose is released into the blood. The hormones **glucagon** and adrenaline stimulate glycogenolysis in response to low blood glucose.

▶ **Gluconeogenesis**

Production of glucose from non-carbohydrate sources (e.g. glycerol, pyruvate, lactate, and amino acids). Adrenaline and glucocorticoid hormones (e.g. cortisol) stimulate gluconeogenesis in response to fasting, starvation, or prolonged periods of exercise when glycogen stores are exhausted. It is also part of the general adaptation syndrome in response to stress.

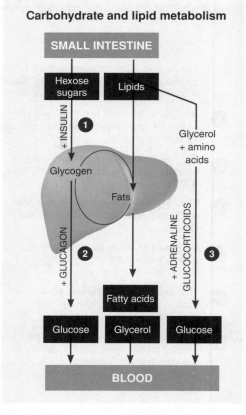

Carbohydrate and lipid metabolism

1. Explain the three important processes of carbohydrate metabolism in the liver, including how these are regulated:

(a) _____

_____

_____

(b) _____

_____

_____

(c) _____

_____

_____

2. Identify the processes occurring at each numbered stage on the diagram above, right:

(a) Process occurring at point 1: _____

(b) Process occurring at point 2: _____

(c) Process occurring at point 3: _____

3. Explain why it is important that the body can readily convert and produce different forms of carbohydrates:

_____

_____

40 Type 1 Diabetes Mellitus

Key Idea: In type 1 diabetes, the insulin-producing cells of the pancreas are destroyed and insulin cannot be made.

Diabetes mellitus is the result of a disruption to the insulin-glucagon system. It is characterised by **hyperglycaemia** (high blood sugar). **Type 1 diabetes** is characterised by **absolute insulin deficiency**. It usually begins in childhood as a result of autoimmune destruction of the insulin-producing cells of the pancreas. For this reason, it was once called juvenile-onset diabetes. It is a severe, incurable condition, and is treated with injections of synthetic insulin.

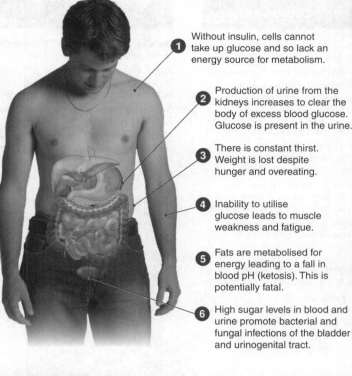

1. Without insulin, cells cannot take up glucose and so lack an energy source for metabolism.

2. Production of urine from the kidneys increases to clear the body of excess blood glucose. Glucose is present in the urine.

3. There is constant thirst. Weight is lost despite hunger and overeating.

4. Inability to utilise glucose leads to muscle weakness and fatigue.

5. Fats are metabolised for energy leading to a fall in blood pH (ketosis). This is potentially fatal.

6. High sugar levels in blood and urine promote bacterial and fungal infections of the bladder and urinogenital tract.

Cause of type 1 diabetes mellitus

Incidence: About 10-15% of all diabetics.

Age at onset: Early; often in childhood.

Symptoms: Hyperglycaemia (high blood sugar), excretion of glucose in the urine (glucosuria), increased urine production, excessive thirst and hunger, weight loss, and ketosis.

Cause: Absolute deficiency of insulin due to lack of insulin production (pancreatic beta cells are destroyed in an autoimmune reaction). There is a genetic component but usually a childhood viral infection triggers the development of the disease. Mumps, coxsackie, and rubella are implicated.

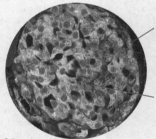

Solimena Lab cc2.5

α **cells** produce glucagon, which promotes glucose release from the liver.

β **cells** (most of the cells in this field of view) produce insulin, the hormone promoting cellular uptake of glucose. Cells are destroyed in type 1 diabetes mellitus.

Cell types in the endocrine region of a normal pancreas

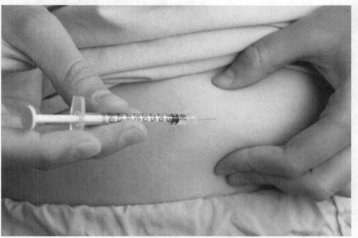

Treatments of type 1 diabetes mellitus

Present treatments: Regular insulin injections are combined with dietary management to keep blood sugar levels stable. Blood glucose levels are monitored regularly with testing kits to guard against sudden, potentially fatal, falls in blood glucose (hypoglycaemia).

Insulin was once extracted from dead animals, but animal-derived insulin produces many side effects. Genetically engineered microbes now provide low cost human insulin, without the side effects associated with animal insulin.

Newer treatments: Cell therapy involves transplanting islet cells into the patient where they produce insulin and regulate blood sugar levels. The islet cells may be derived from stem cells or from the pancreatic tissue of pigs. A new technology, encapsulates the pig islet cells within microspheres so they are protected from destruction by the patient's immune system.

Cell therapy promises to be an effective way to provide sustained relief for diabetes.

1. Describe the **symptoms** of type 1 diabetes mellitus and relate these to the physiological cause of the disease:

_____

_____

_____

_____

2. Explain how regular insulin injections assist the type 1 diabetic to maintain their blood glucose homeostasis:

_____

_____

_____

LINK 42 LINK 41 LINK 37 WEB 40 KNOW

41 Type 2 Diabetes Mellitus

Key Idea: In type 2 diabetes, the pancreas produces insulin, but the body does not respond to it appropriately.

In type 2 diabetes, the pancreas produces insulin, but the quantities are insufficient or the body's cells do not react to it, so blood glucose levels remain high. For this reason, type 2 diabetes is sometimes called insulin resistance diabetes. Type 2 diabetes is a chronic, progressive disease, and gets worse with age if not managed. The long-term effects of high blood sugar include heart disease, strokes, loss of vision, and kidney failure.

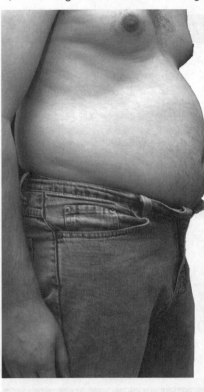

Symptoms of type 2 diabetes mellitus

a Symptoms may be mild at first. The body's cells do not respond appropriately to the insulin that is present and blood glucose levels become elevated. Normal blood glucose level is 60-110 mg dL^{-1}. In diabetics, fasting blood glucose level is 126 mg dL^{-1} or higher.

b Symptoms occur with varying degrees of severity:

▶ Cells are starved of fuel. This can lead to increased appetite and overeating and may contribute to an existing obesity problem.

▶ Urine production increases to rid the body of the excess glucose. Glucose is present in the urine and patients are frequently very thirsty.

▶ The body's inability to use glucose properly leads to muscle weakness and fatigue, irritability, frequent infections, and poor wound healing.

c Uncontrolled elevated blood glucose eventually results in damage to the blood vessels and leads to:

▶ coronary artery disease
▶ peripheral vascular disease
▶ retinal damage, blurred vision and blindness
▶ kidney damage and renal failure
▶ persistent ulcers and gangrene

Risk factors

Obesity: BMI greater than 27. Distribution of weight is also important.

Age: Risk increases with age, although the incidence of type 2 diabetes is increasingly reported in obese children.

Sedentary lifestyle: Inactivity increases risk through its effects on bodyweight.

Family history: There is a strong genetic link for type 2 diabetes. Those with a family history of the disease are at greater risk.

Ethnicity: Certain ethnic groups are at higher risk of developing of type 2 diabetes.

High blood pressure: Up to 60% of people with undiagnosed diabetes have high blood pressure.

High blood lipids: More than 40% of people with diabetes have abnormally high levels of cholesterol and similar lipids in the blood.

Treating type 2 diabetes

Diabetes is not curable but can be managed to minimise the health effects:

▶ Regularly check blood glucose level
▶ Manage diet to reduce fluctuations in blood glucose level
▶ Exercise regularly
▶ Reduce weight
▶ Reduce blood pressure
▶ Reduce or stop smoking
▶ Take prescribed anti-diabetic drugs
▶ Insulin therapy may be required

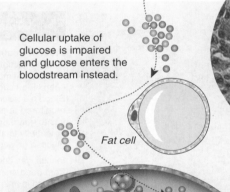

Cellular uptake of glucose is impaired and glucose enters the bloodstream instead.

Fat cell

Insulin

The β cells of the pancreatic islets (above) produce insulin, the hormone responsible for the cellular uptake of glucose. In type 2 diabetes, the body's cells do not utilise the insulin properly, hence the term insulin resistance.

1. Why is type 2 diabetes also known as insulin resistance? _____

_____

2. Distinguish between type 1 and type 2 diabetes, relating the differences to the different methods of treatment:

_____

_____

_____

_____

_____

© 2015 **BIOZONE** International
ISBN: **978-1-927309-14-8**
Photocopying Prohibited

42 Treating Diabetes with Stem Cells

Key Idea: New medical techniques using stem cells show promise in treating diabetes.

Shortages of donors for pancreatic transplants have prompted researchers to explore stem cell therapies as an alternative to donor tissue. Insulin-secreting pancreatic islet cells produced *in-vitro* can be transplanted into diabetes patients, where they produce insulin naturally. Such treatments start with a supply of stem cells either from embryonic stem cells or adult stem cells.

Stem cells for type 1 diabetes?

Type 1 diabetes results from the body's own immune system attacking and destroying the insulin-producing β cells of the pancreas. Research is focussed on how to obtain the stem cells, direct their differentiation into β cells in large numbers, and deliver them effectively to the patient. Many different techniques are currently being investigated.

Important steps

In 2014, two important pieces of research in the development of insulin producing β cells were published. In one study (labelled flow 1 right), human embryonic stem cells were treated with cell regulatory molecules to produce fully functional β cells (a difficult task on its own). β cells could also be produced from induced pluripotent cells (flow 2). What made this piece of research important was that the researchers were able to use the process to produce large numbers of β cells - enough for transplantation. The cells would be placed in a transplantation device to keep them safe from attack by the immune system. Trials with mice have been successful and human trials could begin by 2017.

A second study involved taking skin cells from diabetic mice, reprogramming them (using pluripotent-associated genes) into pluripotent (embryonic) stem cells, and then into β cells, which were injected into the pancreas. The cells behaved as functioning β cells and, because they were derived from the mouse 'patient's' own cells, they did not elicit an immune response.

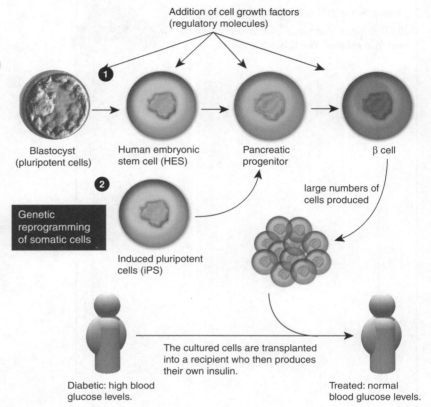

Addition of cell growth factors (regulatory molecules)

Blastocyst (pluripotent cells) → Human embryonic stem cell (HES) → Pancreatic progenitor → β cell

❶

❷ Genetic reprogramming of somatic cells

Induced pluripotent cells (iPS)

large numbers of cells produced

Diabetic: high blood glucose levels.

The cultured cells are transplanted into a recipient who then produces their own insulin.

Treated: normal blood glucose levels.

1. Why is type 1 diabetes a good candidate for stem cell therapy? _____

_____

_____

2. What is the difference between pluripotent stem cells and induced pluripotent stem cells? _____

_____

3. (a) Why was the first investigation (illustrated above) an important step in developing a treatment for type 1 diabetes?

_____

_____

(b) Why can't the β cells generated be transplanted directly into a type 1 diabetes patient? _____

_____

_____

4. (a) Why was the second investigation on mice an important step in developing a treatment for type 1 diabetes? _____

_____

_____

(b) Why would this treatment (as it currently stands) not be effective as a long term treatment for type 1 diabetes?

_____

_____

KNOW

43 Chapter Review

Summarise what you know about this topic under the headings and sub-headings provided. You can draw diagrams or mind maps, or write short notes to organise your thoughts. Use the images and hints to help you and refer back to the introduction to check the points covered:

Hormones and the endocrine system

HINT: Explain the basis of hormonal regulation and the role of the adrenal glands.

Control of blood glucose

HINT: Explain the hormonal regulation of blood glucose, including the role of the liver.

Diabetes

HINT: Distinguish between type 1 and 2 diabetes and outline current and future treatments.

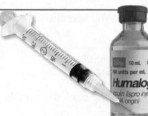

44 KEY TERMS: Did You Get?

1. Use the clues below to find the key terms in

```
P I P D I A B E T E S M E L L I T U S Z R C N G M
D G O P E N D O C R I N E G L A N D T T S V Q D L
G T C P B T N K B B K O A U C E Q K C Q J U P W E
O J V I M P E G Z M J L V M E D U L L A F D V N E
A J I S L E T S O F L A N G E R H A N S W V I J J
Z P Y H R M U N M H O Q V B S Y Z P J I O L O P D
G Q K O O F K V V N V F X V U B E H A N A O L Q K
F C G R L U O N T R S J Q D T P X X L N A P C U W
E B A M T J L R C J L V J T H W P Q E M C R K U A
Q E X O C R I N E G L A N D A W L R Z B E R P R I
E U N N B C K W O S D P S G S V D B C I L P E E V
O I O E I N S U L I N Z B Q Y A C T J N T H O A V
X H L S W Q H S J A Y A D R E N A L G L A N D S S
Z B L N O T G L U C A G O N U M H S V P U N Q A G
```

(a) Chemical messengers produced by endocrine glands.

(b) A ductless gland secreting hormones directly into the blood. (2 words)

(c) The hormone that lowers blood glucose, primarily through the cellular uptake of glucose, but also by promoting storage of glucose as glycogen.

(d) An abdominal organ with both endocrine and exocrine functions.

(e) The hormone responsible for the flight or fight response in the body.

(f) The hormone that brings about physiological processes to elevate blood glucose levels if they become too low.

(g) Ductless cell clusters found within pancreatic tissue, which have an endocrine function in the regulation of blood glucose.(3 words)

(h) A gland that delivers secretions via a duct. (2 words)

(i) A disease caused by the body's inability to produce or react to insulin. (2 words)

(j) Endocrine glands that sit on top of the kidneys. They play a function in regulating metabolism, water balance, and stress. (2 words)

(k) The inner region of the adrenal gland, it produces the catecholamine hormones adrenaline and noradrenaline.

2. For the image of the adrenal gland, right, label the medulla, capsule, and cortex:

3. (a) The hormones secreted by α and β cells together act to…

_____

(b) What mechanism controls the secretion of these hormones?

_____

(c) In which organ are α and β cells found? _____

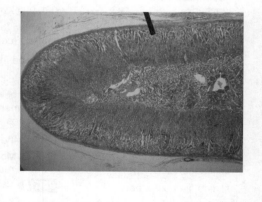

4. (a) What is the difference between glycogenesis and glycogenolysis?

_____

_____

(b) Where do these metabolic processes occur? _____

TEST

Module 5.1.5
Plant and Animal Responses

Key terms

- actin
- adrenaline
- apical dominance
- autonomic nervous system
- auxin
- cardiac muscle
- cell signalling
- central nervous system
- cerebellum
- cerebrum
- creatine phosphate
- cyclic AMP (cAMP)
- endocrine system
- fight or flight response
- geotropism (=gravitropism)
- gibberellin
- hormone
- hypothalamus
- involuntary muscle
- medulla oblongata
- midbrain
- muscle fibre
- muscle fatigue
- myosin
- nervous system
- neuromuscular junction
- peripheral nervous system
- phototropism
- phytohormone
- pons
- reflex
- second messenger
- signal transduction
- skeletal muscle
- sliding filament theory
- somatic nervous system
- thalamus
- tropism

Plant responses

Learning outcomes

	Activity number
□ 1 Describe the range of plant responses to abiotic and biotic factors, including chemical defences and nastic responses (e.g. leaf folding in *Mimosa pudica*).	45 46
□ 2 Describe and explain tropisms, including phototropism and geotropism (more commonly called gravitropism), and their roles in plant growth and orientation.	47
□ 3 Describe the experimental evidence for the proposed role of auxins in tropisms.	48 49
□ 4 **PAG11** Investigate a tropic response in a named plant.	50
□ 5 Explain the role of plant hormones in regulating the adaptive responses and life cycle activities of plants, e.g. leaf loss, seed germination, and stomatal closure.	51
□ 6 Describe and explain the experimental evidence for the role of auxins in regulating apical dominance.	52 53
□ 7 Describe and explain the experimental evidence for the role of gibberellins in controlling stem elongation and seed germination.	54
□ 8 **PAG11** Investigate the effect of a named plant hormone on plant growth.	54
□ 9 Describe the commercial use of plant hormones to control ripening in fruit, promote root development, and kill weeds.	55

Tangopaso   Ell   Ell

The mammalian nervous system

Learning outcomes

	Activity number
□ 10 Describe the structural and functional organisation of the mammalian nervous system, with reference to the central nervous system (CNS) and peripheral nervous system (PNS) and the somatic and autonomic divisions of the PNS.	56
□ 11 Describe the gross structure of the human brain and the functions of its main regions (cerebrum, cerebellum, hypothalamus, medulla oblongata, pituitary gland).	57
□ 12 Describe the structure of a simple monosynaptic reflex arc and its adaptive value, e.g. the corneal (blink) reflex or the patellar tendon (knee jerk) reflex.	58
□ 13 Explain how the nervous and endocrine systems coordinate responses to environmental stimuli, e.g. the fight or flight response in animals. Explain how hormones act as signal molecules in signal transduction pathways.	59 60
□ 14 Explain the nervous and hormonal regulation of heart rate.	60 61
□ 15 **PAG11** Monitor physiological functions, such as pulse rate or muscle fatigue, in response to exercise. Compare the mean responses of two populations **PAG10** using Student's *t* test or by comparing standard deviations.	62 70
□ 16 Describe the structure of cardiac, skeletal, and smooth (involuntary) muscle in mammals. Understand how muscles bring about movement by contraction.	63 64
□ 17 Describe the mechanism of muscular contraction, including the details of events at the neuromuscular junction, the sliding filament model of muscle contraction, the role of ATP, and the maintenance of ATP supply by creatine phosphate.	65-69
□ 18 **PAG11** Identify features of skeletal muscle in stained sections or photomicrographs.	63

45 Plant Responses to Abiotic Stress and Herbivory

Key Idea: Plants have a range of chemical defences that are responses to abiotic (physical) factors and herbivory. Herbivory (the consumption of plants) and abiotic (physical) factors can adversely affect the growth and productivity of plants. Common abiotic plant stressors include extremes of temperature, drought, and high salinity. Plants have evolved a variety of physical and chemical defences to minimise damage and conserve resources for growth and reproduction.

Plant responses to abiotic stress

Plants must be able to adapt to changes in abiotic factors in order to survive. Some responses are rapid, while others take place over a longer time in response to seasonal changes.

Rapid responses to environmental stimuli

Plants are capable of quite rapid responses. Examples include the closing of stomata in response to water loss and the opening and closing of flowers in response to temperature. These responses may follow a daily rhythm and are protective in that they reduce the plant's exposure to abiotic stress or mitigate against the stressor's effects.

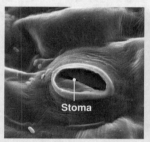 

Stoma

Plants normally close their stomata (above left) during periods of high temperature or high wind. This limits or prevents water loss, although it means that gas exchange and therefore photosynthesis, also stops. Severe water shortage combined with a failure to limit water loss can result in wilting, which can be severe enough to cause plant death.

Life cycle responses

Plants use seasonal changes (such as falling temperatures or decreasing daylength) as cues for starting or ending particular life cycle stages.

Such changes are mediated by plant growth factors, such as phytochrome and gibberellin and enable the plant to avoid conditions unfavourable to growth or survival. Examples include flowering (right), dormancy and germination, and leaf fall.

Plant responses to herbivory

Plants use a variety of physical defences (e.g. thorns and spines) and chemical strategies to deter herbivores. Many secrete chemicals or accumulate them in their tissues in order to deter potential herbivores. Some of these chemicals taste unpleasant, some are toxic, and others lower the nutritional value of the plant material. Common chemical defences include:

Tannins

Tannins are found in the leaves, bark, fruits, and seeds of many plants. The unpleasant, astringent taste of tannins in this persimmon fruit (right) acts as a deterrent to herbivores. Tannins bind the digestive enzymes of some herbivores and inactivate them so that they can no longer carry out their function.

Alkaloids

Alkaloids are bitter-tasting nitrogenous compounds and are found in many plants. They can have strong physiological or toxic effects if consumed. Caffeine (in tea, coffee, and cocoa plants) and nicotine (in tobacco plants) are examples of alkaloids. Capsaicinoids are alkaloids that cause chili peppers to be spicy. The hot, burning sensation produced when eaten stops the herbivore from eating them.

Pheromones and other chemical signals

In response to stress, plants may release chemicals that influence the activity of other organisms. Pheromones are chemicals that affect members of the same species, as when a grazed plant releases a chemical to induce other plants in the area to increase their production of tannins. In other plants, the chemicals released influence the behaviour of animals with which the plant has a mutually beneficial relationship. For example, in the 'ant-plants' (myrmecophytes), leaf damage triggers a release of chemicals that induce ant defenders to attack the animal causing the damage. The attacks are highly effective, killing small invertebrates and irritating vertebrate herbivores until they stop grazing.

Acacia ants rely on the acacia for food and a place to live. In return, it aggressively defends its plant against herbivores and plant competitors.

Ryan Somma

1. (a) Why do plants need to have mechanisms to cope with abiotic stress? _____

    _____

    (b) Describe an example of how plants can rapidly adapt to abiotic stress: _____

    _____

    _____

2. Describe the physical and chemical means by which plants protect themselves from herbivory: _____

    _____

    _____

    _____

    _____

LINK
46
WEB
45
KNOW

46 Nastic Responses

Key Idea: Nastic responses are plant responses in which the direction of the plant response is independent of the stimulus direction. They are often rapid and reversible movements.

Nastic responses in plants are independent of the stimulus direction and may involve quite rapid, reversible movements, often resulting from localised changes in turgor.

Nastic responses can occur in response to temperature (thermonasty), light (photonasty), or touch (thigmonasty). Plant 'sleep movements' (nyctinasties), in which flowers close or leaves droop at night, are specialised photonasties. The mechanisms involved in *Mimosa*'s thigmonasty (below) are also responsible for the leaf movements of the Venus flytrap.

Touch responses in plants

Mimosa pudica has long leaves composed of small leaflets. When a leaf is touched, it collapses and its leaflets fold together. Strong disturbances cause the entire leaf to droop from its base. This response takes only a few seconds and is caused by a rapid loss of turgor pressure from the cells at the bases of the leaves and leaflets. The message that the plant has been disturbed is passed quickly around the plant by electrical signals (changes in membrane potential), not by plant hormones (as occurs in tropisms). Although the response could be likened to the nerve impulse in animal nervous systems, it is not nearly as rapid. After the disturbance is removed, turgor is restored to the cells, and the leaflets will slowly return to their normal state.

Leaf

Leaflets

Unstimulated leaf

Disturbed leaf

When an insect touches the hairs on a leaf of a Venus flytrap (left), the two lobes of the leaf snap shut, trapping the insect. Once the insect has been digested, the empty leaves reopen. The hairs on the leaf must be touched twice in quick succession for the leaf to close. This means false alarms, such as a twig falling onto the leaf, do not set it off.

Tulips show temperature-induced sleep movements with a daily rhythm

Many flowers, including tulips, show sleep movements, opening during the day and closing at night. In many species, these are triggered by daylength, but in tulips the environmental cue is temperature. The photograph series below shows the sleep movements of a single tulip flower over one 12 hour period during spring.

7.00 am   9.30 am   11.00 am

5.00 pm   7.00 pm

1. What is a nastic response? _____

_____

2. Identify the type of nasty involved in each of the following examples:

(a) Opening and closing of tulip flowers to changes in air temperature: _____

(b) Opening of evening-primrose flowers at dusk: _____

3. Describe the basic mechanism behind the sudden leaf movements in *Mimosa*: _____

_____

© 2015 **BIOZONE** International
ISBN: 978-1-927309-14-8
Photocopying Prohibited

47 Tropisms and Growth Responses

Key Idea: Tropisms are directional growth responses to external stimuli. They may be positive (towards a stimulus) or negative (away from a stimulus).

Tropisms are plant growth responses to external stimuli, in which the stimulus direction determines the direction of the growth response. Tropisms are identified according to the stimulus involved, e.g. photo- (light), geo- (gravity), hydro- (water), and are identified as positive (towards the stimulus) or negative (away from the stimulus). Tropisms act to position the plant in the most favourable available environment.

(a) ....
A positive growth response to a chemical stimulus. *Example: Pollen tubes grow towards a chemical, possibly calcium ions, released by the ovule of the flower.*

(b) ....
Stems and coleoptiles (the sheath surrounding the young grass shoot), grow away from the direction of the Earth's gravitational pull.

(c) ....
Growth response to water. Roots are influenced primarily by gravity but will also grow towards water.

(d) ....
Growth responses to light, particularly directional light. Coleoptiles, young stems, and some leaves show a positive response.

(e) ....
Roots respond positively to the Earth's gravitational pull, and curve downward after emerging through the seed coat.

(f) ....
Growth responses to touch or pressure. Tendrils (modified leaves) have a positive coiling response stimulated by touch.

Plant growth responses are adaptive in that they position the plant in a suitable growing environment, within the limits of the position in which it germinated. The responses to stimuli reinforce the appropriate growth behaviour, e.g. roots grow towards gravity and away from the light.

Root mass in a hydroponically grown plant

Sweet pea tendrils

Germinating pollen

Thale cress bending to the light

Kristian Peters

1. Identify each of the plant tropisms described in (a)-(f) above. State whether the response is positive or negative.

2. Describe the adaptive value of the following tropisms:

   (a) Positive geotropism in roots: _____

   (b) Positive phototropism in coleoptiles: _____

   (c) Positive thigmomorphogenesis in weak stemmed plants: _____

   (d) Positive chemotropism in pollen grains: _____

3. Explain the adaptive value of tropisms: _____

   _____

   _____

   _____

LINK **49**　LINK **48**　WEB **47** **KNOW**

48 Investigating Phototropism

Key Idea: Experimental evidence supports the hypothesis that auxin is responsible for tropic responses in stems.

Phototropism in plants was linked to a growth promoting substance in the 1920s. Early experiments using severed coleoptiles gave evidence for the hypothesis that a plant hormone called auxin was responsible for tropic responses in stems. These experiments (below) have been criticised as being too simplistic, although their conclusions have been shown to be valid. Auxins promote cell elongation and are inactivated by light. Thus, when a stem is exposed to directional light, auxin becomes unequally distributed either side of the stem. The stem responds to the unequal auxin concentration by differential growth, i.e. it bends. The mechanisms behind this response are now well understood.

1. **Directional light:** A pot plant is exposed to direct sunlight near a window and as it grows, the shoot tip turns in the direction of the sun. When the plant was rotated, it adjusted by growing towards the sun in the new direction.

    (a) What hormone regulates this growth response?

    _____

    (b) What is the name of this growth response?

    _____

    (c) How do the cells behave to bring about this change in shoot direction at:

    Point **A**?_____

    Point **B**?_____

    (d) Which side (A or B) would have the highest hormone concentration and why?

    _____

    _____

    (e) Draw a diagram of the cells as they appear across the stem from point A to B (in the rectangle on the right).

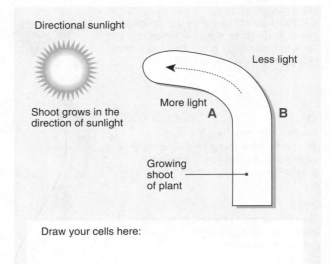

Directional sunlight

Shoot grows in the direction of sunlight

Less light

More light

A   B

Growing shoot of plant

Draw your cells here:

2. **Light excluded from shoot tip:** When a tin-foil cap is placed over the top of the shoot tip, light is prevented from reaching the shoot tip. When growing under these conditions, the direction of growth does not change towards the light source, but grows straight up. State what conclusion can you come to about the source and activity of the hormone that controls the growth response:

    _____

    _____

    _____

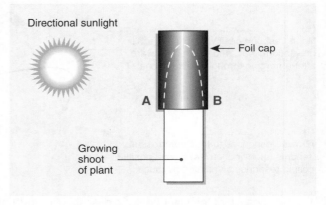

Directional sunlight

Foil cap

A   B

Growing shoot of plant

3. **Cutting into the transport system:** Two identical plants were placed side-by-side and subjected to the same directional light source. Razor blades were cut half-way into the stem, thereby interfering with the transport system of the stem. Plant A had the cut on the same side as the light source, while Plant B was cut on the shaded side. Predict the growth responses of:

    Plant **A**: _____

    _____

    _____

    Plant **B**: _____

    _____

    _____

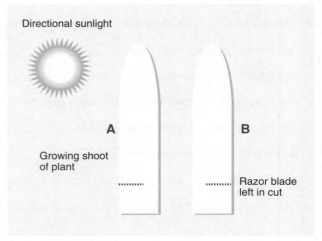

Directional sunlight

A   B

Growing shoot of plant

Razor blade left in cut

© 2015 **BIOZONE** International
ISBN: 978-1-927309-14-8
Photocopying Prohibited

49 Investigating Geotropism

Key Idea: Auxin appears to have a role in the geotropic responses of roots, but its effect may depend on the presence of other plant growth regulators.

The importance of the plant hormone auxin as a plant growth regulator, as well as its widespread occurrence in plants, led to it being proposed as the primary regulator in the geotropic (*aka* gravitropic) response. The basis of auxin's proposed role in geotropism is outlined below. The mechanism is appealing in its simplicity but has been widely criticised because of the use of coleoptiles. The coleoptile (the sheath surrounding the young grass shoot) is a specialised, short-lived structure and is probably not representative of plant tissues generally.

The role of auxins in geotropic responses

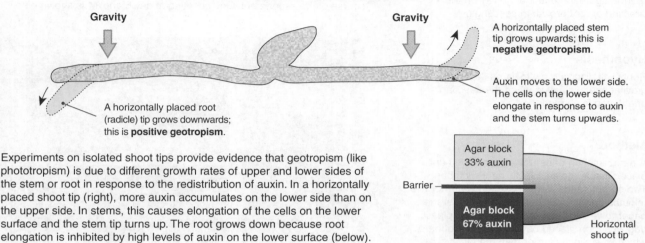

Gravity

A horizontally placed root (radicle) tip grows downwards; this is **positive geotropism**.

Gravity

A horizontally placed stem tip grows upwards; this is **negative geotropism**.

Auxin moves to the lower side. The cells on the lower side elongate in response to auxin and the stem turns upwards.

Experiments on isolated shoot tips provide evidence that geotropism (like phototropism) is due to different growth rates of upper and lower sides of the stem or root in response to the redistribution of auxin. In a horizontally placed shoot tip (right), more auxin accumulates on the lower side than on the upper side. In stems, this causes elongation of the cells on the lower surface and the stem tip turns up. The root grows down because root elongation is inhibited by high levels of auxin on the lower surface (below).

Agar block 33% auxin

Barrier —

Agar block 67% auxin

Horizontal shoot tip

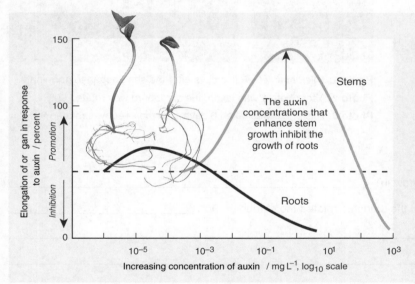

The auxin concentrations that enhance stem growth inhibit the growth of roots

Stems

Roots

Elongation of or gain in response to auxin / percent

Promotion

Inhibition

10^{-5} 10^{-3} 10^{-1} 10^1 10^3

Increasing concentration of auxin / mg L^{-1}, log$_{10}$ scale

Auxin concentration and root growth

In a horizontally placed seedling, auxin moves to the lower side in stems and roots. The stem tip grows upwards and the root tip grows down. Root elongation is inhibited by the same level of auxin that stimulates stem growth (graph left). The higher auxin levels on the lower surface cause growth inhibition there. The longest cells are then on the upper surface and the root turns down. This simple explanation for geotropism has been criticised because the concentrations of auxins measured in the upper and lower surfaces of horizontal stems and roots are too small to account for the growth movements observed. Other studies indicate that growth inhibitors may interact with auxin in geotropic responses.

1. Explain the mechanism proposed for the role of auxin in the geotropic response in:

   (a) Shoots (stems): _____

   _____

   (b) Roots: _____

   _____

   _____

2. (a) From the graph above, state the auxin concentration at which root growth becomes inhibited: _____

   (b) State the response of stem at this concentration: _____

3. Explain why the geotropic response in stems or roots is important to the survival of a seedling:

   (a) Stems: _____

   (b) Roots: _____

LINK **50** LINK **48** LINK **47** WEB **49** KNOW

50 Investigation of Geotropism in Roots

Key Idea: The effect of gravity on the direction of root growth can be easily studied using sprout seeds. The direction of root growth will change if the seedling's orientation is altered. The experiment described below is a simple but effective way in which to investigate geotropism in seedlings. Using the information below, analyse results and draw conclusions about the effect of gravity on the directional growth of seedling roots.

The aim

To investigate the effect of gravity on the direction of root growth in seedlings.

Hypothesis

Roots will always grow towards the Earth's gravitational pull, even when the seedling's orientation is changed.

Method

A damp kitchen paper towel was folded and placed inside a clear plastic sandwich bag. Two sprout seeds were soaked in water for five minutes and then placed in the centre of the paper towel. The bag was sealed. The plastic bag was then placed on a piece of cardboard which was slightly larger than the plastic bag. The plastic bag was stretched tightly so the plastic held the seeds in place, and secured with staples to the cardboard.

The cardboard was placed upright against a wall. Once the first root from each seed reached 2 cm long, the cardboard was turned 90° degrees.

Daily observations and photographs were made of the root length and direction throughout the duration of the experiment. Photos of one seedling from days 5 and 11 are shown right.

Results

The students took photographs to record changes in growth during the course of the experiment. One seedling at day 5 and 11 is shown below.

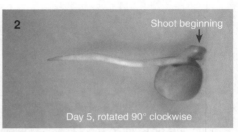
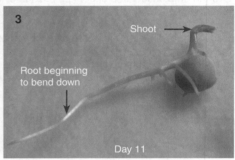

Photo 1: This photo was 5 five days after the seed began to germinate.

Photo 2: After photo 1 was taken, the cardboard was rotated 90°.

Photo 3: This photo was taken 6 days after the seed was rotated 90°.

1. (a) What direction did the root first begin to grow in? _____

    (b) Describe what happened to the root when the students rotated the cardboard 90°: _____

    _____

    _____

    (c) Explain why this occurred: _____

    _____

    _____

    (d) Predict the result after six more days growth if the students rotated the seedling in photo 3 90° clockwise. Draw your answer in the space right:

2. During the course of the experiment a shoot developed.

    (a) In what direction did the shoot grow at first? _____

    _____

    (b) In what direction did the shoot grow after rotation 90°C (photo 3)?

    _____

    (c) Why did this occur? _____

    _____

© 2015 **BIOZONE** International
ISBN: 978-1-927309-14-8
Photocopying Prohibited

51 Regulating Seasonal and Daily Events

Key Idea: Plant hormones play crucial roles in the timing of activities such as leaf loss, germination, and stomatal closure. Plant hormones (or phytohormones) are chemicals that act as signal molecules to regulate plant growth and responses.

Alone or together, plant hormones target specific cells to cause a specific effect. Many have roles in coordinating timing responses in plants including promoting seed germination, leaf loss, and stomatal closure (below).

Seed germination

In plants, germination refers to when a seed begins to sprout (left) and develop into a seedling. This process is controlled by a group of hormones called **gibberellins** (GA). When conditions are favourable for growth (e.g. moist, warm soil temperature) gibberellins break seed dormancy and promote the growth of the seed. Cell division and cell elongation are stimulated, allowing the root to penetrate the seed coat.

The effect of gibberellic acid on the growth of rhododendron seedlings

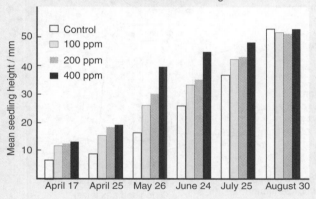

Control
100 ppm
200 ppm
400 ppm

Adapted from Ticknor, R. Journal American Rhododendron Society, Volume 12(2) April 1958

The effect of gibberellic acid (a type of gibberellin) on germination in rhododendron seedlings is shown above. Seeds were initially germinated on sphagnum moss and transferred into soil when two leaves formed. Gibberellic acid of varying concentrations (100, 200, or 400 ppm) was sprayed on the seedlings when they reached 5 mm in height. The controls received no gibberellic acid. The height of the seedlings was measured at varying time intervals (above). Each bar represents the mean height of 15 seedlings.

Leaf loss in deciduous plants

Deciduous plants shed their leaves every autumn in a process called **abscission**. The plant hormones **auxin** and **ethylene** work together to cause leaf loss. As the leaf ages, auxin levels within the leaf drop. The plant becomes more sensitive to the effects of ethylene, and gene expression of enzymes involved in cell wall degradation (e.g. cellulase) increases. These enzymes begin to break down the cell wall in localised regions (the separation layer) at the base of the leaf stalk (petiole). As a result the leaf and its stalk fall away.

Stomatal closure

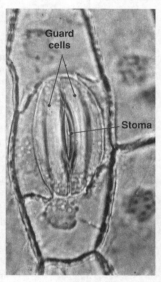

Guard cells

Stoma

Gas exchange and water loss from plants occur via stomata (pores on the surfaces of leaves). Turgor changes in the guard cells flanking the stomata open and close the pore (the pore opens when the guard cells are swollen tight and closes when they are flaccid). This regulates the rate of gas exchange and water loss. The hormone abscisic acid (ABA) is involved in regulating stomatal closure. In times of drought or high salinity, ABA levels increase, causing K^+ and Cl^- to leave the guard cells. Water follows by osmosis and the stomata close, reducing water loss via transpiration and conserving water.

1. Describe the results for the graph above and determine if gibberellic acid has any effect on seedling growth: _____

_____

_____

_____

2. Describe the role of auxin and ethylene in leaf loss: _____

_____

_____

3. Why is ABA important in the survival of plants during times of drought? _____

_____

_____

LINK **45** WEB **51** KNOW

68

52 Transport and Effects of Auxins

Key Idea: Auxin is a plant hormone involved in the differential growth responses of plants to environmental stimuli.
Auxins are plant hormones with a central role in a range of growth and developmental responses in plants. Indole-acetic acid (IAA) is the most potent native auxin in intact plants.

The response of a plant tissue to IAA depends on the tissue itself, the hormone concentration, the timing of its release, and the presence of other hormones. Gradients in auxin concentration during growth prompt differential responses in specific tissues and contribute to directional growth.

Light is an important growth requirement for all plants. Most plants show an adaptive response of growing towards the light. This growth response is called phototropism.
The bending of the plants shown on the right is a phototropism in response to light shining from the left and is caused by the plant hormone **auxin**. Auxin causes the elongation of cells on the shaded side of the stem, causing it to bend (photo right).

Auxin is produced in the shoot tip and is responsible for apical dominance by suppressing growth of the lateral (side) buds.

Auxin movement through the plant is polar. It moves from the shoot tip down the plant.

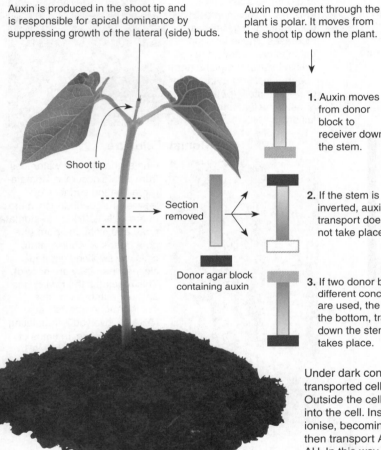

Shoot tip

Section removed

Donor agar block containing auxin

1. Auxin moves from donor block to receiver down the stem.

2. If the stem is inverted, auxin transport does not take place.

3. If two donor blocks of different concentration are used, the higher at the bottom, transport down the stem still takes place.

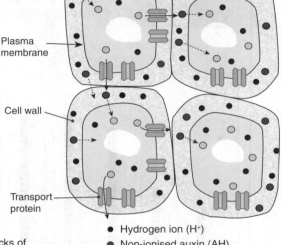

Plasma membrane

Cell wall

Transport protein

- Hydrogen ion (H⁺)
- Non-ionised auxin (AH)
- Ionised auxin (A⁻)
- ····▶ Diffusion
- ──▶ Active transport

Under dark conditions auxin moves evenly down the stem. It is transported cell to cell by diffusion and transport proteins (above right). Outside the cell auxin is a non-ionised molecule (AH) which can diffuse into the cell. Inside the cell the pH of the cytoplasm causes auxin to ionise, becoming A⁻ and H⁺. Transport proteins at the basal end of the cell then transport A⁻ out of the cell where it reacquires an H⁺ ion and reforms AH. In this way auxin is transported in one direction through the plant. When plant cells are illuminated by light from one direction transport proteins in the plasma membrane on the shaded side of the cell are activated and auxin is transported to the shaded side of the plant.

1. What is the term given to the tropism being displayed in the photo (top right)? _____

2. Describe one piece of evidence that demonstrates the transport of auxin is polar: _____

_____

_____

_____

3. What is the effect of auxin on cell growth? _____

_____

KNOW

© 2015 **BIOZONE** International
ISBN: 978-1-927309-14-8
Photocopying Prohibited

53 The Role of Auxins in Apical Dominance

Key Idea: Auxin promotes apical growth in plants and inhibits the growth of lateral (side) buds.

Auxins are responsible for apical dominance in shoots. Auxin is produced in the shoot tip and diffuses down to inhibit the development of the lateral (side) buds. The effect of auxin on preventing the development of lateral buds can be demonstrated by removing the source of the auxin and examining the outcome (below).

Auxin was the first substance to be identified as a plant hormone. Charles Darwin and his son Francis were first to recognise its role in stimulating cell elongation. Frits W. Went isolated this growth-regulating substance, which he called auxin, in 1926. Auxin promotes **apical dominance**, where the shoot tip or apical bud inhibits the formation of lateral (side) buds. As a result, plants tend to grow a single main stem upwards, which dominates over lateral branches.

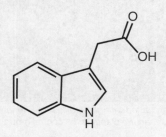

Indole-acetic acid (above) is the only known naturally occurring auxin. It is produced in the apical shoot and young leaves.

No treatment
Apical bud is left intact.

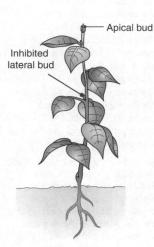

Apical bud
Inhibited lateral bud

In an intact plant, the plant stem elongates and the lateral buds remain inactive. No side growth occurs.

Treatment one
Apical bud is removed; no auxin is applied.

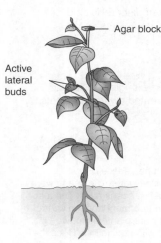

Agar block
Active lateral buds

The apical bud is removed and an agar block without auxin is placed on the cut surface. The seedling begins to develop lateral buds.

Treatment two
Apical bud is removed; auxin is applied.

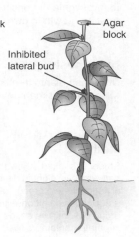

Agar block
Inhibited lateral bud

The apical bud is removed and an agar block containing auxin is placed on the cut surface. Lateral bud development is inhibited.

Two conclusions can be drawn from this experiment.

(1) The apical bud contains a hormone that inhibits lateral growth because its removal promoted lateral growth.

(2) The presence of auxin in the apical bud inhibits lateral growth because auxin applied to a cut stem tip could inhibit lateral growth and mimic the effect of an intact apical bud.

1. Describe the role of auxins in apical dominance: _____

_____

_____

2. Outline the experimental evidence supporting the role of auxins in apical dominance: _____

_____

_____

_____

_____

3. Study the photo (right) and then answer the following questions:

(a) Label the apical bud.

(b) Label the lateral bud(s).

(c) Which buds are the largest? _____

(d) Why would this be important? _____

_____

4. If you were a gardener, how would you make your plants bushier?_____

_____

LINK   WEB

52 **53** **KNOW**

54 How Gibberellins Affect Growth

Key Idea: The effect of gibberellins on plant growth can be tested experimentally by comparing the growth of gibberellin treated plants to plants with no hormonal treatment.

Gibberellins (GA) are a group of plant hormones that affect stem growth. Gibberellic acid is a type of gibberellin. Dwarf pea plants are a selected variety with a mutation that results in impaired GA synthesis. By applying GA to them, the effect of GA on plant growth can easily be demonstrated. The experiment below was performed by a group of students to determine the effect of GA on dwarf pea stem growth.

The aim

To investigate the effect of gibberellic acid on stem growth in dwarf pea plants.

Hypothesis

Dwarf pea plants treated with gibberellic acid will grow taller than untreated dwarf pea plants.

Method

Students soaked 10 dwarf pea seeds (*Pisum sativum*) overnight in distilled water. The seeds were divided into two groups of five seeds each. The test group received gibberellin treatment and the control group did not. The seeds were planted into two separate containers filled with potting mix. Once the seeds had germinated, the test group had gibberellic acid paste (500 ppm) painted on them. Both seed groups were watered daily with distilled water. The heights of the germinating shoots were recorded every few days for 20 days (except for one break in recording between days 11 and 18 when students were away).

Background

Japanese rice farmers documented rapid stem elongation in the 1800s. This process, called **bolting**, resulted in tall, spindly rice plants that set no seed. In 1934, two Japanese scientists isolated the plant hormone responsible for the rapid growth. That hormone was **gibberellin** and it acts by stimulating cell division and cell elongation.

Chemical analysis has revealed that bolting plants contain higher levels of gibberellin than non-bolting plants. The link between gibberellin and bolting can be tested experimentally by applying gibberellin to one group of plants but not to a control group. Both groups are grown in the same conditions and the differences in stem length are measured at the end of set period.

Gibberellin applied

No gibberellin applied

Plants treated with gibberellins have longer stems than the plants in the control group.

The results from the experiment are described in tables 1 and 2.

1. For each table (control and treatment), calculate the mean seedling height for each day and record it in the space provided.

2. For each table (control and treatment), calculate the standard deviation for each day and record it in the space provided.

   Remember: The sample standard deviation (*s*) is a measure of the variability in a set of data. Calculate *s* using either of the equations provided, right. In general, if *s* is small, the mean will more accurately represent the data than if *s* is large. The calculation of population standard deviation (for samples > 40) uses the denominator *n*, rather than *n* - 1 and gives a slightly smaller value.

❶
$$S = \sqrt{\frac{\sum x^2 - ((\sum x)^2 / n)}{n - 1}}$$
where $(\sum x)$ = sum of value x
$\sum x^2$ = sum of value x^2
n = sample size

❷
$$S = \sqrt{\frac{\sum (x - \bar{x})^2}{n - 1}}$$
where $\bar{x}$ = mean

Seed number	Days after germination						
	2	4	6	9	11	18	20
1	1.2	3.1	4.4	6.1	8.3	12.3	16.1
2	1.8	3.6	5.1	7.1	8.8	15.9	19.0
3	1.3	3.3	4.6	6.4	8.9	15.4	18.1
4	0.4	2.9	4.2	6.3	9.5	12.0	13.4
5	1.2	3.7	5.1	6.9	7.2	10.8	12.3
Mean height / cm							
Standard deviation							

Table 1: Height (in cm) of control dwarf pea plants

© 2015 **BIOZONE** International
ISBN: 978-1-927309-14-8
Photocopying Prohibited

Seed number	Days after germination						
	2	4	6	9	11	18	20
1	1.1	5.5	12.1	22.4	25.9	37.5	38.5
2	0.6	5.4	14.6	24.7	28.1	35.8	30.1
3	1.1	6.6	15.0	24.5	26.8	34.8	30.0
4	0.9	6.7	14.2	21.7	26.5	30.2	38.2
5	0.4	4.8	14.1	23.6	25.9	29.0	39.2
Mean height / cm							
Standard deviation							

Table 2: Height (in cm) of gibberellin treated dwarf pea plants

3. (a) Use the grid below to plot a line graph showing the mean plant heights for the two groups of dwarf peas. Plot the standard deviation for each mean as error bars either side of the mean. Include a title and correctly labelled axes.

(b) Describe the effect of gibberellin on the growth of dwarf pea plants:

_____

_____

_____

(c) Do the results support the hypothesis?

_____

(d) Based on the spread of data around the two means at day 20, do you think that the difference between the control and treatment plants is significant? Explain.

_____

_____

_____

(e) If you were to use a statistical test to test this, what test could you use and why?

_____

_____

_____

(f) As extension, perform this test and report the result. Staple it to this page.

5. Why did the students use mutant dwarf peas?

_____

_____

6. In a second experiment, students treated one group of dwarf pea seeds with gibberellin and another group with gibberellin plus gibberellin inhibitor. Predict the result of this experiment:

_____

_____

© 2015 **BIOZONE** International
ISBN: 978-1-927309-14-8
Photocopying Prohibited

55 Commercial Use of Plant Hormones

Key Idea: Plant hormones are used to manipulate plant development and growth for commercial gain.

Plant hormones affect all aspects of plant growth and development. Commercial growers use natural and synthetic plant hormones to manipulate aspects of plant growth for commercial benefit. This allows them to maximise growth and yields, and control the timing of plant growth and development to meet the demands of their customers.

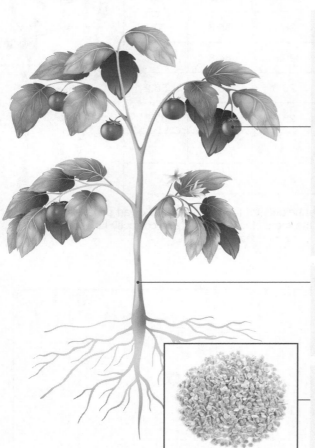

Fruit set and ripening

▸ **Ethylene** is used commercially to speed up fruit ripening or promote fruit fall. For example, bananas (right) are often picked unripe and then ripened with ethylene once at their destination. This prevents them from over-ripening during transport.

▸ **Cytokinins** inhibit fruit fall. Spraying cytokinins on to fruit trees delays fruit fall and allows the fruit more time to ripen. Cytokinins can also be used to prevent discolouration in leafy produce (e.g. lettuce).

▸ **Gibberellins** are used to improve fruit set in apples and pears and to increase fruit size in table grapes.

▸ **Auxin** is also used to increase fruit set and prevent fruit drop, resulting in higher yields.

Growth promotion

▸ **Gibberellins** are used to promote plant stem elongation and growth, producing bigger plants more quickly.

▸ **Auxin** is also used to promote growth, so that plants reach harvesting size more quickly.

Seed dormancy

▸ **Abscisic acid** (ABA) can be used to promote seed dormancy, while gibberellin can be used to promote seed germination in plants usually requiring a cold period to germinate.

Selective weed killers harm some plants but leave others unharmed. They contain artificial hormones which interfere with the growth of the target plant but not those around it. Selectivity may be due to physiological or morphological differences.

Many varieties of fruit (e.g. grapes, citrus fruit, and banana) have seedless varieties, which increases fruit quality and shelf life. Auxins or gibberellins are applied to unpollinated flowers, the growth of the seed is inhibited, but the rest of the fruit grows.

Several small stem cuttings can be taken from one plant to produce many clones (above). The cuttings are dipped into rooting powder containing auxin. The auxin stimulates quick root development, producing many new plants in a short space of time.

1. Discuss how the commercial use of plant hormones can be used to the grower's advantage: _____

_____

_____

_____

_____

_____

_____

© 2015 **BIOZONE** International
ISBN: 978-1-927309-14-8
Photocopying Prohibited

56 The Mammalian Nervous System

Key Idea: The mammalian nervous system consists of the central and peripheral nervous systems. The peripheral nervous system comprises sensory and motor pathways. It is the motor pathways that control the voluntary and autonomic responses of the body to sensory information.

The nervous system is the body's control and communication centre. Its roles are to detect stimuli, interpret them, and coordinate appropriate responses, even those that occur unconsciously. These roles are performed by the central and peripheral nervous systems (below).

The human nervous system

The nervous system has two major divisions, the central nervous system (CNS) and the peripheral nervous system (PNS).

The **central nervous system** comprises the brain and spinal cord. The spinal cord is a cylinder of nervous tissue extending from the base of the brain down the back, protected by the spinal column. It transmits messages to and from the brain, and controls spinal reflexes.

The **peripheral nervous system** comprises all the nerves and sensory receptors outside the central nervous system.

Below: *cross sections through the spinal cord to show entry and exit of neurones.*

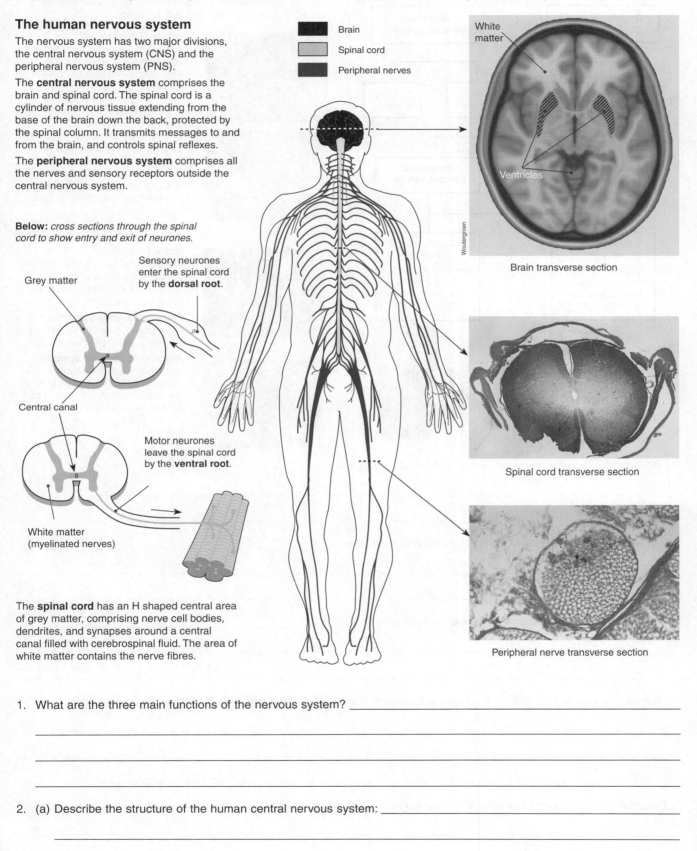

Brain

Spinal cord

Peripheral nerves

White matter

Ventricles

Woutergroen

Brain transverse section

Grey matter

Sensory neurones enter the spinal cord by the **dorsal root**.

Central canal

Motor neurones leave the spinal cord by the **ventral root**.

White matter (myelinated nerves)

Spinal cord transverse section

Peripheral nerve transverse section

The **spinal cord** has an H shaped central area of grey matter, comprising nerve cell bodies, dendrites, and synapses around a central canal filled with cerebrospinal fluid. The area of white matter contains the nerve fibres.

1. What are the three main functions of the nervous system? _____

_____

_____

_____

2. (a) Describe the structure of the human central nervous system: _____

_____

_____

LINK

WEB

57   56   **KNOW**

The divisions of the nervous system

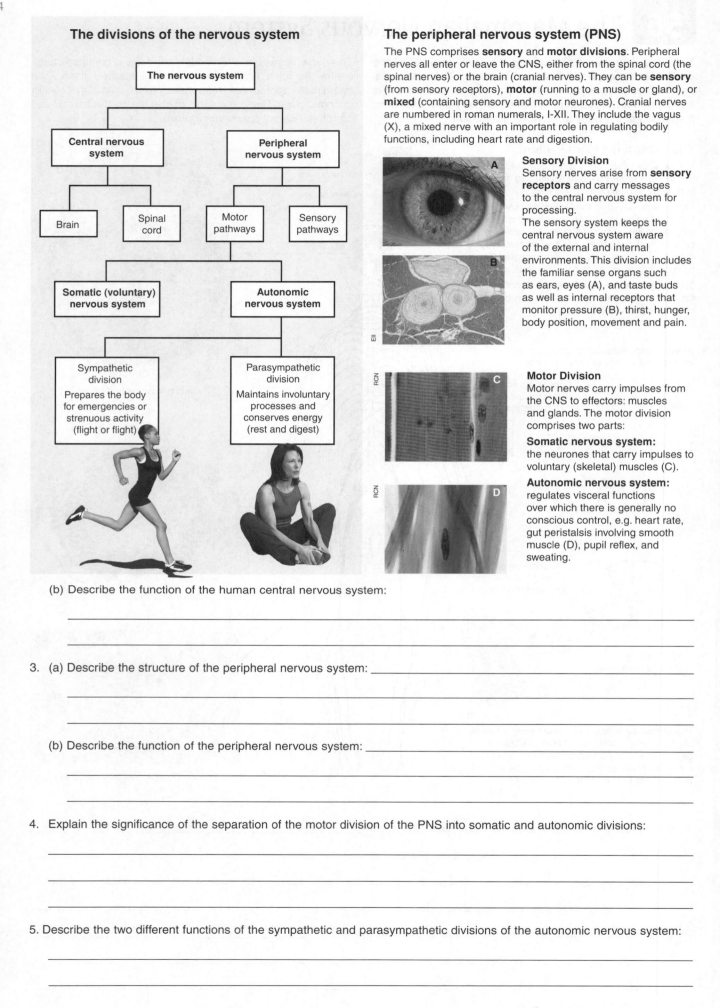

The nervous system

- **Central nervous system**
  - Brain
  - Spinal cord
- **Peripheral nervous system**
  - Motor pathways
  - Sensory pathways

Somatic (voluntary) nervous system

Autonomic nervous system

Sympathetic division
Prepares the body for emergencies or strenuous activity (flight or flight)

Parasympathetic division
Maintains involuntary processes and conserves energy (rest and digest)

The peripheral nervous system (PNS)

The PNS comprises **sensory** and **motor divisions**. Peripheral nerves all enter or leave the CNS, either from the spinal cord (the spinal nerves) or the brain (cranial nerves). They can be **sensory** (from sensory receptors), **motor** (running to a muscle or gland), or **mixed** (containing sensory and motor neurones). Cranial nerves are numbered in roman numerals, I-XII. They include the vagus (X), a mixed nerve with an important role in regulating bodily functions, including heart rate and digestion.

Sensory Division
Sensory nerves arise from **sensory receptors** and carry messages to the central nervous system for processing.
The sensory system keeps the central nervous system aware of the external and internal environments. This division includes the familiar sense organs such as ears, eyes (A), and taste buds as well as internal receptors that monitor pressure (B), thirst, hunger, body position, movement and pain.

Motor Division
Motor nerves carry impulses from the CNS to effectors: muscles and glands. The motor division comprises two parts:

Somatic nervous system: the neurones that carry impulses to voluntary (skeletal) muscles (C).

Autonomic nervous system: regulates visceral functions over which there is generally no conscious control, e.g. heart rate, gut peristalsis involving smooth muscle (D), pupil reflex, and sweating.

(b) Describe the function of the human central nervous system:

_____

_____

3. (a) Describe the structure of the peripheral nervous system: _____

_____

_____

(b) Describe the function of the peripheral nervous system: _____

_____

_____

4. Explain the significance of the separation of the motor division of the PNS into somatic and autonomic divisions:

_____

_____

_____

5. Describe the two different functions of the sympathetic and parasympathetic divisions of the autonomic nervous system:

_____

_____

57 The Human Brain

Key Idea: The brain is the body's control centre. It comprises several distinct but communicating regions, each with a specialised role in physiology or behaviour.

The brain is constantly receiving, processing, and prioritising information, and coordinating appropriate responses to stimuli. The human brain consists of four main regions: the **cerebrum**, **diencephalon** (thalamus and hypothalamus), **brainstem** (midbrain, pons, and medulla oblongata), and **cerebellum**. The **cerebrum** is divided into two hemispheres, each of which has four lobes. The cerebrum is responsible for higher thought processes, whereas reflex activity is mainly the job of the cerebellum and medulla.

Primary structural regions of the brain

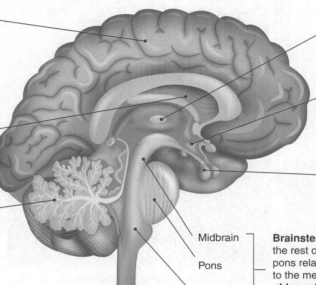

Cerebrum: Divided into the left and right cerebral hemispheres. It has many, complex roles. It contains sensory, motor, and association areas, and is involved in memory, emotion, language, reasoning, and sensory processing.

Ventricles: Cavities containing the CSF, which absorbs shocks and delivers nutritive substances.

Cerebellum is the part of the hindbrain that coordinates body movements, posture, and balance.

Midbrain

Pons

Medulla oblongata

Thalamus acts as the main relay centre for all sensory messages that enter the brain, before they are transmitted to the cerebrum.

Hypothalamus controls the autonomic nervous system and links nervous and endocrine systems. Regulates appetite, thirst, body temperature, and sleep.

Pituitary gland: An endocrine gland often called "the master gland" as it controls the actions of many other glands.

Brainstem: Relay centre for impulses between the rest of the brain and the spinal cord. The pons relays information from the cerebrum to the medulla and cerebellum. The **medulla oblongata** (or medulla) controls the autonomic (involuntary) functions in the body such as breathing, heart rate, swallowing, and the coughing and vomiting reflexes.

Sulci

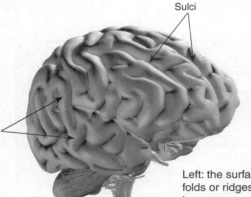

Gyri

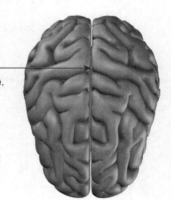

Right: The cerebrum is divided into the left and right hemispheres by a deep fissure (groove) called the cerebral fissure.

Left: the surface of the cerebrum has prominent folds or ridges called **gyri**. The gyri are separated by grooves called **sulci**. Folding increases the surface area of the brain (and therefore the number of neurones) without greatly increasing its size.

1. Identify the regions labelled on the diagram of the human brain (right) and state their function:

A: _____

_____

B: _____

_____

C: _____

_____

D: _____

_____

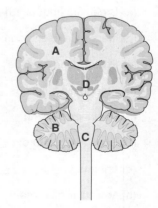

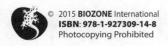
LINK **58** LINK **56** WEB **57** KNOW

Sensory and motor regions in the cerebrum

Primary somatic sensory area receives sensations from receptors in the skin, muscles and viscera, allowing recognition of pain, temperature, or touch. Sensory information from receptors on one side of the body crosses to the opposite side of the cerebral cortex where conscious sensations are produced. The size of the sensory region for different body parts depends on the number of receptors in that particular body part.

Primary motor area controls muscle movement. Stimulation of a point one side of the motor area results in muscular contraction on the opposite side of the body.

Frontal lobe

Primary gustatory area interprets sensations related to taste.

Visual areas within the occipital lobe receive, interpret, and evaluate visual stimuli. In vision, each eye views both sides of the visual field but the brain receives impulses from left and right visual fields separately. The visual cortex combines the images into a single impression or **perception** of the image.

Occipital lobe

Parietal lobe

Temporal lobe

Language areas: The motor speech area (Broca's area) is concerned with speech production. The sensory speech area (Wernicke's area) is concerned with speech recognition and coherence.

Auditory areas interpret the basic characteristics and meaning of sounds.

Olfactory area interprets signals relating to smell

Touch is interpreted in the primary somatic sensory area. The fingertips and the lips have a relatively large amount of area devoted to them.

Humans rely heavily on vision. The importance of this sense in humans is indicated by the large occipital region of the brain.

The olfactory tract connects the olfactory bulb with the cerebral hemispheres where olfactory information is interpreted.

The endothelial tight junctions of the capillaries supplying the brain form a protective **blood-brain barrier** against toxins and infection.

2. Why is damage to the medulla oblongata likely to result in death? _____
_____
_____

3. What is the function of the primary somatic area? _____
_____
_____

4. What is the function of the primary motor area? _____
_____
_____

5. For each of the following bodily functions, identify the region(s) of the brain involved in its control:

   (a) Breathing and heartbeat: _____

   (b) Memory and emotion: _____

   (c) Posture and balance: _____

   (d) Autonomic functions: _____

   (e) Visual processing: _____

   (f) Body temperature: _____

   (g) Language: _____

   (h) Muscular movement: _____

© 2015 **BIOZONE** International
ISBN: 978-1-927309-14-8
Photocopying Prohibited

58 Reflexes

Key Idea: A reflex is an automatic response to a stimulus and involves only a few neurones and a central processing point. A **reflex** is an automatic response to a stimulus. Reflexes require no conscious thought and so act quickly to protect the body from harmful stimuli. Reflexes are controlled by a neural pathway called a reflex arc. A reflex arc involves a small number of neurones and a central nervous system processing point, which is usually the spinal cord, but sometimes the brain stem. Reflexes are classified according to the number of CNS synapses involved. **Monosynaptic reflexes** involve only one CNS synapse (e.g. knee jerk reflex), whereas **polysynaptic reflexes** involve two or more (e.g. pain withdrawal reflex). Both are spinal reflexes. The pupil reflex and the corneal (blink) reflex are cranial reflexes.

The knee-jerk reflex

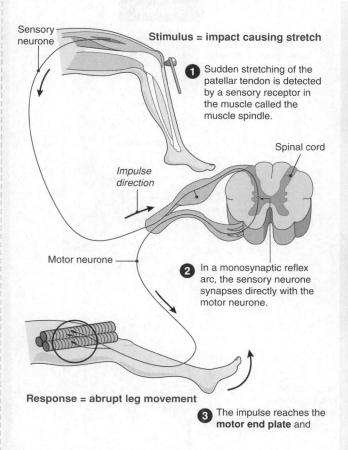

Sensory neurone

Stimulus = impact causing stretch

1 Sudden stretching of the patellar tendon is detected by a sensory receptor in the muscle called the muscle spindle.

Spinal cord

Impulse direction

Motor neurone

2 In a monosynaptic reflex arc, the sensory neurone synapses directly with the motor neurone.

Response = abrupt leg movement

3 The impulse reaches the **motor end plate** and

The patellar (knee jerk) reflex is a simple deep tendon reflex that is used to test the function of the femoral nerve and spinal cord segments L2-L4. It helps to maintain posture and balance when walking.

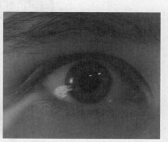

The corneal (blink) reflex is a rapid involuntary blinking of both eyelids occurring when the cornea is stimulated, e.g. by touching. It is mediated by the brainstem and can be used to evaluate coma.

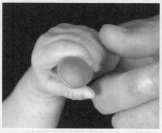

Normal newborns exhibit a number of primitive reflexes in response to particular stimuli. These include the grasp reflex (above) and the startle reflex in which a sudden noise will cause the infant to extend its arms, legs, and head, and cry.

The pupillary light reflex refers to the rapid expansion or contraction of the pupils in response to the intensity of light falling on the retina. It is a polysynaptic cranial reflex and can be used to test for brain death.

1. Explain why higher reasoning or conscious thought are not necessary or desirable features of reflex behaviours:

_____

_____

_____

2. Distinguish between a spinal reflex and a cranial reflex and give an example of each: _____

_____

_____

_____

3. Describe the survival value of the following reflexes:

   (a) Knee-jerk reflex: _____

   (b) Corneal blink reflex: _____

   (c) Grasp reflex: _____

   (d) Pupillary light reflex: _____

59 Coordination by Nerves and Hormones

Key Idea: The nervous and endocrine systems work together to maintain homeostasis.

In mammals, the nervous system and endocrine (hormonal) systems act independently and together to maintain homeostasis. The two systems are quite different in their modes of action, the responses they elicit, and the duration of action. The nervous system stimulates rapid, short-lived responses through electrical signals transmitted directly between adjacent cells. The endocrine system produces a slower, more long-lasting response through blood-borne chemicals called hormones. Hormones control many life processes such as reproduction, growth, and development.

Signalling by neurones (nerve cells)

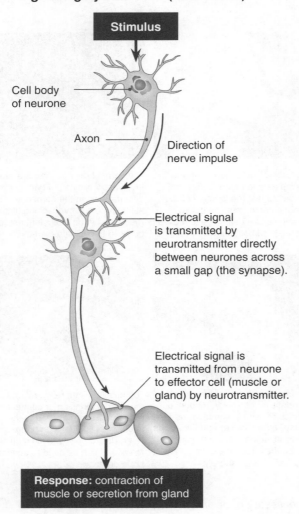

Stimulus

Cell body of neurone

Axon

Direction of nerve impulse

Electrical signal is transmitted by neurotransmitter directly between neurones across a small gap (the synapse).

Electrical signal is transmitted from neurone to effector cell (muscle or gland) by neurotransmitter.

Response: contraction of muscle or secretion from gland

The nervous system transmits electrical impulses directly between cells through electrical junctions or via chemicals called neurotransmitters, which can diffuse across the small gap (synapse) between cells. The response of a cell to nervous stimulation is rapid (milliseconds), short lived, and localised.

Signalling by hormones

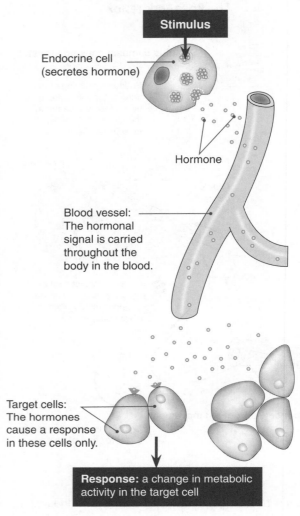

Stimulus

Endocrine cell (secretes hormone)

Hormone

Blood vessel: The hormonal signal is carried throughout the body in the blood.

Target cells: The hormones cause a response in these cells only.

Response: a change in metabolic activity in the target cell

Hormones secreted from endocrine cells are carried in the blood throughout the body, where they interact only with target cells carrying the correct receptor to bring about a response. The speed of hormonal signalling is relatively slow, and it exerts its effects over minutes, hours, or days.

1. Complete the table below to show the comparison between nervous and hormonal signalling:

	Nervous control	**Hormonal control**
Communication	Impulses directly between cells across cell to cell junctions	
Speed		
Duration		
Target pathway		Carried in blood throughout body to target cells
Action		

© 2015 **BIOZONE** International
ISBN: 978-1-927309-14-8
Photocopying Prohibited

60 Flight or Fight

Key Idea: Nerves and hormones mediate the fight or flight response, which prepares the body for exertion.

The **flight or fight response** is a physiological reaction that occurs when someone is confronted with a sudden threat or stressful situation. Stimuli include dangerous situations, when a high level of performance is required, or during athletic competition. The flight or fight response is mediated by both adrenal hormones and the sympathetic nervous system, and coordinated through the hypothalamus. Sympathetic stimulation causes the release of catecholamine hormones, which bring about the physiological reactions that prepare the body for exertion (below). When the stress is relieved, sympathetic stimulation stops and the body's responses return to normal. In cases of unrelieved stress, the anterior pituitary becomes involved, promoting secretion of glucocorticoid stress hormones from the adrenal cortex.

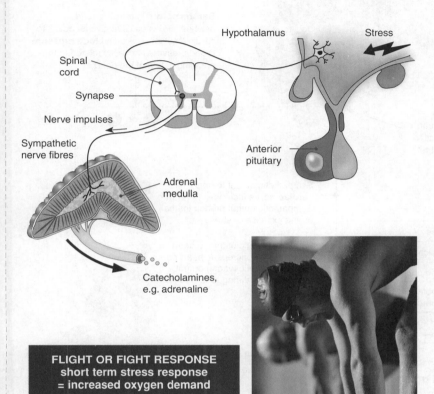

How adrenaline exerts its effect

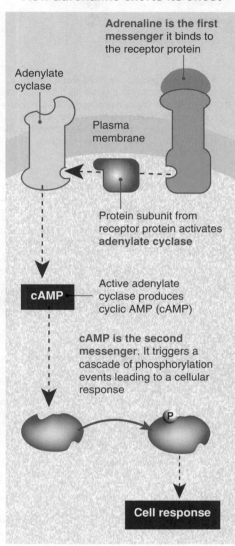

Adrenaline is the first messenger it binds to the receptor protein

Adenylate cyclase

Plasma membrane

Protein subunit from receptor protein activates **adenylate cyclase**

cAMP

Active adenylate cyclase produces cyclic AMP (cAMP)

cAMP is the second messenger. It triggers a cascade of phosphorylation events leading to a cellular response

Cell response

FLIGHT OR FIGHT RESPONSE
short term stress response
= increased oxygen demand

1. Increased heart rate
2. Increased blood pressure
3. Liver converts glycogen to glucose; blood glucose levels increase
4. Dilation of bronchioles
5. Blood flow to gut and kidney reduced

   Blood flow to muscles and brain increased
6. Increased metabolic rate

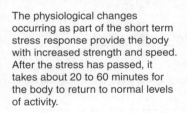

The physiological changes occurring as part of the short term stress response provide the body with increased strength and speed. After the stress has passed, it takes about 20 to 60 minutes for the body to return to normal levels of activity.

1. (a) Briefly outline what occurs during the flight or fight response: _____

_____

_____

(b) How are the body's responses returned to normal after the stress is relieved: _____

_____

2. Explain how adrenaline and cAMP are involved in producing the flight or fight response at the cellular level:

_____

_____

_____

LINK 106   LINK 61   LINK 35   WEB 60   **KNOW**

61 Nerves and Hormones Regulate Heart Rate

Key Idea: The heart's basic rhythm is regulated via the cardiovascular control centre in response to hormones and input from sympathetic and parasympathetic nerves.
The pacemaker sets the basic rhythm of the heart, but this rate is influenced by the cardiovascular control centre, primarily in response to sensory information from pressure receptors in the walls of the blood vessels entering and leaving the heart. The main trigger for changing the basic rate of heart beat is change in blood pressure. The responses are mediated though simple reflexes.

Higher brain centres influence the cardiovascular centre, e.g. excitement or anticipation of an event.

Cardiovascular control	....
Increase in rate	**+**
Decrease in rate	**−**

Baroreceptors in aorta, carotid arteries, and vena cava give feedback to cardiovascular centre on **blood pressure**. Blood pressure is directly related to the pumping action of the heart.

Cardiovascular centre responds directly to noradrenaline and to low pH (high CO_2). It sends output to the sinoatrial node (SAN) to increase heart rate. Changing the rate and force of heart contraction is the main mechanism for controlling cardiac output in order to meet changing demands.

+ or **−**

Sympathetic output to heart via **cardiac nerve** increases heart rate. Sympathetic output predominates during exercise or stress. **+**

Parasympathetic output to heart via **vagus nerve** decreases heart rate. Parasympathetic (vagal) output predominates during rest. **−**

Influences on heart rate

Increase	Decrease
Increased physical activity	Decreased physical activity
Decrease in blood pressure	Increase in blood pressure
Secretion of adrenaline or noradrenaline	Re-uptake and metabolism of adrenaline or noradrenaline
Increase in H^+ or CO_2 concentrations in blood	Decrease in H^+ or CO_2 concentrations in blood

Extrinsic input to SAN

Reflex responses to changes in blood pressure

Reflex	Receptor	Stimulus	Response
Bainbridge reflex	Pressure receptors in vena cava and atrium	Stretch caused by increased venous return	Increase heart rate
Carotid reflex	Pressure receptors in the carotid arteries	Stretch caused by increased arterial flow	Decrease heart rate
Aortic reflex	Pressure receptors in the aorta	Stretch caused by increased arterial flow	Decrease heart rate

Opposing actions keep blood pressure within narrow limits

The intrinsic rhythm of the heart is influenced by the cardiovascular centre, which receives input from sensory neurones and hormones.

1. Explain how each of the following extrinsic factors influences the basic intrinsic rhythm of the heart:

    (a) Increased venous return: _____

    (b) Release of adrenaline in anticipation of an event: _____

    (c) Increase in blood CO_2: _____

2. How do these extrinsic factors bring about their effects? _____

    _____

3. What type of activity might cause increased venous return? _____

4. (a) Identify the nerve that brings about **increased** heart rate: _____

    (b) Identify the nerve that brings about **decreased** heart rate: _____

5. Account for the different responses to stretch in the vena cava and the aorta: _____

    _____

© 2015 **BIOZONE** International
ISBN: 978-1-927309-14-8
Photocopying Prohibited

62 Physiological Response to Exercise

Key Idea: The body's response to exercise can be measured by monitoring changes in heart rate.

The effect of exercise on heart rate can be quantified by measuring heart rate before exercise and then again following exercise. The before and after tests represent two 'populations', so the Student's *t*-test can be used to test the significance of differences between the two population means (mean heart rate before and then after exercise). The steps are outlined below. You can complete the test using a calculator or a spreadsheet programme.

In this practical experiment, students studied how exercise affects heart rate. They did this by comparing their resting heart rate (heart rate before exercise) to their post exercise heart rate.

The students sat quietly in a chair for five minutes, then measured and recorded their heart rate (right). This was their pre-exercise heart rate. Once the students had obtained the pre-exercise heart rate, they carried out star jumps as fast as possible for one minute. Immediately at the end of the one minute exercise period they measured their heart rate again. This was their post exercise heart rate. The class results are presented in the table below.

Measuring heart rate

Heart rate (beats per minute) is obtained by measuring the pulse for 15 seconds and then multiplying by four. Gently press your index and middle fingers, not your thumb, against the carotid artery in the neck (just under the jaw) or the radial artery (on the wrist just under the thumb) until you feel a pulse.

x heart rate / beats per minute		x − x̄ (deviation from the mean)		(x − x̄)² (deviation from mean)²	
Pre-exercise	**Post exercise**	**Pre-exercise**	**Post exercise**	**Pre-exercise**	**Post exercise**
72	87	−16.5	−49.5	272.25	2450.25
116	175	27.5	38.5	756.25	1482.25
79	96				
97	100				
90	176				
67	132				
115	176				
82	141				
95	113				
82	136				
77	96				
105	153				
79	90				
99	152				
82	156				
87	170				
82	128				
98	172				
80	132				
95	141				
79	144				

$n_B = 21$ $n_B = 21$

$\Sigma (x - \bar{x})^2$ $\Sigma (x - \bar{x})^2$

Step 1: Summary statistics

For the data in the table (left), calculate the mean and give the n value for each data set. Calculate the standard deviation (*s*).

Popn A $\bar{x}_A =$ ☐   Popn B $\bar{x}_B =$ ☐

$n_A =$ ☐ $n_B =$ ☐

$s_A =$ ☐ $s_B =$ ☐

Step 2: State your null hypothesis

Step 3: Test is one tailed / two tailed (delete one)

Table of critical values of *t* at different levels of *P*.

Degrees of freedom	Level of Probability		
	0.05	**0.01**	**0.001**
1	12.71	63.66	636.6
2	4.303	9.925	31.60
3	3.182	5.841	12.92
4	2.776	4.604	8.610
5	2.571	4.032	6.869
6	2.447	3.707	5.959
7	2.365	3.499	5.408
8	2.306	3.355	5.041
9	2.262	3.250	4.781
10	2.228	3.169	4.587
15	2.131	2.947	4.073
16	2.120	2.921	4.015
17	2.110	2.898	3.965
18	2.101	2.878	3.922
19	2.093	2.861	3.883
20	2.086	2.845	3.850
25	2.060	2.787	3.725
30	2.042	2.750	3.646
40	2.021	2.704	3.551

© 2015 **BIOZONE** International
ISBN: 978-1-927309-14-8
Photocopying Prohibited

LINK WEB

54 62 PRAC

Step 4: Calculating t

4a: Calculate sums of squares

Complete the computations outlined in the table on the previous page. The sum of each of the final two columns is called the sum of squares.

4b: Calculate the variances

Calculate the variance (s^2) for each data set. This is the sum of squares ÷ by $n - 1$ (number of samples in each data set $- 1$). In this case the n values are the same, but they need not be.

$$s^2_A = \frac{\sum(x - \bar{x})^2}{n_A - 1}_{(A)} \qquad s^2_B = \frac{\sum(x - \bar{x})^2}{n_B - 1}_{(B)}$$

4c: Differences between the means

Calculate the difference between the means

$$(\bar{x}_A - \bar{x}_B)$$

4d: Calculate t

$$t = \frac{(\bar{x}_A - \bar{x}_B)}{\sqrt{\dfrac{s^2_A}{n_A} + \dfrac{s^2_B}{n_B}}}$$

4e: Determine the degrees of freedom

Degrees of freedom (d.f.) = $n_A + n_B - 2$ where n_A and n_B are the number of counts in each of populations A and B.

Step 5: Consult the t table

Consult the t-table on the previous page for the critical t value at the appropriate degrees of freedom and probability levels P = 0.05.

5a: Make your decision

Make a decision whether or not to reject H_0 based on the **absolute value** of the calculated t value. If t_{calc} is large enough, you can reject H_0 at a lower P value (e.g. 0.001), increasing confidence in the alternative hypothesis.

1. The variance for population A: $s^2_A =$ _____

   The variance for population B: $s^2_B =$ _____

2. The difference between the population means:

   $(\bar{x}_A - \bar{x}_B) =$ _____

3. (a) Calculate t:

   (b) $t_{(calculated)} =$ _____

4. Determine the degrees of freedom (d.f.)

   d.f. $(n_A + n_B - 2) =$ _____

5. $t_{(critical\ value)}$ at P = 0.05: _____

6. (a) Do you reject or accept the null hypothesis? _____

   (b) State the reason for the answer you gave in (a): _____

   _____

7. (a) Which population has the greatest variance? _____

   (b) Suggest an possible explanation for this? _____

   _____

8. Write a conclusion for the investigation: _____

   _____

   _____

   _____

63 Types of Muscle

Key Idea: There are three kinds of muscle tissue: skeletal (voluntary), cardiac (heart), and involuntary (smooth) muscle. Mammalian muscles fall into one of three categories, skeletal, cardiac, or involuntary. The muscles used for posture and locomotion are **skeletal muscles** and are largely under conscious (voluntary) control. Cardiac (heart) and involuntary (smooth) muscle are not under conscious control (involuntary). **Cardiac muscle** is located in the heart. **Involuntary muscle** lines hollow organs such as blood vessels, the bladder, and gut. Each muscle type has a distinct structure.

Skeletal muscle	Cardiac muscle	Involuntary (smooth) muscle

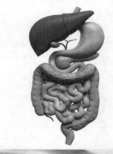

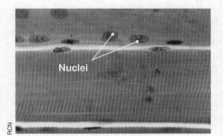

Nuclei

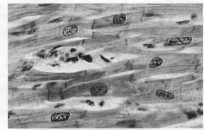

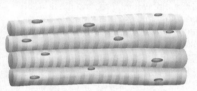

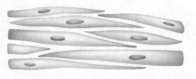

- Skeletal muscle is also called striated or voluntary muscle.
- It is involved in maintaining posture and in movement (e.g. walking).
- It is called voluntary muscle because it is under conscious control.
- It has a striated (striped or banded) appearance and the fibres (cells) contain many nuclei located at the edges.
- The muscle fibres are long and tubular.

- Cardiac muscle is also sometimes called heart muscle.
- Cardiac muscle is striated and does not fatigue because the muscle has a built in rest period after each contraction.
- It is found only in the heart.
- It is an involuntary muscle and is not under conscious control.
- The muscle fibres are branching and uninucleate (have only one nucleus).

- Involuntary muscle is also called smooth muscle. It is not under conscious control.
- It lines the walls of hollow organs (e.g. blood vessels or digestive tract) enabling them to respond to stimuli, e.g. to create gut movements, or expand and contract blood vessels.
- The fibres are spindle shaped with one nucleus. They lack striations.
- They are irregularly arranged so the contraction is not in one direction.

1. Compare the structure and function of **skeletal muscle, cardiac muscle**, and **smooth muscle**: _____

_____

_____

_____

_____

_____

_____

_____

2. In terms of its control, how does skeletal muscle differ from cardiac and smooth muscle? _____

_____

_____

LINK **65** LINK **64** WEB **63** **KNOW**

64 Muscles and Movement

Key Idea: Skeletal muscle provides the contractile force to move body parts. Pairs of muscles work together to bring about movement.

In mammals, movement is caused by the contraction of skeletal muscles across a joint (the junction of two bones) Skeletal muscles are attached to the skeleton by tough connective tissue structures called **tendons**. When skeletal muscles contract, they can only pull on bones (not push) so they must work in pairs to achieve movement. As one muscle of the pair contracts (shortens), the other relaxes (lengthens). The muscle pairs are called **antagonistic muscles** because they have opposite movements.

Muscles and bones work together to create movement

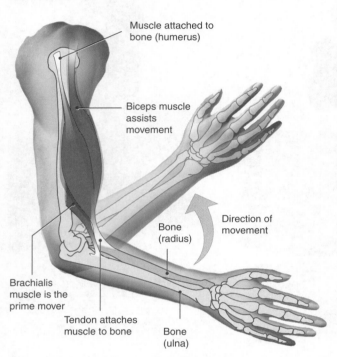

Muscle attached to bone (humerus)

Biceps muscle assists movement

Brachialis muscle is the prime mover

Tendon attaches muscle to bone

Bone (radius)

Bone (ulna)

Direction of movement

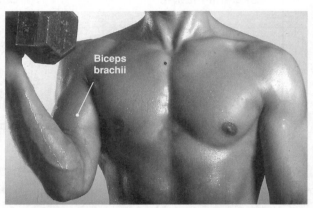

Biceps brachii

While you are sitting at your desk, lay your forearm on the desk, palm facing upwards. Now put your other hand on your upper arm and raise your resting arm towards you, bending at the elbow. You would have felt the muscles in your upper arm move.

What you felt was the muscles of the upper arm (brachialis and biceps brachii) contracting (shortening), causing the bones attached to it to move at the elbow joint, creating movement. Contrary to what most people think, the main muscle causing this movement is the brachialis muscle, underlying the biceps, although the biceps assists in the movement. The antagonistic muscle in this movement is the triceps muscle (located at the back of the upper arm, not shown). It is relaxed when the other two muscles contract.

Types of body movement

The type of movement possible is determined by the joint type. Ball and socket joints (such as the shoulder) allow movement in all planes, whereas a hinge joint, as in the elbow, allows movement in only one plane.

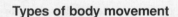

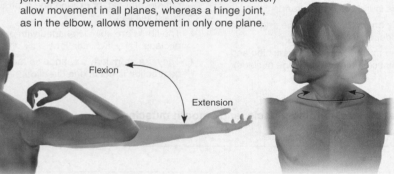

Flexion

Extension

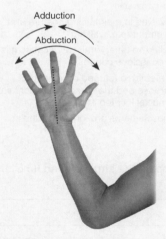

Adduction

Abduction

Flexion decreases the angle of the joint and brings two bones closer together. **Extension** is its opposite.

Rotation is movement of a bone around its longitudinal axis as in ball and socket joints and the movement of the atlas around the axis (neck vertebrae).

Abduction is a movement away from the midline. **Adduction** describes movement towards the midline. The terms also apply to opening and closing the fingers.

1. Why do skeletal muscles work in antagonistic pairs to create movement? _____

_____

_____

2. How does the type of joint influence the freedom of movement possible? _____

_____

© 2015 **BIOZONE** International
ISBN: 978-1-927309-14-8
Photocopying Prohibited

65 Skeletal Muscle Structure and Function

Key Idea: Skeletal muscle is organised into bundles of muscle cells or fibres. The muscle fibres are made up of repeating contractile units called sarcomeres.

Skeletal muscle is organised into bundles of muscle cells or fibres. Each **fibre** is a single cell with many nuclei and each fibre is itself a bundle of smaller **myofibrils** arranged lengthwise. Each myofibril is in turn composed of two kinds of **myofilaments** (thick and thin), which overlap to form light and dark bands. It is the orderly alternation of these light and dark bands which gives skeletal muscle its striated or striped appearance. The **sarcomere**, bounded by dark Z lines, forms one complete contractile unit.

When viewed under a microscope (above), skeletal muscle has a banded appearance. The cells are large with many nuclei (multinucleate).

Skeletal muscles require a conscious action to control them. Physical actions, such as running, writing, and speaking require the contraction of skeletal muscles to occur.

Structure of muscle

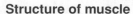

Skeletal muscle enclosed in connective tissue

Bundles of muscle fibres (**fascicles**)

Single muscle fibre

The relationship between muscle, fascicles, and muscle fibres (cells)

Structure of a muscle fibre (cell)

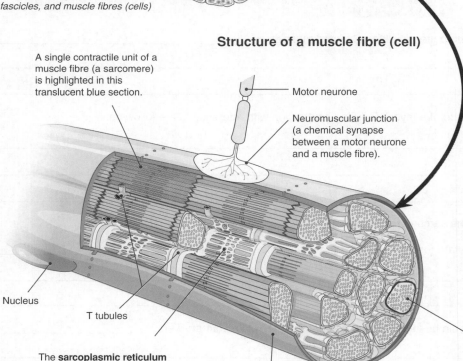

A single contractile unit of a muscle fibre (a sarcomere) is highlighted in this translucent blue section.

Motor neurone

Neuromuscular junction (a chemical synapse between a motor neurone and a muscle fibre).

Nucleus

T tubules

The **sarcoplasmic reticulum** is a specialised type of smooth endoplasmic reticulum. It is associated with the T tubules and forms a network containing a store of calcium ions.

The **sarcolemma** is the plasma membrane of the muscle cell and encloses the sarcoplasm (cytoplasm).

High power light micrograph of skeletal muscle fibres in cross section.

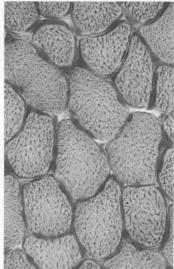

A myofibril (blue outline) with myofilaments in cross section.

LINK
66

WEB
65

KNOW

The banding pattern of myofibrils

Within a myofibril, the thin filaments, held together by the **Z lines**, project in both directions. The arrival of an action potential sets in motion a series of events that cause the thick and thin filaments to slide past each other. This is called **contraction** and it results in shortening of the muscle fibre and is accompanied by a visible change in the appearance of the myofibril: the I band and the sarcomere shorten and H zone shortens or disappears (below).

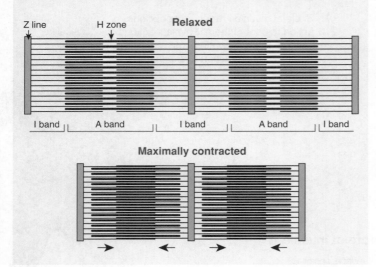

Longitudinal section of a sarcomere

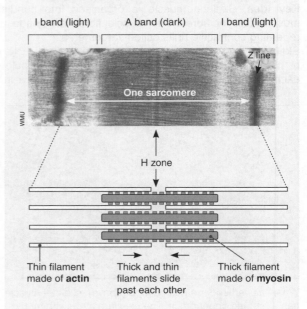

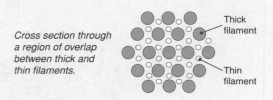

Thin filament made of **actin**

Thick and thin filaments slide past each other

Thick filament made of **myosin**

Fast vs slow twitch muscle

There are two basic types of muscle fibres: **slow twitch** (type I) and **fast twitch** (type II) fibres. Slow twitch fibres contract slowly and produce ATP slowly over a long period of time. This allows them to keep working for a long time. In contrast, fast twitch muscles contract quickly, but also fatigue rapidly because they only produce ATP for a short period of time. Most muscles contain an even mixture of fibre types.

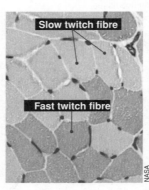

Cross section through a region of overlap between thick and thin filaments.

Thick filament

Thin filament

The photograph of a sarcomere (above) shows the banding pattern arising as a result of the highly organised arrangement of thin and thick filaments. It is represented schematically in longitudinal section and cross section.

1. (a) Explain the cause of the banding pattern visible in striated muscle: _____

_____

_____

(b) Explain the change in appearance of a myofibril during contraction with reference to the following:

The I band: _____

The H zone: _____

The sarcomere: _____

2. Study the electron micrograph of the sarcomere (top, right).

(a) Is it in a contracted or relaxed state (use the diagram, top left to help you decide): _____

(b) Explain your answer: _____

_____

3. What type of fibre (fast or slow) would be in use during a sprint race? Explain your answer: _____

_____

_____

_____

© 2015 **BIOZONE** International
ISBN: 978-1-927309-14-8
Photocopying Prohibited

66 Neuromuscular Junction

Key Idea: The neuromuscular junction is the specialised synapse between a motor neurone and a muscle fibre. Arrival of an action potential at the neuromuscular junction results in contraction of the muscle fibre.

For a muscle fibre to contract, it must receive a threshold stimulus in the form of an action potential. Action potentials are carried by motor neurones from the central nervous system to the muscle fibres they supply. A motor neurone communicates with a muscle fibre across a specialised synapse called the neuromuscular junction. The arrival of an action potential at the neuromuscular junction results in release of the neurotransmitter acetylcholine and contraction of the fibre. The response of a single muscle fibre is **all-or-none**, meaning it contracts maximally or not at all.

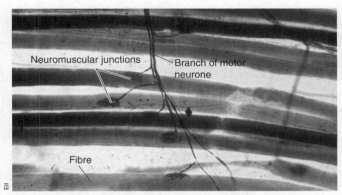

Above: Axon terminals of a motor neurone supplying a muscle. The branches of the axon terminate on the sarcolemma of a fibre at regions called the neuromuscular junction. Each fibre receives a branch of an axon, but one axon may supply many muscle fibres.

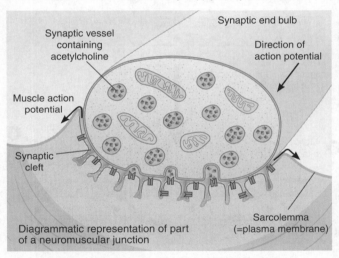

Diagrammatic representation of part of a neuromuscular junction

Above: When an action potential arrives at the neuromuscular junction, it causes the release of acetylcholine, which diffuses across the synaptic cleft to stimulate an action potential in the sarcolemma. The action potential is propagated throughout the muscle fibre via the system of T tubules and causes a release of stored calcium ions from the sarcoplasmic reticulum.

Muscles have graded responses

Muscle fibres respond to an action potential by contracting maximally or not all. This response is called the **all or none law** of muscle contraction. However, skeletal muscles as a whole can produce contractions of varying force. This is achieved by changing the frequency of stimulation (more rapid arrival of action potentials) and by changing the number of fibres active at any one time. A stronger muscle contraction is produced when a large number of muscle fibres are recruited (below left), whereas less strenuous movements, such as picking up a pen, require fewer active fibres (below right).

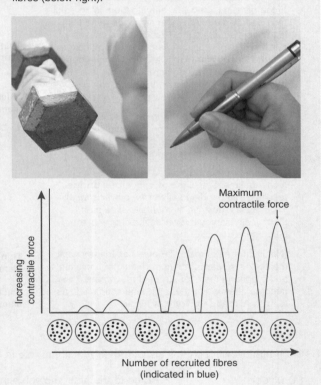

1. (a) Describe the neuromuscular junction: _____
   _____

   (b) What neurotransmitter transmits the signal to the muscle fibre? _____

   (c) What events happen as a result of this? _____
   _____

2. (a) What is meant by the all-or-none response of a muscle fibre? _____
   _____

   (b) How does a muscle as a whole produce contractions of varying force? _____
   _____

67 The Sliding Filament Theory

Key Idea: The sliding filament theory describes how muscle contraction occurs when the thick and thin myofibrils of a muscle fibre slide past one another. Calcium ions and ATP are required for muscle contraction.

The structure and arrangement of the thick and thin filaments in a muscle fibre make it possible for them to slide past each other and cause shortening (contraction) of the muscle. The ends of the thick myosin filaments have cross bridges that can link to adjacent thin actin filaments. When the cross

bridges of the thick filaments connect to the thin filaments, a shape change moves one filament past the other. Two things are necessary for cross bridge formation: calcium ions, which are released from the sarcoplasmic reticulum when the muscle receives an action potential, and ATP, which is present in the muscle fibre and is hydrolysed by ATPase enzymes on the myosin. When cross bridges attach and detach in sarcomeres throughout the muscle cell, the cell shortens.

The sliding filament theory

Muscle contraction requires calcium ions (Ca^{2+}) and energy (in the form of ATP) in order for the thick and thin filaments to slide past each other. The steps are:

1. The binding sites on the **actin** molecule (to which myosin 'heads' will locate) are blocked by a complex of two protein molecules (**tropomyosin** and **troponin**).

2. Prior to muscle contraction, ATP binds to the heads of the myosin molecules, priming them in an erect high energy state. Arrival of an action potential is transmitted along the T tubules and causes a release of Ca^{2+} from the sarcoplasmic reticulum into the sarcoplasm. The Ca^{2+} binds to the troponin and causes the blocking complex to move so that the myosin binding sites on the actin filament become exposed.

3. The heads of the cross-bridging myosin molecules attach to the binding sites on the actin filament. Release of energy from the hydrolysis of ATP accompanies the cross bridge formation.

4. The energy released from ATP hydrolysis causes a change in shape of the myosin **cross bridge**, resulting in a bending action (*the power stroke*). This causes the actin filaments to slide past the myosin filaments towards the centre of the sarcomere.

5. (Not illustrated). Fresh ATP attaches to the myosin molecules, releasing them from the binding sites and repriming them for a repeat movement. They become attached further along the actin chain as long as ATP and Ca^{2+} are available.

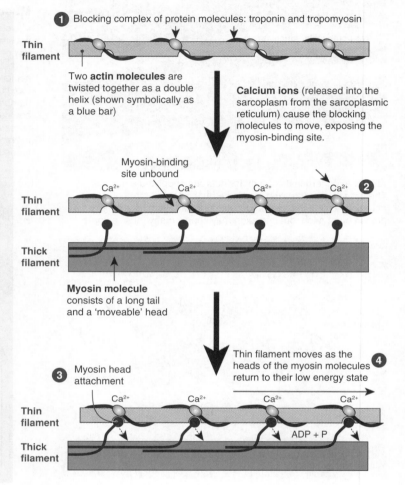

1. Blocking complex of protein molecules: troponin and tropomyosin

Thin filament

Two **actin molecules** are twisted together as a double helix (shown symbolically as a blue bar)

Calcium ions (released into the sarcoplasm from the sarcoplasmic reticulum) cause the blocking molecules to move, exposing the myosin-binding site.

Myosin-binding site unbound

Ca^{2+} 2

Thin filament

Thick filament

Myosin molecule consists of a long tail and a 'moveable' head

3 Myosin head attachment

Thin filament moves as the heads of the myosin molecules return to their low energy state 4

Ca^{2+}

Thin filament

Thick filament

ADP + P

---

1. Match the following chemicals with their functional role in muscle movement (draw a line between matching pairs):

   (a) Myosin   • Bind to the actin molecule in a way that prevents myosin head from forming a cross bridge

   (b) Actin   • Supplies energy for the flexing of the myosin 'head' (power stroke)

   (c) Calcium ions   • Has a moveable head that provides a power stroke when activated

   (d) Troponin-tropomyosin   • Two protein molecules twisted in a helix shape that form the thin filament of a myofibril

   (e) ATP   • Bind to the blocking molecules, causing them to move and expose the myosin binding site

2. (a) Identify the two things necessary for cross bridge formation: _____

   (b) Explain where each of these comes from: _____

   _____

   _____

3. Why are there abundant mitochondria in a muscle fibre?_____

   _____

© 2015 **BIOZONE** International
ISBN: 978-1-927309-14-8
Photocopying Prohibited

68 Energy for Muscle Contraction

Key Idea: Three energy systems supply energy (ATP) to carry out muscle contraction: the ATP-CP system, the glycolytic system, and the oxidative system.

During exercise, the energy demands of skeletal muscle can increase up to 20 times. In order to continue to contract during exercise, energy in the form of ATP must be supplied. Three energy systems do this: the ATP-CP system, the glycolytic system, and the oxidative system. The ultimate sources of energy for ATP generation in muscle via these systems are glucose, and stores of glycogen and triglycerides. Prolonged exercise utilises the oxidative system and relies on a constant supply of oxygen to the tissues. Anaerobic pathways provide lower yields of ATP and are important for brief periods of high intensity, but unsustained exercise.

CP provides enough energy to fuel about 10 s of maximum effort (e.g. a 100 m race).

The ATP-CP system

The simplest of the energy systems is the ATP-CP system. CP or **creatine phosphate** is a high energy compound that stores energy sufficient for brief periods of muscular effort. Energy released from the breakdown of CP is not used directly to accomplish cellular work. Instead it rebuilds ATP to maintain a relatively constant supply. This process is anaerobic, occurs very rapidly, and is accomplished without any special structures in the cell.

CP levels decline steadily as it is used to replenish depleted ATP levels. The ATP-CP system maintains energy levels for 3-15 seconds. Beyond this, the muscle must rely on other processes for ATP generation.

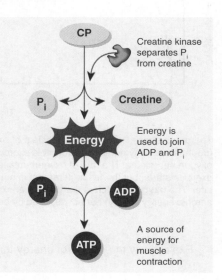

Creatine kinase separates P_i from creatine

Energy is used to join ADP and P_i

A source of energy for muscle contraction

Soccer and other field sports demand brief intense efforts with recovery in-between.

The glycolytic system

ATP can also be provided by **glycolysis**. The ATP yield from glycolysis is low (only net 2 ATP per molecule of glucose), but it produces ATP rapidly and does not require oxygen. The fuel for the glycolytic system is glucose in the blood, or glycogen, which is stored in the muscle or liver and broken down to glucose-6-phosphate. Pyruvate is reduced to lactate, regenerating NAD^+ and allowing further glycolysis.

Glycolysis provides ATP for exercise for just a few minutes. Its main limitation is that it causes an accumulation of H^+ (because protons are not being removed via mitochondrial respiration) and lactate ($C_3H_5O_3$) in the tissues. These changes lead to impairment of muscle function.

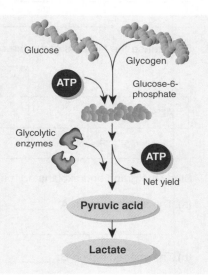

Glucose

Glycogen

Glucose-6-phosphate

Glycolytic enzymes

Net yield

Pyruvic acid

Lactate

Prolonged aerobic effort (e.g. distance running) requires a sustained ATP supply.

The oxidative system

In the oxidative system, glucose is completely broken down to yield around 36 molecules of ATP. This process uses oxygen and occurs in the mitochondria. Aerobic metabolism has a high energy yield and is the primary method of energy production during sustained high activity. It relies on a continued supply of oxygen and therefore on the body's ability to deliver oxygen to the muscles. The fuels for aerobic respiration are glucose, stored glycogen, or stored **triglycerides**. Triglycerides provide free fatty acids, which are oxidised in the mitochondria by the successive removal of two-carbon fragments (a process called beta-oxidation). These two carbon units enter the Krebs cycle as acetyl coenzyme A (acetyl CoA).

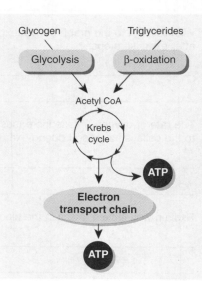

Glycogen

Triglycerides

Glycolysis

β-oxidation

Acetyl CoA

Krebs cycle

Electron transport chain

LINK 87   LINK 86

KNOW

Oxygen uptake during exercise and recovery

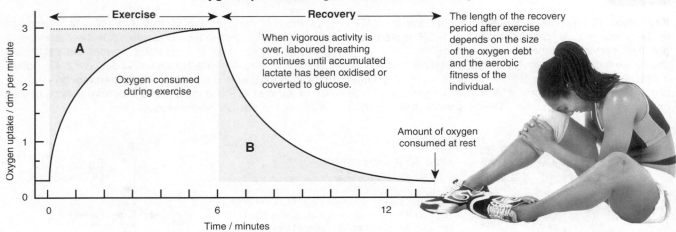

The graph above illustrates the principle of **oxygen debt**. In the graph, the energy demands of aerobic exercise require 3 dm³ of oxygen per minute. The rate of oxygen uptake increases immediately exercise starts, but the full requirement is not met until six minutes later. The **oxygen deficit** is the amount of oxygen needed (for aerobic energy supply) but not supplied by breathing. During the first

six minutes, energy is supplied largely from anaerobic pathways: the ATP-CP and glycolytic systems. After exercise, oxygen uptake per minute does not drop immediately to resting level. The extra oxygen that is taken in despite the drop in energy demand is the **oxygen debt**. The oxygen debt is used to replace oxygen reserves, restore creatine phosphate, and oxidise the lactate or convert it to glucose.

1. Explain why the supply of energy through the glycolytic system is limited: _____

_____

_____

2. Summarise the features of the three energy systems in the table below:

	ATP-CP system	Glycolytic system	Oxidative system
ATP supplied by:			
Duration of ATP supply:			

3. Study the graph and explanatory paragraph above, then identify and describe what is represented by:

   (a) The shaded region **A**: _____

   _____

   (b) The shaded region **B**: _____

   _____

4. With respect to the graph above, explain why the rate of oxygen uptake does not immediately return to its resting level after exercise stops:

   _____

   _____

5. The rate of oxygen uptake increases immediately exercise starts. Explain how the oxygen supply from outside the body to the cells is increased during exercise:

   _____

   _____

6. Explain why lactate levels in the blood continue to rise for a time after a period of high intensity exercise has stopped:

   _____

   _____

© 2015 **BIOZONE** International
ISBN: 978-1-927309-14-8
Photocopying Prohibited

69 Muscle Fatigue

Key Idea: Muscle fatigue refers to the decline in a muscle's ability to generate force in a prolonged or repeated contraction. Long or intense periods of vigorous activity can result in muscle fatigue, which refers to a muscle's decline in ability to contract efficiently, i.e. generate force. Muscles can fatigue because of shortage of fuel or because of the accumulation of metabolites which interfere with the activity of calcium in the muscle. Contrary to older thinking, muscle fatigue is not caused by the toxic effects of lactic acid accumulation in oxygen-starved muscle. In fact, lactate formed during exercise is an important source of fuel (though conversion to glucose) and delays fatigue and metabolic acidosis during moderate activity by acting as a buffer. However, during sustained exhausting exercise, more of the muscle's energy needs must be met by glycolysis, and some lactate does accumulate. This is transported to the liver and metabolised.

At rest

▶ Muscles produce a surplus of ATP

▶ This extra energy is stored in CP (creatine phosphate) and glycogen

During moderate activity

▶ ATP requirements are met by the aerobic metabolism of glycogen and lipids.

▶ There is no proton accumulation in the cell

During peak activity

▶ Effort is limited by ATP. ATP production is ultimately limited by availability of oxygen.

▶ During short-term, intense activity, more of the muscle's ATP needs must be met by glycolysis. This leads to an increase in H+.

▶ Removal of H+ is slow because mitochondrial respiration is hampered. Lactate may accumulate and is coincident with metabolic acidosis but not the cause of it.

▶ Muscle contraction is impaired (fatigue).

The complex causes of muscle fatigue

During intense exercise, oxygen is limited and more of the muscle's energy needs must be met through anaerobic metabolism. The effects of this are:

▶ An increase in H+ (acidosis) because protons are not being removed via the mitochondrial electron transport system.

▶ Lactate accumulates faster than it can be oxidised.

▶ Accumulation of phosphate (Pi) from breakdown of ATP and creatine phosphate

These metabolic changes lead to a fall in ATP and impaired calcium release from the sarcoplasmic reticulum (SR), both of which contribute to muscle fatigue.

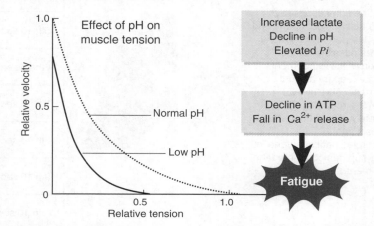

Effect of pH on muscle tension

Relative velocity

Relative tension

Normal pH

Low pH

Increased lactate
Decline in pH
Elevated Pi

Decline in ATP
Fall in Ca^{2+} release

Fatigue

Short term maximal exertion (sprint)

▶ Accumulation of lactate and H+

▶ Depletion of creatine phosphate

▶ Buildup of phosphate (P_i) affects the sensitivity of the muscle to Ca^{2+}

Mixed aerobic and anaerobic (5 km race)

▶ Accumulation of lactate and H+

▶ Build-up of ADP and P_i

▶ Decline in Ca^{2+} release affects the ability of the muscle to contract

Extended sub-maximal effort (marathon)

▶ Depletion of all energy stores (glycogen, lipids, amino acids) leads to a failure of Ca^{2+} release

▶ Repetitive overuse damages muscle fibres

1. Identify the two physiological changes in the muscle that ultimately result in a decline in muscle performance:

_____

_____

_____

2. Suggest why the reasons for fatigue in a long distance race are different to those in a 100 m sprint: _____

_____

_____

LINK

68 KNOW

70 Measuring Muscle Fatigue

Key Idea: A simple experiment can be used to show how muscles fatigue in response prolonged work.

When skeletal muscle undergoes prolonged or repetitive work, it becomes fatigued, meaning it loses its ability to produce contractile force. Muscle fatigue can be measured electronically by recording the force of the contraction over time, or can be studied more simply by measuring the number of repetitive contractions that can take place over a set time. In the activity below you will work in a group of three to test the effect of muscle fatigue in your fingers.

In this practical, you will demonstrate the effects of muscle fatigue in fingers by opening and closing a spring-loaded peg over ten 10 second intervals. You will need to work in a group of three for this experiment.

Test subject: The person who opens and closes the peg.

Time keeper: Calls out the time in 10 second intervals.

Recorder: Records the number of times the peg is opened in each 10 second interval.

The test subject holds the clothes peg comfortably with the thumb and forefinger of their dominant hand (the hand they write with). They should practise opening and closing the peg fully several times before beginning the experiment.

When the timekeeper says go, the test subject opens and closes the peg fully as many times as possible for the duration of the experiment. The timekeeper calls out each 10 second interval so that the recorder can accurately record the data in the chart right.

Switch roles until everyone in your group has completed the experiment.

	Student 1	Student 2	Student 3
1st 10 sec			
2nd 10 sec			
3rd 10 sec			
4th 10 sec			
5th 10 sec			
6th 10 sec			
7th 10 sec			
8th 10 sec			
9th 10 sec			
10th 10 sec			

1. (a) On the grid (right) plot the data for all three individuals:

   (b) Describe the results: _____

   _____

   _____

   _____

   _____

   _____

   (c) Are these results what you expected? Why or why not?

   _____

   _____

   _____

   _____

   (d) Predict what would happen if the experiment was repeated using the non-dominant hand:

   _____

   _____

© 2015 **BIOZONE** International
ISBN: 978-1-927309-14-8
Photocopying Prohibited

71 Chapter Review

Summarise what you know about this topic under the headings and sub-headings provided. You can draw diagrams or mind maps, or write short notes to organise your thoughts. Use the images and hints to help you and refer back to the introduction to check the points covered:

The mammalian nervous system

HINT: Describe the structure and function of the human nervous system, including reference to the brain, reflexes, and coordination by nerves and hormones.

Plant responses and plant hormones

HINT: Describe plant responses. What role do hormones play in plant growth and timing responses?

Muscle contraction

HINT: Compare the structure and function of cardiac, smooth, and skeletal muscle. Describe how skeletal muscle contracts.

REVISE

72 KEY TERMS: Did You Get It?

1. (a) What is the name given to a plant growth response to directional light? _____

   (b) What is the name given to a plant growth response to gravity? _____

   (c) What is the name given to a plant response that is independent of stimulus direction? _____

   (d) What plant hormone is principally responsible for the phototropic effect? _____

2. (a) What responses are being shown by the orchid in the photo (right):

   _____

   _____

   _____

   _____

   (b) What is the stimulus involved? _____

   _____

3. Test your vocabulary by matching each term to its definition, as identified by its preceding letter code.

actin	**A** The portion of the nervous system comprising the brain and spinal cord.
auxin	**B** A molecule that relays signals from receptors on the cell surface to target molecules inside the cell.
cardiac muscle	**C** An automatic response to a stimulus involving a small number of neurones and a central nervous system (CNS) processing point.
central nervous system	**D** Muscle cell containing a bundle of myofibrils.
cerebellum	**E** A class of plant hormones involved in stem elongation and in breaking seed dormancy.
cerebrum	**F** The decline in a muscle's ability to maintain force in a prolonged or repeated contraction. It is the normal result of vigorous exercise.
cyclic AMP	**G** The theory of how thin and thick filaments slide past each other to produce muscle contraction.
gibberellin	**H** The muscle responsible for autonomic movements such as peristalsis. It is not under conscious control. Cells are spindle shaped with one central nucleus.
muscle fatigue	**I** A protein found in the thin myofilaments of the sarcomere of a muscle fibre.
muscle fibre	**J** The junction between a motor neurone and a skeletal muscle fibre.
myosin	**K** The part of the nervous system that comprises all the nerves and sensory receptors outside the central nervous system.
neuromuscular junction	**L** An important intracellular signal transduction molecule, derived from ATP. The second messenger in many signal transduction pathways.
peripheral nervous system	**M** Muscle that is attached to the skeleton and responsible for the movement of bone around joints or movement of some organs, e.g. the eyes.
reflex	**N** The largest region of the brain. It controls and integrates motor, sensory, and higher mental functions (e.g. reason and emotion).
second messenger	**O** Specialised striated muscle that does not fatigue. It is found only in the walls of the heart and is not under conscious control.
skeletal muscle	**P** A part of the hindbrain that coordinates body movements, posture, and balance
sliding filament hypothesis	**Q** A contractile protein found in the thick myofilaments of the sarcomere of a muscle fibre.
smooth muscle	**R** A plant hormone responsible for apical dominance, phototropism, and cell elongation.

TEST

Photosynthesis

Key terms

absorption spectrum

accessory pigment

action spectrum

ATP

ATP synthase

Calvin cycle

carotenoid

cellular respiration

chemiosmosis

chloroplast

chlorophyll

cyclic photophosphorylation

glycerate 3-phosphate (G3P or GP)

grana

light dependent phase

light independent phase

NADP

NON-cyclic photophosphorylation

photolysis

photosynthesis

photosystem

ribulose bisphosphate (RuBP)

RuBisCo

stroma

stroma lamellae

thin layer chromatography

thylakoid discs

triose phosphate

Photosynthesis, chloroplasts, and light capture

Learning outcomes

Activity number

☐ 1 Compare and contrast cellular respiration and photosynthesis as energy transformation processes. Include reference to the relationship between the raw materials and products of the two processes. — 73 74

☐ 2 Describe the structure of a chloroplasts to include the double membrane, stroma lamellae, thylakoids arranged into grana, stroma, and DNA. Identify the sites of the two stages of photosynthesis (light capture and carbon fixation). — 75

☐ 3 Explain the role of chlorophyll *a* and accessory pigments (chlorophyll *b* and carotenoids) in light capture by green plants. Include reference to the role of chlorophyll in the photosystems (the protein complexes involved in the absorption of light and the transfer of energy and electrons). — 76

☐ 4 Explain what is meant by the terms absorption spectrum and action spectrum with respect to light absorbing pigments. — 76

☐ 5 **PAG6** Use thin layer chromatography to separate photosynthetic pigments. — 77

Kristian Peters

Dartmouth College

The biochemistry of photosynthesis

Learning outcomes

Activity number

☐ 6 Describe the light dependent reactions of photosynthesis, including reference to the absorption of light by the photosystems, the transfer of excited electrons between carriers in the thylakoid membranes, the generation of ATP and NADPH, and the photolysis of water to generate replacement electrons in non-cyclic photophosphorylation. — 78

☐ 7 Compare and contrast cyclic and non-cyclic photophosphorylation. — 78

☐ 8 Describe the light independent reactions (Calvin cycle), including the role of the catalysing enzyme RuBisCo, the carboxylation of ribulose bisphosphate (RuBP) to form glycerate 3-phosphate (GP), and the production of triose phosphate using reduced NADPH and ATP. Describe the fate of the triose phosphate generated in the Calvin cycle and explain how the RuBP is regenerated. — 79

☐ 9 Appreciate the experimental work that elucidated the processes involved in photosynthesis, e.g. Hill's experiment and Calvin's lollipop experiment. — 80

☐ 10 Describe the uses of triose phosphate. — 81

☐ 11 Describe and explain limiting factors for photosynthesis (to include carbon dioxide concentration, light intensity, and temperature). Explain the implications of water stress and closure of stomata to photosynthesis. — 82

☐ 12 **PAG11** Investigate the effect of environmental factors, e.g. light intensity or carbon dioxide concentration, on the rate of photosynthesis.
PAG10 Use sensors, dataloggers, or software to process data. — 83

73 Energy in Cells

Key Idea: Photosynthesis uses energy from the sun to produce glucose. Glucose breakdown produces ATP, which is used by all cells to provide the energy for metabolism.

A summary of the flow of energy within a plant cell is illustrated below. Heterotrophic cells (animals and fungi) have a similar flow except the glucose is supplied by ingestion or absorption of food molecules rather than by photosynthesis. The energy not immediately stored in chemical bonds is lost as heat. Note that ATP provides the energy for most metabolic reactions, including photosynthesis.

Summary of energy transformations in a photosynthetic plant cell

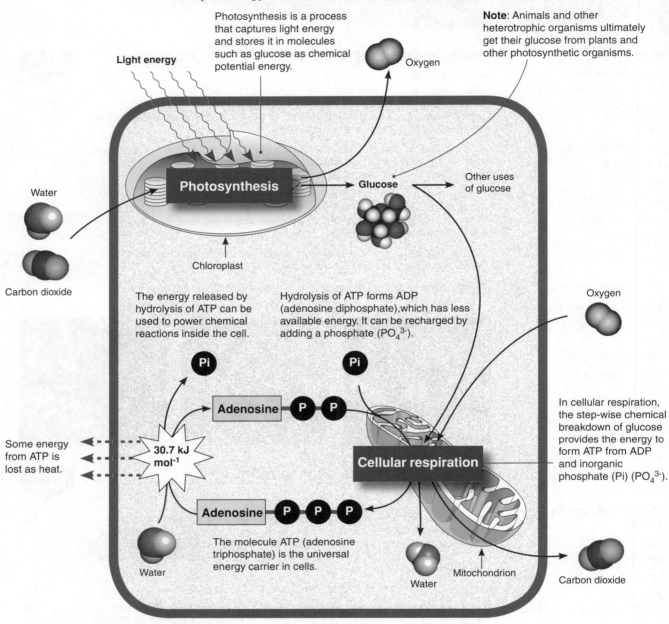

Photosynthesis is a process that captures light energy and stores it in molecules such as glucose as chemical potential energy.

Note: Animals and other heterotrophic organisms ultimately get their glucose from plants and other photosynthetic organisms.

Light energy

Oxygen

Water

Photosynthesis

Glucose

Other uses of glucose

Chloroplast

Carbon dioxide

The energy released by hydrolysis of ATP can be used to power chemical reactions inside the cell.

Hydrolysis of ATP forms ADP (adenosine diphosphate), which has less available energy. It can be recharged by adding a phosphate (PO_4^{3-}).

Oxygen

Pi

Pi

Adenosine – **P** **P**

In cellular respiration, the step-wise chemical breakdown of glucose provides the energy to form ATP from ADP and inorganic phosphate (Pi) (PO_4^{3-}).

Some energy from ATP is lost as heat.

30.7 kJ mol⁻¹

Cellular respiration

Adenosine – **P** **P** **P**

The molecule ATP (adenosine triphosphate) is the universal energy carrier in cells.

Water

Water

Mitochondrion

Carbon dioxide

1. (a) What are the raw materials for photosynthesis? _____

   _____

   (b) What are the raw materials for respiration? _____

   _____

2. What is the immediate source of energy for reforming ATP from ADP? _____

3. What is the ultimate source of energy for plants? _____

4. What is the ultimate source of energy for animals? _____

LINK 86 LINK 87

KNOW

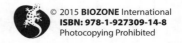

© 2015 **BIOZONE** International
ISBN: 978-1-927309-14-8
Photocopying Prohibited

74 Photosynthesis

Key Idea: Photosynthesis is the process by which light energy is used to convert CO_2 and water into glucose and oxygen. **Photosynthesis** is of fundamental importance to living things because it transforms sunlight energy into chemical energy stored in molecules, releases free oxygen gas, and absorbs carbon dioxide (a waste product of cellular metabolism).

Photosynthetic organisms use special pigments, called **chlorophylls**, to absorb light of specific wavelengths and capture the light energy. Photosynthesis involves reduction and oxidation (redox) reactions. In photosynthesis, water is split and electrons are transferred together with hydrogen ions from water to CO_2, reducing it to sugar.

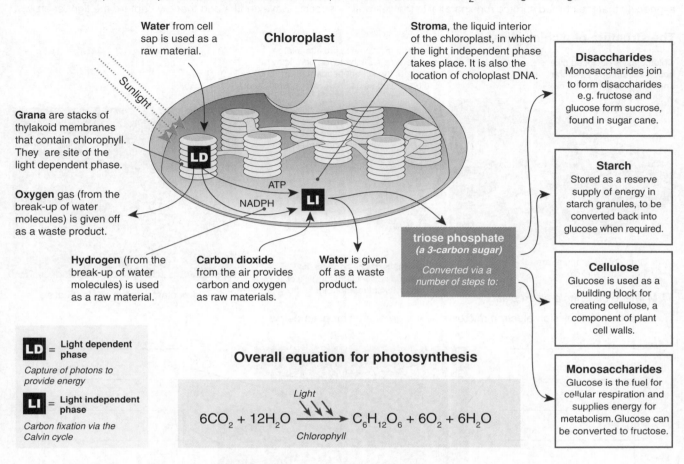

Water from cell sap is used as a raw material.

Chloroplast

Stroma, the liquid interior of the chloroplast, in which the light independent phase takes place. It is also the location of choloplast DNA.

Sunlight

Grana are stacks of thylakoid membranes that contain chlorophyll. They are site of the light dependent phase.

Oxygen gas (from the break-up of water molecules) is given off as a waste product.

Hydrogen (from the break-up of water molecules) is used as a raw material.

Carbon dioxide from the air provides carbon and oxygen as raw materials.

Water is given off as a waste product.

ATP

NADPH

triose phosphate *(a 3-carbon sugar)*

Converted via a number of steps to:

Disaccharides
Monosaccharides join to form disaccharides e.g. fructose and glucose form sucrose, found in sugar cane.

Starch
Stored as a reserve supply of energy in starch granules, to be converted back into glucose when required.

Cellulose
Glucose is used as a building block for creating cellulose, a component of plant cell walls.

Monosaccharides
Glucose is the fuel for cellular respiration and supplies energy for metabolism. Glucose can be converted to fructose.

LD = **Light dependent phase**
Capture of photons to provide energy

LI = **Light independent phase**
Carbon fixation via the Calvin cycle

Overall equation for photosynthesis

$$6CO_2 + 12H_2O \xrightarrow[\text{Chlorophyll}]{\text{Light}} C_6H_{12}O_6 + 6O_2 + 6H_2O$$

1. Distinguish between the two different regions of a chloroplast and describe the biochemical processes that occur in each:

   (a) _____

   _____

   _____

   (b) _____

   _____

   _____

2. State the origin and fate of the following molecules involved in photosynthesis:

   (a) Carbon dioxide: _____

   (b) Oxygen: _____

   (c) Hydrogen: _____

3. Discuss the potential uses for the end products of photosynthesis: _____

   _____

   _____

   _____

LINK **81**   LINK **79**   LINK **78**   LINK **75**   WEB **74**   **KNOW**

75 Chloroplasts

Key Idea: Chloroplasts have a complicated internal membrane structure that provides the sites for the light dependent reactions of photosynthesis.

Chloroplasts are the specialised plastids in which photosynthesis occurs. A mesophyll leaf cell contains between 50-100 chloroplasts. The chloroplasts are generally aligned so that their broad surface runs parallel to the cell wall

to maximise the surface area available for light absorption. Chloroplasts have an internal structure characterised by a system of membranous structures called **thylakoids** arranged into stacks called **grana**. Special pigments, called **chlorophylls** and **carotenoids**, are bound to the membranes as part of light-capturing photosystems. They absorb light of specific wavelengths and thereby capture the light energy.

The structure of a chloroplast

Chloroplast is enclosed by a double membrane envelope (inner and outer membrane)

Thylakoid membranes provide a large surface area for light absorption. They are the site of the light dependent phase and are organised so as not to shade each other.

Liquid **stroma** contains the enzymes for the light independent phase. It also contains the chloroplast's DNA.

Starch granule

Lipid droplet

Grana (*sing.* granum) are stacks of thylakoids

Stroma lamellae connect the grana. They account for 20% of the thylakoid membrane.

TEM image of a single chloroplast

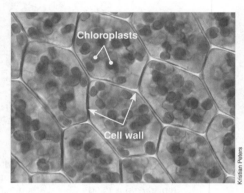

Chloroplasts

Cell wall

Kristian Peters

Chloroplasts visible in plant cells

1. Label the transmission electron microscope image of a chloroplast below:

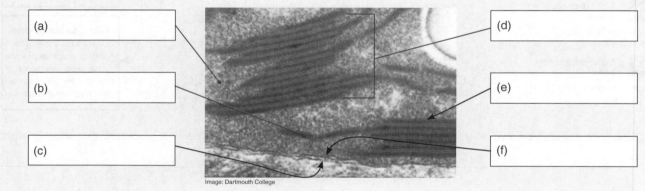

(a)

(b)

(c)

(d)

(e)

(f)

Image: Dartmouth College

2. (a) Where is chlorophyll found in a chloroplast? _____

_____

(b) Why is chlorophyll found there? _____

_____

_____

3. Explain how the internal structure of chloroplasts helps absorb the maximum amount of light: _____

_____

_____

_____

4. Explain why plant leaves appear green: _____

_____

_____

LINK
76

KNOW

76 Pigments and Light Absorption

Key Idea: Chlorophyll pigments absorb light of specific wavelengths and capture light energy for photosynthesis. Substances that absorb visible light are called **pigments**, and different pigments absorb light of different wavelengths. The ability of a pigment to absorb particular wavelengths of light can be measured with a spectrophotometer. The light absorption vs the wavelength is called the **absorption**

spectrum of that pigment. The absorption spectrum of different photosynthetic pigments provides clues to their role in photosynthesis, since light can only perform work if it is absorbed. An **action spectrum** profiles the effectiveness of different wavelengths of light in fuelling photosynthesis. It is obtained by plotting wavelength against a measure of photosynthetic rate (e.g. O_2 production).

The electromagnetic spectrum

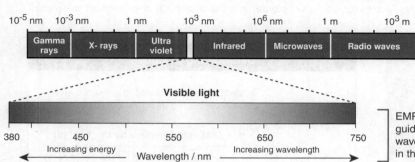

Light is a form of energy known as electromagnetic radiation (EMR). The segment of the electromagnetic spectrum most important to life is the narrow band between about 380 nm and 750 nm. This radiation is known as visible light because it is detected as colours by the human eye. It is visible light that drives photosynthesis.

EMR travels in waves, where wavelength provides a guide to the energy of the photons. The greater the wavelength of EMR, the lower the energy of the photons in that radiation.

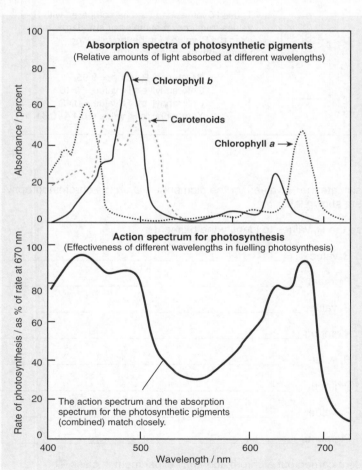

The photosynthetic pigments of plants

The photosynthetic pigments of plants fall into two categories: **chlorophylls** (which absorb red and blue-violet light) and **carotenoids** (which absorb strongly in the blue-violet and appear orange, yellow, or red). The pigments are located on the chloroplast membranes (the thylakoids) and are associated with membrane transport systems.

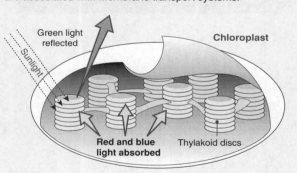

The pigments of chloroplasts in higher plants (above) absorb blue and red light, and the leaves therefore appear green (which is reflected). Each photosynthetic pigment has its own characteristic absorption spectrum (top left). Only chlorophyll *a* participates directly in the light reactions of photosynthesis, but the accessory pigments (chlorophyll *b* and carotenoids) can absorb wavelengths of light that chlorophyll *a* cannot and pass the energy (photons) to chlorophyll *a*, thus broadening the spectrum that can effectively drive photosynthesis.

Left: Graphs comparing absorption spectra of photosynthetic pigments compared with the action spectrum for photosynthesis.

1. What is meant by the absorption spectrum of a pigment? _____

_____

2. Why doesn't the **action spectrum** for photosynthesis exactly match the absorption spectrum of chlorophyll *a*?

_____

77 Separation of Pigments by Chromatography

Key Idea: Photosynthetic pigments can be separated from a mixture using chromatography.

Chromatography involves passing a mixture dissolved in a mobile phase (a solvent) through a stationary phase, which separates the molecules according to their specific characteristics (e.g. size or charge). In thin layer chromatography, the stationary phase is a thin layer of adsorbent material (e.g. silica gel or cellulose) attached to a solid plate. A sample is placed near the bottom of the plate which is placed in an appropriate solvent (the mobile phase).

Separation of photosynthetic pigments

The four primary pigments of green plants can be easily separated and identified using thin layer chromatography. The pigments from the leaves are first extracted by crushing leaves, together with acetone, using a mortar and pestle. The extract is dotted on to the chromatography plate. Acetone is used as the mobile phase (solvent). During thin layer chromatography, the pigments separate out according to differences in their relative solubilities. Two major classes of pigments are detected: the two greenish chlorophyll pigments and two yellowish carotenoid pigments.

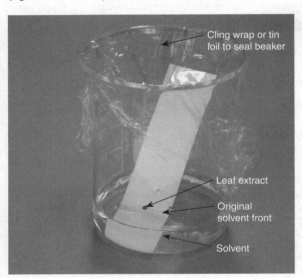

Cling wrap or tin foil to seal beaker

Leaf extract

Original solvent front

Solvent

Determining R$_f$ values

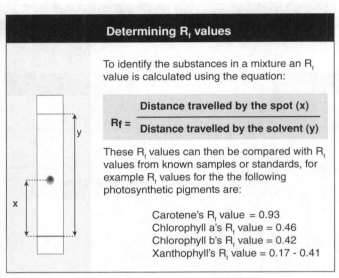

To identify the substances in a mixture an R$_f$ value is calculated using the equation:

$$R_f = \frac{\text{Distance travelled by the spot (x)}}{\text{Distance travelled by the solvent (y)}}$$

These R$_f$ values can then be compared with R$_f$ values from known samples or standards, for example R$_f$ values for the the following photosynthetic pigments are:

Carotene's R$_f$ value = 0.93
Chlorophyll a's R$_f$ value = 0.46
Chlorophyll b's R$_f$ value = 0.42
Xanthophyll's R$_f$ value = 0.17 - 0.41

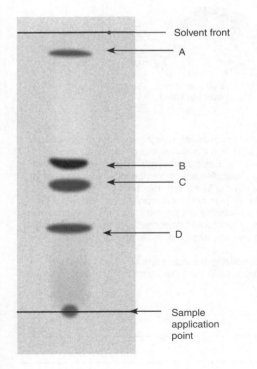

Solvent front

A

B

C

D

Sample application point

1. (a) Calculate the R$_f$ values for the pigments A-D on the chromatography plate shown left.

   (b) Use the R$_f$ values to identify the pigments:

   A: R$_f$ value: _____

   Pigment: _____

   B: R$_f$ value: _____

   Pigment: _____

   C: R$_f$ value: _____

   Pigment: _____

   D: R$_f$ value: _____

   Pigment: _____

2. A student carried out a chromatography experiment in class. The instructions said to leave the plate in the solvent for 30 minutes, but the student instead removed the plate after 20 minutes. How would this affect the R$_f$ values and pigment separations obtained?

   _____

   _____

   _____

   _____

© 2015 **BIOZONE** International
ISBN: 978-1-927309-14-8
Photocopying Prohibited

78 Light Dependent Reactions

Key Idea: In light dependent reactions of photosynthesis, the energy from photons of light is used to drive the reduction of $NADP^+$ and the production of ATP.

Like cellular respiration, photosynthesis is a redox process, but in photosynthesis, water is split, and electrons and hydrogen ions, are transferred from water to CO_2, reducing it to sugar. The electrons increase in potential energy as they move from water to sugar. The energy to do this is provided by light. Photosynthesis has two phases. In the **light dependent**

reactions, light energy is converted to chemical energy (ATP and NADPH). In the **light independent reactions**, the chemical energy is used to synthesise carbohydrate. The light dependent reactions most commonly involve **non-cyclic phosphorylation**, which produces ATP and NADPH in roughly equal quantities. The electrons lost are replaced from water. In **cyclic phosphorylation**, the electrons lost from photosystem II are replaced by those from photosystem I. ATP is generated, but not NADPH.

Non-cyclic phosphorylation

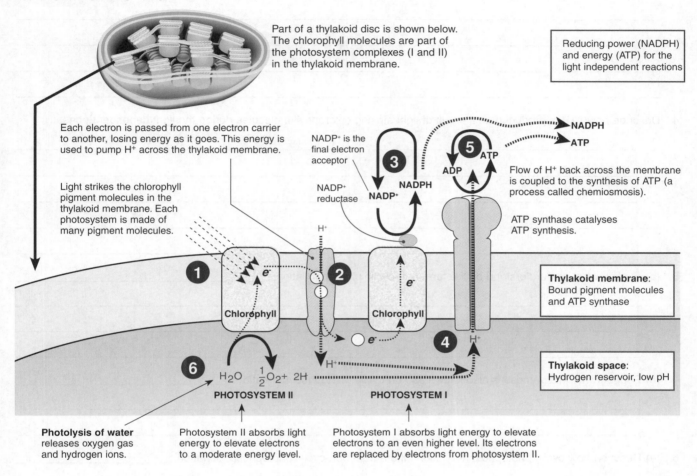

Part of a thylakoid disc is shown below. The chlorophyll molecules are part of the photosystem complexes (I and II) in the thylakoid membrane.

Reducing power (NADPH) and energy (ATP) for the light independent reactions

Each electron is passed from one electron carrier to another, losing energy as it goes. This energy is used to pump H^+ across the thylakoid membrane.

Light strikes the chlorophyll pigment molecules in the thylakoid membrane. Each photosystem is made of many pigment molecules.

$NADP^+$ is the final electron acceptor

$NADP^+$ reductase

Flow of H^+ back across the membrane is coupled to the synthesis of ATP (a process called chemiosmosis).

ATP synthase catalyses ATP synthesis.

Thylakoid membrane: Bound pigment molecules and ATP synthase

Thylakoid space: Hydrogen reservoir, low pH

PHOTOSYSTEM II

PHOTOSYSTEM I

Photolysis of water releases oxygen gas and hydrogen ions.

Photosystem II absorbs light energy to elevate electrons to a moderate energy level.

Photosystem I absorbs light energy to elevate electrons to an even higher level. Its electrons are replaced by electrons from photosystem II.

Cyclic phosphorylation

Cyclic phosphorylation involves only photosystem I and NADPH is not generated. Electrons from photosystem I are shunted back to the electron carriers in the membrane. This pathway produces ATP only. The Calvin cycle uses more ATP than NADPH, so cyclic phosphorylation makes up the difference. It is activated when NADPH levels build up, and remains active until enough ATP is made to meet demand.

Electrons are cycled through a pathway that takes them away from $NADP^+$ reductase.

ATP is produced while NADPH production ceases.

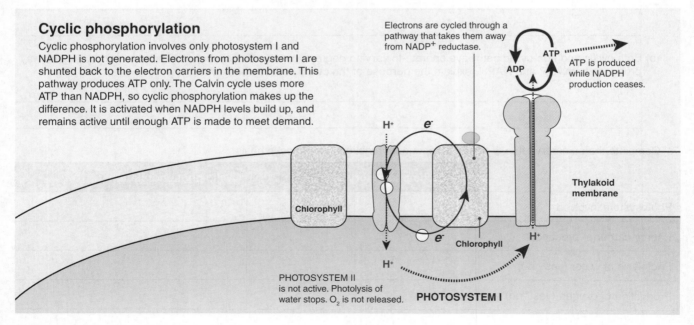

Thylakoid membrane

Chlorophyll

PHOTOSYSTEM II is not active. Photolysis of water stops. O_2 is not released.

PHOTOSYSTEM I

LINK 90   LINK 80   LINK 79   WEB 78   KNOW

1. Describe the role of the carrier molecule **NADP** in photosynthesis: _____

_____

2. Explain the role of chlorophyll molecules in photosynthesis: _____

_____

_____

_____

3. Summarise the events of the light dependent reactions and identify where they occur: _____

_____

_____

_____

_____

4. Describe how ATP is produced as a result of light striking chlorophyll molecules during the light dependent phase:

_____

_____

_____

_____

_____

5. (a) Explain what you understand by the term non-cyclic phosphorylation: _____

_____

_____

_____

(b) Suggest why this process is also known as non-cyclic photophosphorylation: _____

_____

_____

6. (a) Describe how cyclic photophosphorylation differs from non-cyclic photophosphorylation: _____

_____

_____

(b) Both cyclic and non-cyclic pathways operate to varying degrees during photosynthesis. Since the non-cyclic pathway produces both ATP and NAPH, explain the purpose of the cyclic pathway of electron flow:

_____

_____

7. Complete the summary table of the light dependent reactions of photosynthesis

	Non-cyclic phosphorylation	Cyclic phosphorylation
Photosystem involved		
Energy carrier(s) produced		
Photolysis of water (yes / no)		
Production of oxygen (yes / no)		

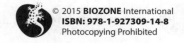

79 Light Independent Reactions

Key Idea: The light independent reactions of photosynthesis take place in the stroma of the chloroplast and do not require light to proceed.

In the **light independent reactions** (the **Calvin cycle**) hydrogen (H^+) is added to CO_2 and a 5C intermediate to make carbohydrate. The H^+ and ATP are supplied by the light dependent reactions. The Calvin cycle uses more ATP than NADPH, but the cell uses cyclic phosphorylation (which does not produce NADPH) when it runs low on ATP to make up the difference.

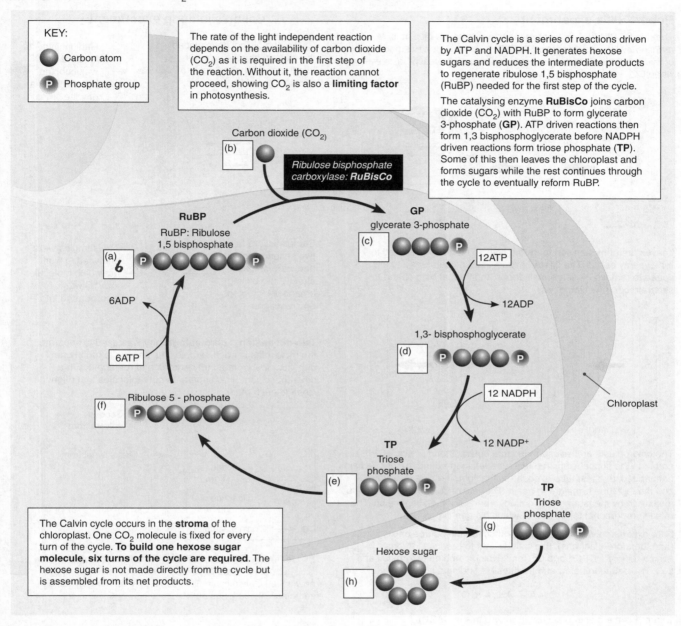

KEY:
- ● Carbon atom
- ⓟ Phosphate group

The rate of the light independent reaction depends on the availability of carbon dioxide (CO_2) as it is required in the first step of the reaction. Without it, the reaction cannot proceed, showing CO_2 is also a **limiting factor** in photosynthesis.

The Calvin cycle is a series of reactions driven by ATP and NADPH. It generates hexose sugars and reduces the intermediate products to regenerate ribulose 1,5 bisphosphate (RuBP) needed for the first step of the cycle.

The catalysing enzyme **RuBisCo** joins carbon dioxide (CO_2) with RuBP to form glycerate 3-phosphate (**GP**). ATP driven reactions then form 1,3 bisphosphoglycerate before NADPH driven reactions form triose phosphate (**TP**). Some of this then leaves the chloroplast and forms sugars while the rest continues through the cycle to eventually reform RuBP.

Carbon dioxide (CO_2)
(b)

Ribulose bisphosphate carboxylase: RuBisCo

RuBP
RuBP: Ribulose 1,5 bisphosphate
(a) **6** ⓟ ●●●●● ⓟ

GP
glycerate 3-phosphate
(c) ●●● ⓟ

12ATP

12ADP

1,3- bisphosphoglycerate
(d) ⓟ ●●● ⓟ

6ADP

6ATP

12 NADPH

Chloroplast

Ribulose 5 - phosphate
(f) ⓟ ●●●●

12 NADP⁺

TP
Triose phosphate
(e) ●●● ⓟ

TP
Triose phosphate
(g) ●●● ⓟ

Hexose sugar

(h) ●●●●●●

The Calvin cycle occurs in the **stroma** of the chloroplast. One CO_2 molecule is fixed for every turn of the cycle. **To build one hexose sugar molecule, six turns of the cycle are required**. The hexose sugar is not made directly from the cycle but is assembled from its net products.

1. In the boxes on the diagram above, write the number of molecules formed at each step during the formation of **one hexose sugar molecule**. The first one has been done for you:

2. Explain the importance of RuBisCo in the Calvin cycle: _____

_____

3. Identify the actual end product on the Calvin cycle: _____

4. Write the equation for the production of one hexose sugar molecule from carbon dioxide: _____

_____

5. Explain why the Calvin cycle is likely to cease in the dark for most plants, even though it is independent of light:

_____

© 2015 **BIOZONE** International
ISBN: 978-1-927309-14-8
Photocopying Prohibited

LINK **80** LINK **78** WEB **79** KNOW

80 Experimental Investigation of Photosynthesis

Key Idea: Hill's experiment using isolated chloroplasts and Calvin's "lollipop" experiment provided important information on the process of photosynthesis.

In the 1930s Robert Hill devised a way of measuring oxygen evolution and the rate of photosynthesis in isolated chloroplasts. During the 1950s Melvin Calvin led a team using radioisotopes of carbon to work out the steps of the light independent reactions (the Calvin cycle).

Robert Hill's experiment

The dye **DCPIP** (2,6-dichlorophenol-indophenol) is blue. It is reduced by H^+ ions and forms $DCPIPH_2$ (colourless). Hill made use of this dye to show that O_2 is produced during photosynthesis even when CO_2 is not present.

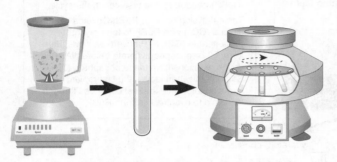

Leaves are homogenised to form a slurry. The slurry is filtered to remove any debris. The filtered extract is then centrifuged at low speed to remove the larger cell debris and then at high speed to separate out the chloroplasts.

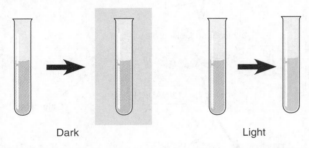

Dark	Light

The chloroplasts are resuspended in a buffer. The blue dye **DCPIP** is added to the suspension. In a test tube left in the dark, the dye remains unchanged. In a test tube exposed to the light, the blue dye fades and the test tube turns green again. The rate of colour change can be measured by measuring the light absorbance of the suspension. The rate is proportional to the rate at which oxygen is produced.

Hill's experiment showed that water must be the source of oxygen (and therefore electrons). It is split by light to produce H^+ ions (which reduce DCPIP) and O^{2-} ions (which combine to form O_2 and $2e^-$). The equation below summarises his findings:

$$H_2O + A \rightarrow AH_2 + \frac{1}{2} O_2$$

where A is the electron acceptor (*in vivo* this is NADP)

Calvin's lollipop experiment

Calvin and his colleges placed the algae *Chlorella vulgaris* in a thin bulb shaped flask to simulate a leaf (the lollipop).

Radioactive ^{14}C labelled CO_2 was bubbled into the flask at precise times.

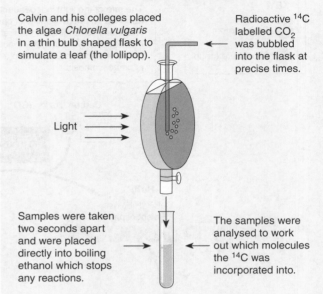

Samples were taken two seconds apart and were placed directly into boiling ethanol which stops any reactions.

The samples were analysed to work out which molecules the ^{14}C was incorporated into.

Two-dimensional chromatography was used to separate the molecules in each sample. The sample is run in one direction, then rotated 90 degrees and run again with a different solvent. This separates out molecules that might be close to each other.

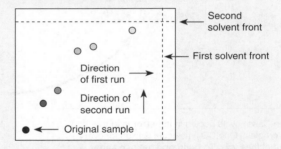

By identifying the order that the molecules incorporating the ^{14}C appeared it was possible to work out the steps of the now called Calvin cycle. This could only be done by taking samples only seconds apart.

---

1. Write an equation for the formation of $DCPIPH_2$ from DCPIP: _____

   _____

2. What important finding about photosynthesis did Hill's experiment show? _____

   _____

3. Why did the samples in Calvin's lollipop experiment need to be taken just seconds apart? ___

   _____

   _____

   _____

© 2015 **BIOZONE** International
ISBN: 978-1-927309-14-8
Photocopying Prohibited

81 The Fate of Triose Phosphate

Key Idea: The triose phosphate molecules produced in photosynthesis can be combined and rearranged to form monosaccharides such as glucose. Glucose is an important energy source and a precursor of many other molecules.

The triose phosphate molecules produced in photosynthesis can be combined and rearranged to form the hexose monosaccharide glucose. Glucose has three main fates:

immediate use to produce ATP molecules (available energy for work), storage for later ATP production, or for use in building other molecules. Plants use the glucose they make in photosynthesis to build all the molecules they require. Animals obtain their glucose by consuming plants or other animals. Other molecules (e.g. amino acids and fatty acids) are also obtained by animals this way.

The fate of glucose

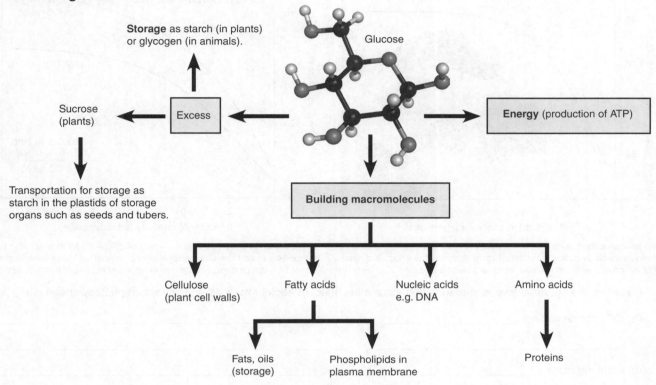

Storage as starch (in plants) or glycogen (in animals).

Sucrose (plants) ← Excess ← Glucose → **Energy** (production of ATP)

Transportation for storage as starch in the plastids of storage organs such as seeds and tubers.

Building macromolecules

Cellulose (plant cell walls) — Fatty acids — Nucleic acids e.g. DNA — Amino acids

Fats, oils (storage) — Phospholipids in plasma membrane — Proteins

How do we know how glucose is used?

► Labelling the carbon atoms in a glucose molecule with isotopes shows how glucose is incorporated into other molecules.

► An isotope is an element (e.g. carbon) whose atoms have a particular number of neutrons in their nucleus. The different number of neutrons allows the isotopes to be identified by their density (e.g. a carbon atom with 13 neutrons is denser than a carbon atom with 12 neutrons).

► Some isotopes are radioactive. These radioactive isotopes can be traced using X-ray film or devices that detect the disintegration of the isotopes, such as Geiger counters.

The carbon atom

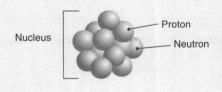

Nucleus — Proton — Neutron

The nucleus of an atom is made up of neutrons and protons. For any element, the number of protons remains the same, but the number of neutrons can vary. Electrons (not shown) are found outside the nucleus.

Naturally occurring C isotopes

^{12}C
6 protons
6 neutrons
Stable. 99.9% of all C isotopes.

^{13}C
6 protons
7 neutrons
Stable

^{14}C
6 protons
8 neutrons
Radioactive

1. What are the three main fates of glucose? _____

_____

2. Identify a use for glucose in a plant that does not occur in animals: _____

_____

3. How can isotopes of carbon be used to find the fate of glucose molecules? _____

_____

LINK
74

KNOW

82 Factors Affecting Photosynthesis

Key Idea: Environmental factors, such as CO_2 availability and light intensity, affect the rate of photosynthesis.

The photosynthetic rate is the rate at which plants make carbohydrate. It is dependent on environmental factors, particularly the availability of light and carbon dioxide (CO_2). Temperature is important, but its influence is less clear because it depends on the availability of the other two limiting factors (CO_2 and light) and the temperature tolerance of the plant. The relative importance of these factors can be tested experimentally by altering one of the factors while holding the others constant. The results for such an experiment are shown below.

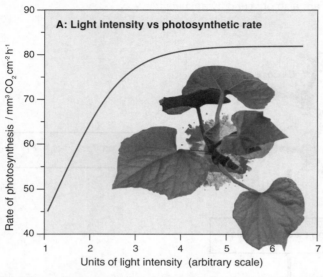

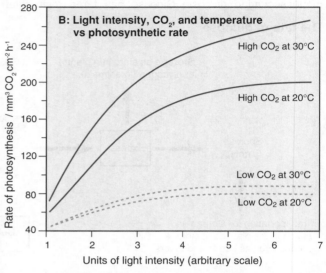

These figures illustrate the effect of different limiting factors on the rate of photosynthesis in cucumber plants. Figure A shows the effect of different light intensities when the temperature and carbon dioxide (CO_2) level are kept constant. Figure B shows the effect of different light intensities at two temperatures and two CO_2 concentrations. In each of these experiments, either CO_2 level or temperature was changed at each light intensity in turn.

1. Based on the figures above, summarise and explain the effect of each of the following factors on photosynthetic rate:

    (a) CO_2 concentration: _____

    _____

    (b) Light intensity: _____

    _____

    (c) Temperature: _____

    _____

2. Why does photosynthetic rate decline when the CO_2 level is reduced?_____

    _____

    _____

3. (a) In figure B, explain how the effects of CO_2 concentration were distinguished from the effects of temperature:

    _____

    (b) Which factor (CO_2 or temperature) had the greatest effect on photosynthetic rate: _____

    (c) How can you tell this from the graph? _____

    _____

4. How can glasshouses be used to create an environment in which photosynthetic rates are maximised?

    _____

    _____

    _____

5. Design an experiment to demonstrate the effect of temperature on photosynthetic rate. You should include a hypothesis, list of equipment, and methods. Staple your experiment to this page.

© 2015 **BIOZONE** International
ISBN: 978-1-927309-14-8
Photocopying Prohibited

83 Investigating Photosynthetic Rate

Key Idea: Measuring the production of oxygen provides a simple means of measuring the rate of photosynthesis. The rate of photosynthesis can be investigated by measuring the substances involved in photosynthesis. These include measuring the uptake of carbon dioxide, the production of oxygen, or the change in biomass over time. Measuring the rate of oxygen production provides a good approximation of the photosynthetic rate and is relatively easy to carry out.

The aim

To investigate the effect of light intensity on the rate of photosynthesis in an aquatic plant, *Cabomba aquatica*.

Cabomba aquatica, a common aquarium plant

Piotr Kuczynski CC 3.0

The method

► 0.8-1.0 grams of *Cabomba* stem were weighed on a balance. The stem was cut and inverted to ensure a free flow of oxygen bubbles.

► The stem was placed into a beaker filled with a solution containing 0.2 mol L^{-1} sodium hydrogen carbonate (to supply carbon dioxide). The solution was at approximately 20°C. A funnel was inverted over the *Cabomba* and a test tube filled with the sodium hydrogen carbonate solution was inverted on top to collect any gas produced.

► The beaker was placed at distances (20, 25, 30, 35, 40, 45 cm) from a 60W light source and the light intensity measured with a lux meter at each interval. One beaker was not exposed to the light source (5 lx).

► Before recording data, the *Cabomba* stem was left to acclimatise to the new light level for 5 minutes. Because the volumes of oxygen gas produced are very low, bubbles were counted for a period of three minutes at each distance.

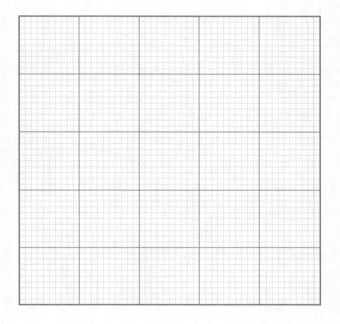

The results

Light intensity / lx	Bubbles counted in three minutes	Bubbles per minute
5	0	
13	6	
30	9	
60	12	
95	18	
150	33	
190	35	

1. Complete the table by calculating the rate of oxygen production (bubbles of oxygen gas per minute):

2. Use the data to draw a graph of the bubble produced per minute vs light intensity:

3. Although the light source was placed set distances from the *Cabomba* stem, light intensity in lux was recorded at each distance rather than distance *per se*. Explain why this would be more accurate:

_____

_____

_____

4. The sample of gas collected during the experiment was tested with a glowing splint. The splint reignited when placed in the gas. What does this confirm about the gas produced?

_____

5. What could be a more accurate way of measuring the gas produced in the experiment? _____

_____

_____

LINK
82

WEB
83

DATA

84 Chapter Review

Summarise what you know about this topic under the headings and sub-headings provided. You can draw diagrams or mind maps, or write short notes to organise your thoughts. Use the images and hints to help you and refer back to the introduction to check the points covered:

Photosynthesis

HINT: State the general equation for photosynthesis. Outline the light dependent and independent reactions.

Experimental Investigations

HINT: Describe and explain factors affecting photosynthesis. Explain how the products of photosynthesis can be tracked.

© 2015 **BIOZONE** International
ISBN: 978-1-927309-14-8
Photocopying Prohibited

85 KEY TERMS: Did You Get It?

1. Complete the schematic diagram of photosynthesis below:

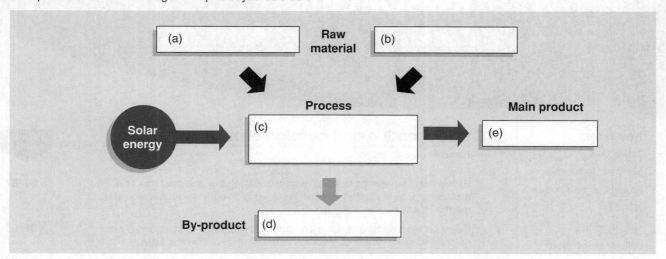

2. (a) Write the process of photosynthesis as:

A word equation: _____

A chemical equation: _____

(b) Where does photosynthesis occur? _____

3. Test your vocabulary by matching each term to its correct definition, as identified by its preceding letter code.

absorption spectrum ....

accessory pigments ....

action spectrum ....

Calvin cycle ....

chlorophyll ....

grana ....

light dependent phase ....

photosynthesis ....

ribulose bisphosphate ....

stroma ....

thylakoid discs ....

A The biochemical process that uses light energy to convert carbon dioxide and water into glucose molecules and oxygen.

B A 5-carbon molecule which acts as the primary CO_2 acceptor in photosynthesis.

C Membrane-bound compartments in chloroplasts. They are the site of the light dependent reactions of photosynthesis.

D The phase in photosynthesis where chemical energy is used for the synthesis of carbohydrate. Also called the light independent phase.

E The liquid interior of the chloroplast where the light independent phase takes place.

F The phase in photosynthesis when light energy is converted to chemical energy.

G The term to describe the light absorption of a pigment vs the wavelength of light.

H Plant pigments that absorb wavelengths of light that chlorophyll *a* does not absorb.

I A profile of the effectiveness of different wavelengths of light in fuelling photosynthesis.

J The green, membrane-bound pigment involved in the light dependent reactions of photosynthesis.

K The stacks of thylakoids within the chloroplasts of plants.

4. Label the following features of a chloroplast on the diagram below: granum, stroma, thylakoid disc, stroma lamellae

TEST

Respiration

Key terms

acetyl coA

alcoholic fermentation

anaerobic metabolism

ATP

ATP synthase

cellular respiration

chemiosmosis

cristae

decarboxylation

dehydrogenation

electron transport chain

ethanol

FAD

fermentation

glycolysis

Krebs cycle

lactic acid fermentation

link reaction

matrix

mitochondrion

NAD

oxidative phosphorylation

pyruvate

substrate level phosphorylation

triose phosphate

Mitochondria and cellular respiration

Learning outcomes

Activity number

☐ 1 Explain why organisms need to respire, recalling the universal role of ATP in metabolism, as illustrated by examples, e.g. active transport, named metabolic reactions, and movement.　86 87

☐ 2 Describe the structure of a mitochondrion, identifying the inner and outer mitochondrial membranes, matrix, cristae, and mitochondrial DNA.　88 89

☐ 3 Identify the location of the main steps in the complete oxidation of glucose: glycolysis, the link reaction, Krebs cycle, and electron transport chain.　88

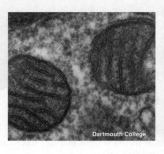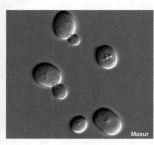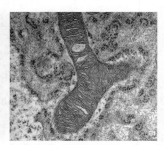

Dartmouth College　　Masur　　EM

The biochemistry of respiration

Learning outcomes

Activity number

☐ 4 Describe glycolysis and recognise it as the major anaerobic pathway in cells. Include reference to the phosphorylation of glucose to hexose bisphosphate, the splitting of this intermediate to two triose phosphates, and further oxidation to pyruvate. State the net yield of ATP and $NADH_2$ from glycolysis.　88 89

☐ 5 Describe the link reaction to include decarboxylation of pyruvate, reduction of NAD, and formation of acetyl coenzyme A.　88 89

☐ 6 Describe the events in the Krebs (citric acid) cycle including reference to the stepwise oxidation of intermediates in the cycle and the importance of decarboxylation, dehydrogenation, reduction of NAD and FAD, and substrate level phosphorylation.　88 89

☐ 7 Describe the role of coenzymes (NAD, FAD, coenzyme A) in cellular respiration.　89

☐ 8 Explain oxidative phosphorylation in the electron transport chain to include the roles of electron carriers in the mitochondrial cristae and the role of oxygen as the terminal electron acceptor.　88 89

☐ 9 Describe chemiosmotic theory as an explanation for ATP generation in oxidative phosphorylation and photophosphorylation (in photosynthesis).　90

☐ 10 Describe anaerobic pathways for ATP generation in eukaryotes to include alcoholic fermentation in yeast and lactic acid fermentation in mammalian muscle. Describe benefits of these anaerobic pathways. Compare and explain the differences in ATP yield from aerobic respiration and from fermentation.　91

☐ 11 **PAG11** Investigate fermentation in yeast.　92

☐ 12 Describe and explain the relative energy values of carbohydrates, lipids, and proteins as respiratory substrates. Describe the use of respiratory quotients (RQ) to determine the respiratory substrate being utilised. Calculate and interpret RQ values for organisms in different conditions.　93

☐ 13 **PAG11** Use a simple respirometer to investigate respiration rate, e.g. in germinating seeds, under different conditions.　94

86 The Role of ATP in Cells

Key Idea: ATP transports chemical energy within the cell for use in metabolic processes.

All organisms require energy to be able to perform the metabolic processes required for them to function and reproduce. This energy is obtained by cellular respiration, a set of metabolic reactions which ultimately convert biochemical energy from 'food' into the nucleotide **adenosine triphosphate** (ATP). ATP is considered to be a universal energy carrier, transferring chemical energy within the cell for use in metabolic processes such as biosynthesis, cell division, cell signalling, thermoregulation, cell mobility, and active transport of substances across membranes.

Adenosine triphosphate (ATP)

The ATP molecule consists of three components; a purine base (**adenine**), a pentose sugar (**ribose**), and **three phosphate groups** which attach to the 5' carbon of the pentose sugar. The structure of ATP is described below.

The bonds between the phosphate groups contain electrons in a high energy state which store a large amount of energy. The energy is released during ATP hydrolysis. Typically, hydrolysis is coupled to another cellular reaction to which the energy is transferred. The end products of the reaction are adenosine diphosphate (ADP) and an inorganic phosphate (Pi).

Note that energy is released during the formation of bonds during the hydrolysis reaction, not the breaking of bonds between the phosphates (which requires energy input).

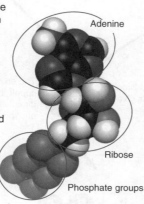

Adenine

Ribose

Phosphate groups

The mitochondrion

Cellular respiration and ATP production occur in mitochondria. A mitochondrion is bounded by a double membrane. The inner and outer membranes are separated by an intermembrane space, compartmentalising the regions where the different reactions of cellular respiration take place. The folded inner membranes provide a large surface area for reactions.

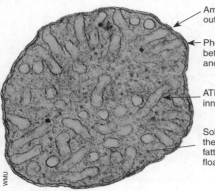

Amine oxidases on the outer membrane surface

Phosphorylases between the inner and outer membranes

ATP synthases on the inner membranes (cristae)

Soluble enzymes for the Krebs cycle and fatty acid degradation floating in the matrix

ATP powers metabolism

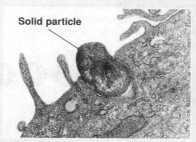

Solid particle

The energy released from the removal of a phosphate group of ATP is used to actively transport molecules and substances across the cellular membrane. **Phagocytosis** (left), which involves the engulfment of solid particles, is one such example.

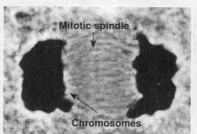

Mitotic spindle

Chromosomes

Cell division (mitosis), as observed in this onion cell, requires ATP to proceed. Formation of the mitotic spindle and chromosome separation are two aspects of cell division which require energy from ATP hydrolysis to occur.

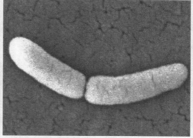

ATP is required when bacteria divide by binary fission (left). For example, ATP is required in DNA replication and to synthesise components of the peptidoglycan cell wall.

Maintaining body temperature requires energy. To maintain body heat, muscular activity increases (e.g. shivering). Cooling requires expenditure of energy too. For example, sweating is an energy requiring process involving secretion from glands in the skin.

1. Why do organisms need to respire? _____

_____

2. (a) Describe the general role of mitochondria in cell respiration: _____

_____

   (b) Explain the importance of compartmentalisation in the mitochondrion: _____

_____

3. Explain why thermoregulation is associated with energy expenditure: _____

_____

_____

LINK **87**   WEB **86**   KNOW

87 ATP and Energy

Key Idea: ATP is the universal energy carrier in cells. Energy is stored in the covalent bonds between phosphate groups. The molecule ATP (adenosine triphosphate) is the universal energy carrier for the cell. ATP can release its energy quickly by hydrolysis of the terminal phosphate. This reaction is catalysed by the enzyme ATPase. Once ATP has released its energy, it becomes ADP (adenosine diphosphate), a low energy molecule that can be recharged by adding a phosphate. The energy to do this is supplied by the controlled breakdown of respiratory substrates in cellular respiration.

How does ATP provide energy?

ATP releases its energy during hydrolysis. Water is split and added to the terminal phosphate group resulting in ADP and Pi. For every mole of ATP hydrolysed **30.7 kJ** of energy is released. Note that energy is released during the formation of chemical bonds not from the breaking of chemical bonds.

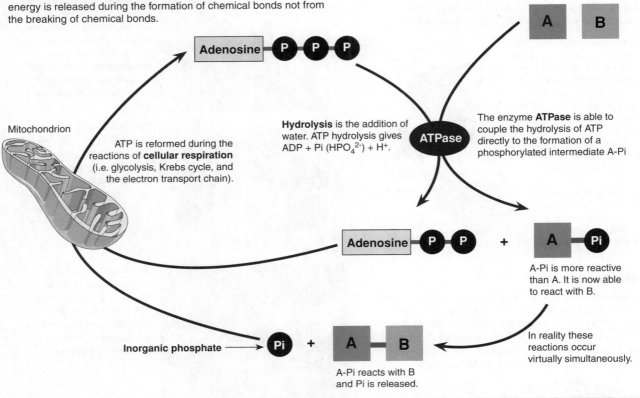

The reaction of A + B is endergonic. It requires energy to proceed and will not occur spontaneously.

Mitochondrion

ATP is reformed during the reactions of **cellular respiration** (i.e. glycolysis, Krebs cycle, and the electron transport chain).

Hydrolysis is the addition of water. ATP hydrolysis gives ADP + Pi (HPO_4^{2-}) + H^+.

The enzyme **ATPase** is able to couple the hydrolysis of ATP directly to the formation of a phosphorylated intermediate A-Pi

A-Pi is more reactive than A. It is now able to react with B.

Inorganic phosphate

In reality these reactions occur virtually simultaneously.

A-Pi reacts with B and Pi is released.

Note! The phosphate bonds in ATP are often referred to as high energy bonds. This can be misleading. The bonds contain *electrons in a high energy state* (making the bonds themselves relatively weak). A small amount of energy is required to break the bonds, but when the intermediates recombine and form new chemical bonds a large amount of energy is released. The final product is less reactive than the original reactants.

In many textbooks the reaction series above is simplified and the intermediates are left out:

1. (a) How does ATP supply energy to power metabolism? _____

_____

(b) In what way is the ADP/ATP system like a rechargeable battery? _____

_____

2. What is the immediate source of energy for reforming ATP from ADP? _____

3. Explain the purpose of the folded inner membrane in mitochondria: _____

_____

_____

4. Explain why highly active cells (e.g. sperm cells) have large numbers of mitochondria: _____

_____

88 ATP Production in Cells

Key Idea: Cellular respiration is the process by which the energy in glucose is transferred to ATP.

Cellular respiration can be **aerobic** (requires oxygen) or **anaerobic** (does not require oxygen). Some plants and animals can generate ATP anaerobically for short periods of time. Other organisms (anaerobic bacteria) use only anaerobic respiration and live in oxygen-free environments. Cellular respiration occurs in the cytoplasm and mitochondria. The overall process is summarised by the word equation:

glucose + oxygen → carbon dioxide + water + ATP.

An overview of ATP production in cells

Respiration involves three metabolic stages (plus a link reaction) summarised below. The first two stages are the catabolic pathways that decompose glucose and other organic fuels. In the third stage, the electron transport chain accepts electrons from the first two stages and passes these from one electron acceptor to another. The energy released at each stepwise transfer is used to make ATP. The final electron acceptor in this process is molecular oxygen.

1. **Glycolysis**. In the cytoplasm, glucose is broken down into two molecules of pyruvate.

2. **The link reaction**. In the mitochondrial matrix, pyruvate is split and added to coenzyme A.

3. **Krebs cycle**. In the mitochondrial matrix, a derivative of pyruvate is decomposed to CO_2.

4. **Electron transport and oxidative phosphorylation**. This occurs in the inner membranes of the mitochondrion and accounts for almost 90% of the ATP generated by respiration.

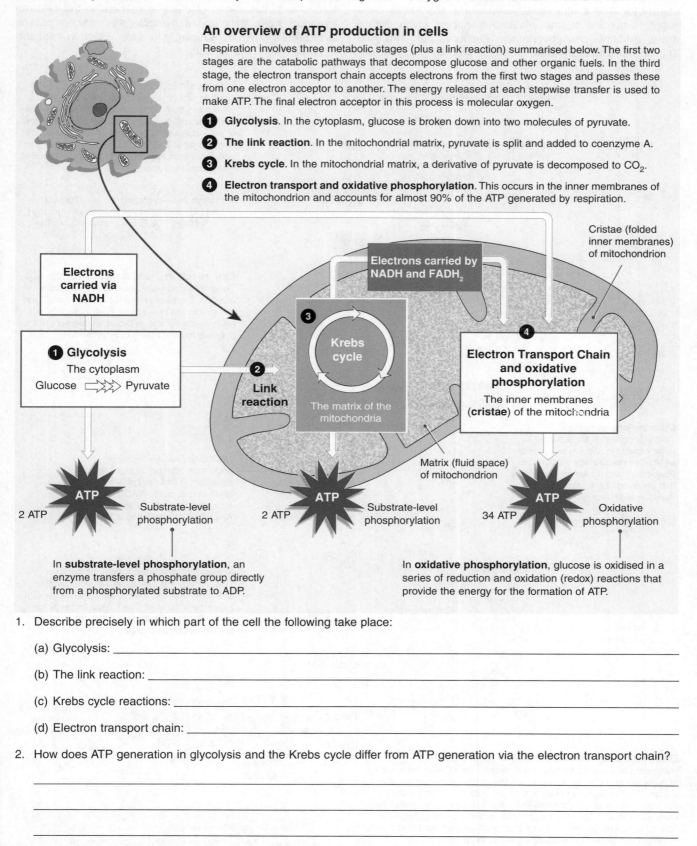

In **substrate-level phosphorylation**, an enzyme transfers a phosphate group directly from a phosphorylated substrate to ADP.

In **oxidative phosphorylation**, glucose is oxidised in a series of reduction and oxidation (redox) reactions that provide the energy for the formation of ATP.

1. Describe precisely in which part of the cell the following take place:

   (a) Glycolysis: _____

   (b) The link reaction: _____

   (c) Krebs cycle reactions: _____

   (d) Electron transport chain: _____

2. How does ATP generation in glycolysis and the Krebs cycle differ from ATP generation via the electron transport chain?

   _____
   _____
   _____
   _____

© 2015 **BIOZONE** International
ISBN: **978-1-927309-14-8**
Photocopying Prohibited

LINK **90** LINK **89** **KNOW**

89 The Biochemistry of Respiration

Key Idea: During cellular respiration, the energy in glucose is transferred to ATP in a series of enzyme controlled steps. The oxidation of glucose is a catabolic, energy yielding pathway. The breakdown of glucose and other organic fuels (such as fats and proteins) to simpler molecules releases energy for ATP synthesis. Glycolysis and the Krebs cycle supply electrons to the electron transport chain, which drives oxidative phosphorylation. Glycolysis nets two ATP. The conversion of pyruvate (the end product of glycolysis) to acetyl CoA links glycolysis to the Krebs cycle. One "turn" of the cycle releases carbon dioxide, forms one ATP, and passes electrons to three NAD+ and one FAD. Most of the ATP generated in cellular respiration is produced by oxidative phosphorylation when NADH + H+ and FADH$_2$ donate electrons to the series of electron carriers in the electron transport chain. At the end of the chain, electrons are passed to molecular oxygen, reducing it to water. Electron transport is coupled to ATP synthesis.

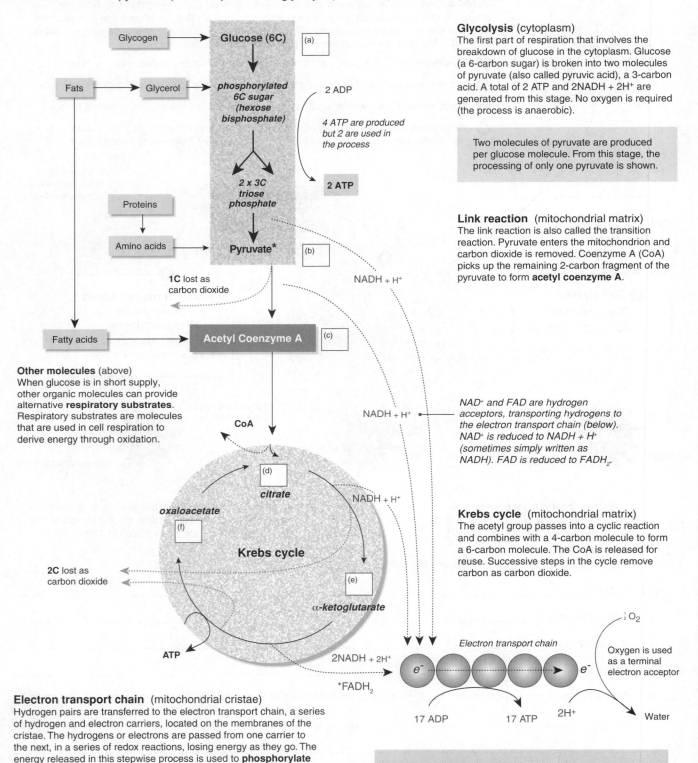

Glycolysis (cytoplasm)
The first part of respiration that involves the breakdown of glucose in the cytoplasm. Glucose (a 6-carbon sugar) is broken into two molecules of pyruvate (also called pyruvic acid), a 3-carbon acid. A total of 2 ATP and 2NADH + 2H+ are generated from this stage. No oxygen is required (the process is anaerobic).

Two molecules of pyruvate are produced per glucose molecule. From this stage, the processing of only one pyruvate is shown.

Link reaction (mitochondrial matrix)
The link reaction is also called the transition reaction. Pyruvate enters the mitochondrion and carbon dioxide is removed. Coenzyme A (CoA) picks up the remaining 2-carbon fragment of the pyruvate to form **acetyl coenzyme A**.

Other molecules (above)
When glucose is in short supply, other organic molecules can provide alternative **respiratory substrates**. Respiratory substrates are molecules that are used in cell respiration to derive energy through oxidation.

NAD+ and FAD are hydrogen acceptors, transporting hydrogens to the electron transport chain (below). NAD+ is reduced to NADH + H+ (sometimes simply written as NADH). FAD is reduced to FADH$_2$.

Krebs cycle (mitochondrial matrix)
The acetyl group passes into a cyclic reaction and combines with a 4-carbon molecule to form a 6-carbon molecule. The CoA is released for reuse. Successive steps in the cycle remove carbon as carbon dioxide.

Oxygen is used as a terminal electron acceptor

Electron transport chain (mitochondrial cristae)
Hydrogen pairs are transferred to the electron transport chain, a series of hydrogen and electron carriers, located on the membranes of the cristae. The hydrogens or electrons are passed from one carrier to the next, in a series of redox reactions, losing energy as they go. The energy released in this stepwise process is used to **phosphorylate** ADP to form ATP. Oxygen is the final electron acceptor and is reduced to water (hence the term **oxidative phosphorylation**).
Note FAD enters the electron transport chain at a lower energy level than NAD, and only 2ATP are generated per FADH$_2$.

Total ATP yield per glucose
Glycolysis: 2 ATP, *Krebs cycle*: 2 ATP, *Electron transport*: 34 ATP

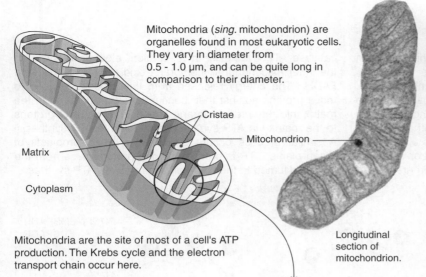

Mitochondria (*sing.* mitochondrion) are organelles found in most eukaryotic cells. They vary in diameter from 0.5 - 1.0 μm, and can be quite long in comparison to their diameter.

Cristae

Matrix

Cytoplasm

Mitochondrion

Mitochondria are the site of most of a cell's ATP production. The Krebs cycle and the electron transport chain occur here.

Longitudinal section of mitochondrion.

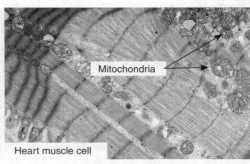

Mitochondria

Heart muscle cell

Cells that require a lot of ATP for cellular processes have a lot of mitochondria. Sperm cells contain a large number of mitochondria near the base of the tail. Liver cells have around 2000 mitochondria per cell, taking up 25% of the cytoplasmic space. Heart muscle cells (above) may have 40% of the cytoplasmic space taken up by mitochondria.

Location of cellular respiration

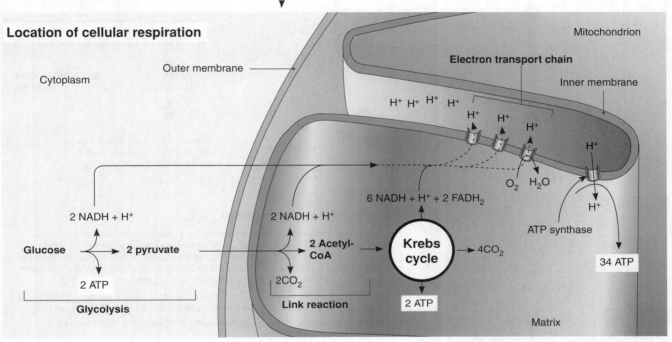

Mitochondrion

Cytoplasm

Outer membrane

Electron transport chain

Inner membrane

H^+ H^+ H^+ H^+

H^+ H^+ H^+

H^+

O_2 H_2O

H^+

ATP synthase

H^+

2 NADH + H^+

2 NADH + H^+

6 NADH + H^+ + 2 FADH$_2$

Glucose → **2 pyruvate**

2 ATP

2 Acetyl-CoA

Krebs cycle

$4CO_2$

34 ATP

$2CO_2$

2 ATP

Glycolysis

Link reaction

Matrix

1. In the longitudinal section of a mitochondrion (above), label the matrix and cristae.

2. Explain the purpose of the link reaction: _____

_____

_____

3. On the diagram of cell respiration (previous page), state the number of carbon atoms in each of the molecules (a)-(f):

4. How many ATP molecules **per molecule of glucose** are generated during the following stages of respiration?

    (a) Glycolysis: _____ (b) Krebs cycle: _____ (c) Electron transport chain: _____ (d) Total: _____

5. Explain what happens to the carbon atoms lost during respiration: _____

6. Explain what happens during oxidative phosphorylation: _____

_____

_____

_____

_____

_____

90 Chemiosmosis

Key Idea: Chemiosmosis is the process in which electron transport is coupled to ATP synthesis.

Chemiosmosis occurs in the membranes of mitochondria, the chloroplasts of plants, and across the plasma membrane of bacteria. It involves establishing and using a proton gradient to drive ATP synthesis. Chemiosmosis has two key components: an **electron transport chain** sets up a proton gradient as electrons pass along it to a final electron acceptor, and an enzyme, **ATP synthase**, uses the proton gradient to

catalyse ATP synthesis. In respiration, electron carriers on the inner mitochondrial membrane oxidise NADH + H$^+$ and FADH$_2$. The energy released from this process is used to move protons against their concentration gradient, from the matrix into the intermembrane space. The return of protons to the matrix via ATP synthase is coupled to ATP synthesis. A similar process occurs Similarly, in the chloroplasts of green plants, ATP is produced when protons pass from the thylakoid lumen to the chloroplast stroma via ATP synthase.

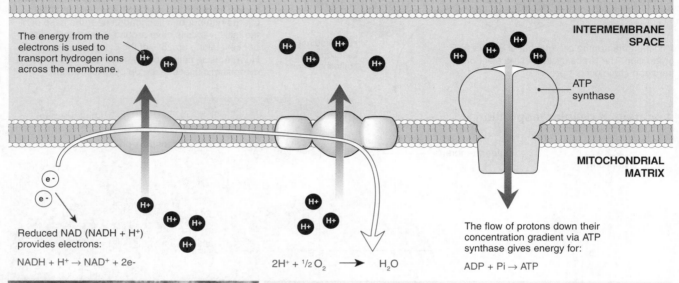

The energy from the electrons is used to transport hydrogen ions across the membrane.

INTERMEMBRANE SPACE

ATP synthase

MITOCHONDRIAL MATRIX

Reduced NAD (NADH + H$^+$) provides electrons:

NADH + H$^+$ → NAD$^+$ + 2e-

$2H^+ + \frac{1}{2}O_2 \longrightarrow H_2O$

The flow of protons down their concentration gradient via ATP synthase gives energy for:

ADP + Pi → ATP

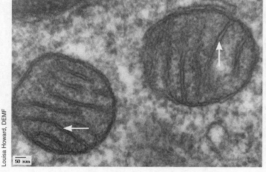

The intermembrane spaces can be seen (arrows) in this transverse section of mitochondria.

The evidence for chemiosmosis

The British biochemist Peter Mitchell proposed the chemiosmotic hypothesis in 1961. He proposed that, because living cells have membrane potential, electrochemical gradients could be used to do work, i.e. provide the energy for ATP synthesis. Scientists at the time were sceptical, but the evidence for chemiosmosis was extensive and came from studies of isolated mitochondria and chloroplasts. Evidence included:

▸ The outer membranes of mitochondria were removed leaving the inner membranes intact. Adding protons to the treated mitochondria increased ATP synthesis.

▸ When isolated chloroplasts were illuminated, the medium in which they were suspended became alkaline.

▸ Isolated chloroplasts were kept in the dark and transferred first to a low pH medium (to acidify the thylakoid interior) and then to an alkaline medium (low protons). They then spontaneously synthesised ATP (no light was needed).

1. Summarise the process of chemiosmosis: _____

_____

_____

2. Why did the addition of protons to the treated mitochondria increase ATP synthesis?_____

_____

_____

3. Why did the suspension of isolated chloroplasts become alkaline when illuminated?_____

_____

4. (a) What was the purpose of transferring the chloroplasts first to an acid then to an alkaline medium? _____

_____

(b) Why did ATP synthesis occur spontaneously in these treated chloroplasts? _____

_____

© 2015 **BIOZONE** International
ISBN: **978-1-927309-14-8**
Photocopying Prohibited

91 Anaerobic Pathways

Key Idea: Glucose can be metabolised aerobically and anaerobically to produce ATP. The ATP yield from aerobic processes is higher than from anaerobic processes.

Aerobic respiration occurs in the presence of oxygen. Organisms can also generate ATP when oxygen is absent by using a molecule other than oxygen as the terminal electron acceptor for the pathway. In alcoholic fermentation in yeasts, the electron acceptor is ethanal. In lactic acid fermentation, which occurs in mammalian muscle even when oxygen is present, the electron acceptor is pyruvate itself.

Alcoholic fermentation

In alcoholic fermentation, the H^+ acceptor is ethanal which is reduced to ethanol with the release of carbon dioxide (CO_2). Yeasts respire aerobically when oxygen is available but can use alcoholic fermentation when it is not. At ethanol levels above 12-15%, the ethanol produced by alcoholic fermentation is toxic and this limits their ability to use this pathway indefinitely. The root cells of plants also use fermentation as a pathway when oxygen is unavailable but the ethanol must be converted back to respiratory intermediates and respired aerobically.

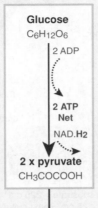

Glucose
$C_6H_{12}O_6$
2 ADP
→ 2 ATP Net
NAD.H_2
2 x pyruvate
$CH_3COCOOH$

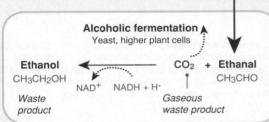

Alcoholic fermentation
Yeast, higher plant cells

Ethanol		CO_2 + Ethanal
CH_3CH_2OH	NAD$^+$ NADH + H$^+$	CH_3CHO
Waste product		*Gaseous waste product*

Lactic acid fermentation

Skeletal muscles produce ATP in the absence of oxygen using lactic acid fermentation. In this pathway, pyruvate is reduced to lactic acid, which dissociates to form lactate and H^+. The conversion of pyruvate to lactate is reversible and this pathway operates alongside the aerobic system all the time to enable greater intensity and duration of activity. Lactate can be metabolised in the muscle itself or it can enter the circulation and be taken up by the liver to replenish carbohydrate stores. This 'lactate shuttle' is an important mechanism for balancing the distribution of substrates and waste products.

Glucose
$C_6H_{12}O_6$
2 ADP
→ 2 ATP Net
NAD.H_2
2 x pyruvate
$CH_3COCOOH$

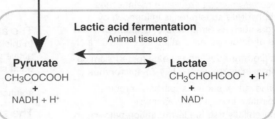

Lactic acid fermentation
Animal tissues

Pyruvate		Lactate
$CH_3COCOOH$		$CH_3CHOHCOO^-$ + H$^+$
+ NADH + H$^+$		+ NAD$^+$

The alcohol and CO_2 produced from alcoholic fermentation form the basis of the brewing and baking industries. In baking, the dough is left to ferment and the yeast metabolises sugars to produce ethanol and CO_2. The CO_2 causes the dough to rise.

Yeasts are used to produce almost all alcoholic beverages (e.g. wine and beers). The yeast used in the process breaks down the sugars into ethanol (alcohol) and CO_2. The alcohol produced is a metabolic by-product of fermentation by the yeast.

The lactate shuttle in vertebrate skeletal muscle works alongside the aerobic system to enable maximal muscle activity. Lactate moves from its site of production to regions within and outside the muscle (e.g. liver) where it can be respired aerobically.

1. Describe the key difference between aerobic respiration and fermentation: _____

_____

2. (a) Refer to page 114 and determine the efficiency of fermentation compared to aerobic respiration: _____ %

   (b) Why is the efficiency of these anaerobic pathways so low? _____

   _____

3. Why can't alcoholic fermentation go on indefinitely? _____

_____

_____

LINK **92** LINK **69** WEB **91** **KNOW**

92 Investigating Yeast Fermentation

Key Idea: Brewer's yeast preferentially uses alcoholic fermentation when there is excess sugar, releasing CO_2, which can be collected as a measure of fermentation rate. Brewer's yeast is a facultative anaerobe (meaning it can respire aerobically or use fermentation). It will preferentially use alcoholic fermentation when sugars are in excess. One would expect glucose to be the preferred substrate, as it is the starting molecule in cellular respiration, but brewer's yeast is capable of utilising a variety of sugars, including disaccharides, which can be broken down into single units.

The aim

To investigate the suitability of different mono- and disaccharide sugars as substrates for alcoholic fermentation in yeast.

The hypothesis

If glucose is the preferred substrate for fermentation in yeast, then the rate of fermentation will be highest when the yeast is grown on glucose rather than on other sugars.

Background

The rate at which brewer's or baker's yeast (*Saccharomyces cerevisiae*) metabolises carbohydrate substrates is influenced by factors such as temperature, solution pH, and type of carbohydrate available.

The literature describes yeast metabolism as optimal in warm, acid (pH 4-6) environments.

High levels of sugars suppress aerobic respiration in yeast, so yeast will preferentially use the fermentation pathway in the presence of excess substrate.

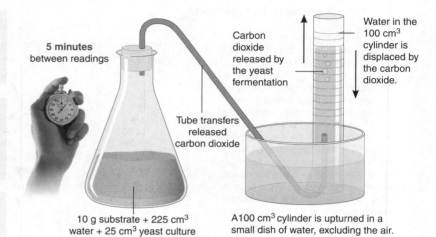

5 minutes between readings

Carbon dioxide released by the yeast fermentation

Tube transfers released carbon dioxide

Water in the 100 cm³ cylinder is displaced by the carbon dioxide.

10 g substrate + 225 cm³ water + 25 cm³ yeast culture

A 100 cm³ cylinder is upturned in a small dish of water, excluding the air.

The apparatus

In this experiment, all substrates tested used the same source culture of 30 g active yeast dissolved in 150 cm³ of room temperature (24°C) tap water. 25 g of each substrate to be tested was added to 225 cm³ room temperature (24°C) tap water buffered to pH 4.5. Then 25 cm³ of source culture was added to the test solution. The control contained yeast solution but no substrate.

The substrates

Glucose is a monosaccharide, maltose (glucose-glucose), sucrose (glucose-fructose), and lactose (glucose-galactose) are disaccharides.

Substrate / Time / min	Volume of carbon dioxide collected / cm³				
	None	**Glucose**	**Maltose**	**Sucrose**	**Lactose**
0	0	0	0	0	0
5	0	0	0.8	0	0
10	0	0	0.8	0	0
15	0	0	0.8	0.1	0
20	0	0.5	2.0	0.8	0
25	0	1.2	3.0	1.8	0
30	0	2.8	3.6	3.0	0
35	0	4.2	5.4	4.8	0
40	0	4.6	5.6	4.8	0
45	0	7.4	8.0	7.2	0
50	0	10.8	8.9	7.6	0
55	0	13.6	9.6	7.7	0
60	0	16.1	10.4	9.6	0
65	0	22.0	12.1	10.2	0
70	0	23.8	14.4	12.0	0
75	0	26.7	15.2	12.6	0
80	0	32.5	17.3	14.3	0
85	0	37.0	18.7	14.9	0
90	0	39.9	21.6	17.2	0

1. Write the equation for the fermentation of glucose by yeast:

   _____

2. The results are presented on the table left. Using the final values, calculate the rate of CO_2 production per minute for each substrate:

   (a) None: _____

   (b) Glucose: _____

   (c) Maltose: _____

   (d) Sucrose: _____

   (e) Lactose: _____

3. What assumptions are being made in this experimental design and do you think they were reasonable?

   _____

   _____

   _____

   _____

   _____

   _____

Experimental design and results adapted from Tom Schuster, Rosalie Van Zyl, & Harold Coller , California State University Northridge 2005

LINK
DATA 91

4. Use the tabulated data to plot an appropriate graph of the results on the grid provided:

5. (a) Identify the **independent variable**: _____

   (b) State the range of values for the independent variable: _____

   (c) Name the unit for the independent variable: _____

6. (a) Identify the **dependent variable**: _____

   (b) Name the unit for the dependent variable: _____

7. (a) Summarise the results of the fermentation experiment: _____

   _____

   _____

   _____

   (b) Why do you think CO_2 production was highest when glucose was the substrate? _____

   _____

   _____

   (c) Suggest why fermentation rates were lower on maltose and sucrose than on glucose:

   _____

   _____

   (d) Suggest why there was no fermentation on the lactose substrate: _____

   _____

8. Predict what would happen to CO_2 production rates if the yeast cells were respiring aerobically: _____

   _____

   _____

93 Respiratory Quotient

Key Idea: The respiratory quotient is the ratio of the amount of carbon dioxide produced during cellular respiration to the amount of oxygen consumed.
The ratio of carbon dioxide produced to the amount of oxygen being consumed during cellular respiration in a set period of time is called the **respiratory quotient** (RQ). It is often calculated to provide a useful indication about the respiratory substrate being respired.

Calculating RQ

The RQ is the amount of carbon dioxide (CO_2) produced, divided by the amount of oxygen (O_2) used in a set period of time. The equation for calculating RQ is very simple and is given below.

$$RQ = \frac{CO_2 \text{ produced}}{O_2 \text{ consumed}}$$

For the equation below, the RQ value would be 1:
($6CO_2 \div 6O_2$)

$$6O_2 + C_6H_{12}O_6 \longrightarrow 6CO_2 + 6H_2O$$

Different substrates have different RQ values

Different respiratory substrates have different RQ values (see table below). When pure carbohydrate is oxidised in cellular respiration, the RQ is 1.0. More oxygen is required to oxidise fatty acids (RQ = 0.7). The RQ for protein is about 0.9. Organisms usually respire a mix of substrates, and produce RQ values of between 0.8 and 0.9.

RQ	Substrate
> 1.0	Carbohydrate with some anaerobic respiration
1.0	Carbohydrate e.g. glucose
0.9	Protein
0.7	Fat
0.5	Fat with associated carbohydrate synthesis
0.3	Carbohydrate with associated organic acid synthesis

1. This equation shows aerobic respiration of compound A: $C_{55}H_{100}O_6 + 77O_2 \rightarrow 55CO_2 + 50H_2O$

   (a) Calculate the RQ value: _____

   (b) Based on the RQ value, what substrate is being respired? _____

2. The table (right) shows the results of an experiment to measure the rates of oxygen consumption and carbon dioxide production of crickets 1 hour and 48 hours after feeding at different temperatures:

   (a) Calculate the RQ at 20°C, 1 hour after feeding:

   _____

   (b) Calculate the RQ at 20°C, 48 hours after feeding:

   _____

   (c) Explain the difference between the two results: _____

   _____

   (d) Did increasing the temperature to 30°C have any effect on RQ value? Explain your answer: _____

   _____

   _____

   _____

Time after last feed / hours	Temperature / °C	Rate of O_2 consumption / cm³ g⁻¹ h⁻¹	Rate of CO_2 production / cm³ g⁻¹ h⁻¹
1	20	2.82	2.82
48	20	2.82	1.97
1	30	5.12	5.12
48	30	5.12	3.57

3. The graph (right) shows the RQ values for germinating wheat seeds. Study the graph state the most likely respiratory substances at:

   Point A: _____

   Point B: _____

   Point C: _____

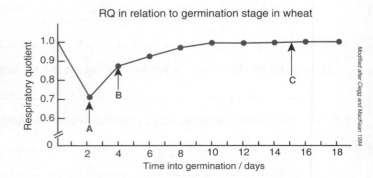

RQ in relation to germination stage in wheat

Modified after Clegg and MacKean 1994

94 Measuring Respiration

Key Idea: Oxygen consumption and carbon dioxide production in respiring organisms can be measured with a respirometer. A respirometer measures the amount of oxygen consumed and the amount of carbon dioxide produced during cellular respiration. Respirometers are quite simple pieces of apparatus but can give accurate results if set up carefully.

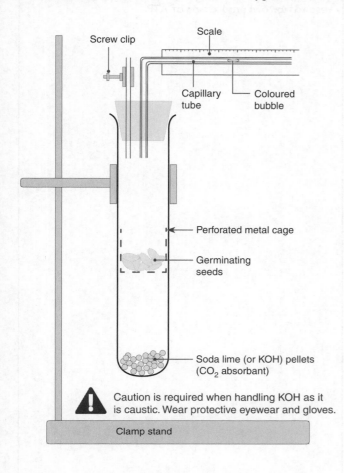

Screw clip

Scale

Capillary tube

Coloured bubble

Perforated metal cage

Germinating seeds

Soda lime (or KOH) pellets (CO_2 absorbant)

Caution is required when handling KOH as it is caustic. Wear protective eyewear and gloves.

Clamp stand

Measuring respiration with a simple respirometer

The diagram on the left shows a **simple respirometer**. It measures the change in gases as respiration occurs.

▶ Respiring organisms, in this case germinating seeds, are placed into the bottom of the chamber.

▶ Soda lime or potassium hydroxide is added to absorb any carbon dioxide produced during respiration. Therefore the respirometer measures oxygen consumption.

▶ Once the organisms have been placed into the chamber the screw clip is closed. The start position of the coloured bubble is measured (this is the time zero reading).

▶ The coloured bubble in the capillary tube moves in response to the change in oxygen consumption. Measuring the movement of the liquid (e.g. with a ruler) allows the change in volume of gas to be estimated.

▶ Care needs to be taken when using a simple respirometer because changes in temperature or atmospheric pressure may change the readings and give a false measure of respiration.

▶ **Differential respirometers** (not shown) use two chambers (a control chamber with no organisms and a test chamber) connected by a U-tube. Changes in temperature or atmospheric pressure act equally on both chambers. Observed changes are only due to the activities of the respiring organism.

1. Why does the bubble in the capillary tube move?

   _____

   _____

   _____

2. A student used a simple respirometer (like the one above) to measure respiration in maggots. Their results are presented in the table (right). The maggots were left to acclimatise for 10 minutes before the experiment was started.

   (a) Calculate the rate of respiration and record this in the table. The first two calculations have been done for you.

   (b) Plot the rate of respiration on the grid, below right.

   (c) Describe the results in your plot: _____

   _____

   _____

   _____

   (d) Why was there an acclimatisation period before the experiment began?

   _____

   _____

3. Why would it have been better to use a differential respirometer? _____

   _____

   _____

   _____

Time / minutes	Distance bubble moved / mm	Rate/ mm min⁻¹
0	0	–
5	25	5
10	65	
15	95	
20	130	
25	160	

DATA

95 Chapter Review

Summarise what you know about this topic under the headings and sub-headings provided. You can draw diagrams or mind maps, or write short notes to organise your thoughts. Use the images and hints to help you and refer back to the introduction to check the points covered:

Mitochondrial structure

HINT: Use a drawing to describe the structure of the mitochondrion.

Cellular respiration

HINT: Summarise the stages of cellular respiration and production of ATP.

Anaerobic metabolism

HINT: Describe the benefits and disadvantages of ATP generation without oxygen using fermentation.

Respiratory quotient (RQ)

HINT: How can RQ be used to determine which substance is being respired?

96 KEY TERMS: Did You Get It?

1. Match each term to its definition, as identified by its preceding letter code.

aerobic respiration

alcoholic fermentation

anaerobic respiration

ATP

cellular respiration

chemiosmosis

electron transport chain

glycolysis

Krebs cycle

lactic acid fermentation

link reaction

matrix

mitochondria

oxidative phosphorylation

pyruvate

respiratory substrate

substrate level phosphorylation

A A series of reactions that convert glucose into pyruvate. The energy released is used to produce ATP.

B The process in which the synthesis of ATP is coupled to electron transport and the movement of protons.

C Organelle responsible for producing the cell's ATP. They appear oval in shape with an outer double membrane and a convoluted interior membrane.

D The stage in cellular respiration where pyruvate enters the mitochondrion and carbon dioxide is removed.

E An anaerobic pathway where ethanal acts as the electron acceptor, and the end product is ethanol.

F A type of metabolic reaction that results in the formation of ATP by direct transfer of a phosphate group to ADP from a phosphorylated reactive intermediate.

G An anaerobic pathway occurring in the skeletal muscle of mammals. Pyruvate is reduced to lactic acid.

H Respiration requiring oxygen as the terminal electron acceptor.

I A substance required for cellular respiration to derive energy through oxidation. Examples are carbohydrates (especially glucose), fats, and proteins.

J Also known as the citric acid cycle. Part of a metabolic pathway involved in the chemical conversion of carbohydrates, fats and proteins to CO_2 and water to generate a form of usable energy (ATP).

K The catabolic process in which the chemical energy in complex organic molecules is coupled to ATP production.

L A product of glycolysis. An important intermediate in many metabolic pathways.

M The inner region of the mitochondrion enclosed by the inner mitochondrial membrane.

N Chain of enzyme based redox reactions which pass electrons from high to low redox potentials. The energy released is used to pump protons across a membrane and produce ATP.

O The process in cellular respiration which involves the oxidation of glucose by a series of redox reactions that provide the energy for the formation of ATP.

P A form of respiration that occurs without oxygen.

Q A nucleoside triphosphate used in the transfer of energy in cells.

2. The RQs of two species of seeds were calculated at two day intervals after germination. Results are tabulated to the right:

(a) Plot the change in RQ of the two species during early germination:

(b) Explain the values in terms of the possible substrates being respired:

_____

_____

_____

_____

_____

_____

_____

Days after germination	RQ	
	Seedling A	Seedling B
2	0.65	0.70
4	0.35	0.91
6	0.48	0.98
8	0.68	1.00
10	0.70	1.00

TEST

Cellular Control

Key terms

apoptosis

beneficial mutation

cell differentiation

cyclic AMP

deletion mutation

exons

frame shift

gene expression

gene mutation

harmful mutation

homeobox genes

Hox genes

insertion mutation

introns

lac operon

mitosis

morphogenesis

neutral mutation

point mutation

primary mRNA
transcript

substitution mutation

transcription

transcription factors

translation

Mutation

Learning outcomes

□ 1 Describe types of gene mutations to include substitution, insertion, and deletion   97 98
of one or more nucleotides. Explain what is meant by a point mutation.

□ 2 Describe the possible effect of gene mutations in terms of the products of gene   98 99 100
expression (e.g. proteins) and identify them as beneficial, harmful, or neutral.
Explain the significance of code degeneracy on the effect of point mutations.

□ 3 Describe examples of gene mutations and their phenotypic effects, e.g. the   101 102
sickle cell mutation as an example of a substitution mutation and the most
common CFTR (cystic fibrosis) mutation as an example of a triplet deletion.

 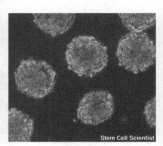 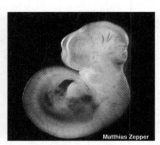

Control of gene expression

Learning outcomes

□ 4 Describe transcriptional control in prokaryotes as illustrated by the *lac* operon   103
(gene induction) in *E. coli*. Include reference to the role of regulator, promoter,
and operator genes, and the repressor molecule.

□ 5 Describe transcriptional control in eukaryotes, including the role of transcription   104
factors and the formation of an initiation complex.

□ 6 Describe post-transcriptional control of gene expression with reference to the   105
editing of the primary mRNA transcript and removal of introns.

□ 7 Describe post-translational control of gene expression as illustrated by the   106
activation of proteins by the second messenger cyclic AMP.

The genetic control of development

Learning outcomes

□ 8 Recall that changes in gene expression result in cell differentiation.   109

□ 9 Explain the role of homeobox gene sequences in plants, animals, and fungi and   107
suggest why these gene sequences are highly conserved across phyla.

□ 10 Describe the role of Hox genes, a family of homeobox genes in animals that   107
control development of the embryo along the head-tail axis. Explain how diversity
of body form can arise through small changes in the genes controlling development.

□ 11 Describe the role of mitosis and apoptosis in normal cell differentiation and   108 109
morphogenesis (development of body form). Describe the consequences
of excessive or insufficient apoptosis during development. Appreciate that
development occurs as a result of the sequential expression of genes in response
to internal and external cell stimuli.

97 Gene Mutations

Key Idea: Gene mutations are localised changes to the DNA base sequence.

Gene mutations are localised changes in the base sequence of a DNA strand caused by a mutagen or an error during DNA replication. The changes may involve a single nucleotide (a point mutation) or a triplet. Point mutations can occur by substitution, insertion, or deletion of bases. These changes alter the mRNA transcribed from the DNA. A point mutation may not alter the amino acid sequence because more than one codon can code for the same amino acid. These mutations are called **silent**. Mutations that result in a change in the amino acid sequence will most often be harmful.

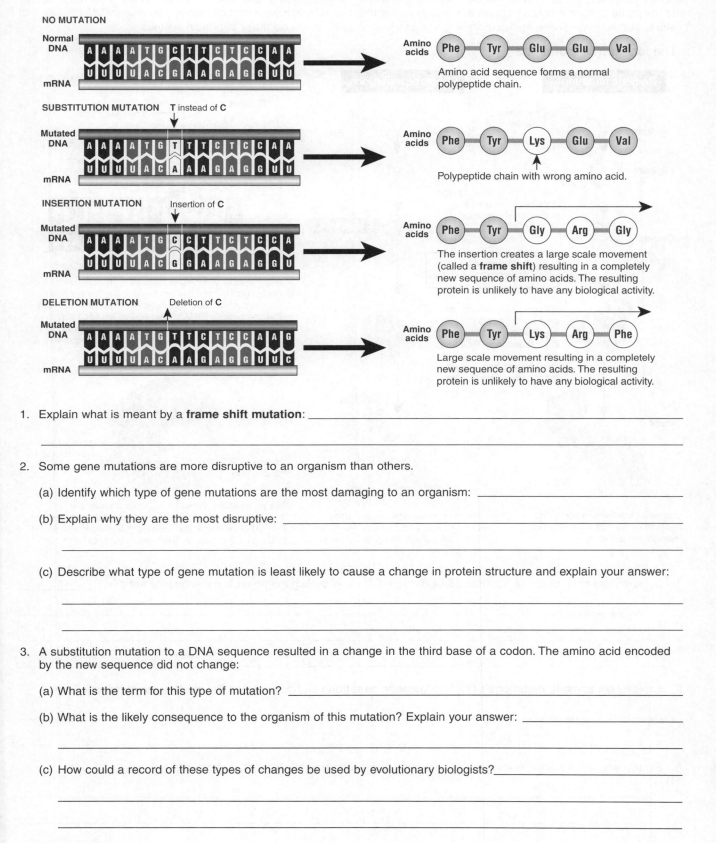

1. Explain what is meant by a **frame shift mutation**: _____

_____

2. Some gene mutations are more disruptive to an organism than others.

   (a) Identify which type of gene mutations are the most damaging to an organism: _____

   (b) Explain why they are the most disruptive: _____

   _____

   (c) Describe what type of gene mutation is least likely to cause a change in protein structure and explain your answer:

   _____

   _____

3. A substitution mutation to a DNA sequence resulted in a change in the third base of a codon. The amino acid encoded by the new sequence did not change:

   (a) What is the term for this type of mutation? _____

   (b) What is the likely consequence to the organism of this mutation? Explain your answer: _____

   _____

   (c) How could a record of these types of changes be used by evolutionary biologists?_____

   _____

   _____

© 2015 **BIOZONE** International
ISBN: **978-1-927309-14-8**
Photocopying Prohibited

98 The Nature of Mutation

Key Idea: A mutation is any change to the DNA sequence. Most mutations are harmful, but if a mutation causes no change in the amino acid sequence, it is said to be silent. Occasionally a mutation produces a new and useful protein. A mutation is a change in the genetic sequence of a genome. Only those affecting gametic cells will be heritable. Mutations may occur spontaneously, as a result of errors during meiosis or DNA replication, or they may be induced. Induced mutations are the result of agents called mutagens, which increase the natural mutation rate. These agents include ionising radiation,

some viruses, and chemicals such as formaldehyde, coal tar, and components of tobacco smoke. While changes to DNA are likely to be harmful, there are many documented cases of mutations conferring a survival advantage. Mutations that cause no change in the amino acid sequence are called **silent**. Until recently, it was supposed that these were also **neutral**, i.e. carried without effect until subjected to selection pressure at a later time. However, recent research indicates that even these silent mutations may alter mRNA stability and affect the accuracy of protein synthesis.

The location of mutations

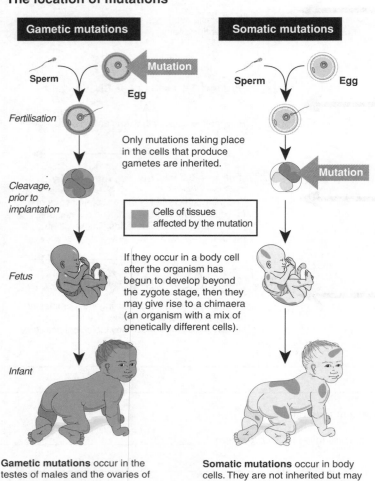

Gametic mutations occur in the testes of males and the ovaries of females and are inherited.

Only mutations taking place in the cells that produce gametes are inherited.

Cells of tissues affected by the mutation

If they occur in a body cell after the organism has begun to develop beyond the zygote stage, then they may give rise to a chimaera (an organism with a mix of genetically different cells).

Somatic mutations occur in body cells. They are not inherited but may affect the person during their lifetime.

The effect of mutagens on DNA

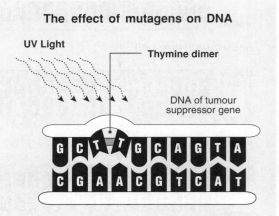

In some cases, mutations trigger the onset of cancer by disrupting the normal controls regulating the cell cycle. After exposure to UV light (a potent mutagen), adjacent thymine bases in DNA become cross-linked to form a 'thymine dimer'. This disrupts the normal base pairing and throws the controlling gene's instructions into chaos.

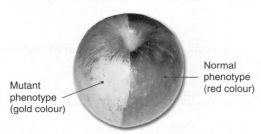

Mutant phenotype (gold colour)

Normal phenotype (red colour)

The photo above shows an example of a somatic mutation in a red delicious apple. A mutation occurred in the part of the flower that eventually developed into the fleshy part of the apple. The seeds would not be mutant.

1. Using an example, describe how mutagens damage DNA and explain the possible consequences of this: _____

_____

_____

_____

2. Explain how **somatic mutations** differ from **gametic mutations** and comment on the significance of the difference: _____

_____

_____

3. Explain why the mutation seen in the red delicious apple (above right) will not be inherited: _____

_____

_____

© 2015 **BIOZONE** International
ISBN: **978-1-927309-14-8**
Photocopying Prohibited

Albinism: a common harmful mutation

Albinism is caused by any one of a number of gene mutations to enzymes in the metabolic pathway that produces the skin pigment melanin. Mutations to this metabolic pathway are common in most vertebrate taxa, including humans, and most commonly albino individuals are homozygous for the mutation.

Albinos lack pigment in their hair/fur and eyes are so more visible to predators or prey (left). Usually their vision is impaired and they are also more susceptible to the damaging effects of ultraviolet radiation because they lack protective pigmentation.

Beneficial mutations in microbes

 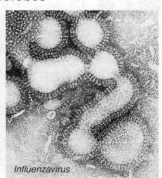

Salmonella · Influenzavirus

Bacteria reproduce asexually by binary fission. They are susceptible to antibiotics (substances that harm them or inhibit their growth) but can acquire antibiotic resistance through mutation. The genes for resistance can be transferred within and between bacterial species. New, multi-resistant bacterial superbugs have arisen in this way.

Viruses, including HIV and *Influenzavirus*, have glycoprotein coated envelopes, which confer virulence but also enable the host to detect the virus and destroy it. The genes encoding these glycoproteins are constantly mutating, so each new viral 'strain' goes undetected by the immune system until well after the infection is established.

Are silent mutations really silent?

So-called **silent mutations** are those that result in no change in the sequence of amino acids making up a protein. The redundancy of the genetic code provides a buffer against the effect of DNA changes affecting the third base. Such mutations have routinely been assumed to be neutral, meaning that, at that time, they have no effect on the phenotype or fitness of the individual carrying the mutation.

Right: A change to the third base of a codon may not change the amino acid encoded, but it does change the exonic sequence.

However, so-called silent changes still affect transcription, splicing, and mRNA stability, even though they do not change the codon information. Disruptions to RNA splicing sequences can cause exon skipping and lead to RNA not being processed properly. Silent variations have been associated with a number of diseases including cystic fibrosis. For example, one silent mutation causes the dopamine receptor D2 gene to be less stable and degrade faster, under-expressing the gene. Experimental evidence with the CFTR gene also shows that silent mutations cause exon skipping, yielding a short CFTR protein.

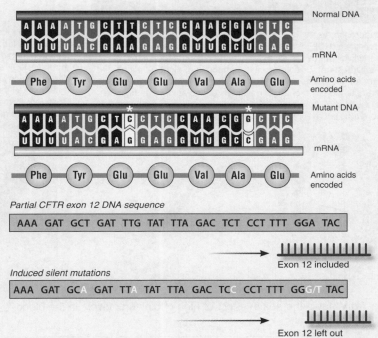

Partial CFTR exon 12 DNA sequence
AAA GAT GCT GAT TTG TAT TTA GAC TCT CCT TTT GGA TAC — Exon 12 included

Induced silent mutations
AAA GAT GCA GAT TTA TAT TTA GAC TCC CCT TTT GGG/T TAC — Exon 12 left out

4. Giving examples, distinguish between beneficial and harmful mutations:

5. (a) Explain what is meant by a silent mutation:

(b) Explain why silent mutations are now no longer seen as always being neutral in their effect:

99 A Beneficial Mutation

Key Idea: A change to a single amino acid in a lipoprotein causes it to be far more efficient at mopping up cholesterol. High blood cholesterol in humans is detrimental and associated with cardiovascular disease (CVD). In 1979, a citizen born in Limone sul Garda (Italy), had a medical checkup, which revealed high levels of cholesterol, but no CVD. This amazed doctors and sparked studies into one of the most famous beneficial mutations ever studied in humans.

Blood tests of a man from Limone showed he had very high levels of blood cholesterol, but he had no signs of damage to his heart or arteries. Further tests found his blood contained an anomalous protein similar to **Apolipoprotein A-1** (ApoA1), the protein that aids clearance of cholesterol from the blood. The protein, now called **Apolipoprotein A-1 Milan** (ApoA1 Milan), was able to remove cholesterol from the blood many times more efficiently than ApoA1.

Steep mountains behind the village

Lake Garda

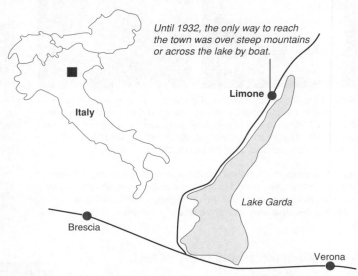

Until 1932, the only way to reach the town was over steep mountains or across the lake by boat.

Limone

Italy

Lake Garda

Brescia

Verona

The protein ApoA1 is a major component of high density lipoprotein (HDL) in blood plasma. HDL transports cholesterol to the liver where it is excreted into the bile (and then into the small intestine). Structurally it is composed of eight α-helices that form a twisted loop (below). Studies have shown ApoA1 Milan is characterised by a change in a single amino acid, from arginine at position 173 to cysteine. This small change makes it ten times more efficient at removing excess cholesterol to the liver.

Researchers tested the blood of the man's family members and found the blood of his father and daughter both contained ApoA1 Milan. Blood tests were then conducted on all Limone's residents (the population at the time being around 1000), and found that many also had the mutated protein in their blood. The genealogy of the town was constructed using town and church records and found all the people who carried the ApoA1 Milan gene were related to Cristoforo Pomaroli and Rosa Giovanelli, who were married in 1644. Because the town was relatively isolated from the outside world until 1932, the gene spread through the population with little dilution from outside genes.

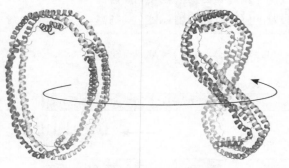

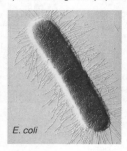

E. coli

The bacterium *E. coli* was engineered to produce the ApoA1 Milan protein in order to try to produce a useful cholesterol reducing drug. In 2003 researchers in the United States produced an experimental drug for human testing. It was administered to 47 patients with heart disease. After a six week period there was an average 4.2% reduction in plaque along the arteries. Shortly after, Pfizer paid US$1.3 billion for the rights to the drug's production. However, due to technical difficulties little progress was made and Pfizer sold the rights for US$160 million in 2008.

1. (a) What is the health effect of high cholesterol levels in the blood? _____

    _____

    (b) Describe the function of ApoA1: _____

    _____

    (c) How is the amino acid structure of ApoA1 Milan different to ApoA1? _____

    _____

2. Why do people with the ApoA1 Milan gene show no sign of heart disease, even though they may have high levels of blood cholesterol?

    _____

    _____

3. Explain why Limone sul Garda's isolation may have helped the spread of the gene in the population: _____

    _____

    _____

© 2015 **BIOZONE** International
ISBN: **978-1-927309-14-8**
Photocopying Prohibited

100 Gene Mutations and Genetic Diseases

Key Idea: Many genetic diseases in humans are the result of mutations to recessive alleles, but some are also caused by dominant or codominant alleles.

There are more than 6000 human diseases attributed to mutations in single genes, although most are uncommon. The three genetic diseases described below occur with relatively high frequency and are the result of recessive, dominant, and codominant allele mutations respectively.

Cystic Fibrosis (CF)	Huntington Disease (HD)	Sickle Cell Anaemia

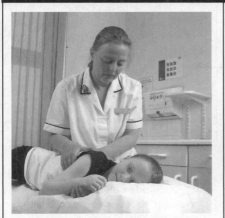

Cystic fibrosis is traditionally treated with physical therapy to clear mucus from the airways.

Incidence: Varies with populations:
United States: 1 in 1000 (0.1%).
Asians in England: 1 in 10 000
European descent: 1 in 20-28 are carriers.

Gene type: Autosomal recessive. The most common mutation is ΔF508, which accounts for around 70% of all defective CF genes. The mutation is a deletion of the 508th triplet in the DNA code for the chloride transport protein CFTR. As a result, the amino acid phenylalanine is missing and the CFTR protein cannot carry out its function of regulating chloride ion balance in the cell.

Gene location: Chromosome 7

CFTR

Symptoms: Disruption of all glands including pancreas, bronchial glands (chronic lung infections), and sweat glands (high salt content of which becomes depleted). Infertility.

Inheritance: Autosomal recessive pattern. Affected people are homozygous recessive for the mutation. Heterozygotes (carriers) have largely no symptoms and are less susceptible to cholera than people without the mutation.

American singer-songwriter and folk musician Woody Guthrie died from complications of HD

Incidence: An uncommon disease affecting 3-7 per 100 000 people of European descent. Less common in other ethnicities, including people of Japanese, Chinese, and African descent.

Gene type: Autosomal dominant mutation of the HTT gene caused by a trinucleotide repeat expansion on the short arm of chromosome 4. In the mutation (**mHTT**), the number of CAG repeats increases from the normal 6-30 to 36-125. The severity of the disease increases with the number of repeats. The repeats result in the production of an abnormally long version of the huntingtin protein.

Gene location: Short arm of chromosome 4

HTT

Symptoms: The long huntingtin protein is cut into smaller toxic fragments, which accumulate in nerve cells and eventually kill them. The disease becomes apparent in mid-adulthood, with jerky, involuntary movements and loss of memory, reasoning, and personality.

Inheritance: Autosomal dominance pattern. Affected people may be homozygous or heterozygous for the mutant allele.

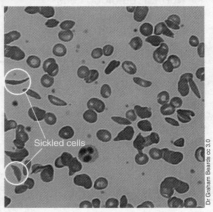

In a person heterozygous for the sickle cell allele, only some of the red blood cells are deformed.

Sickled cells

Dr Graham Beards cc 3.0

Incidence: Occurs most commonly in people of African descent. West Africans: 1% (10-45% are carriers). West Indians: 0.5%.

Gene type: Autosomal mutation involving substitution of a single nucleotide in the HBB gene that codes for the beta chain of haemoglobin. The allele is codominant. The substitution causes a change in a single amino acid. The mutated haemoglobin behaves differently when deprived of oxygen, causing distortion of the red blood cells, anaemia, and circulatory problems.

Gene location: Short arm of chromosome 11

HBB

Symptoms: Sickling of the red blood cells, which are removed from circulation, anaemia, pain, damage to tissues and organs.

Inheritance: Autosomal codominance pattern. People who are homozygous for the mutant allele have sickle cell disease. Heterozygotes (carriers) are only mildly affected and show greater resistance to malaria than people without the mutation.

1. For each of genetic disorder below, indicate the following:

   (a) Sickle cell anaemia: Gene name: _____ Chromosome: _____ Mutation type: _____

   (b) Cystic fibrosis: Gene name: _____ Chromosome: _____ Mutation type: _____

   (c) Huntington disease: Gene name: _____ Chromosome: _____ Mutation type: _____

2. Explain why mHTT, which is dominant and lethal, does not disappear from the population: _____

   _____

   _____

3. Suggest why the sickle cell and CF mutations have been maintained in populations, despite being lethal mutations:

   _____

   _____

LINK 102 | LINK 101 | LINK 98 | WEB 100 | KNOW

101 Sickle Cell Mutation

Key Idea: The substitution of one nucleotide from T to A results in sickle cell disease. The mutation is codominant. Sickle cell disease is an inherited blood disorder caused by a gene mutation (Hb^s), which produces a faulty beta (β) chain haemoglobin (Hb) protein. This in turn produces red blood cells with a deformed sickle appearance and a reduced capacity to carry oxygen. Many aspects of metabolism are also affected. The mutation is codominant (both alleles equally expressed), and people heterozygous for the mutation (carriers) have enough functional haemoglobin and suffer only minor effects.

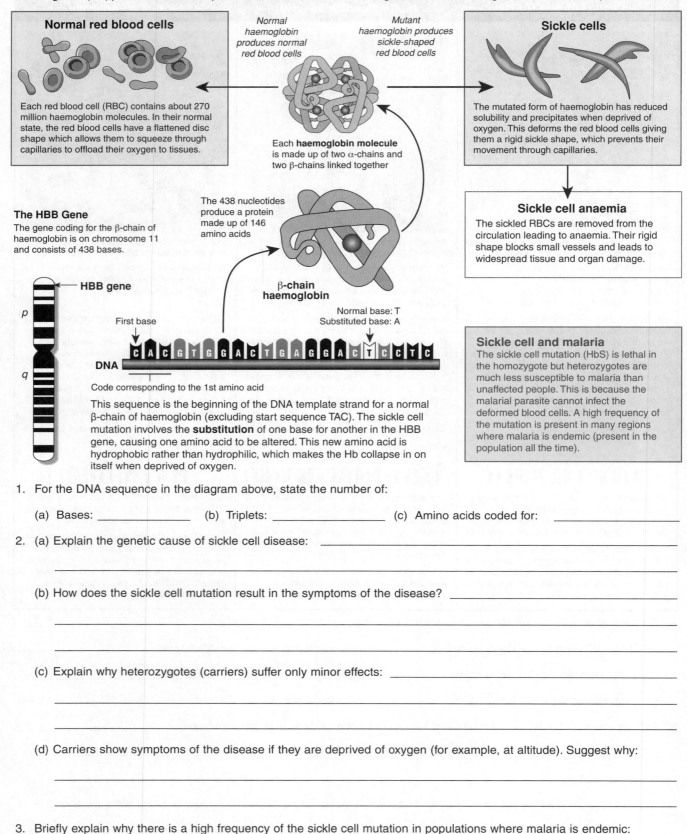

Normal red blood cells

Each red blood cell (RBC) contains about 270 million haemoglobin molecules. In their normal state, the red blood cells have a flattened disc shape which allows them to squeeze through capillaries to offload their oxygen to tissues.

Normal haemoglobin produces normal red blood cells

Mutant haemoglobin produces sickle-shaped red blood cells

Each **haemoglobin molecule** is made up of two α-chains and two β-chains linked together

Sickle cells

The mutated form of haemoglobin has reduced solubility and precipitates when deprived of oxygen. This deforms the red blood cells giving them a rigid sickle shape, which prevents their movement through capillaries.

Sickle cell anaemia

The sickled RBCs are removed from the circulation leading to anaemia. Their rigid shape blocks small vessels and leads to widespread tissue and organ damage.

The HBB Gene

The gene coding for the β-chain of haemoglobin is on chromosome 11 and consists of 438 bases.

The 438 nucleotides produce a protein made up of 146 amino acids

β-chain haemoglobin

HBB gene

p

q

First base

Normal base: T
Substituted base: A

DNA CACGTGGACTGAGGACTCCTC

Code corresponding to the 1st amino acid

This sequence is the beginning of the DNA template strand for a normal β-chain of haemoglobin (excluding start sequence TAC). The sickle cell mutation involves the **substitution** of one base for another in the HBB gene, causing one amino acid to be altered. This new amino acid is hydrophobic rather than hydrophilic, which makes the Hb collapse in on itself when deprived of oxygen.

Sickle cell and malaria

The sickle cell mutation (HbS) is lethal in the homozygote but heterozygotes are much less susceptible to malaria than unaffected people. This is because the malarial parasite cannot infect the deformed blood cells. A high frequency of the mutation is present in many regions where malaria is endemic (present in the population all the time).

1. For the DNA sequence in the diagram above, state the number of:

(a) Bases: _____ (b) Triplets: _____ (c) Amino acids coded for: _____

2. (a) Explain the genetic cause of sickle cell disease: _____

_____

(b) How does the sickle cell mutation result in the symptoms of the disease? _____

_____

_____

(c) Explain why heterozygotes (carriers) suffer only minor effects: _____

_____

_____

(d) Carriers show symptoms of the disease if they are deprived of oxygen (for example, at altitude). Suggest why:

_____

_____

3. Briefly explain why there is a high frequency of the sickle cell mutation in populations where malaria is endemic:

_____

© 2015 **BIOZONE** International
ISBN: **978-1-927309-14-8**
Photocopying Prohibited

102 Cystic Fibrosis Mutation

Key Idea: Cystic fibrosis most often results from a triplet deletion in the CFTR gene, producing a protein that is unable to regulate chloride transport.

Cystic fibrosis (CF) is an inherited disorder caused by a mutation of the CFTR gene. It is one of the most common lethal autosomal recessive conditions affecting people of European descent (4% are carriers). The CFTR gene's protein product is a membrane-based protein that regulates chloride transport in cells. Over 500 mutations of the CFTR gene are known, causing disease symptoms of varying severity. The δ(delta)F508 mutation accounts for more than 70% of all defective CFTR genes. This mutation leads to an abnormal CFTR, which cannot take its proper position in the membrane (below) nor perform its transport function.

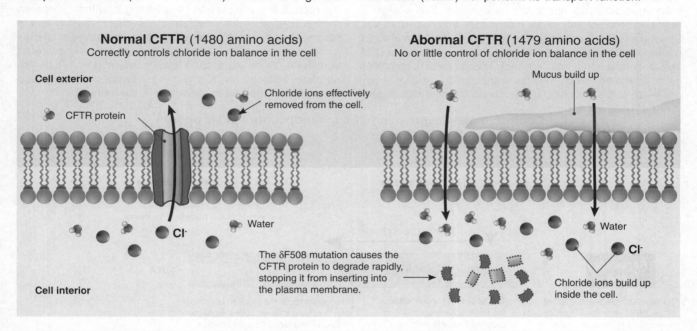

Normal CFTR (1480 amino acids)
Correctly controls chloride ion balance in the cell

Cell exterior

CFTR protein

Chloride ions effectively removed from the cell.

Cl⁻

Water

Cell interior

Abormal CFTR (1479 amino acids)
No or little control of chloride ion balance in the cell

Mucus build up

Water

Cl⁻

Chloride ions build up inside the cell.

The δF508 mutation causes the CFTR protein to degrade rapidly, stopping it from inserting into the plasma membrane.

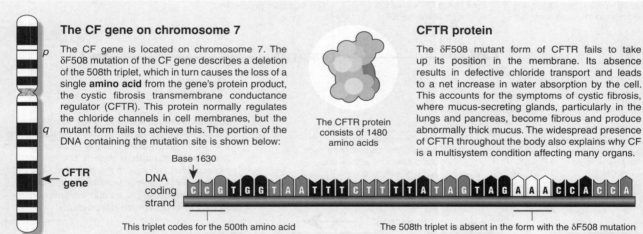

The CF gene on chromosome 7

The CF gene is located on chromosome 7. The δF508 mutation of the CF gene describes a deletion of the 508th triplet, which in turn causes the loss of a single **amino acid** from the gene's protein product, the cystic fibrosis transmembrane conductance regulator (CFTR). This protein normally regulates the chloride channels in cell membranes, but the mutant form fails to achieve this. The portion of the DNA containing the mutation site is shown below:

p

q

CFTR gene

The CFTR protein consists of 1480 amino acids

CFTR protein

The δF508 mutant form of CFTR fails to take up its position in the membrane. Its absence results in defective chloride transport and leads to a net increase in water absorption by the cell. This accounts for the symptoms of cystic fibrosis, where mucus-secreting glands, particularly in the lungs and pancreas, become fibrous and produce abnormally thick mucus. The widespread presence of CFTR throughout the body also explains why CF is a multisystem condition affecting many organs.

Base 1630

DNA coding strand

C C G T G G T A A T T T C T T T T A T A G T A G A A A C C A C C A

This triplet codes for the 500th amino acid

The 508th triplet is absent in the form with the δF508 mutation

1. (a) Write the mRNA sequence for the transcribing DNA strand above: _____

_____

   (b) Rewrite the mRNA sequence for the mutant DNA strand: _____

_____

   (c) What kind of mutation is δF508? _____

2. (a) Explain why the abnormal CFTR fails to transport Cl⁻ correctly: _____

_____

   (b) What effect does this have on water movement in and out of the cell? _____

_____

LINK
100

WEB
102

KNOW

103 Gene Induction in Prokaryotes

Key Idea: The presence of the inducer molecule lactose, switches the *lac* operon on so that the genes for lactose metabolism are transcribed.

In prokaryotes, an operon consists of a group of closely linked genes, which act together and code for the enzymes that control a particular metabolic pathway. The operon model **applies only to prokaryotes** because genes in eukaryotic cells are not found as operons. The operon is made up of structural genes, a promoter, and operator sites. Structural genes encoding the enzymes in the metabolic pathway are transcribed as a single transcription unit (a DNA sequence that constitutes a gene). This process is controlled by a promoter, which initiates transcription, and a region upstream of the structural genes called the operator. A gene

outside the operon, called the regulator gene, produces a repressor molecule that can bind to the operator and block the transcription of the structural genes. It is the repressor that switches the structural genes on or off and controls the metabolic pathway. Two mechanisms operate in the operon model: gene induction and gene repression. Gene induction occurs when genes are switched on by an inducer binding to the repressor molecule and deactivating it. In the *lac* operon model (below), lactose acts as the inducer, binding to the repressor and permitting transcription of the structural genes for the utilisation of lactose (an infrequently encountered substrate). Gene repression occurs when genes that are normally switched on (e.g. genes for synthesis of an amino acid) are switched off by activation of the repressor.

Control of gene expression through induction: the *lac* operon

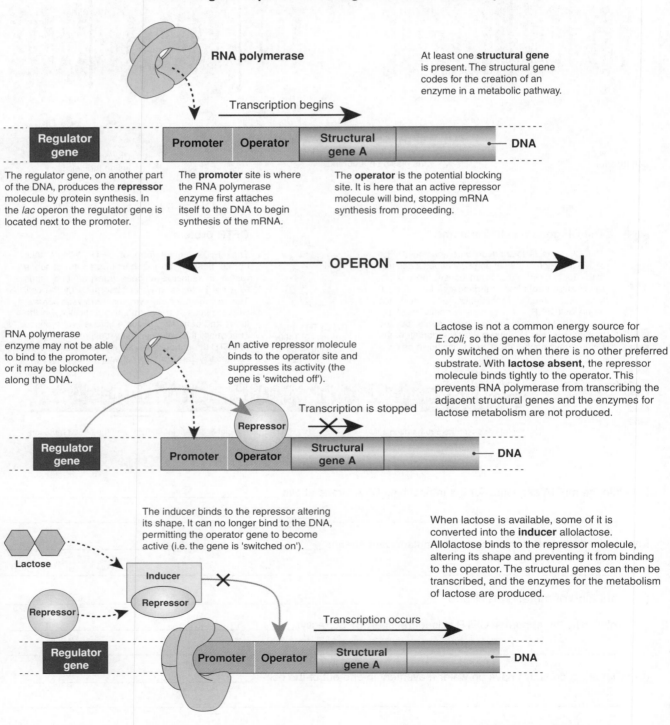

RNA polymerase

Transcription begins

At least one **structural gene** is present. The structural gene codes for the creation of an enzyme in a metabolic pathway.

| Regulator gene | | Promoter | Operator | Structural gene A | | DNA |

The regulator gene, on another part of the DNA, produces the **repressor** molecule by protein synthesis. In the *lac* operon the regulator gene is located next to the promoter.

The **promoter** site is where the RNA polymerase enzyme first attaches itself to the DNA to begin synthesis of the mRNA.

The **operator** is the potential blocking site. It is here that an active repressor molecule will bind, stopping mRNA synthesis from proceeding.

OPERON

RNA polymerase enzyme may not be able to bind to the promoter, or it may be blocked along the DNA.

An active repressor molecule binds to the operator site and suppresses its activity (the gene is 'switched off').

Repressor

Transcription is stopped

Lactose is not a common energy source for *E. coli*, so the genes for lactose metabolism are only switched on when there is no other preferred substrate. With **lactose absent**, the repressor molecule binds tightly to the operator. This prevents RNA polymerase from transcribing the adjacent structural genes and the enzymes for lactose metabolism are not produced.

The inducer binds to the repressor altering its shape. It can no longer bind to the DNA, permitting the operator gene to become active (i.e. the gene is 'switched on').

Lactose

Inducer

Repressor

Repressor

When lactose is available, some of it is converted into the **inducer** allolactose. Allolactose binds to the repressor molecule, altering its shape and preventing it from binding to the operator. The structural genes can then be transcribed, and the enzymes for the metabolism of lactose are produced.

Transcription occurs

| Regulator gene | | Promoter | Operator | Structural gene A | | DNA |

© 2015 **BIOZONE** International
ISBN: **978-1-927309-14-8**
Photocopying Prohibited

Diauxie in *E.coli*

Diauxie means two growth phases. **Diauxic growth** describes how microbes grown on a mixed sugar source in batch culture will preferentially metabolise one sugar source before moving on to the second. This sequential metabolism results in two distinct growth phases (right).

In the example (right) *E.coli* is grown on a mixed substrate of glucose and lactose. Diauxie occurs because the presence of glucose in excess suppresses the *lac* operon so that only the enzymes required for glucose metabolism are produced. As the glucose supply diminishes, the *lac* operon becomes activated, and *E.coli* begins to metabolise lactose.

The lag period represents the time taken for the *lac* operon to become active and the synthesis of the enzymes required for lactose metabolism to begin. This mechanism allows *E.coli* to preferentially metabolise the substrate it can grow fastest on, before moving to the second substrate.

The diauxic growth curve of *E.coli* when grown on glucose and lactose

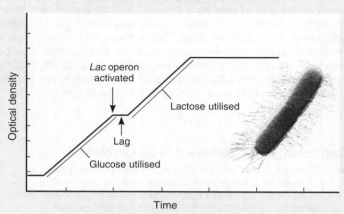

Jacques Monod discovered diauxic growth in 1941 prior to the discovery of the lac operon, which explained the lag phenomenon at the genetic level.

1. Explain the functional role of each of the following in relation to gene regulation in a prokaryote, e.g. *E. coli*:

   (a) Operon: _____

   _____

   (b) Regulator gene: _____

   _____

   (c) Operator: _____

   _____

   (d) Promoter: _____

   _____

   (e) Structural genes: _____

   _____

2. (a) Explain the advantage in having an inducible enzyme system that is regulated by the presence of a substrate:

   _____

   _____

   (b) Suggest when it would not be adaptive to have an inducible system for metabolism of a substrate: _____

   _____

   _____

   (c) Suggest how gene control in a non-inducible system might be achieved: _____

   _____

   _____

3. Explain how the operon model explains the diauxic growth of bacteria on two sugar substrates: _____

   _____

   _____

   _____

104 Gene Control in Eukaryotes

Key Idea: Eukaryote transcription occurs when transcription factors bind to an enhancer sequence and RNA polymerase. Although all the cells in your body contain identical copies of your genetic instructions, these cells appear very different (e.g. muscle, nerve, and epithelial cells). These differences reflect differences in gene expression during the cell's development. For example, muscle cells express the genes for the proteins that make up the contractile elements of the muscle fibre. This diversity of cell structure and function reflects precise control over the time, location, and extent of expression of a huge variety of genes. The physical state of the DNA in or near a gene is important in helping to control whether the gene is even available for transcription. To be transcribed, a gene must first be unpacked from its condensed state. Once unpacked, control of gene expression involves the interaction of transcription factors with DNA sequences that control the specific gene. Initiation of transcription is the most important and universally used control point in gene expression.

Control of gene expression in eukaryotes

▶ Eukaryotic genes are very different from prokaryotic genes: they have introns (which are removed after the primary transcript is made) and a relatively large number of **control elements** (non-coding DNA sequences that help regulate transcription by binding proteins called transcription factors).

▶ Each functional eukaryotic gene has a **promoter region** at the upstream end of the gene: a DNA sequence where RNA polymerase binds and starts transcription.

▶ Eukaryotic RNA polymerase alone cannot initiate the transcription of a gene; it is dependent on **transcription factors** in order to recognise and bind to the **promoter** (step 1).

▶ Transcription is activated when a hairpin loop in the DNA brings the transcription factors (activators) attached to the **enhancer sequence** in contact with the transcription factors bound to RNA polymerase at the promoter (step 2).

▶ Protein-protein interactions are crucial to eukaryotic transcription. Only when the complete initiation complex is assembled can the polymerase move along the DNA template strand and produce the complementary strand of RNA.

▶ Transcription is deactivated when a terminator sequence is encountered. Terminators are nucleotide sequences that function to stop transcription. *Do not confuse these with stop codons, which are the stop signals for translation.*

▶ A range of transcription factors and enhancer sequences throughout the genome may selectively activate the expression of specific genes at appropriate stages during cell development.

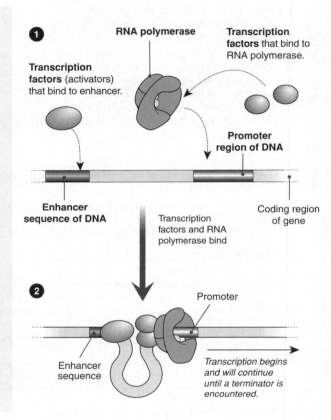

1. Explain the functional role of each of the following in relation to gene regulation in a eukaryote:

(a) Promoter: _____

_____

(b) Transcription factors: _____

_____

(c) Enhancer sequence: _____

_____

(d) RNA polymerase: _____

_____

(e) Terminator sequence: _____

_____

2. Identify one difference between the mechanisms of gene control in eukaryotes and prokaryotes: _____

_____

WEB 104 LINK 107

© 2015 **BIOZONE** International
ISBN: **978-1-927309-14-8**
Photocopying Prohibited

105 Post Transcriptional Modification

Key Idea: Primary mRNA molecules are modified before they are translated into proteins.

Human DNA contains only 25 000 genes, but produces possibly up to 1 million different proteins. Each gene must therefore produce more than one protein. This is achieved by both **post transcriptional** and **post translational** **modification**. Primary mRNA contains exons and introns. Usually introns are removed after transcription and the exons are spliced together. However, the number of exons and the way they are spliced varies. This creates variations in the translated polypeptide chain. These mechanisms allow for the production of the diverse range of proteins.

Post transcriptional modification

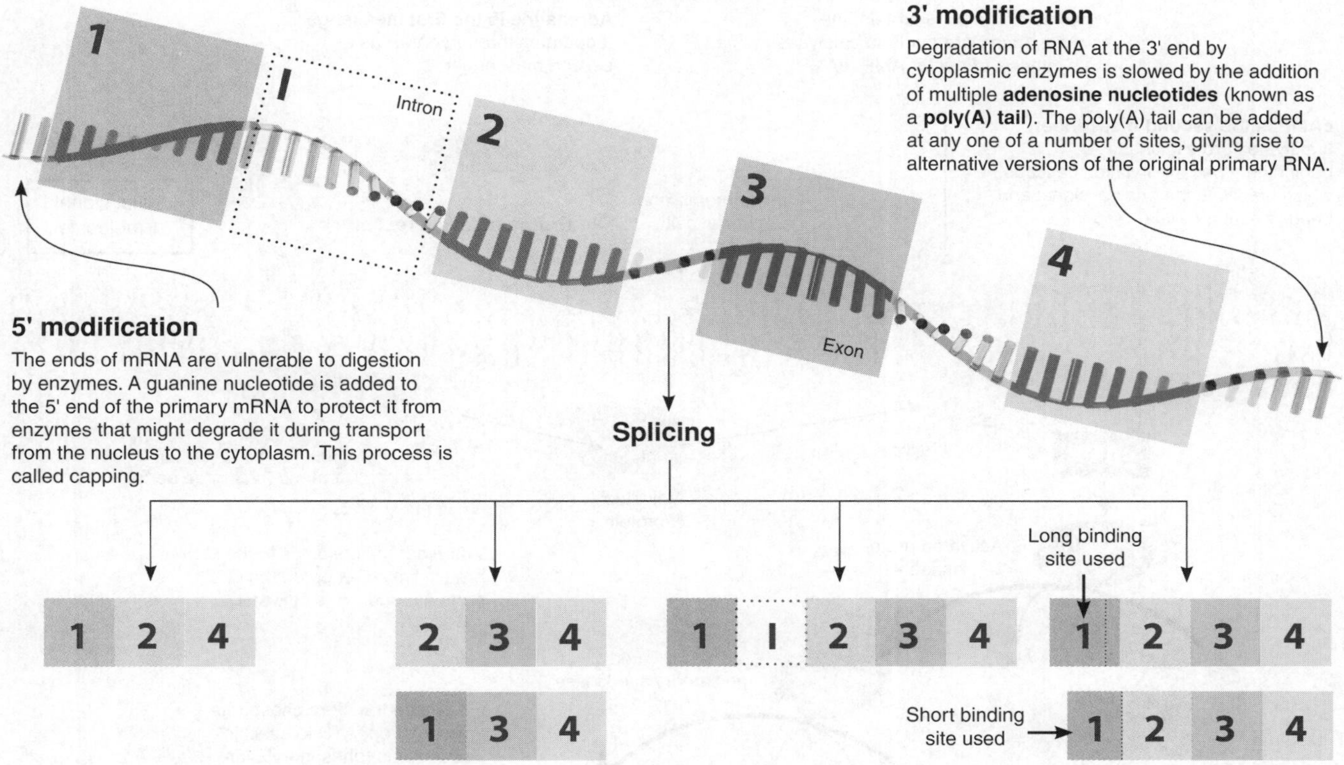

3' modification

Degradation of RNA at the 3' end by cytoplasmic enzymes is slowed by the addition of multiple **adenosine nucleotides** (known as a **poly(A) tail**). The poly(A) tail can be added at any one of a number of sites, giving rise to alternative versions of the original primary RNA.

Intron

Exon

5' modification

The ends of mRNA are vulnerable to digestion by enzymes. A guanine nucleotide is added to the 5' end of the primary mRNA to protect it from enzymes that might degrade it during transport from the nucleus to the cytoplasm. This process is called capping.

Splicing

Long binding site used

Short binding site used

Exon skipping

During splicing, an exon may be skipped. This is a relatively common way to produce protein variants in mammals.

Mutually exclusive exons

In some cases, only one of two exons (but never both) will be incorporated into the mature mRNA.

Intron retention

Introns are not always removed during the splicing process. In some rare cases the intron is retained in the mature mRNA.

Alternative binding sites

Exons may contain more than one site for binding to other exons. If the shorter version is used, the remaining code is discarded, and results in a shorter mRNA sequence.

1. Explain how so many proteins can be produced from so few genes: _____

_____

_____

_____

2. Describe the ways in which mRNA can be modified to code for different proteins: _____

_____

_____

_____

3. Explain the advantage of being able to modify the mRNA to produce different proteins: _____

_____

_____

_____

_____

106 Protein Activation by Cyclic AMP

Key Idea: Cyclic AMP acts as a second messenger to bring about an amplified response to an extracellular signal.

Cells can regulate metabolic activity by activating or deactivating enzymes as they are needed. When the enzyme is needed by the cell, it can quickly be activated, saving the cell energy and reducing cellular response time. **Cyclic AMP (cAMP)** is a signalling molecule that works in conjunction

with protein kinase A to amplify the effect of an extracellular signaling molecule (such as hormone) and bring about the activation of enzymes in a metabolic pathway. In the example below, the cell receives a signal via the hormone adrenaline. cAMP is produced from ATP and activates protein kinase A, beginning a cascade of reactions that ends with the production of glucose from glycogen.

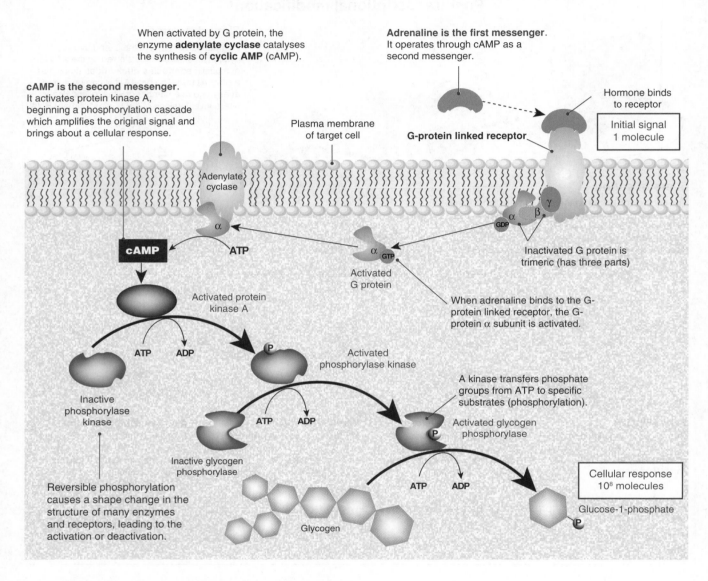

When activated by G protein, the enzyme **adenylate cyclase** catalyses the synthesis of **cyclic AMP** (cAMP).

Adrenaline is the first messenger. It operates through cAMP as a second messenger.

cAMP is the second messenger. It activates protein kinase A, beginning a phosphorylation cascade which amplifies the original signal and brings about a cellular response.

Hormone binds to receptor

Initial signal 1 molecule

Plasma membrane of target cell

G-protein linked receptor

Adenylate cyclase

cAMP

ATP

Inactivated G protein is trimeric (has three parts)

Activated G protein

When adrenaline binds to the G-protein linked receptor, the G-protein α subunit is activated.

Activated protein kinase A

ATP   ADP

P

Activated phosphorylase kinase

A kinase transfers phosphate groups from ATP to specific substrates (phosphorylation).

Inactive phosphorylase kinase

ATP   ADP

Inactive glycogen phosphorylase

Activated glycogen phosphorylase

Reversible phosphorylation causes a shape change in the structure of many enzymes and receptors, leading to the activation or deactivation.

Glycogen

ATP   ADP

Cellular response 10^8 molecules

Glucose-1-phosphate

1. (a) What is the role of adrenaline in the example above? _____

_____

   (b) What is the role of cAMP in the example above and how does it result in an amplification of the original signal?

_____

_____

2. (a) What is the role of reversible phosphorylation in signal cascades such as the one described above? _____

_____

   (b) What are the advantages of this method of regulation? Why are enzymes not just degraded when not required?

_____

_____

© 2015 **BIOZONE** International
ISBN: **978-1-927309-14-8**
Photocopying Prohibited

107 Homeobox Genes and Development

Key Idea: Homeobox genes contain a highly conserved region called the homeobox, which encodes a protein domain that can bind to DNA and regulate transcription.

Homeobox genes are genes containing a highly conserved gene sequence, called the **homeobox**. The homeobox codes for a string of 60 amino acids, called the **homeodomain**, which regulates gene expression by binding to DNA. Homeobox genes are found in all eukaryotes and the homeobox itself has changed very little throughout evolution. *Hox* genes are a subset of homeobox genes found in animals. They are found in clusters and determine where body segments and limbs grow. Very different organisms share this set of genes, but regulate them differently, leading to the differences in form and function we see amongst animals.

What are homeobox genes?

Homeobox genes are genes containing a highly conserved (unchanging) sequence called the **homeobox**. The homeobox is about 180 base pairs long and encodes a string of about 60 amino acids called a homeodomain that can bind to DNA. Homeodomain-containing proteins act as transcription factors and so regulate transcription of other genes. A homeobox gene is not a specific gene. It is a large, ancient group of genes that all contain the homeobox sequence. In humans, there are about 235 homeobox genes, but homeobox genes are found in all eukaryotes, including plants, animals, and fungi. The genes themselves may be different, but the homeobox sequence itself hasn't changed much at all throughout evolution.

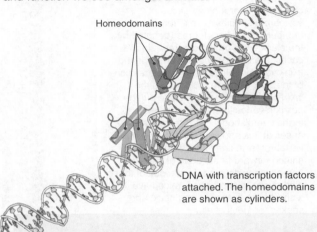

Homeodomains

DNA with transcription factors attached. The homeodomains are shown as cylinders.

The role of *Hox* genes

Hox genes are a special group of homeobox genes that are found only in animals. *Hox* genes control the development of the back and front parts of the animal body. The same genes (or homologous ones) are present in essentially all animals, including humans.

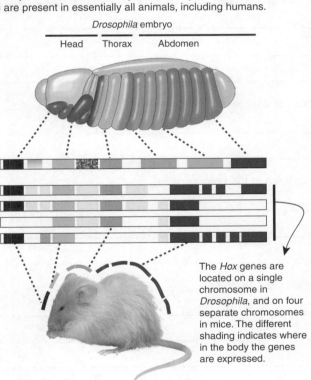

Drosophila embryo

Head   Thorax   Abdomen

The *Hox* genes are located on a single chromosome in *Drosophila*, and on four separate chromosomes in mice. The different shading indicates where in the body the genes are expressed.

The evolution of novel forms

Even very small changes (mutations) in the *Hox* genes can have a profound effect on morphology. Such changes to the genes controlling development have almost certainly been important in the evolution of novel structures and body plans. Four principles underlie the role of developmental genes in the evolution of novel forms:

- **Evolution works with what is already present**: New structures are modifications of pre-existing structures.

- **Multifunctionality** and **redundancy**: Functional redundancy in any part of a multifunctional structure allows for specialisation and division of labour through the development of two separate structures.

  Example: the diversity of appendages (including mouthparts) in arthropods.

- **Modularity**: Modular architecture in animals (arthropods, vertebrates) allows for the modification and specialisation of individual body parts. Genetic switches allow changes in one part of a structure, independent of other parts.

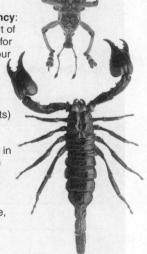

1. (a) What is a homeobox gene? _____

_____

_____

(b) Describe the function of the homeodomain: _____

_____

_____

_____

© 2015 **BIOZONE** International
ISBN: **978-1-927309-14-8**
Photocopying Prohibited

Shifting *Hox* expression

Huge diversity in morphology in organisms within and across phyla could have arisen through small changes in the genes controlling development.

Differences in neck length in vertebrates provide a good example of how changes in gene expression can bring about changes in morphology. Different vertebrate species have different numbers of neck vertebrae (denoted by the black ovals on the diagram). In all cases, the boundary between neck and trunk vertebrae is marked by expression of the ***Hox c6* gene** (c6 denotes the sixth cervical or neck vertebra) but the position varies in each animal relative to the overall body. The forelimb (arrow) arises at this boundary in all four-legged vertebrates. In snakes, the boundary is shifted forward to the base of the skull and no limbs develop. As a result of these differences in expression, mice have a short neck, geese a long neck, and snakes, no neck at all.

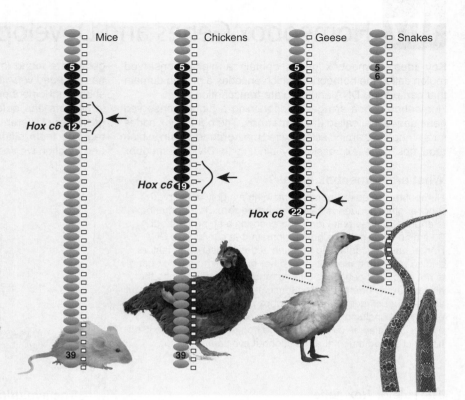

2. (a) What are *Hox* genes? _____

_____

(b) What is the general function of *Hox* genes? _____

_____

3. (a) What does it mean when the homeobox gene sequences are said to be highly conserved? _____

_____

_____

(b) What does this tell you about the evolution and the importance of the homeobox? _____

_____

_____

4. Suggest why the *Hox* genes are found in clusters (i.e. grouped tightly together): _____

_____

_____

_____

5. Using an example, discuss how changes in gene expression can bring about changes in morphology:

_____

_____

_____

_____

_____

_____

© 2015 **BIOZONE** International
ISBN: **978-1-927309-14-8**
Photocopying Prohibited

108 The Timing of Development

Key Idea: Embryonic development is regulated by signal molecules that affect gene expression.

The differentiation of cells is controlled by cell signalling, either by producing a gradient of molecules through the embryo or by signalling a specific cell that then signals other cells in sequence. Cell signals regulate transcription factors that in turn control the differential gene expression that shapes embryos. This process, called **embryonic induction**, takes hours to days, while the time a cell can respond to an inducing signal is strictly limited.

Development in *Drosophila*

Morphogen concentration and cell fate

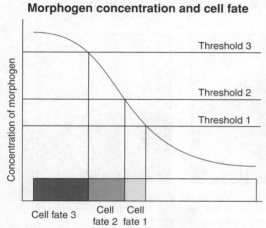

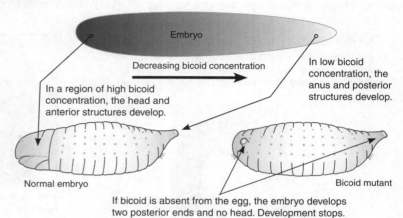

Morphogens are signal molecules that govern patterns of tissue development. Morphogens induce cells in different positions to adopt different fates by diffusing from an area of production through a field of cells.

The **bicoid** gene is important in *Drosophila* development. After fertilisation, bicoid mRNA from the mother is passed to the egg where it is translated into bicoid protein. Bicoid protein forms a concentration gradient in the developing embryo, which determine where the anterior and posterior develop.

Development in *Caenorhabditis elegans*

A second way of inducing change in embryonic cells is through **sequential induction**. A signal molecule reaches cell A, which responds by developing and producing signal B and so on.

The fate of all of *C. elegans*' 1090 somatic cells are known. 131 somatic cells undergo cell death (apoptosis). The death of these cells is controlled by the genes *ced-3* and *ced-4*, which are themselves regulated by gene *ced-9*. There are three waves of apoptosis. The first removes 113 of 628 cells, the second removes 18 more cells, and the third removes half of the developing oocytes.

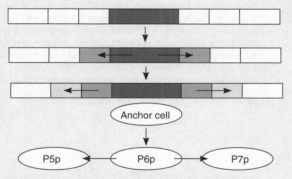

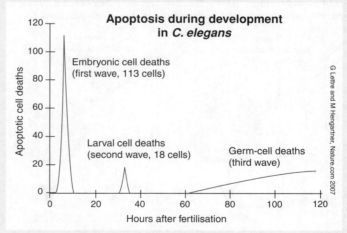

The nematode worm, *Caenorhabditis elegans*, is a model organism for developmental studies. The cells that form the vulva (ventral opening for copulation and egg laying) display sequential induction. Signals from the anchor cell induce a change in cell P6p. Cell P6p then signals cells P5p and P7p to develop.

1. (a) Describe the role of **morphogens**: _____

(b) Explain the purpose of the **bicoid protein** in *Drosophila*: _____

2. Describe **sequential induction** in *C. elegans*: _____

LINK 109 LINK 3 WEB 108 KNOW

109 Controlling the Development of Body Form

Key Idea: Control over the rate and timing of cell division and apoptosis (programmed cell death) maintains cell numbers and produces the sculpting of body parts during development. The growth, development, and maintenance of a multicellular organism involves an increase in cell numbers though mitotic division, differentiation of those cells to perform specific tasks, and programmed death (apoptosis) of cells at certain points to sculpt tissues in the embryo and maintain cell numbers in the adult. Both apoptosis and cell division are orderly processes and both are tightly regulated. Signalling molecules regulate the cell cycle to ensure that the cell passes essential regulatory checkpoints before dividing. Apoptosis is regulated by a balance between signals that promote cell survival and those that trigger cell death. Defects in cell cycle regulation and apoptotic processes are implicated in many diseases, including cancers.

The cell cycle

Recall that there are three **checkpoints** (critical regulatory points) during the cell cycle. Specific conditions must be met before the cell progresses past the checkpoint to the next phase.

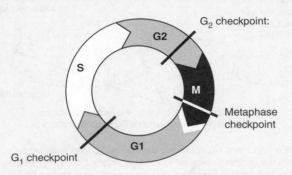

G_2 checkpoint:

Metaphase checkpoint

G_1 checkpoint

During the normal cell cycle, genes that regulate the cell cycle are switched on and off in a regular way. However during a time of stress (e.g. a lack of glucose) these genes must be switched on and off in a different pattern as the cell responds. This may result in the slowing down of the cell cycle until the stress element is removed, at which time the cell cycle will return to normal.

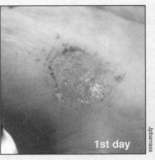

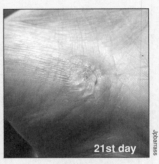

1st day

21st day

The events of mitosis are virtually the same for all eukaryotes. However, aspects of the cell cycle can vary enormously between species and even between cells of the same organism. For example, the length of the cell cycle varies between cells such as intestinal, liver, and muscle cells. Intestinal cells divide around twice a day, whereas cells in the liver divide once a year, and those in muscle tissue do not divide at all. Under certain conditions, e.g. stress, the cell cycle can be slowed down or speeded up. Skin cells have a high rate of division. When tissue is damaged the rate of cell division increases to repair the damage. Here a wound on the heel of the hand heals over the course of 21 days. Note how the deeper central part of the wound takes longer to heal.

Cells divide in response to internal stimuli

The cell cycle in controlled by numerous genes and signal molecules. The movement of cells into M-phase (mitosis and cytokinesis) is regulated by M-phase promoting factor (MPF). This was originally discovered during experiments with the eggs of the African clawed frog (*Xenopus laevis*).

Other studies have shown that MPF is made up of two subunits. The first subunit is a **protein kinase** which activates proteins by transferring a phosphate group from ATP to the protein. The second subunit, called a **cyclin**, activates the first subunit (and thus the first subunit is called a **cyclin-dependent kinase** or **CDK**). CDK is constantly present in the cell, whereas cyclin is not.

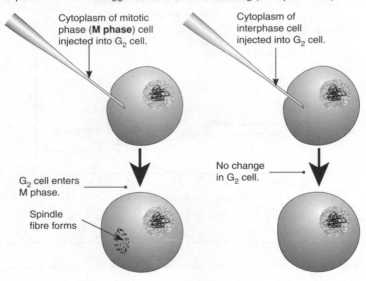

Cytoplasm of mitotic phase (**M phase**) cell injected into G_2 cell.

Cytoplasm of interphase cell injected into G_2 cell.

G_2 cell enters M phase.

No change in G_2 cell.

Spindle fibre forms

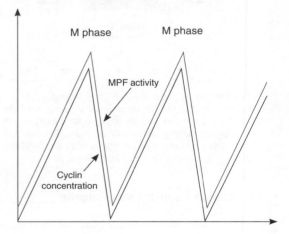

M phase

M phase

MPF activity

Cyclin concentration

1. How do the genes controlling the cell cycle respond to a stress stimulus? _____

_____

2. (a) Explain why the cytoplasm from a M-phase cell could induce a G_2 cell to enter M phase: _____

_____

_____

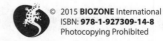

© 2015 **BIOZONE** International
ISBN: **978-1-927309-14-8**
Photocopying Prohibited

The role of programmed cell death (apoptosis)

Apoptosis is a normal and necessary mechanism in multicellular organisms to trigger the death of a cell. It helps to maintain adult cell numbers and is a defence against damaged or infected cells. Apoptosis also has a role in "sculpting" embryonic tissue during development, e.g. in the formation of digits in developing embryos. Apoptosis occurs in response to specific cell signals. The cell and its nucleus shrink and there is an orderly dissection of chromatin by endonucleases. Death is finalised by a rapid engulfment of the dying cell by phagocytosis.

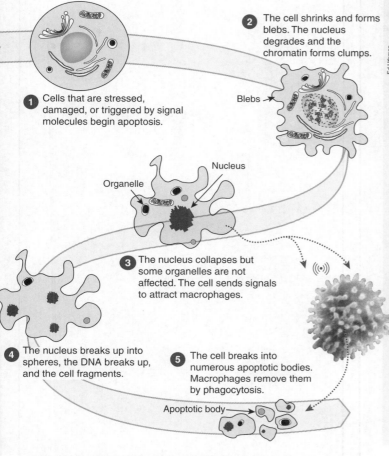

2 The cell shrinks and forms blebs. The nucleus degrades and the chromatin forms clumps.

1 Cells that are stressed, damaged, or triggered by signal molecules begin apoptosis.

Blebs

Nucleus

Organelle

3 The nucleus collapses but some organelles are not affected. The cell sends signals to attract macrophages.

4 The nucleus breaks up into spheres, the DNA breaks up, and the cell fragments.

5 The cell breaks into numerous apoptotic bodies. Macrophages remove them by phagocytosis.

Apoptotic body

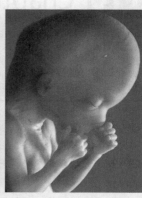

Ed Uthman

In humans, the mesoderm initially formed between the fingers and toes is removed by apoptosis. Forty one days after fertilisation (above, left), the digits of the hands and feet are webbed, appearing paddle-like. Apoptosis selectively destroys this superfluous webbing, sculpting them into digits, which can be seen later in development (above, right).

Regulating apoptosis

Apoptosis is a tightly controlled process, distinct from necrosis (uncontrolled cell death), in which the cell contents are spilled. Apoptosis is regulated by a balance between factors promoting cell survival and those triggering cell death:

Positive signals prevent apoptosis and allow a cell to function normally. They include:
▶ interleukin-2
▶ bcl-2 protein and growth factors

Interleukin-2 is a positive signal for cell survival. Like other signalling molecules, it binds to cell surface receptors to regulate metabolism.

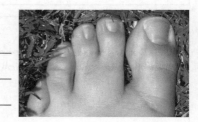

Negative signals (death activators), which trigger the changes leading to cell death. They include:
▶ inducer signals generated from within the cell itself in response to stress, e.g. DNA damage or cell starvation.
▶ signalling proteins and peptides such as lymphotoxin.

(b) Explain how the activity of MPF is regulated: _____

_____

_____

3. The photograph (right) shows a condition called syndactyly. Explain what might have happened during development to result in this condition:

_____

_____

_____

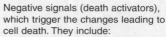

4. What is the role of apoptosis in the normal functioning of the body?

_____

_____

5. Describe two situations, other than digit formation in development, in which apoptosis plays a crucial role:

(a) _____

_____

(b) _____

_____

110 Chapter Review

Summarise what you know about this topic under the headings and sub-headings provided. You can draw diagrams or mind maps, or write short notes to organise your thoughts. Use the images and hints to help you and refer back to the introduction to check the points covered:

The nature of mutations
HINT: Describe substitution, insertion, and deletion mutation. Describe the causes and symptoms of sickle cell disease and cystic fibrosis.

Gene control
HINT: Explain operons in prokaryotes and gene regulation in eukaryotes.

Timing and development
HINT: Outline the role of homeobox (including Hox) genes and their role. Describe the mechanisms controlling the development of body form.

© 2015 BIOZONE International
ISBN: 978-1-927309-14-8
Photocopying Prohibited

111 KEY TERMS: Did You Get It?

1. Match each term to its definition, as identified by its preceding letter code.

apoptosis _____

gene expression _____

gene induction _____

homeobox genes _____

Hox genes _____

lac operon _____

morphogens _____

mutation _____

transcription factors _____

A The entire process of transferring of information encoded in a gene into a gene product.

B A process of genetically programmed cell death that is part of normal growth and development, and cellular regulation in multicellular organisms.

C Developmental control genes that are involved in establishing the anterior-posterior axis of an organism. They are shared by almost all organisms.

D Activation of an inactive gene to carry out transcription.

E Proteins that bind to specific DNA sequences to regulate transcription.

F Cluster of genes in *E. coli* that regulates the metabolism of lactose.

G A change to the DNA sequence of an organism. This may be a deletion, insertion, duplication, inversion or translocation of DNA in a gene or larger regions of a chromosome.

H Signal molecules that control and direct the development of cells and tissues by producing a concentration gradient.

I A group of ancient genes that all contain a highly conserved sequence of 180 base pairs encoding a protein domain that can bind to DNA.

2. (a) Describe the structure of an operon: _____

_____

_____

_____

   (b) Is an operon present in prokaryotes or eukaryotes? _____

3. For the following DNA sequence, identify the mutations that have occurred:

   Original DNA sequence: GTT GCG CAT AAT GCA TGA ATA

   (a) GTT GCC ATA ATG CAT GAA TA

   (b) GTT GCG CAT AAA TGC ATG AAT A

4. Explain why a mutation that may be harmful in one environment may be beneficial in another: _____

_____

_____

_____

_____

5. In relation to developing and maintaining shape and form, explain why organisms need to tightly control gene expression:

_____

_____

_____

_____

_____

© 2015 **BIOZONE** International
ISBN: **978-1-927309-14-8**
Photocopying Prohibited

TEST

Module 6.1.2

Patterns of Inheritance I

Key terms

allele

back cross

codominance (of alleles)

continuous variation

diploid

dihybrid cross

discontinuous variation

dominant (of alleles)

epistasis

F_1 / F_2 generation

gene interactions

genotype

haploid

heterozygous

homologous chromosomes

homozygous

independent assortment

linkage (linked genes)

locus

meiosis

monogenic inheritance

monohybrid cross

multiple alleles

multiple genes

phenotype

phenotypic ratio

polygenes

Punnett square

pure (true)-breeding

recessive (of alleles)

recombination

sex linkage

test cross

trait

Variation and inheritance

Learning outcomes

		Activity number
☐	1 Explain how genotype and environment contribute to phenotypic variation. Using examples, describe the contribution of environment to phenotypic variation in plants and animals.	112
☐	2 Explain how sexual reproduction contributes to genetic variation within a species, including reference to linkage and recombination in meiosis and random fusion of gametes at fertilisation.	112

Studying inheritance

Learning outcomes

		Activity number
☐	3 Demonstrate appropriate use of the terms used in studying inheritance: allele, locus, trait, heterozygous, homozygous, genotype, phenotype, cross, test cross, back cross, carrier, F_1/F_2 generation.	112-114
☐	4 Use genetic diagrams to show patterns of monogenic inheritance (inheritance of traits controlled by only one gene).	114 115
☐	5 Use a Punnett square to solve problems involving monohybrid crosses with a simple dominant-recessive pattern.	115 116
☐	6 Describe and explain inheritance involving codominance, multiple alleles, and sex linked genes.	117-120
☐	7 Use a Punnett square to solve problems involving dihybrid inheritance of unlinked, autosomal genes for two independent characteristics. Use the test cross to determine an unknown dominant genotype.	121 127
☐	8 Solve problems involving dihybrid inheritance of linked genes. Understand that the probability of linked genes being inherited together as a unit is a function of the distance between them.	122-124
☐	9 Use phenotypic ratios to identify autosomal and sex linkage in genetic crosses.	122 124
☐	10 Use the chi-squared test (for goodness of fit) to test the significance of differences between the observed and expected results of genetic crosses.	125 126
☐	11 Describe how two or more genes can interact to control a single phenotype (epistasis). Use phenotypic ratios to identify epistasis in genetic crosses.	128 129
☐	12 Describe and explain polygenic inheritance (polygenes are also called multiple genes). Distinguish between continuous and discontinuous variation in phenotypes. Explain the genetic basis for each pattern.	130

112 Sources of Phenotypic Variation

Key Idea: Genes and the environment interact to produce the variations we observe between individuals.

An organism's phenotype is the set of observable characteristics that result from the interaction between the organism's genetic complement (genotype) and the environment the organism is exposed to. This interaction can result in large differences in appearance between even closely related individuals.

Meiosis and variation

Meiosis produces gametes for sexual reproduction. It also produces variation in the genetic make-up of the gametes. This variation occurs as a result of crossing over and independent assortment. The random union of two gametes in fertilisation produces further variation.

Crossing over: In meiosis I, sister chromatids can swap genetic material (alleles) causing differences between them and the parent chromosome. Alleles are recombined so that different gametes receive different allele combinations.

Independent assortment:
The separation of each homologous pair is random with respect to all the other pairs. Each chromosome has a 1 in 4 chance of ending up in any one gamete.

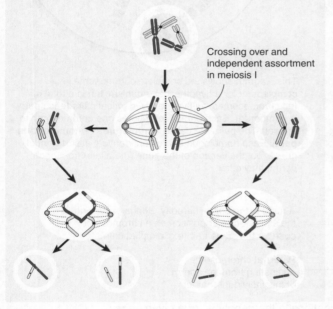

Crossing over and independent assortment in meiosis I

The environment and variation

Every organism has a certain genetic potential, i.e. what its genes could make possible given ideal circumstances. In reality, the ideal circumstances never occur, because a constantly changing environment creates deficiencies and surpluses in the factors required for an organism to reach its genetic potential.

This leaf has a condition called chlorosis. The pale areas around the edge of the leaf are caused by a lack of chlorophyll. There are many reasons for a lack of chlorophyll, including a lack of nutrients such as magnesium and iron, or even water logged roots. It is not a genetic disease.

Etiolation is the apparent rapid growth of the plant caused by the elongation of cells. It occurs when plants lack light and it increases the plant's chances of reaching light by growing above whatever is blocking the light (e.g. a seedling may be covered by soil or leaves).

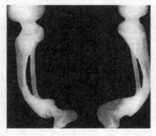

Diet, including over- or under nutrition and lack of balanced nutritional intake, makes a large contribution to an animal's phenotype. Lack of vitamins or minerals can result in major growth abnormalities, e.g. rickets (left) is caused by a deficiency or impaired metabolism of vitamin D, phosphorus, or calcium.

1. (a) At which two points during meiosis is there the ability to increase genetic variation in the possible gametes?

_____

(b) Explain how these two mechanisms increase variation in the gametes:

i: _____

_____

_____

ii: _____

_____

_____

2. Using examples, explain how the environment can influence an organism's phenotype: _____

_____

_____

_____

LINK
113

KNOW

113 Describing Alleles

Key Idea: Eukaryotes generally have paired chromosomes. Each chromosome contains many genes and each gene may have a number of versions called alleles.

Sexually reproducing organisms usually have paired sets of chromosomes, one set from each parent. The equivalent chromosomes that form a pair are termed **homologues**. They carry equivalent sets of genes, but there is the potential for different versions of a gene (**alleles**) to exist in a population.

Homologous chromosomes

In sexually reproducing organisms, most cells have a homologous pair of chromosomes (one coming from each parent). This diagram shows the position of three different genes on the same chromosome that control three different traits (A, B and C).

Chromosomes are formed from DNA and proteins. DNA tightly winds around special proteins to form the chromosome.

Having two different versions (alleles) of gene A is a **heterozygous** condition. Only the dominant allele (A) will be expressed. Alleles differ by only a few bases.

When both chromosomes have identical copies of the dominant allele for gene B the organism is **homozygous dominant** for that gene.

When both chromosomes have identical copies of the recessive allele for gene C the organism is said to be **homozygous recessive** for that gene.

Maternal chromosome originating from the egg of this individual's mother.

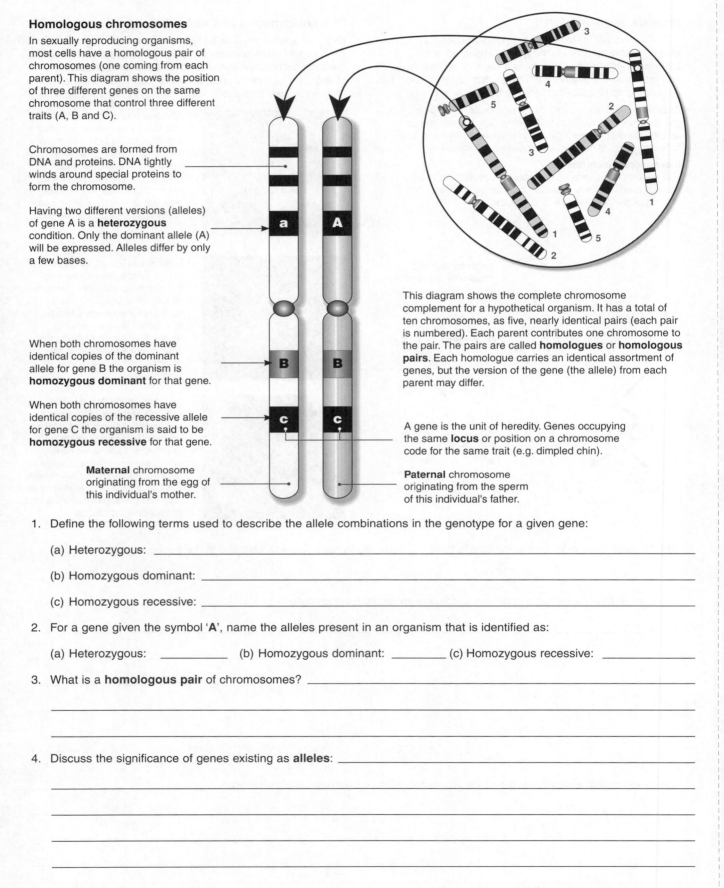

This diagram shows the complete chromosome complement for a hypothetical organism. It has a total of ten chromosomes, as five, nearly identical pairs (each pair is numbered). Each parent contributes one chromosome to the pair. The pairs are called **homologues** or **homologous pairs**. Each homologue carries an identical assortment of genes, but the version of the gene (the allele) from each parent may differ.

A gene is the unit of heredity. Genes occupying the same **locus** or position on a chromosome code for the same trait (e.g. dimpled chin).

Paternal chromosome originating from the sperm of this individual's father.

1. Define the following terms used to describe the allele combinations in the genotype for a given gene:

   (a) Heterozygous: _____

   (b) Homozygous dominant: _____

   (c) Homozygous recessive: _____

2. For a gene given the symbol '**A**', name the alleles present in an organism that is identified as:

   (a) Heterozygous: _____   (b) Homozygous dominant: _____   (c) Homozygous recessive: _____

3. What is a **homologous pair** of chromosomes? _____

   _____

   _____

4. Discuss the significance of genes existing as **alleles**: _____

   _____

   _____

   _____

   _____

LINK
114

KNOW

© 2015 **BIOZONE** International
ISBN: **978-1-927309-14-8**
Photocopying Prohibited

114 Basic Genetic Crosses

Key Idea: The outcome of a cross depends on the parental genotypes and can be determined using Punnett squares. Examine the diagrams below on monohybrid (one gene) and dihybrid (two gene) inheritance. The F_1 generation describes the offspring of a cross between **true-breeding** (homozygous) parents. A **back cross** is a cross between an offspring and one of its parents. If the back cross is to a homozygous recessive, it can be used as a **test cross**.

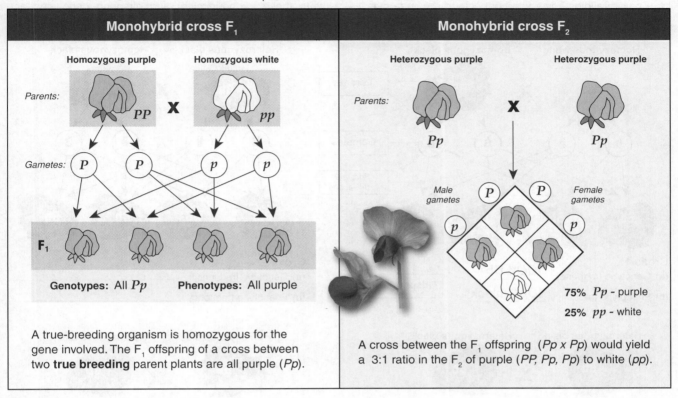

Monohybrid cross F_1

Homozygous purple **X** Homozygous white

Parents: PP pp

Gametes: P P p p

F_1

Genotypes: All Pp **Phenotypes:** All purple

A true-breeding organism is homozygous for the gene involved. The F_1 offspring of a cross between two **true breeding** parent plants are all purple (Pp).

Monohybrid cross F_2

Heterozygous purple **X** Heterozygous purple

Parents: Pp Pp

Male gametes P P *Female gametes*

p p

75% Pp - purple
25% pp - white

A cross between the F_1 offspring ($Pp \times Pp$) would yield a 3:1 ratio in the F_2 of purple (PP, Pp, Pp) to white (pp).

Dihybrid cross

A dihybrid cross studies the inheritance patterns of two genes. In pea seeds, yellow colour (Y) is dominant to green (y) and round shape (R) is dominant to wrinkled (r). Each **true breeding** parental plant has matching alleles for each of these characters ($YYRR$ or $yyrr$). F_1 offspring will all have the same genotype and phenotype (yellow-round: $YyRr$).

Parents: Homozygous yellow-round **X** Homozygous green-wrinkled

Gametes: YR yr

F_1 all yellow-round $YyRr$ **X** $YyRr$ for the F_2

1. Fill in the Punnett square (below right) to show the genotypes of the F_2 generation.

2. In the boxes below, use fractions to indicate the numbers of each phenotype produced from this cross.

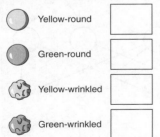

   Yellow-round

   Green-round

   Yellow-wrinkled

   Green-wrinkled

3. Express these numbers as a ratio:

_____

Offspring (F_2)

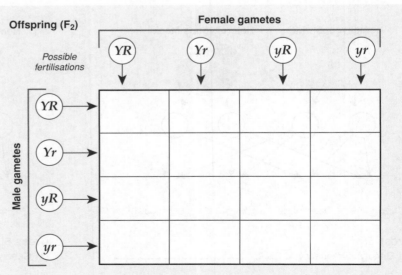

Possible fertilisations

Female gametes

YR Yr yR yr

Male gametes

YR

Yr

yR

yr

LINK   LINK   WEB
121 **115** **114**   **KNOW**

115 Monohybrid Cross

Key Idea: A monohybrid cross studies the inheritance pattern of one gene. The offspring of these crosses occur in predictable ratios.

In this activity, you will examine six types of matings possible for a pair of alleles governing coat colour in guinea pigs. A dominant allele (**B**) produces black hair and its recessive allele (**b**), produces white. Each parent can produce two types of gamete by meiosis. Determine the **genotype** and **phenotype frequencies** for the crosses below. For crosses 3 to 6, also determine the gametes produced by each parent (write these in the circles) and offspring genotypes and phenotypes (write these inside the offspring shapes).

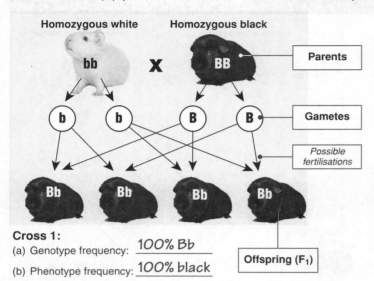

Homozygous white   Homozygous black

bb   X   BB   — Parents

b   b   B   B   — Gametes

⟶ Possible fertilisations

Bb   Bb   Bb   Bb

Cross 1:
(a) Genotype frequency: _100% Bb_
(b) Phenotype frequency: _100% black_

Offspring (F₁)

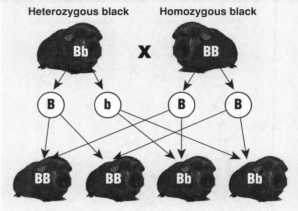

Heterozygous black   Homozygous black

Bb   X   BB

B   b   B   B

BB   BB   Bb   Bb

Cross 2:
(a) Genotype frequency: _____
(b) Phenotype frequency: _____

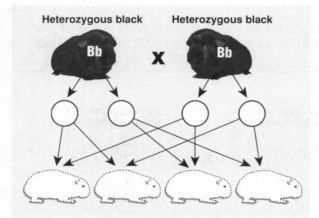

Heterozygous black   Heterozygous black

Bb   X   Bb

Cross 3:
(a) Genotype frequency: _____
(b) Phenotype frequency: _____

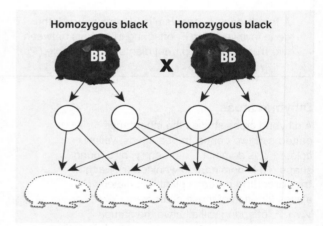

Homozygous black   Homozygous black

BB   X   BB

Cross 4:
(a) Genotype frequency: _____
(b) Phenotype frequency: _____

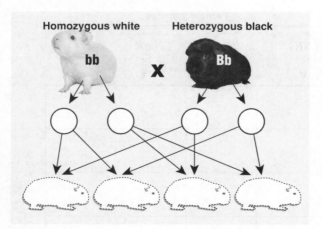

Homozygous white   Heterozygous black

bb   X   Bb

Cross 5:
(a) Genotype frequency: _____
(b) Phenotype frequency: _____

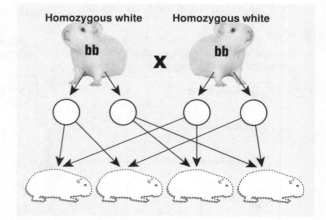

Homozygous white   Homozygous white

bb   X   bb

Cross 6:
(a) Genotype frequency: _____
(b) Phenotype frequency: _____

© 2015 **BIOZONE** International
ISBN: **978-1-927309-14-8**
Photocopying Prohibited

116 Problems Involving Monohybrid Inheritance

Key Idea: For monohybrid crosses involving autosomal unlinked genes, the offspring appear in predictable ratios. The following problems involve Mendelian crosses. The alleles involved are associated with various phenotypic traits controlled by a single gene. The problems are to give you practise in problem solving using Mendelian genetics.

1. A dominant gene (**W**) produces wire-haired texture in dogs; its recessive allele (**w**) produces smooth hair. A group of heterozygous wire-haired individuals are crossed and their F_1 progeny are then test-crossed. Determine the expected genotypic and phenotypic ratios among the **test cross** progeny:

   _____

   _____

   _____

   _____

   _____

2. In sheep, black wool is due to a recessive allele (**b**) and white wool to its dominant allele (**B**). A white ram is crossed to a white ewe. Both animals carry the black allele (b). They produce a white ram lamb, which is then back crossed to the female parent. Determine the probability of the **back cross** offspring being black:

   _____

   _____

3. A homozygous recessive allele, **aa**, is responsible for albinism. Humans can exhibit this phenotype. In each of the following cases, determine the possible genotypes of the mother and father, and their children:

   (a) Both parents have normal phenotypes; some of their children are albino and others are unaffected: _____

   _____

   (b) Both parents are albino and have only albino children: _____

   (c) The woman is unaffected, the man is albino, and they have one albino child and three unaffected children:

   _____

4. Two mothers give birth to sons at a busy hospital. The son of the first couple has haemophilia, a recessive, X-linked disease. Neither parent from couple #1 has the disease. The second couple has an unaffected son, despite the fact that the father has haemophilia. The two couples challenge the hospital in court, claiming their babies must have been swapped at birth. You must advise as to whether or not the sons could have been swapped. What would you say?

   _____

   _____

   _____

5. In a dispute over parentage, the mother of a child with blood group O identifies a male with blood group A as the father. The mother is blood group B. Draw Punnett squares to show possible genotype/phenotype outcomes to determine if the male is the father and the reasons (if any) for further dispute:

   _____

   _____

   _____

   _____

LINK 119 LINK 115 **TEST**

117 Codominance of Alleles

Key Idea: In inheritance involving codominant alleles, neither allele is recessive and both alleles are equally and independently expressed in the heterozygote.

Codominance is an inheritance pattern in which both alleles in a heterozygote contribute to the phenotype and both alleles are **independently** and **equally expressed**. Examples include the human blood group AB and certain coat colours in horses and cattle. Reddish coat colour is equally dominant with white. Animals that have both alleles have coats that are roan (both red and white hairs are present).

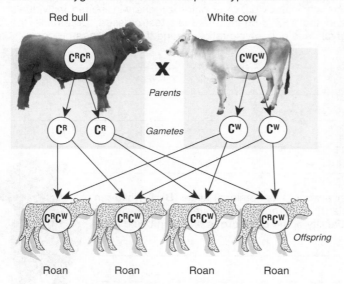

Red bull White cow

C^RC^R X C^WC^W

Parents

C^R C^R *Gametes* C^W C^W

C^RC^W C^RC^W C^RC^W C^RC^W *Offspring*

Roan Roan Roan Roan

A roan shorthorn heifer

In the shorthorn cattle breed, coat colour is inherited. White shorthorn parents always produce calves with white coats. Red parents always produce red calves. However, when a red parent mates with a white one, the calves have a coat colour that is different from either parent; a mixture of red and white hairs, called roan. Use the example (left) to help you to solve the problems below.

1. Explain how codominance of alleles can result in offspring with a phenotype that is different from either parent:

   _____

2. A white bull is mated with a roan cow (right):

   (a) Fill in the spaces to show the genotypes and phenotypes for parents and calves:

   (b) What is the phenotype ratio for this cross?

   _____

   (c) How could a cattle farmer control the breeding so that the herd ultimately consisted of only red cattle:

   _____
   _____
   _____
   _____
   _____

White bull Roan cow

X

3. A farmer has only roan cattle on his farm. He suspects that one of the neighbours' bulls may have jumped the fence to mate with his cows earlier in the year because half the calves born were red and half were roan. One neighbour has a red bull, the other has a roan.

   (a) Fill in the spaces (right) to show the genotype and phenotype for parents and calves.

   (b) Which bull serviced the cows? **red** or **roan** (*delete one*)

4. Describe the classical phenotypic ratio for a codominant gene resulting from the cross of two heterozygous parents (e.g. a cross between two roan cattle):

   _____
   _____

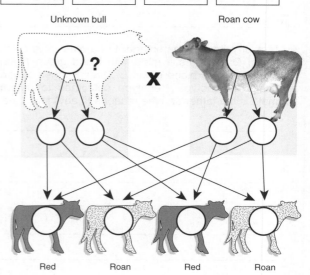

Unknown bull Roan cow

? X

Red Roan Red Roan

WEB LINK

KNOW

© 2015 **BIOZONE** International
ISBN: **978-1-927309-14-8**
Photocopying Prohibited

118 Codominance in Multiple Allele Systems

Key Idea: The human ABO blood group system is a multiple allele system involving the codominant alleles *A* and *B* and the recessive allele *O*.

The four common blood groups of the human 'ABO blood group system' are determined by three alleles: *A*, *B*, and *O*. The ABO antigens consist of sugars attached to the surface of red blood cells. The alleles code for enzymes (proteins) that join these sugars together. The allele O produces a non-functioning enzyme that is unable to make any changes to the basic antigen (sugar) molecule. The other two alleles (*A*, *B*) are **codominant** and are expressed equally. They each produce a different functional enzyme that adds a different, specific sugar to the basic sugar molecule. The blood group A and B antigens are able to react with antibodies present in the blood of other people so blood must always be matched for transfusion.

Recessive allele: **O** produces a non-functioning protein
Dominant allele: **A** produces an enzyme which forms **A antigen**
Dominant allele: **B** produces an enzyme which forms **B antigen**

Blood group (phenotype)	Possible genotypes	Frequency in the UK
O	OO	47%
A	AA, AO	42%
B		8%
AB		3%

Source: http://www.transfusionguidelines.org.uk/ Allele terminology follows latest recommended (use of *I* allele terminology has been discontinued as inaccurate)

If a person has the **AO** allele combination then their blood group will be group **A**. The presence of the recessive allele has no effect on the blood group in the presence of a dominant allele. Another possible allele combination that can create the same blood group is **AA**.

1. Use the information above to complete the table for the possible genotypes for blood group B and group AB.

2. Below are four crosses possible between couples of various blood group types. The first example has been completed for you. Complete the genotype and phenotype for the other three crosses below:

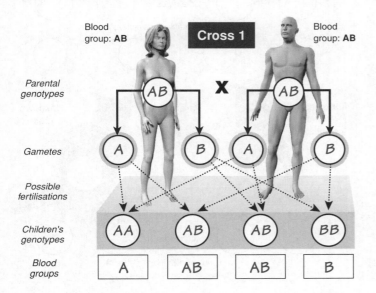

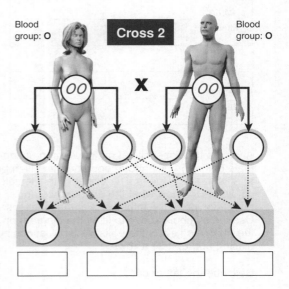

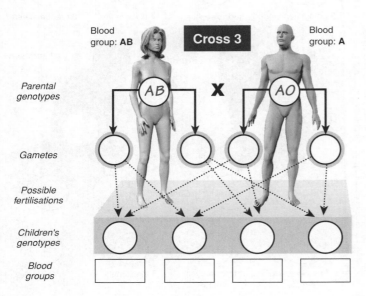

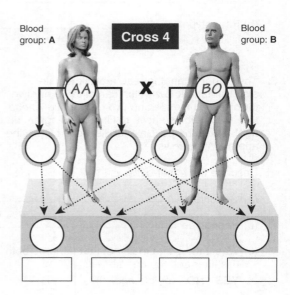

LINK   WEB

117 118 KNOW

119 Sex Linked Genes

Key Idea: Many genes on the X chromosome do not have a match on the Y chromosome. In males, a recessive allele on the X chromosome cannot therefore be masked by a dominant allele.

Sex linkage occurs when a gene is located on a sex chromosome (usually the X). The result of this is that the character encoded by the gene is usually seen only in one sex (the heterogametic sex). In humans, recessive sex linked genes cause a number of heritable disorders in males, e.g. haemophilia. Women who have a recessive allele are said to be carriers. One of the gene loci controlling coat colour in cats is sex-linked. The two alleles, red and non-red (or black), are found only on the X-chromosome.

Allele types

X^o = Non-red (=black)
X^O = Red

Genotypes   **Phenotypes**

X^oX^o, X^oY = Black coated female, male
X^OX^O, X^OY = Orange coated female, male
X^OX^o = Tortoiseshell (intermingled black and orange in fur) in female cats only)

1. An owner of a cat is thinking of mating her black female cat with an orange male cat. Before she does this, she would like to know what possible coat colours could result from such a cross. Use the symbols above to fill in the diagram on the right. Summarise the possible genotypes and phenotypes of the kittens in the tables below.

	Genotypes	Phenotypes
Male kittens		

	Genotypes	Phenotypes
Female kittens		

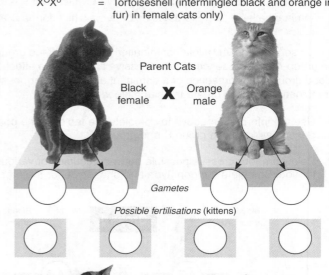

Parent Cats

Black female **X** Orange male

Gametes

Possible fertilisations (kittens)

2. A female tortoiseshell cat mated with an unknown male cat in the neighbourhood and has given birth to a litter of six kittens. The owner of this female cat wants to know what the appearance and the genotype of the father was of these kittens. Use the symbols above to fill in the diagram on the right. Also show the possible fertilisations by placing appropriate arrows.

Describe the father cat's:

(a) Genotype: _____

(b) Phenotype: _____

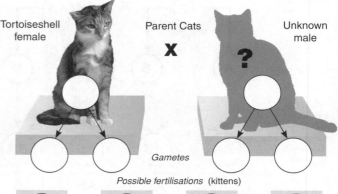

Tortoiseshell female   Parent Cats   Unknown male

X   **?**

Gametes

Possible fertilisations (kittens)

2 orange females   1 tortoiseshell female   1 black male   2 orange males

3. The owner of another cat, a black female, also wants to know which cat fathered her two tortoiseshell female and two black male kittens. Use the symbols above to fill in the diagram on the right. Show the possible fertilisations by placing appropriate arrows.

Describe the father cat's:

(a) Genotype: _____

(b) Phenotype: _____

(c) Was it the same male cat that fathered both this litter and the one above?

     YES / NO (*delete one*)

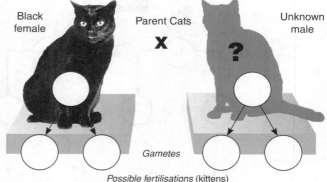

Black female   Parent Cats   Unknown male

X   **?**

Gametes

Possible fertilisations (kittens)

1 tortoiseshell female   1 tortoiseshell female   1 black male   1 black male

© 2015 **BIOZONE** International
ISBN: **978-1-927309-14-8**
Photocopying Prohibited

Dominant allele in humans

A rare form of rickets in humans is determined by a **dominant** allele of a gene on the **X chromosome** (it is not found on the Y chromosome). This condition is not successfully treated with vitamin D therapy. The allele types, genotypes, and phenotypes are as follows:

Allele types	Genotypes	Phenotypes
X^R = affected by rickets	X^RX^R, X^RX =	Affected female
X = normal	X^RY =	Affected male
	XX, XY =	Normal female, male

As a genetic counsellor you are presented with a married couple where one of them has a family history of this disease. The husband is affected by this disease and the wife is normal. The couple, who are thinking of starting a family, would like to know what their chances are of having a child born with this condition. They would also like to know what the probabilities are of having an affected boy or affected girl. Use the symbols above to complete the diagram right and determine the probabilities stated below (expressed as a proportion or percentage).

4. Determine the probability of having:

   (a) Affected children: _____

   (b) An affected girl: _____

   (c) An affected boy: _____

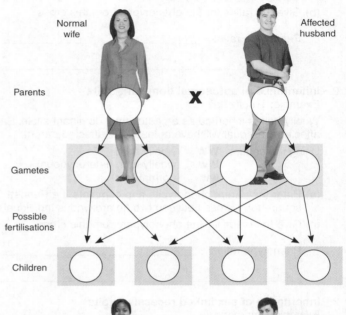

Another couple with a family history of the same disease also come in to see you to obtain genetic counselling. In this case, the husband is normal and the wife is affected. The wife's father was not affected by this disease. Determine what their chances are of having a child born with this condition. They would also like to know what the probabilities are of having an affected boy or affected girl. Use the symbols above to complete the diagram right and determine the probabilities stated below (expressed as a proportion or percentage).

5. Determine the probability of having:

   (a) Affected children: _____

   (b) An affected girl: _____

   (c) An affected boy: _____

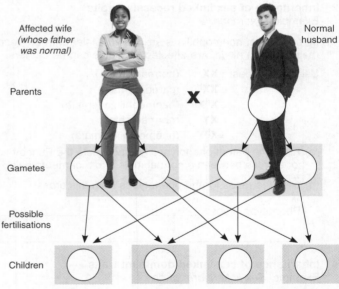

6. Describing examples other than those above, discuss the role of **sex linkage** in the inheritance of genetic disorders:

   _____

   _____

   _____

   _____

120 Inheritance Patterns

Key Idea: Sex-linked traits and autosomal traits have different inheritance patterns.

Complete the following monohybrid crosses for different types of inheritance patterns in humans: autosomal recessive, autosomal dominant, sex linked recessive, and sex linked dominant inheritance.

1. **Inheritance of autosomal recessive traits**
   Example: *Albinism*

   Albinism (lack of pigment in hair, eyes and skin) is inherited as an autosomal recessive allele (not sex-linked).

   Using the codes: **PP** (normal) **Pp** (carrier)
   pp (albino)

   (a) Enter the parent phenotypes and complete the Punnett square for a cross between two carrier genotypes.

   (b) Give the ratios for the phenotypes from this cross.

   Phenotype ratios: _____

   _____

2. **Inheritance of autosomal dominant traits**
   Example: *Woolly hair*

   Woolly hair is inherited as an autosomal dominant allele. Each affected individual will have at least one affected parent.

   Using the codes: **WW** (woolly hair)
   Ww (woolly hair, heterozygous)
   ww (normal hair)

   (a) Enter the parent phenotypes and complete the Punnett square for a cross between two heterozygous individuals.

   (b) Give the ratios for the phenotypes from this cross.

   Phenotype ratios: _____

   _____

3. **Inheritance of sex linked recessive traits**
   Example: *Haemophilia*

   Inheritance of haemophilia is sex linked. Males with the recessive (haemophilia) allele, are affected. Females can be carriers.

   Using the codes: **XX** (normal female)
   XX^h (carrier female)
   X^{h}X^h (haemophiliac female)
   XY (normal male)
   X^{h}Y (haemophiliac male)

   (a) Enter the parent phenotypes and complete the Punnett square for a cross between a normal male and a carrier female.

   (b) Give the ratios for the phenotypes from this cross.

   Phenotype ratios: _____

   _____

4. **Inheritance of sex linked dominant traits**
   Example: *Sex linked form of rickets*

   A rare form of rickets is inherited on the X chromosome.

   Using the codes: **XX** (normal female); **XY** (normal male)
   X^{R}X (affected heterozygote female)
   X^{R}X^R (affected female)
   X^{R}Y (affected male)

   (a) Enter the parent phenotypes and complete the Punnett square for a cross between an affected male and heterozygous female.

   (b) Give the ratios for the phenotypes from this cross.

   Phenotype ratios: _____

   _____

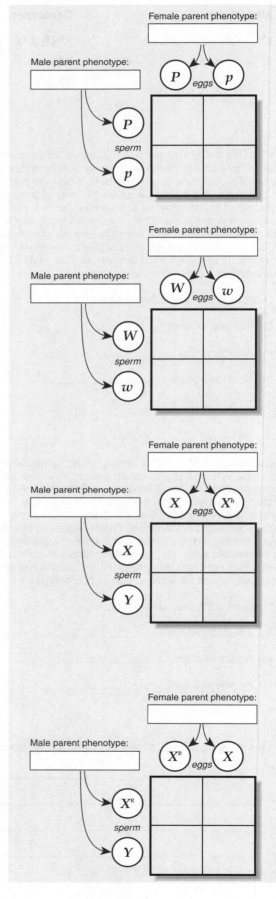

© 2015 **BIOZONE** International
ISBN: **978-1-927309-14-8**
Photocopying Prohibited

121 Dihybrid Cross

Key Idea: A dihybrid cross studies the inheritance pattern of two genes. In crosses involving unlinked autosomal genes, the offspring occur in predictable ratios.

There are four types of gamete produced in a cross involving two genes, where the genes are carried on separate chromosomes and are sorted independently of each other during meiosis. The two genes in the example below are on separate chromosomes and control two unrelated characteristics, **hair colour** and **coat length**. Black (B) and short (L) are dominant to white and long.

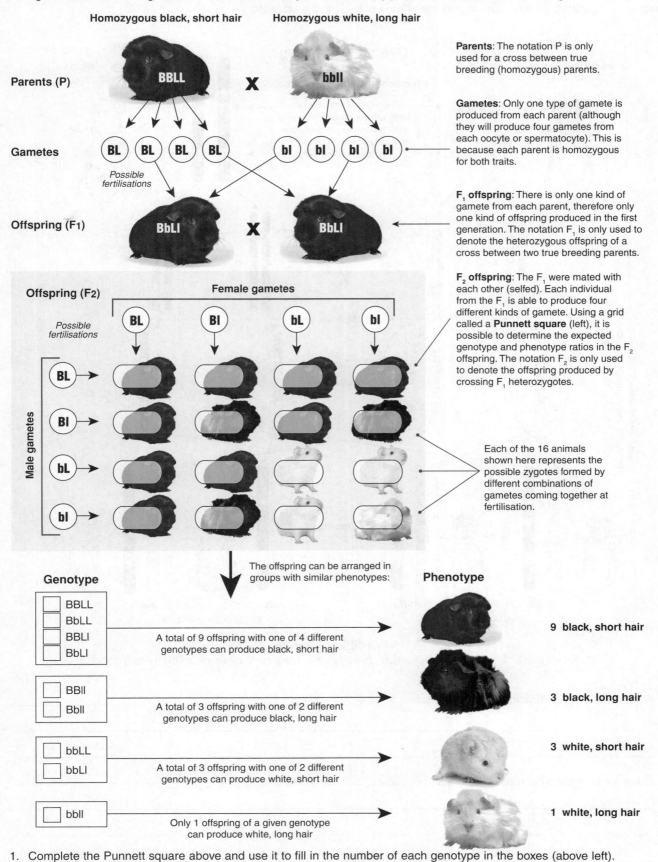

Parents: The notation P is only used for a cross between true breeding (homozygous) parents.

Gametes: Only one type of gamete is produced from each parent (although they will produce four gametes from each oocyte or spermatocyte). This is because each parent is homozygous for both traits.

F₁ offspring: There is only one kind of gamete from each parent, therefore only one kind of offspring produced in the first generation. The notation F₁ is only used to denote the heterozygous offspring of a cross between two true breeding parents.

F₂ offspring: The F₁ were mated with each other (selfed). Each individual from the F₁ is able to produce four different kinds of gamete. Using a grid called a **Punnett square** (left), it is possible to determine the expected genotype and phenotype ratios in the F₂ offspring. The notation F₂ is only used to denote the offspring produced by crossing F₁ heterozygotes.

Each of the 16 animals shown here represents the possible zygotes formed by different combinations of gametes coming together at fertilisation.

1. Complete the Punnett square above and use it to fill in the number of each genotype in the boxes (above left).

LINK 127 LINK 123 LINK 122 WEB 121 KNOW

122 Inheritance of Linked Genes

Key Idea: Linked genes are genes found on the same chromosome and tend to be inherited together. Linkage reduces the genetic variation in the offspring.

Genes are **linked** when they are on the same chromosome. Linked genes tend to be inherited together and the extent of crossing over depends on how close together they are on the chromosome. In genetic crosses, linkage is indicated when a greater proportion of the offspring from a cross are of the parental type (than would be expected if the alleles were on separate chromosomes and assorting independently). Linkage reduces the genetic variation that can be produced in the offspring.

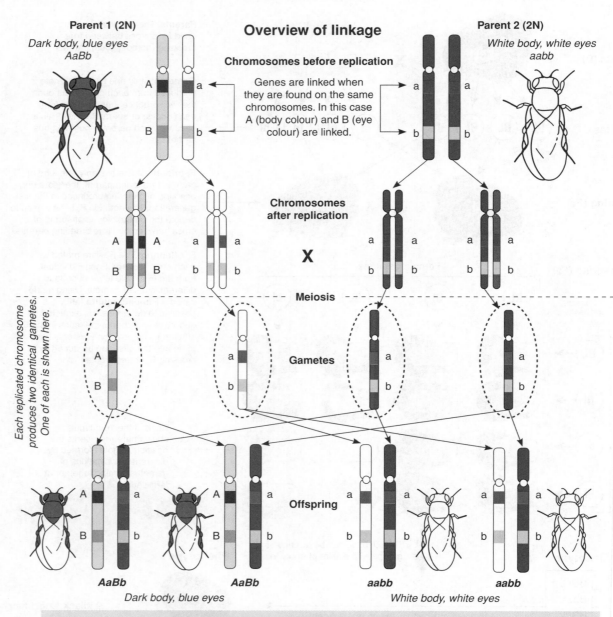

Parent 1 (2N)
Dark body, blue eyes
AaBb

Parent 2 (2N)
White body, white eyes
aabb

Overview of linkage

Chromosomes before replication

Genes are linked when they are found on the same chromosomes. In this case A (body colour) and B (eye colour) are linked.

Chromosomes after replication

X

Meiosis

Each replicated chromosome produces two identical gametes. One of each is shown here.

Gametes

Offspring

AaBb **AaBb**
Dark body, blue eyes

aabb **aabb**
White body, white eyes

Possible offspring
Only two kinds of genotype combinations are possible. They are they same as the parent genotype.

1. What is the effect of **linkage** on the inheritance of genes? _____

_____

_____

2. Explain how linkage decreases the amount of genetic variation in the offspring: _____

_____

_____

_____

© 2015 **BIOZONE** International
ISBN: **978-1-927309-14-8**
Photocopying Prohibited

An example of linked genes in *Drosophila*

The genes for wing shape and body colour are linked (they are on the same chromosome).

	Wild type female	Mutant male
Parent		
Phenotype	Straight wing Grey body	Curled wing Ebony body
Genotype	Cucu Ebeb	cucu ebeb

Linkage

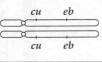

Cu   Eb   *cu   eb*

cu   eb   *cu   eb*

---------- **Meiosis** ----------

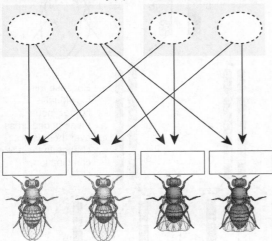

Gametes from female fly (N)   Gametes from male fly (N)

Sex of offspring is irrelevant in this case

Contact **Newbyte Educational Software** for details of their superb *Drosophila Genetics* software package which includes coverage of linkage and recombination. *Drosophila* images © Newbyte Educational Software.

Drosophila and linked genes

In the example shown left, wild type alleles are dominant and are given an upper case symbol of the mutant phenotype (Cu or Eb). This notation used for *Drosophila* departs from the convention of using the dominant gene to provide the symbol. This is necessary because there are many mutant alternative phenotypes to the wild type (e.g. curled and vestigial wings). A lower case symbol of the wild type (e.g. ss for straight wing) would not indicate the mutant phenotype involved.

Drosophila melanogaster is known as a model organism. Model organisms are used to study particular biological phenomena, such as mutation. *Drosophila melanogaster* is particularly useful because it produces such a wide range of heritable mutations. Its short reproduction cycle, high offspring production, and low maintenance make it ideal for studying in the lab.

Drosophila melanogaster examples showing variations in eye and body colour. The wild type is marked with a w in the photo above.

3. Complete the linkage diagram above by adding the gametes in the ovals and offspring genotypes in the rectangles.

4. (a) List the possible genotypes in the offspring (above, left) if genes Cu and Eb had been on **separate chromosomes**:

   _____

   (b) If the female *Drosophila* had been homozygous for the dominant wild type alleles (CuCu EbEb), state:

   The genotype(s) of the F_1: _____   The phenotype(s) of the F_1: _____

5. A second pair of *Drosophila* are mated. The female genotype is Vgvg EbEb (straight wings, grey body), while the male genotype is vgvg ebeb (vestigial wings, ebony body). Assuming the genes are linked, carry out the cross and list the genotypes and phenotypes of the offspring. Note vg = vestigial (no) wings:

   _____

   _____

   _____

   The genotype(s) of the F_1: _____   The phenotype(s) of the F_1: _____

6. Explain why *Drosophila* are often used as model organisms in the study of genetics: _____

   _____

   _____

123 Recombination and Dihybrid Inheritance

Key Idea: Recombination is the exchange of alleles between homologous chromosomes as a result of crossing over. Recombination increases the genetic variation in the offspring. The alleles of parental linkage groups separate and new associations of alleles are formed in the gametes. Offspring formed from these gametes are called **recombinants** and show combinations of characteristics not seen in the parents.

In contrast to linkage, recombination increases genetic variation in the offspring. Recombination between the alleles of parental linkage groups is indicated by the appearance of non-parental types in the offspring, although not in the numbers that would be expected had the alleles been on separate chromosomes (independent assortment).

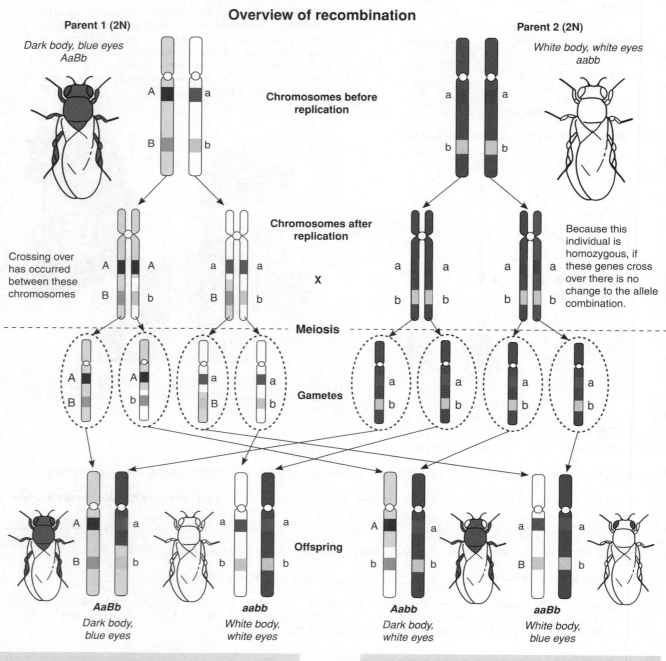

Overview of recombination

Parent 1 (2N)
Dark body, blue eyes
AaBb

Parent 2 (2N)
White body, white eyes
aabb

Chromosomes before replication

Chromosomes after replication

Crossing over has occurred between these chromosomes

Because this individual is homozygous, if these genes cross over there is no change to the allele combination.

Meiosis

Gametes

Offspring

AaBb
Dark body, blue eyes

aabb
White body, white eyes

Aabb
Dark body, white eyes

aaBb
White body, blue eyes

Non-recombinant offspring
These two offspring show allele combinations that are expected as a result of independent assortment during meiosis. Also called parental types.

Recombinant offspring
These two offspring show unexpected allele combinations. They can only arise if one of the parent's chromosomes has undergone crossing over.

1. Describe the effect of **recombination** on the inheritance of genes: _____

_____

_____

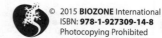 © 2015 **BIOZONE** International
ISBN: **978-1-927309-14-8**
Photocopying Prohibited

An example of recombination

In the female parent, crossing over occurs between the linked genes for wing shape and body colour

Parent	Wild type female	Mutant male
Phenotype	Straight wing Grey body	Curled wing Ebony body
Genotype	Cucu Ebeb	cucu ebeb

Linkage

Cu   Eb   cu   eb

cu   eb   cu   eb

Meiosis

Gametes from female fly (N)

Crossing over has occurred, giving four types of gametes

Gametes from male fly (N)

Only one type of gamete is produced in this case

Non-recombinant offspring   **Recombinant offspring**

The sex of the offspring is irrelevant in this case

Contact **Newbyte Educational Software** for details of their superb *Drosophila Genetics* software package which includes coverage of linkage and recombination. *Drosophila* images © Newbyte Educational Software.

The cross (left) uses the same genotypes as the previous activity but, in this case, crossing over occurs between the alleles in a linkage group in one parent. The symbology used is the same.

Recombination produces variation

If crossing over does not occur, the possible combinations in the gametes is limited. **Crossing over and recombination increase the variation in the offspring**. In humans, even without crossing over, there are approximately $(2^{23})^2$ or 70 trillion genetically different zygotes that could form for every couple. Taking crossing over and recombination into account produces at least $(4^{23})^2$ or 5000 trillion trillion genetically different zygotes for every couple.

Family members may resemble each other, but they'll never be identical (except for identical twins).

Using recombination

Analysing recombination gave geneticists a way to map the genes on a chromosome. Crossing over is less likely to occur between genes that are close together on a chromosome than between genes that are far apart. By counting the number of offspring of each phenotype, the **frequency of recombination** can be calculated. The higher the frequency of recombination between two genes, the further apart they must be on the chromosome.

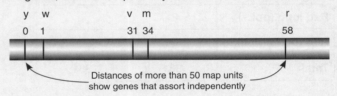

Distances of more than 50 map units show genes that assort independently

Map of the X chromosome of *Drosophila*, showing the relative distances between five different genes (in map units).

2. Complete the recombination diagram above, adding the gametes in the ovals and offspring genotypes and phenotypes in the rectangles:

3. Explain how recombination increases the amount of genetic variation in offspring: _____

_____

_____

4. Explain why it is not possible to have a recombination frequency of greater than 50% (half recombinant progeny):

_____

_____

5. A second pair of *Drosophila* are mated. The female is Cucu YY (straight wing, grey body), while the male is Cucu yy (straight wing, yellow body). Assuming recombination, perform the cross and list the offspring genotypes and phenotypes:

_____

_____

_____

124 Detecting Linkage in Dihybrid Crosses

Key Idea: Linkage between genes can be detected by observing the phenotypic ratios in the offspring.

Shortly after the rediscovery of Mendel's work early in the 20th century, it became apparent that his ratios of 9:3:3:1 for heterozygous dihybrid crosses did not always hold true.

Experiments on sweet peas by William Bateson and Reginald Punnett, and on *Drosophila* by Thomas Hunt Morgan, showed that there appeared to be some kind of coupling between genes. This coupling, which we now know to be linkage, did not follow any genetic relationship known at the time.

Sweet pea cross

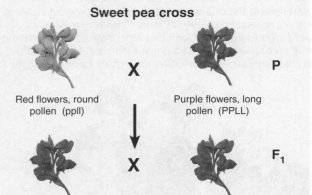

Red flowers, round pollen (ppll)   X   Purple flowers, long pollen (PPLL)   **P**

Purple flowers, long pollen (PpLl)   X   Purple flowers, long pollen (PpLl)   **F₁**

Bateson and Punnett studied sweet peas in which purple flowers (P) are dominant to red (p), and long pollen grains (L) are dominant to round (l). If these genes were unlinked, the outcome of an cross between two heterozygous sweet peas should have been a 9:3:3:1 ratio.

Table 1: Sweet pea cross results

	Observed	Expected
Purple long (P_L_)	284	
Purple round (P_ll)	21	
Red long (ppL_)	21	
Red round (ppll)	55	
Total	381	381

Morgan performed experiments to investigate linked genes in *Drosophila*. He crossed a heterozygous red-eyed normal-winged (Prpr Vgvg) fly with a homozygous purple-eyed vestigial-winged (prpr vgvg) fly. The table (below) shows the outcome of the cross.

   X

Red eyed normal winged (Prpr Vgvg)   Purple eyed vestigial winged (prpr vgvg)

Table 2: *Drosophila* cross results

Genotype	Observed	Expected	Gamete type
Prpr Vgvg	1339	710	Parental
prpr Vgvg	152		
Prpr vgvg	154		
prpr vgvg	1195		
Total	2840	2840	

1. Fill in the missing numbers in the **expected** column of **Table 1**, remembering that a 9:3:3:1 ratio is expected:

2. (a) Fill in the missing numbers in the **expected** column of **Table 2**, remembering that a 1:1:1:1 ratio is expected:

   (b) Add the gamete type (parental/recombinant) to the gamete type column in Table 2:

   (c) What type of cross did Morgan perform here?

   _____

3. (a) Use the pedigree chart below to determine if nail-patella syndrome is dominant or recessive, giving reasons for your choice:

   _____
   _____
   _____
   _____

   (b) What evidence is there that nail-patella syndrome is linked to the ABO blood group locus?

   _____
   _____
   _____

   (c) Suggest a likely reason why individual III-3 is not affected despite carrying the B allele:

   _____
   _____
   _____

Pedigree for nail-patella syndrome

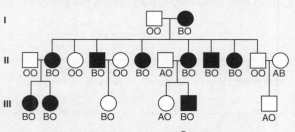

Individual with nail-patella syndome   ●♀   ■♂
Blood types   OO, BO, AO, AB

Linked genes can be detected by pedigree analysis. The diagram above shows the pedigree for the inheritance of nail-patella syndrome, which results in small, poorly developed nails and kneecaps in affected people. Other body parts such as elbows, chest, and hips can also be affected. The nail-patella syndrome gene is linked to the ABO blood group locus.

LINK
KNOW 125

© 2015 **BIOZONE** International
ISBN: **978-1-927309-14-8**
Photocopying Prohibited

125 Chi-Squared Test in Genetics

Key Idea: The chi-squared test (χ^2) can be used for testing the outcome of dihybrid crosses against an expected (predicted) Mendelian ratio.

When using the chi-squared test, the null hypothesis predicts the ratio of offspring of different phenotypes according to the expected Mendelian ratio for the cross, assuming independent assortment of alleles (no linkage). Significant departures from the predicted Mendelian ratio indicate linkage of the alleles in question. Raw counts should be used and a large sample size is required for the test to be valid.

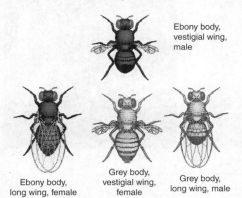

Ebony body, vestigial wing, male

Ebony body, long wing, female

Grey body, vestigial wing, female

Grey body, long wing, male

Images of *Drosophila* courtesy of **Newbyte Educational Software**: *Drosophila* Genetics Lab (www.newbyte.com)

Using χ^2 in Mendelian genetics

In a *Drosophila* genetics experiment, two individuals were crossed (the details of the cross are not relevant here). The predicted Mendelian ratios for the offspring of this cross were 1:1:1:1 for each of the four following phenotypes: grey body-long wing, grey body-vestigial wing, ebony body-long wing, ebony body-vestigial wing. The observed results of the cross were not exactly as predicted. The following numbers for each phenotype were observed in the offspring of the cross:

Observed results of the example *Drosophila* cross			
Grey body, long wing	98	Ebony body, long wing	102
Grey body, vestigial wing	88	Ebony body, vestigial wing	112

Using χ^2, the probability of this result being consistent with a 1:1:1:1 ratio could be tested. Worked example as follows:

Step 1: Calculate the expected value (E)

In this case, this is the sum of the observed values divided by the number of categories (see note below)

$$\frac{400}{4} = 100$$

Step 2: Calculate O – E

The difference between the observed and expected values is calculated as a measure of the deviation from a predicted result. Since some deviations are negative, they are all squared to give positive values. This step is usually performed as part of a tabulation (right, darker blue column).

Category	O	E	O – E	$(O - E)^2$	$\dfrac{(O - E)^2}{E}$
Grey, long wing	98	100	–2	4	0.04
Grey, vestigial wing	88	100	–12	144	1.44
Ebony, long wing	102	100	2	4	0.04
Ebony, vestigial wing	112	100	12	144	1.44

Total = 400 $\chi^2 \quad \Sigma = 2.96$

Step 3: Calculate the value of χ^2

$$\chi^2 = \sum \frac{(O - E)^2}{E}$$

Where:
O = the observed result
E = the expected result
Σ = sum of

The calculated χ^2 value is given at the bottom right of the last column in the tabulation.

Step 5a: Using the χ^2 table

On the χ^2 table (part reproduced in Table 1 below) with 3 degrees of freedom, the calculated value for χ^2 of 2.96 corresponds to a probability of between 0.2 and 0.5 (see arrow). *This means that by chance alone a χ^2 value of 2.96 could be expected between 20% and 50% of the time.*

Step 4: Calculating degrees of freedom

The probability that any particular χ^2 value could be exceeded by chance depends on the number of degrees of freedom. This is simply *one less than the total number of categories* (this is the number that could vary independently without affecting the last value). *In this case: 4–1 = 3.*

Step 5b: Using the χ^2 table

The probability of between 0.2 and 0.5 is higher than the 0.05 value which is generally regarded as significant. The null hypothesis cannot be rejected and we have no reason to believe that the observed results differ significantly from the expected (at $P = 0.05$).

Footnote: Many Mendelian crosses involve ratios other than 1:1. For these, calculation of the expected values is not simply a division of the total by the number of categories. Instead, the total must be apportioned according to the ratio. For example, for a total of 400 as above, in a predicted 9:3:3:1 ratio, the total count must be divided by 16 (9+3+3+1) and the expected values will be 225: 75: 75: 25 in each category.

Table 1: Critical values of χ^2 at different levels of probability. By convention, the critical probability for rejecting the null hypothesis (H_0) is 5%. If the test statistic is less than the tabulated critical value for $P = 0.05$ we cannot reject H_0 and the result is not significant. If the test statistic is greater than the tabulated value for $P = 0.05$ we reject H_0 in favour of the alternative hypothesis.

Degrees of freedom	Level of probability (P)									
	0.98	0.95	0.80	0.50	0.20	0.10	0.05	0.02	0.01	0.001
1	0.001	0.004	0.064	0.455	1.64	2.71	3.84	5.41	6.64	10.83
2	0.040	0.103	0.466	1.386	3.22	4.61	5.99	7.82	9.21	13.82
3	0.185	0.352	1.005	2.366	4.64	6.25	7.82	9.84	11.35	16.27
4	0.429	0.711	1.649	3.357	5.99	7.78	9.49	11.67	13.28	18.47
5	0.752	0.145	2.343	4.351	7.29	9.24	11.07	13.39	15.09	20.52

(χ^2 at row 1 col 0.50; arrow pointing down to row 3)

←———— Do not reject H_0 Reject H_0 ————→

126 Chi-Squared Exercise in Genetics

Key Idea: The following problems examine the use of the chi-squared (χ^2) test in genetics.

A worked example illustrating the use of the chi-squared test for a genetic cross is provided on the previous page.

1. In a tomato plant experiment, two heterozygous individuals were crossed (the details of the cross are not relevant here). The predicted Mendelian ratios for the offspring of this cross were **9:3:3:1** for each of the **four following phenotypes**: purple stem-jagged leaf edge, purple stem-smooth leaf edge, green stem-jagged leaf edge, green stem-smooth leaf edge.

   The observed results of the cross were not exactly as predicted.
   The numbers of offspring with each phenotype are provided below:

Observed results of the tomato plant cross			
Purple stem-jagged leaf edge	12	Green stem-jagged leaf edge	8
Purple stem-smooth leaf edge	9	Green stem-smooth leaf edge	0

   (a) State your null hypothesis for this investigation (H0): _____

   _____

   (b) State the alternative hypothesis (HA): _____

   _____

2. Use the chi-squared (χ^2) test to determine if the differences observed between the phenotypes are significant. The table of critical values of χ^2 at different P values is provided on the previous page.

   (a) Enter the observed values (number of individuals) and complete the table to calculate the χ^2 value:

Category	O	E	O — E	(O — E)^2	$\frac{(O — E)^2}{E}$
Purple stem, jagged leaf					
Purple stem, smooth leaf					
Green stem, jagged leaf					
Green stem, smooth leaf					
	Σ				Σ

   (b) Calculate χ^2 value using the equation:

   $$\chi^2 = \Sigma \ \frac{(O - E)^2}{E} \qquad \chi^2 = \ _____$$

   (c) Calculate the degrees of freedom: _____

   (d) Using the χ^2 table, state the P value corresponding to your calculated χ^2 value:

   _____

   (e) State your decision: *(circle one)*

   reject H0 / do not reject H0

3. Students carried out a pea plant experiment, where two heterozygous individuals were crossed. The predicted Mendelian ratios for the offspring were **9:3:3:1** for each of the **four following phenotypes**: round-yellow seed, round-green seed, wrinkled-yellow seed, wrinkled-green seed.

   The observed results were as follows:

Round-yellow seed	441	Wrinkled-yellow seed	143
Round-green seed	159	Wrinkled-green seed	57

   Use a separate piece of paper to complete the following:

   (a) State the null and alternative hypotheses (H0 and HA).

   (b) Calculate the χ^2 value.

   (c) Calculate the degrees of freedom and state the P value corresponding to your calculated χ^2 value.

   (d) State whether or not you reject your null hypothesis: reject H0 / do not reject H0 (circle one)

4. Comment on the whether the χ^2 values obtained above are similar. Suggest a reason for any difference:

   _____

   _____

   _____

© 2015 **BIOZONE** International
ISBN: **978-1-927309-14-8**
Photocopying Prohibited

127 Problems Involving Dihybrid Inheritance

Key Idea: For dihybrid crosses involving autosomal unlinked genes, the offspring appear in predictable ratios.

Test your understanding of dihybrid inheritance by solving problems involving the inheritance of two genes.

1. In cats, the following alleles are present for coat characteristics: black (**B**), brown (**b**), short (**L**), long (**l**), tabby (**T**), blotched tabby (**tb**). Use the information to complete the dihybrid crosses below:

(a) A black short haired (**BBLl**) male is crossed with a black long haired (**Bbll**) female. Determine the genotypic and phenotypic ratios of the offspring:

Genotype ratio: _____

_____

Phenotype ratio: _____

_____

_____

(b) A tabby, short haired male (**TtbLl**) is crossed with a blotched tabby, short haired (**tbtbLl**) female. Determine ratios of the offspring:

Genotype ratio: _____

_____

Phenotype ratio: _____

_____

_____

2. A plant with orange-striped flowers was cultivated from seeds. The plant was self-pollinated and the F_1 progeny appeared in the following ratios: 89 orange with stripes, 29 yellow with stripes, 32 orange without stripes, 9 yellow without stripes.

(a) Describe the dominance relationships of the alleles responsible for the phenotypes observed: _____

_____

_____

(b) Determine the genotype of the original plant with orange striped flowers: _____

_____

_____

3. In rabbits, spotted coat **S** is dominant to solid colour **s**, while for coat colour, black **B** is dominant to brown **b**. A brown spotted rabbit is mated with a solid black one and all the offspring are black spotted (the genes are not linked).

(a) State the genotypes:

Parent 1: _____

Parent 2: _____

Offspring: _____

(b) Use the Punnett square to show the outcome of a cross between the F_1 (the F_2):

(c) Using ratios, state the phenotypes of the F_2 generation: _____

_____

_____

_____

LINK
121 **TEST**

4. In guinea pigs, rough coat **R** is dominant over smooth coat **r** and black coat **B** is dominant over white **b**. The genes are not linked.
A homozygous rough black animal was crossed with a homozygous smooth white:

(a) State the genotype of the **F₁**: _____

(b) State the phenotype of the **F₁**: _____

(c) Use the Punnett square (top right) to show the outcome of a cross between the F₁ (the F₂):

(d) Using ratios, state the phenotypes of the F₂ generation: _____

_____

_____

(e) Use the Punnett square (right) to show the outcome of a **back cross** of the **F₁** to the rough, black parent:

(f) Using ratios, state the phenotype of the F₂ generation: _____

_____

(g) A rough black guinea pig was crossed with a rough white one produced the following offspring: 28 rough black, 31 rough white, 11 smooth black, and 10 smooth white. Determine the genotypes of the parents:

_____

5. The Himalayan colour-pointed, long-haired cat is a breed developed by crossing a pedigree (true-breeding), uniform-coloured, long-haired Persian with a pedigree colour-pointed (darker face, ears, paws, and tail) short-haired Siamese.

The genes controlling hair colouring and length are on separate chromosomes: uniform colour **U**, colour pointed **u**, short hair **S**, long hair **s**.

Persian   Siamese   Himalayan

(a) Using the symbols above, indicate the genotype of each breed below its photograph (above, right).
_____ _____ _____

(b) State the genotype of the **F₁** (Siamese X Persian): _____

(c) State the phenotype of the **F₁**: _____

(d) Use the Punnett square to show the outcome of a cross between the F₁ (the F₂):

(e) State the ratio of the F₂ that would be Himalayan: _____

(f) State whether the Himalayan would be true breeding: _____

(g) State the ratio of the F₂ that would be colour-point, short-haired cats: _____

6. A *Drosophila* male with genotype **Cucu Ebeb** (straight wing, grey body) is crossed with a female with genotype **cucu ebeb** (curled wing, ebony body). The phenotypes of the F₁ were recorded and the percentage of each type calculated. The percentages were: Straight wings, grey body 45%, curled wings, ebony body 43%, straight wings, ebony body 6%, and curled wings grey body 6%.

(a) Is there evidence of crossing over in the offspring? _____

(b) Explain your answer: _____

_____

_____

(c) Determine the genotypes of the offspring: _____

_____

*Straight wing Cucu
Grey body, Ebeb*

*Curled wing cucu
Ebony body, ebeb*

128 Gene Interactions

Key Idea: Epistatic genes interact to control the expression of a single characteristic.

Although one gene product (e.g. an enzyme) may independently produce a single phenotypic character, genes frequently interact to produce the phenotype we see. Two or more loci may interact to produce new phenotypes, or an allele at one locus may mask or modify the effect of alleles at other loci. These epistatic gene interactions result in characteristic phenotypic ratios in the offspring that are different from those expected under independent assortment.

In the example of pea seeds (see *Basic Genetic Crosses*) the alleles R and r, and Y and y act independently on seed shape and colour respectively. If the Y or y allele is present there is no effect on the phenotype produced by the R or r allele. But consider a situation where the Y or y allele works together with the R and r alleles to produce a single phenotype? A simple example of this is the comb type of chickens.

There are four comb types in chickens (right). The four phenotypes are produced by the interactions of two alleles R and P. In a cross between two individuals heterozygous for both alleles (RrPp), the phenotypic ratio is 9:3:3:1, as would be expected in a dihybrid cross involving independent assortment. However, there are many examples of gene interactions that produce different phenotypic ratios. The ratio can be diagnostic in that it can indicate the type of interaction involved.

Single comb	Pea comb	Rose comb	Walnut comb
Genotypes:	Genotypes:	Genotypes:	Genotypes:
rrpp	**rrP_**	**R_pp**	**R_P_**
rrpp	rrPp, rrPP	Rrpp, RRpp	RRPP RrPP, RrPp, RRPp

Comb photos: Marc King

In chickens, new phenotypes result from interaction between dominant alleles, as well as from the interaction between homozygous recessives.

How do genes interact?

Gene interaction usually occurs when the protein products or enzymes of several genes are all part of the same metabolic process. In the example below, enzyme A (produced from gene A) acts on a precursor substance to produce a colourless intermediate. Enzyme B (from gene B) acts on the intermediate to produce the final product. If either gene A or gene B produces a non-functional enzyme, the end product will be affected. The way gene A or B act on their substrates affects the appearance of the final product and produces different phenotypic ratios. The ratios can be used to identify the type of gene interaction, but they all come under the title of **epistasis**.

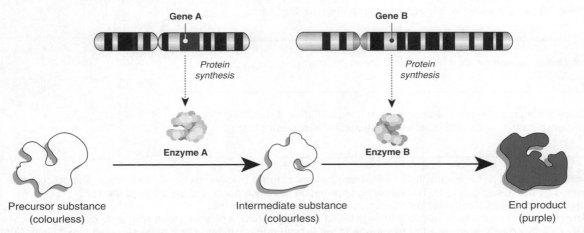

Gene A · Protein synthesis · Enzyme A · Gene B · Protein synthesis · Enzyme B

Precursor substance (colourless) → Intermediate substance (colourless) → End product (purple)

1. (a) For the example of the comb type in chickens, determine the ratios of each comb type in a heterozygous cross:

    _____

   (b) What phenotype is produced by the interaction of dominant alleles? _____

   (c) What phenotype is produced by the interaction of recessive alleles? _____

2. In the metabolic process shown above, gene A has the alleles A and a. Allele a produces a non-functional enzyme. Gene B has the alleles B and b. Allele b produces a non-functional enzyme. What is the effect on the end product if:

   (a) Gene A has the allele a and Gene B has the allele B: _____

   (b) Gene A has the allele A and Gene B has the allele b: _____

   (c) Gene A has the allele A and Gene B has the allele B: _____

   (d) Gene A has the allele a and Gene B has the allele b: _____

   (e) On a separate sheet, use a Punnett square to determine the ratio of purple to colourless from a cross AABb x AaBb:

    _____

Table of gene interactions

This table shows five common dihybrid gene interactions and a dihybrid cross with no gene interaction as a comparison. The important point to note is the change to the expected dihybrid 9:3:3:1 ratio in each case. Note that there is independent assortment at the genotypic level. Epistasis is indicated by the change in the phenotypic ratio. Collaboration is usually not considered an epistatic effect because the phenotypic ratio is unchanged, but it does fit in the broad definition of epistasis being an interaction of two or more genes to control a single phenotype.

No of offspring (out of 16)

Possible genotypes from AaBb x AaBb

Type of gene interaction	AABB 1	AABb 2	AaBB 2	AaBb 4	AAbb 1	Aabb 2	aaBB 1	aaBb 2	aabb 1	F$_1$ dihybrid ratio	Example Organism	Character
No interaction	Yellow round				Yellow wrinkled		Green round		Green wrinkled	9:3:3:1	Peas	seed colour/ coat colour
Collaboration	Walnut				Rose		Pea		Single	9:3:3:1	Chickens	Comb shape
Recessive epistasis	Black				Brown		White			9:3:4	Mice	Coat colour
Duplicate recessive epistasis	Purple				Colourless					9:7	Sweet pea flowers	Colour
Dominant epistasis	White						Yellow		Green	12:3:1	Squash	Fruit colour
Duplicate dominant epistasis	Coloured								Colour- less	15:1	Wheat	Kernel colour

3. In a species of freshwater fish, the allele G produces a green pattern on the dorsal fin when in the presence of the allele Y. A fish that is homozygous recessive for the both genes produces no green pattern to the dorsal fin.

   (a) Write the genotypes for a fish with a green patterned dorsal fin: _____

   _____

   (b) Write the genotypes for a fish with no green pattern: _____

   _____

   (c) Carry out a cross for the heterozygous genotype (GgYy). From the phenotypic ratio, what kind of epistatic interaction is occurring here?

   _____

4. In a second species of freshwater fish, the tail can be one of three colours, red, pink, or orange. The colours are controlled by the genes B and H. The following information is known about the breeding of the fish:
   i   Any orange tailed fish crossed together only produce orange tailed fish.
   ii Any red tailed fish crossed with any orange tailed fish may produce offspring with red, pink, or orange tails.
   iii Any pink tailed fish crossed with any orange tailed fish produces offspring that have either all pink tails or 50% with pink tails and 50% with orange tails.

   Use the information above and the space below to work out the type of gene interaction that is being examined here:

   The gene interaction is: _____

© 2015 **BIOZONE** International
ISBN: **978-1-927309-14-8**
Photocopying Prohibited

129 Epistasis

Key Idea: Epistatic interactions by genes that control coat colour typically produce three coat colours.

Epistatic genes often mask the effect of other genes. In this case there are typically three possible phenotypes for a dihybrid cross involving masking interactions. One example is in the genes controlling coat colour in rodents and other mammals. Skin and hair colour is the result of melanin, a pigment which may be either black/brown (eumelanin) or reddish/yellow (phaeomelanin). Melanin itself is synthesised

via several biochemical steps from the amino acid tyrosine. The control of coat colour and patterning in mammals is complex and involves at least five major interacting genes. One of these genes (gene C), controls the production of the pigment melanin, while another gene (gene B), is responsible for whether the colour is black or brown (this interaction is illustrated for mice, below). In albinism, the homozygous recessive condition, cc, blocks the expression of the other coat colours.

Mice that are homozygous recessive for the colour gene (cc) have a defective enzyme and produce no pigment. They are **albino** regardless of what other colour genes they have.

Albino (_ _ cc)

Gene C

Tyrosinase

Tyrosine

Gene **C** codes for the enzyme tyrosinase, which converts tyrosine to the dark pigment melanin. The C gene therefore controls melanin **production**.

Gene B

TYRP1

Melanin

Gene **B** encodes the tyrosinase related protein Tyrp1, which determines the level of pigment expression, producing black or brown.

Brown (bb C_)
Mice with genotype bb are brown

Black (B_ C_)
A dominant B allele produces black.

1. State how many phenotypes are possible for a dihybrid cross involving this type of epistasis:

_____

2. State which alleles must be present/absent for the following phenotypes:

Black: _____

Brown: _____

Albino: _____

3. Complete the Punnett square for the F2 (right) by entering the **genotype** and **phenotype** for each possible offspring from BbCc x BbCc. Determine the **ratio** of the phenotypes in this type of cross:

_____

_____

_____

For the following crosses between parent rats (all homozygous for the genes involved), determine the **phenotypes** and possible **genotypes** of the offspring:

4. A mating of albino with black:

_____

_____

5. A mating of brown with black:

_____

_____

Brown (bbCC)   Parent generation (true breeding)   **Albino** (BBcc)

X

Black (Bb Cc)   Inbred (mated with siblings)

Sperm

	BC	Bc	bC	bc
BC				
Bc				
bC				
bc				

Eggs

© 2015 **BIOZONE** International
ISBN: **978-1-927309-14-8**
Photocopying Prohibited

Allele combinations and coat colour

Epistatic interactions also regulate coat colour in Labrador dogs. The basic coat colour is controlled by the interaction of two genes, each with two alleles. The epistatic E gene determines if pigment will be present in the coat, and the B gene determines the pigment density (depth of colour). Dogs with genotype ee will always be yellow. As a result, three main coat colour variations are possible in Labradors: black, chocolate, and yellow. The yellow coat colour can have two possible phenotypes, giving a total of 4 phenotypes.

ee
No dark pigment in coat

E_
Dark pigment in coat

eebb
yellow coat, brown nose, lips, and eye rims

eeB_
yellow coat, black nose, lips, and eye rims

E_bb
Chocolate coat, brown nose, lips, and eye rims

E_B_
black coat, black nose, lips, and eye rims

6. State how many main phenotypes are possible for a dihybrid cross involving the genes E and B: _____

7. State which alleles must be present and absent for the following phenotypes:

Black: _____

Brown: _____

Yellow: _____

8. (a) State the phenotype and genotype of the F$_1$ in a cross between a male black and a female yellow Labrador. Both dogs are homozygous for the alleles involved:

_____

_____

Working space

(b) F$_1$ male Labradors were crossed with F$_1$ female Labradors. In the working space provided right, show this cross and state the genotype and phenotype ratios of the offspring:

_____

_____

(c) From the phenotypic ratio, what type of gene interaction is this?

_____

9. Yellow Labradors can have either a black nose, lips, and eye rims, or a brown nose, lips, and eye rims.

(a) What are the genotypes for a yellow coated dog with a black nose, lips, and eye rims:

_____

(b) What is the genotype for a yellow coated dog with a brown nose, lips, and eye rims:

_____

(c) Furthermore, yellow coated Labradors display variations of the C gene from dark (CC) to light (cc). What is the genotype of a dark yellow Labrador with a black nose, lips, and eye rims:

_____

130 Polygenes

Key Idea: Many phenotypes are affected by multiple genes. Some phenotypes (e.g. kernel colour in maize and skin colour in humans) are determined by more than one gene and show **continuous variation** in a population. The production of the skin pigment melanin in humans is controlled by at least three genes. The amount of melanin produced is directly proportional to the number of dominant alleles for either gene (from 0 to 6).

Very pale	Light	Medium light	Medium	Medium dark	Dark	Black
0	1	2	3	4	5	6

A light-skinned person

A dark-skinned person

There are seven shades skin colour ranging from very dark to very pale, with most individual being somewhat intermediate in skin colour. No dominant allele results in a lack of dark pigment (aabbcc). Full pigmentation (black) requires six dominant alleles (AABBCC).

1. Complete the Punnett square for the F$_2$ generation (below) by entering the genotypes and the number of dark alleles resulting from a cross between two individuals of intermediate skin colour. Colour-code the offspring appropriately for easy reference.

   (a) How many of the 64 possible offspring of this cross will have darker skin than their parents:

   _____

   (b) How many genotypes are possible for this type of gene interaction:

   _____

2. Explain why we see many more than seven shades of skin colour in reality:

   _____

   _____

Parental generation

X

Black (AABBCC)   Pale (aabbcc)

Medium (AaBbCc)

F$_2$ generation (AaBbCc X AaBbCc)

GAMETES	ABC	ABc	AbC	Abc	aBC	aBc	abC	abc
ABC								
ABc								
AbC								
Abc								
aBC								
aBc								
abC								
abc								

WEB

3. Discuss the differences between **continuous** and **discontinuous variation**, giving examples to illustrate your answer:

_____

_____

_____

_____

_____

4. From a sample of no less than 30 adults, collect data for one continuous variable (e.g. height, weight, shoe size, hand span). Record and tabulate your results in the space below, and then plot a frequency histogram on the grid below:

Raw data

Tally chart (frequency table)

Variable: _____

Frequency

(a) Calculate the following for your data and attach your working.

Mean: _____ **Mode:** _____ **Median:** _____

Standard deviation: _____

(b) Describe the pattern of distribution shown by the graph, giving a reason for your answer: _____

_____

(c) What is the genetic basis of this distribution? _____

(d) What is the importance of a large sample size when gathering data relating to a continuous variable? _____

_____

© 2015 **BIOZONE** International
ISBN: **978-1-927309-14-8**

131 Chapter Review

Summarise what you know about this topic under the headings and sub-headings provided. You can draw diagrams or mind maps, or write short notes to organise your thoughts. Use the images and hints to help you and refer back to the introduction to check the points covered:

Alleles and sources of variation

HINT: What are alleles? What is the source of genetic and physical variation?.

Genetic crosses

HINT: Explain monohybrid and dihybrid crosses. Linkage and recombination.

Gene interactions

HINT: Types of gene interactions. How can different interactions be detected?

REVISE

132 KEY TERMS: Did You Get It?

1. Complete the crossword:

Across

2. Offspring of parents with linked genes that do not display the parental phenotypes are called _____ offspring.

9. The specific allele combination of an organism.

10. An inheritance patten in which both alleles in the heterozygous condition contribute to the phenotype.

13. A diagram that is used to predict an outcome of a particular genetic cross (2 words: 7, 6)

15. The allele that expresses its characteristics when in both homozygous and heterozygous conditions.

16. A particular phenotypic character. Refers to the physical appearance as opposed to the mode of appearance, e.g. blue eyes rather than eye colour.

17. The position of a gene on a chromosome.

18. Possessing two alleles at a locus that are the same.

19. Possessing two different alleles at a locus.

Down

1. The physical appearance of the genotype.

3. A reduction division responsible for the production of haploid gametes or spores.

4. One of two or more forms of a particular gene.

5. Variation that falls into discrete groups.

6. Allele that expresses its characteristics only when in the homozygous condition.

7. Variation that exhibits a wide range of graduated phenotypes.

8. A diagnostic cross involving breeding with a recessive with known genotype.(2 words: 4, 5)

11. Any cross between an offspring and one of its parents (2 words: 4, 5)

12. Some genes have more than two types of alleles, such as the ABO alleles in humans. These are called _____ alleles.

14. The term to describe genes that are located on the same chromosome.

2. Use lines to match the statements in the table below to form complete sentences:

Mutations are the ultimate...	... of a gene.
Alleles are variations...	... dominant or recessive.
A person carrying two of the same alleles (one on each homologous chromosome)...	... for the gene, they are heterozygous.
If the person carries two different alleles...	... is said to be homozygous for that gene.
Alleles may be...	... expresses its trait if it is in the homozygous condition.
A dominant allele...	... source of new alleles.
A recessive allele only...	... always expresses its trait whether it is in the homozygous or the heterozygous condition.

TEST

Module 6.1.2

Patterns of Inheritance II

Key terms

adaptation
allele frequency
allopatric speciation
artificial selection
Darwin
deme
differential survival
directional selection
disruptive selection
evolution
inbreeding depression
fitness
fixation (of alleles)
founder effect
gene flow (=migration)
gene pool
genetic bottleneck
genetic diversity
genetic drift
genetic equilibrium
genotype
Hardy-Weinberg principle
mate choice
migration
mutation
natural selection
phenotype
polyploidy
population
reproductive isolating mechanism
selective breeding
species
stabilising selection
sympatric speciation

Gene pools and evolution

Learning outcomes

		Activity number
☐	1 Recall the principles of Darwin's "Theory of evolution by natural selection".	
☐	2 Understand the concept of the gene pool and explain how allele frequencies are expressed for populations. Explain the effect of mutation, gene flow (migration), natural selection, and genetic drift on the allele frequencies of populations.	134 135 145 146
☐	3 State the conditions required for genetic equilibrium in a population and explain the consequences of these conditions rarely, if ever, being satisfied.	134
☐	4 Use the Hardy-Weinberg equation to calculate the allele frequencies in populations. Analyse changes in allele frequencies for a real population.	136 137
☐	5 Explain the role of natural selection in sorting the variability within a gene pool and establishing adaptive genotypes. Distinguish between stabilising, directional, and (as required) disruptive selection.	138
☐	6 Describe and evaluate examples of selection in real populations over time. Examples include selection for beak size in Galápagos finches, selection for human birth weight, industrial melanism in peppered moths, selection for coat colour in rock pocket mice, and selection for skin colour in humans.	139-144
☐	7 Recognise genetic drift as an important process in evolution. Describe its consequences and the conditions under which it is important.	147
☐	8 Explain the genetic and evolutionary consequences of the founder effect.	148
☐	9 Explain the genetic and evolutionary consequences of genetic bottlenecks.	149

Speciation

Learning outcomes

		Activity number
☐	10 Describe and explain mechanisms of reproductive isolation, distinguishing between prezygotic and postzygotic reproductive isolating mechanisms.	150 151
☐	11 Explain allopatric speciation in terms of migration, geographic isolation, and adaptation leading to reproductive (genetic) isolation of gene pools.	133 150 152 154
☐	12 Describe and explain sympatric speciation. Discuss the role of polyploidy in instant speciation events.	153 159

Artificial selection

Learning outcomes

		Activity number
☐	13 Describe and explain the principles of artificial selection to include examples of selective breeding in plants (e.g. crops) and animals (e.g. livestock and pets).	155-159
☐	14 Describe problems with selective breeding (e.g. inbreeding depression and loss of genetic diversity) and explain the importance of maintaining a resource of genetic material (e.g. wild types) for use in selective breeding.	155-159
☐	15 Describe the ethical considerations (e.g. welfare issues) associated with the use of artificial selection, e.g. in selecting for particular traits in pets and livestock.	155-159

133 Small Flies and Giant Buttercups

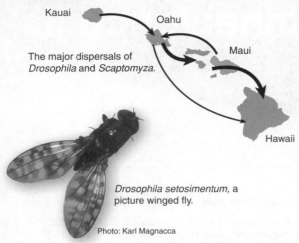

Kauai
Oahu
Maui
Hawaii

The major dispersals of *Drosophila* and *Scaptomyza*.

Drosophila setosimentum, a picture winged fly.

Photo: Karl Magnacca

Photo: Velela

Drosophilidae (commonly known as fruit flies) are a group of small flies found almost everywhere in the world. Two genera, *Drosophila* and *Scaptomyza* are found in the Hawaiian islands and between them there are more than 800 species present on a land area of just 16 500 km^2; it is one of the densest concentrations of related species found anywhere. The flies range from 1.5 mm to 20 mm in length and display a startling range of wing forms and patterns, body shapes and colours, and head and leg shapes. This diverse array of species and characteristics has made these flies the subject of much evolutionary and genetics research. Genetic analyses show that they are all related to a single species that may have arrived on the islands around 8 million years ago and diversified to exploit a range of unoccupied niches. Older species appear on the older islands and more recent species appear as one moves from the oldest to the newest islands. Such evidence points to numerous colonisation events as new islands emerged from the sea. The volcanic nature of the islands means that newly isolated environments are a frequent occurrence. For example, forested areas may become divided by lava flows, so that flies in one region diverge rapidly from flies in another just tens of metres away. One such species is *D. silvestris*. Males have a series of hairs on their forelegs, which they brush against females during courtship. Males in the northeastern part of the island have many more of these hairs than the males on the southwestern side of the island. While still the same species, the two demes are already displaying structural and behavioural isolation. Behavioural isolation is clearly an important phenomenon in drosophilid speciation. A second species, *D. heteroneura*, is closely related to *D. silvestris* and the two species live sympatrically. Although hybrid offspring are fully viable, hybridisation rarely occurs because male courtship displays are very different.

New Zealand alpine buttercups (*Ranunculus*) are some of the largest in the world and are also the product of repeated speciation events. There are 14 species of *Ranunculus* in New Zealand; more than in the whole of North and South America combined. They occupy five distinct habitats ranging from snowfields and scree slopes to bogs. Genetic studies have shown that this diversity is the result of numerous isolation events following the growth and recession of glaciers. As the glaciers retreat, alpine habitat becomes restricted and populations are isolated at the tops of mountains. This restricts gene flow and provides the environment for species divergence. When the glaciers expand again, the extent of the alpine habitat increases, allowing isolated populations to come in contact and closely related species to hybridise.

1. Explain why so many drosophilidae are present in Hawaii: _____

_____

_____

_____

2. Explain why these flies are of interest: _____

_____

_____

3. Describe the relationship between the age of the islands and the age of the fly species: _____

_____

_____

_____

4. Explain why New Zealand has so many alpine buttercups: _____

_____

_____

_____

_____

_____

_____

LINK
COMP 152

© 2015 **BIOZONE** International
ISBN: **978-1-927309-14-8**

134 Gene Pools and Evolution

Key Idea: The proportions of alleles in a gene pool can be altered by the processes that increase or decrease variation. This activity portrays two populations of a beetle species. Each beetle is a 'carrier' of genetic information, represented by the alleles (A and a) for a gene that controls colour and has a dominant/recessive inheritance pattern. There are normally two phenotypes: black and pale. Mutations may create new alleles. Some of the **microevolutionary processes** (natural selection, genetic drift, gene flow, and mutation) that affect the genetic composition (**allele frequencies**) of gene pools are shown below. Simulate the effect of these using the *Gene Pool Exercise*.

Immigration: Populations can gain alleles when they are introduced from other gene pools. Immigration is one aspect of gene flow.

Mutations: Spontaneous mutations can create new alleles. Mutation is very important to evolution, because it is the original source of genetic variation that provides new material for natural selection.

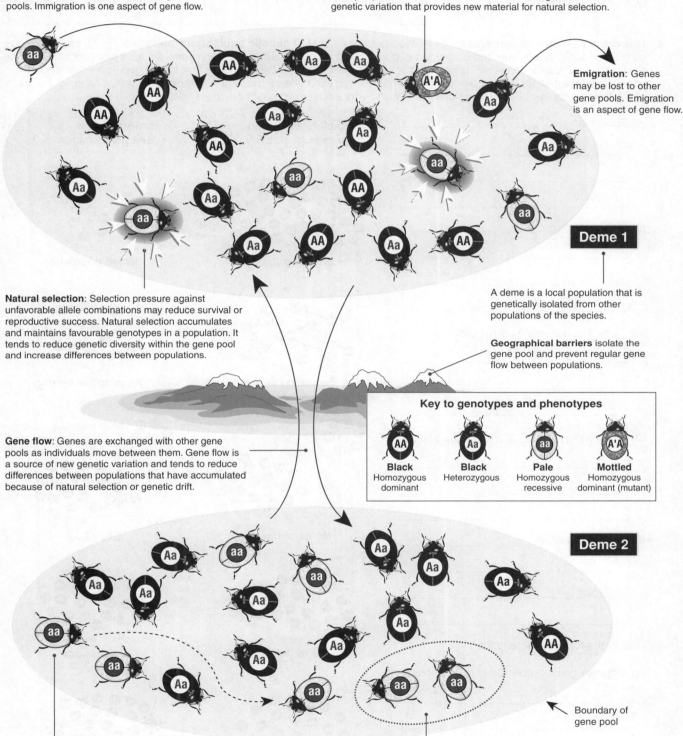

Emigration: Genes may be lost to other gene pools. Emigration is an aspect of gene flow.

Deme 1

A deme is a local population that is genetically isolated from other populations of the species.

Natural selection: Selection pressure against unfavorable allele combinations may reduce survival or reproductive success. Natural selection accumulates and maintains favourable genotypes in a population. It tends to reduce genetic diversity within the gene pool and increase differences between populations.

Geographical barriers isolate the gene pool and prevent regular gene flow between populations.

Gene flow: Genes are exchanged with other gene pools as individuals move between them. Gene flow is a source of new genetic variation and tends to reduce differences between populations that have accumulated because of natural selection or genetic drift.

Key to genotypes and phenotypes

AA — **Black** Homozygous dominant

Aa — **Black** Heterozygous

aa — **Pale** Homozygous recessive

A'A — **Mottled** Homozygous dominant (mutant)

Deme 2

Boundary of gene pool

Mate choice (non-random mating): Individuals may not select their mate randomly and may seek out particular phenotypes, increasing the frequency of the associated alleles in the population.

Genetic drift: Chance events cause the allele frequencies of small populations to 'drift' (change) randomly from generation to generation. Genetic drift has a relatively greater effect on the genetics of small populations and can be important in their evolution. Small populations may occur as a result of the **founder effect** (where a small number of individuals colonise a new area) or **genetic bottlenecks** (where the population size is dramatically reduced by a catastrophic event) .

LINK **145**   LINK **135**   WEB **134**   **DATA**

1. For each of the two demes shown on the previous page (treating the mutant in deme 1 as a AA):

   (a) Count up the numbers of **allele types** (**A** and **a**).

   (b) Count up the numbers of **allele combinations** (**AA, Aa, aa**).

2. Calculate the frequencies as percentages (%) for the allele types and combinations:

Deme 1		Number counted	%	Deme 2		Number counted	%
Allele types	A			Allele types	A		
	a				a		
Allele combinations	AA			Allele combinations	AA		
	Aa				Aa		
	aa				aa		

3. One of the fundamental concepts for population genetics is that of **genetic equilibrium**, stated as: *"For a very large, randomly mating population, the proportion of dominant to recessive alleles remains constant from one generation to the next"*. If a gene pool is to remain unchanged, it must satisfy all of the criteria below that favour gene pool stability. Few populations meet all (or any) of these criteria and their genetic makeup must therefore by continually changing. For each of the five factors (a-e) below, state briefly **how** and **why** each would affect the allele frequency in a gene pool:

   (a) Population size: _____

   _____

   _____

   (b) Mate selection: _____

   _____

   _____

   (c) Gene flow between populations:

   _____

   _____

   _____

   (d) Mutations: _____

   _____

   _____

   _____

   (e) Natural selection: _____

   _____

   _____

   _____

4. Identify the factors that tend to:

   (a) Increase genetic variation in populations:

   _____

   _____

   (b) Decrease genetic variation in populations:

   _____

   _____

Factors favouring gene pool stability	Factors favouring gene pool change

Large population — Small population

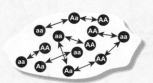

Random mating — Assortative mating

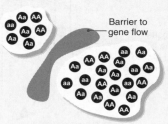
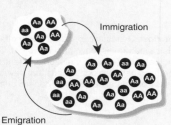

No gene flow — Gene flow

Barrier to gene flow

Immigration

Emigration

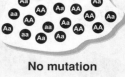

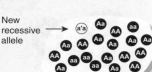

No mutation — Mutations

New recessive allele

No natural selection — Natural selection

© 2015 **BIOZONE** International
ISBN: **978-1-927309-14-8**
Photocopying Prohibited

135 Changes in a Gene Pool

Key Idea: Natural selection and migration can alter the allele frequencies in gene pools.

The diagram below shows an hypothetical population of beetles undergoing changes as it is subjected to two 'events'. The three phases represent a progression in time (i.e. the same gene pool, undergoing change). The beetles have two phenotypes (black and pale) determined by the amount of pigment deposited in the cuticle. The gene controlling this character is represented by two alleles **A** and **a**. Your task is to analyse the gene pool as it undergoes changes.

1. For each phase in the gene pool below fill in the tables provided as follows; (some have been done for you):

   (a) Count the number of A and a alleles separately. Enter the count into the top row of the table (left hand columns).
   (b) Count the number of each type of allele combination (AA, Aa and aa) in the gene pool. Enter the count into the top row of the table (right hand columns).
   (c) For each of the above, work out the frequencies as percentages (bottom row of table):

$$\text{Allele frequency} = \text{No. counted alleles} \div \text{Total no. of alleles} \times 100$$

Phase 1: Initial gene pool

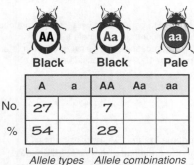

Black (AA) · Black (Aa) · Pale (aa)

	A	a	AA	Aa	aa
No.	27		7		
%	54		28		

Allele types — Allele combinations

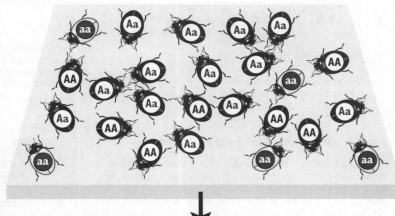

Two pale individuals died. Their alleles are removed from the gene pool.

Phase 2: Natural selection

In the same gene pool at a later time there was a change in the allele frequencies. This was due to the loss of certain allele combinations due to natural selection. Some of those with a genotype of aa were eliminated (poor fitness).

These individuals (surrounded by small white arrows) are not counted for allele frequencies; they are dead!

	A	a	AA	Aa	aa
No.					
%					

This individual is entering the population and will add its alleles to the gene pool.

This individual is leaving the population, removing its alleles from the gene pool.

Phase 3: Immigration and emigration

This particular kind of beetle exhibits wandering behaviour. The allele frequencies change again due to the introduction and departure of individual beetles, each carrying certain allele combinations.

Individuals coming into the gene pool (AA) are counted for allele frequencies, but those leaving (aa) are not.

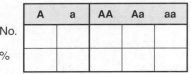

	A	a	AA	Aa	aa
No.					
%					

LINK 145 · LINK 134 · WEB 135 **DATA**

136 Hardy-Weinberg Calculations

Key Idea: The Hardy-Weinberg equation is a mathematical model used to calculate allele and genotype frequencies in populations.

The Hardy-Weinberg equation provides a simple mathematical model of genetic equilibrium in a gene pool, but its main application in population genetics is in calculating allele and genotype frequencies in populations, particularly as a means of studying changes and measuring their rate.

Punnett square

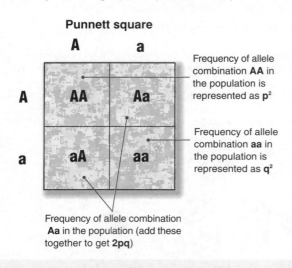

Frequency of allele combination **AA** in the population is represented as p^2

Frequency of allele combination **aa** in the population is represented as q^2

Frequency of allele combination **Aa** in the population (add these together to get **2pq**)

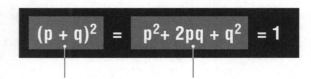

$$(p + q)^2 = p^2 + 2pq + q^2 = 1$$

Frequency of allele types

p = Frequency of allele A
q = Frequency of allele a

Frequency of allele combinations

p^2 = Frequency of AA (homozygous dominant)
2pq = Frequency of Aa (heterozygous)
q^2 = Frequency of aa (homozygous recessive)

The Hardy-Weinberg equation is applied to populations with a simple genetic situation: dominant and recessive alleles controlling a single trait. The frequency of all of the dominant (A) and recessive alleles (a) equals the total genetic complement, and adds up to 1 or 100% of the alleles present (i.e. p + q = 1).

How To solve Hardy-Weinberg problems

In most populations, the frequency of two alleles of interest is calculated from the proportion of homozygous recessives (q^2), as this is the only genotype identifiable directly from its phenotype. If only the dominant phenotype is known, q^2 may be calculated (1 – the frequency of the dominant phenotype). The following steps outline the procedure for solving a Hardy-Weinberg problem:

Remember that all calculations must be carried out using proportions, NOT PERCENTAGES!

1. Examine the question to determine what piece of information you have been given about the population. In most cases, this is the percentage or frequency of the homozygous recessive phenotype q^2, or the dominant phenotype p^2 + 2pq (see note above).

2. The first objective is to find out the value of p or q, If this is achieved, then every other value in the equation can be determined by simple calculation.

3. Take the square root of q^2 to find q.

4. Determine p by subtracting q from 1 (i.e. p = 1 – q).

5. Determine p^2 by multiplying p by itself (i.e. p^2 = p x p).

6. Determine 2pq by multiplying p times q times 2.

7. Check that your calculations are correct by adding up the values for p^2 + q^2 + 2pq (the sum should equal 1 or 100%).

Worked example

Among white-skinned people in the USA, approximately 70% of people can taste the chemical phenylthiocarbamide (PTC) (the dominant phenotype), while 30% are non-tasters (the recessive phenotype).

Determine the frequency of:	*Answers*
(a) Homozygous recessive phenotype (q^2).	30% - provided
(b) The dominant allele (**p**).	45.2%
(c) Homozygous tasters (p^2).	20.5%
(d) Heterozygous tasters (**2pq**).	49.5%

Data: The frequency of the dominant phenotype (70% tasters) and recessive phenotype (30% non-tasters) are provided.

Working:

Recessive phenotype: q^2 = 30%

use 0.30 for calculation

therefore: q = 0.5477

square root of 0.30

therefore: p = 0.4523

1 – q = p
1 – 0.5477 = 0.4523

Use p and q in the equation (top) to solve any unknown:

Homozygous dominant p^2 = 0.2046

(p x p = 0.4523 x 0.4523)

Heterozygous: **2pq** = 0.4953

---

1. A population of hamsters has a gene consisting of 90% M alleles (black) and 10% m alleles (grey). Mating is random.

   Data: Frequency of recessive allele (10% m) and dominant allele (90% M).

   Determine the proportion of offspring that will be black and the proportion that will be grey (show your working):

   _____

   _____

Recessive allele:	q =	
Dominant allele:	p =	
Recessive phenotype:	q^2 =	
Homozygous dominant:	p^2 =	
Heterozygous:	2pq =	

2. You are working with pea plants and found 36 plants out of 400 were dwarf.
   Data: Frequency of recessive phenotype (36 out of 400 = 9%)

   (a) Calculate the frequency of the tall gene: _____

   (b) Determine the number of heterozygous pea plants:

   _____

   _____

Recessive allele:	q =	
Dominant allele:	p =	
Recessive phenotype:	q² =	
Homozygous dominant:	p² =	
Heterozygous:	2pq =	

3. In humans, the ability to taste the chemical phenylthiocarbamide (PTC) is inherited as a simple dominant characteristic. Suppose you found out that 360 out of 1000 college students could not taste the chemical.
   Data: Frequency of recessive phenotype (360 out of 1000).

   (a) State the frequency of the gene for tasting PTC:

   _____

   (b) Determine the number of heterozygous students in this population:

   _____

Recessive allele:	q =	
Dominant allele:	p =	
Recessive phenotype:	q² =	
Homozygous dominant:	p² =	
Heterozygous:	2pq =	

4. A type of deformity appears in 4% of a large herd of cattle. Assume the deformity was caused by a recessive gene.
   Data: Frequency of recessive phenotype (4% deformity).

   (a) Calculate the percentage of the herd that are carriers of the gene:

   _____

   (b) Determine the frequency of the dominant gene in this case:

   _____

Recessive allele:	q =	
Dominant allele:	p =	
Recessive phenotype:	q² =	
Homozygous dominant:	p² =	
Heterozygous:	2pq =	

5. Assume you placed 50 pure bred black guinea pigs (dominant allele) with 50 albino guinea pigs (recessive allele) and allowed the population to attain genetic equilibrium (several generations have passed).
   Data: Frequency of recessive allele (50%) and dominant allele (50%).

   Determine the proportion (%) of the population that becomes white:

   _____

Recessive allele:	q =	
Dominant allele:	p =	
Recessive phenotype:	q² =	
Homozygous dominant:	p² =	
Heterozygous:	2pq =	

6. It is known that 64% of a large population exhibit the recessive trait of a characteristic controlled by two alleles (one is dominant over the other).
   Data: Frequency of recessive phenotype (64%). Determine the following:

   (a) The frequency of the recessive allele: _____

   (b) The percentage that are heterozygous for this trait: _____

   (c) The percentage that exhibit the dominant trait: _____

   (d) The percentage that are homozygous for the dominant trait: _____

   (e) The percentage that has one or more recessive alleles: _____

7. Albinism is recessive to normal pigmentation in humans. The frequency of the albino allele was 10% in a population.
   Data: Frequency of recessive allele (10% albino allele).

   Determine the proportion of people that you would expect to be albino:

   _____

   _____

Recessive allele:	q =	
Dominant allele:	p =	
Recessive phenotype:	q² =	
Homozygous dominant:	p² =	
Heterozygous:	2pq =	

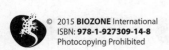

137 Analysis of a Squirrel Gene Pool

Key Idea: Allele frequencies for real populations can be calculated using the Hardy-Weinberg equation. Analysis of those allele frequencies can show how the population's gene pool changes over time.

In Olney, Illinois, there is a unique population of albino (white) and grey squirrels. Between 1977 and 1990, students at Olney Central College carried out a study of this population. They recorded the frequency of grey and albino squirrels. The albinos displayed a mutant allele expressed as an albino phenotype only in the homozygous recessive condition. The data they collected are provided in the table below. Using the **Hardy-Weinberg equation**, it was possible to estimate the frequency of the normal 'wild' allele (G) providing grey fur colouring, and the frequency of the mutant albino allele (g) producing white squirrels when homozygous.

Thanks to **Dr. John Stencel**, Olney Central College, Olney, Illinois, US, for providing the data for this exercise.

Grey squirrel, usual colour form

Albino form of grey squirrel

Population of grey and white squirrels in Olney, Illinois (1977-1990)

Year	Grey	White	Total	GG	Gg	gg	Freq. of g	Freq. of G
1977	602	182	784	26.85	49.93	23.21	48.18	51.82
1978	511	172	683	24.82	50.00	25.18	50.18	49.82
1979	482	134	616	28.47	49.77	21.75	46.64	53.36
1980	489	133	622	28.90	49.72	21.38	46.24	53.76
1981	536	163	699	26.74	49.94	23.32	48.29	51.71
1982	618	151	769	31.01	49.35	19.64	44.31	55.69
1983	419	141	560	24.82	50.00	25.18	50.18	49.82
1984	378	106	484	28.30	49.79	21.90	46.80	53.20
1985	448	125	573	28.40	49.78	21.82	46.71	53.29
1986	536	155	691	27.71	49.86	22.43	47.36	52.64
1987	No data collected this year							
1988	652	122	774	36.36	47.88	15.76	39.70	60.30
1989	552	146	698	29.45	49.64	20.92	45.74	54.26
1990	603	111	714	36.69	47.76	15.55	39.43	60.57

1. **Graph population changes**: Use the data in the first 3 columns of the table above to plot a line graph. This will show changes in the phenotypes: numbers of grey and white (albino) squirrels, as well as changes in the total population. Plot: **grey**, **white**, and **total** for each year:

(a) Determine by how much (as a %) total population numbers have fluctuated over the sampling period:

_____

(b) Describe the overall trend in total population numbers and any pattern that may exist:

_____
_____
_____
_____
_____
_____
_____

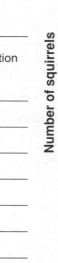
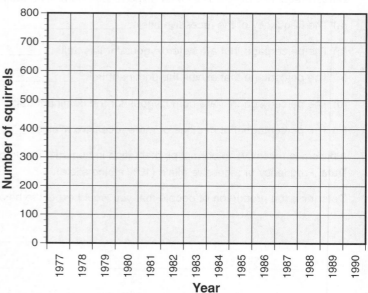

Number of squirrels / Year

2. Graph genotype changes: Use the data in the genotype columns of the table on the opposite page to plot a line graph. This will show changes in the allele combinations (**GG, Gg, gg**). Plot: **GG, Gg,** and **gg** for each year:

Describe the overall trend in the frequency of:

(a) Homozygous dominant (**GG**) genotype:

_____

_____

(b) Heterozygous (**Gg**) genotype:

_____

_____

(c) Homozygous recessive (**gg**) genotype:

_____

_____

_____

Graph: Y-axis labelled "Percentage frequency of genotype" from 0 to 60 in increments of 10. X-axis labelled "Year" from 1977 to 1990.

3. Graph allele changes: Use the data in the last two columns of the table on the previous page to plot a line graph. This will show changes in the allele frequencies for each of the dominant (**G**) and recessive (**g**) alleles. Plot: the frequency of **G** and the frequency of **g**:

(a) Describe the overall trend in the frequency of the dominant allele (**G**):

_____

_____

_____

(b) Describe the overall trend in the frequency of the recessive allele (**g**):

_____

_____

_____

_____

_____

_____

Graph: Y-axis labelled "Percentage frequency of allele" from 0 to 70 in increments of 10. X-axis labelled "Year" from 1977 to 1990.

4. (a) State which of the three graphs best indicates that a significant change may be taking place in the gene pool of this population of squirrels:

_____

(b) Give a reason for your answer: _____

_____

_____

5. Describe a possible cause of the changes in allele frequencies over the sampling period: _____

_____

_____

_____

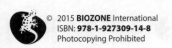

138 Natural Selection

Key Idea: Natural selection acts on phenotypes and results in the differential survival of some genotypes over others. It is an important cause of change in gene pools.

Natural selection operates on the phenotypes of individuals, produced by their particular combinations of alleles. It results in the differential survival of some genotypes over others. As a result, organisms with phenotypes most suited to the prevailing environment are more likely to survive and breed than those with less suited phenotypes. Favourable phenotypes

will become relatively more numerous than unfavourable phenotypes. Over time, natural selection may lead to a permanent change in the genetic makeup of a population. Natural selection is always linked to phenotypic suitability in the prevailing environment so it is a dynamic process. It may favour existing phenotypes or shift the phenotypic median, as is shown in the diagrams below. The top row of diagrams below represents the population phenotypic spread before selection, and the bottom row the spread afterwards.

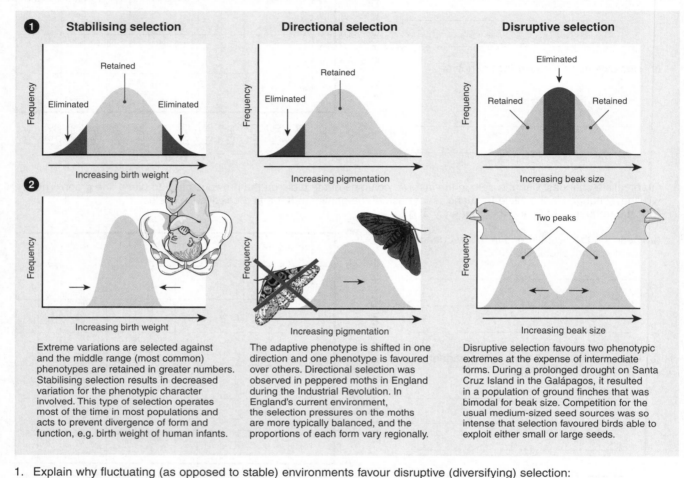

① Stabilising selection

Directional selection

Disruptive selection

Extreme variations are selected against and the middle range (most common) phenotypes are retained in greater numbers. Stabilising selection results in decreased variation for the phenotypic character involved. This type of selection operates most of the time in most populations and acts to prevent divergence of form and function, e.g. birth weight of human infants.

The adaptive phenotype is shifted in one direction and one phenotype is favoured over others. Directional selection was observed in peppered moths in England during the Industrial Revolution. In England's current environment, the selection pressures on the moths are more typically balanced, and the proportions of each form vary regionally.

Disruptive selection favours two phenotypic extremes at the expense of intermediate forms. During a prolonged drought on Santa Cruz Island in the Galápagos, it resulted in a population of ground finches that was bimodal for beak size. Competition for the usual medium-sized seed sources was so intense that selection favoured birds able to exploit either small or large seeds.

1. Explain why fluctuating (as opposed to stable) environments favour disruptive (diversifying) selection:

_____

_____

_____

2. Disruptive selection can be important in the formation of new species:

(a) Describe the evidence from the ground finches on Santa Cruz Island that provides support for this statement:

_____

_____

(b) The ground finches on Santa Cruz Island are one interbreeding population with a strongly bimodal distribution for the phenotypic character beak size. Suggest what conditions could lead to the two phenotypic extremes diverging further:

_____

_____

(c) Predict the consequences of the end of the drought and an increased abundance of medium size seeds as food:

_____

WEB LINK LINK LINK LINK

138 139 140 141 142

© 2015 **BIOZONE** International
ISBN: **978-1-927309-14-8**
Photocopying Prohibited

139 Directional Selection in Darwin's Finches

Key Idea: The effect of directional selection on a population can be verified by making measurements of phenotypic traits. Natural selection acts on the phenotypes of a population. Individuals with phenotypes that increase their fitness produce more offspring, increasing the proportion of the genes corresponding to that phenotype in the next generation. Many population studies have shown natural selection can cause phenotypic changes in a population relatively quickly.

The finches on the Galápagos island (Darwin's finches) are famous in that they are commonly used as examples of how evolution produces new species. In this activity you will analyse data from the measurement of beaks depths of the medium ground finch (*Geospiza fortis*) on the island of Daphne Major near the centre of the Galápagos Islands. The measurements were taken in 1976 before a major drought hit the island and in 1978 after the drought (survivors and survivors' offspring).

Beak depth / mm	No. 1976 birds	No. 1978 survivors	Beak depth of offspring / mm	Number of birds
7.30-7.79	1	0	7.30-7.79	2
7.80-8.29	12	1	7.80-8.29	2
8.30-8.79	30	3	8.30-8.79	5
8.80-9.29	47	3	8.80-9.29	21
9.30-9.79	45	6	9.30-9.79	34
9.80-10.29	40	9	9.80-10.29	37
10.30-10.79	25	10	10.30-10.79	19
10.80-11.29	3	1	10-80-11.29	15
11.30+	0	0	11.30+	2

1. Use the data above to draw two separate sets of histograms:

   (a) On the left hand grid draw side-by-side histograms for the number of 1976 birds per beak depth and the number of 1978 survivors per beak depth.

   (b) On the right hand grid draw a histogram of the beak depths of the offspring of the 1978 survivors.

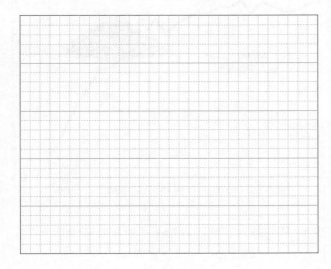

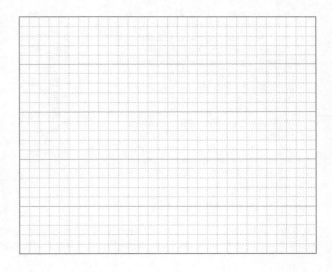

2. (a) Mark the approximate mean beak depth on the graphs of the 1976 beak depths and the 1978 offspring.

   (b) How much has the average moved from 1976 to 1978? _____

   (c) Is beak depth heritable? What does this mean for the process of natural selection in the finches?

   _____

   _____

3. The 1976 drought resulted in plants dying back and not producing seed. Based on the graphs, what can you say about competition between the birds for the remaining seeds, i.e. in what order were the seeds probably used up?

   _____

   _____

   _____

LINK 141   LINK 140   WEB 139   DATA

140 Directional Selection in Moths

Key Idea: Directional selection pressures on the peppered moth during the Industrial Revolution shifted the common phenotype from the grey form to the melanic (dark) form. Natural selection may act on the frequencies of phenotypes (and hence genotypes) in populations in one of three different ways (through stabilising, directional, or disruptive selection).

Colour change in the **peppered moth** (*Biston betularia*) during the Industrial Revolution is often used to show **directional selection** in a polymorphic population (polymorphic means having two or more forms). Intensive coal burning during this time caused trees to become dark with soot, and the dark form (morph) of peppered moth became dominant.

The gene controlling colour in the peppered moth, is located on a single locus. The allele for the melanic (dark) form (**M**) is dominant over the allele for the grey (light) form (**m**).

Olaf Leillinger

Melanic form
Genotype: MM or Mm

Olaf Leillinger

Grey form
Genotype: mm

The peppered moth, *Biston betularia*, has two forms: a grey mottled form, and a dark melanic form. During the Industrial Revolution, the relative abundance of the two forms changed to favour the dark form. The change was thought to be the result of selective predation by birds. It was proposed that the grey form was more visible to birds in industrial areas where the trees were dark. As a result, birds preyed upon them more often, resulting in higher numbers of the dark form surviving.

Museum collections of the peppered moth over the last 150 years show a marked change in the frequency of the melanic form (above right). Moths collected in 1850, prior to the major onset of the Industrial Revolution in England, were mostly the grey form (above left). Fifty years later the frequency of the darker melanic forms had increased.

In the 1940s and 1950s, coal burning was still at intense levels around the industrial centres of Manchester and Liverpool. During this time, the melanic form of the moth was still very dominant. In the rural areas further south and west of these industrial centres, the occurrence of the grey form increased dramatically. With the decline of coal burning factories and the introduction of the Clean Air Act in cities, air quality improved between 1960 and 1980. Sulfur dioxide and smoke levels dropped to a fraction of their previous levels. This coincided with a sharp fall in the relative numbers of melanic moths (right).

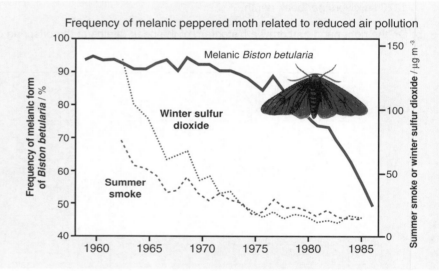

Frequency of melanic peppered moth related to reduced air pollution

1. The populations of peppered moth in England have undergone changes in the frequency of an obvious phenotypic character over the last 150 years. What is the phenotypic character?

_____

2. Describe how the selection pressure on the grey form has changed with change in environment over the last 150 years:

_____

_____

_____

3. Describe the relationship between allele frequency and phenotype frequency: _____

_____

_____

4. The level of pollution dropped around Manchester and Liverpool between 1960 and 1985. How did the frequency of the darker melanic form change during this period?

_____

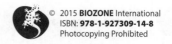
© 2015 **BIOZONE** International
ISBN: **978-1-927309-14-8**
Photocopying Prohibited

141 Disruptive Selection in Darwin's Finches

Key Idea: Disruptive selection in the finch *Geospiza fortis* produces a bimodal distribution for beak size.

The Galápagos Islands, 970 km west of Ecuador, are home to the finch species *Geospiza fortis*. A study during a prolonged drought on Santa Cruz Island showed how **disruptive selection** can change the distribution of genotypes in a population. During the drought, large and small seeds were more abundant than the preferred intermediate seed size.

Beak sizes of *G. fortis* were measured over a three year period (2004-2006), at the start and end of each year. At the start of the year, individuals were captured, banded, and their beaks were measured.

The presence or absence of banded individuals was recorded at the end of the year when the birds were recaptured. Recaptured individuals had their beaks measured.

The proportion of banded individuals in the population at the end of the year gave a measure of fitness. Absent individuals were presumed dead (fitness = 0).

Fitness related to beak size showed a bimodal distribution (left) typical of disruptive selection.

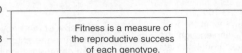
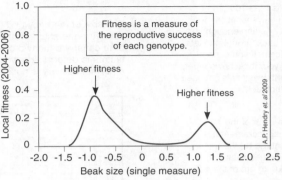

*Fitness showed a **bimodal distribution** (arrowed) being highest for smaller and larger beak sizes.*

Measurements of the beak length, width, and depth were combined into one **single measure**.

Beak size pairing in *Geospiza fortis*

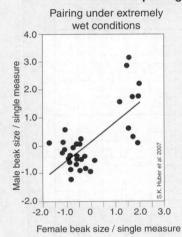
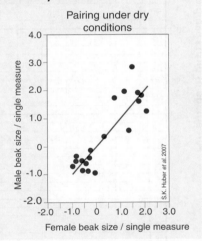

Large beak *G. fortis*

Small beak *G. fortis*

A 2007 study found that breeding pairs of birds had similar beak sizes. Male and females with small beaks tended to breed together, and males and females with large beaks tended to breed together. Mate selection maintained the biomodal distribution in the population during extremely wet conditions. If beak size wasn't a factor in mate selection, the beak size would even out.

1. (a) How did the drought affect seed size on Santa Cruz Island? _____

(b) How did the change in seed size during the drought create a selection pressure for changes in beak size?

2. How does beak size relate to fitness (differential reproductive success) in *G. fortis*? _____

3. (a) Is mate selection in *G. fortis* random / non-random? (delete one)

(b) Give reasons for your answer: _____

142 Selection for Human Birth Weight

Key Idea: Stabilising selection operates to keep human birth weight within relatively narrow constraints.

Selection pressures operate on populations in such a way as to reduce mortality. In a study of human birth weights it is possible to observe the effect of selection pressures operating to constrain human birth weight within certain limits. This is a good example of **stabilising selection**. This activity explores the selection pressures acting on the birth weight of human babies. Carry out the steps below:

Step 1: Collect the birth weights from 100 birth notices from your local newspaper (or 50 if you are having difficulty getting enough; this should involve looking back through the last 2-3 weeks of birth notices). If you cannot obtain birth weights in your local newspaper, a set of 100 sample birth weights is provided in the Model Answers booklet.

Step 2: Group the weights into each of the 12 weight classes (of 0.5 kg increments). Determine what percentage (of the total sample) fall into each weight class (e.g. 17 babies weigh 2.5-3.0 kg out of the 100 sampled = 17%)

Step 3: Graph these in the form of a histogram for the 12 weight classes (use the graphing grid provided right). Be sure to use the scale provided on the left vertical (y) axis.

Step 4: Create a second graph by plotting percentage mortality of newborn babies in relation to their birth weight. Use the scale on the right y axis and data provided (below).

Step 5: Draw a line of 'best fit' through these points.

Mortality of newborn babies related to birth weight

Weight / kg	Mortality / %
1.0	80
1.5	30
2.0	12
2.5	4
3.0	3
3.5	2
4.0	3
4.5	7
5.0	15

Source: Biology: The Unity & Diversity of Life (4th ed), by Starr and Taggart

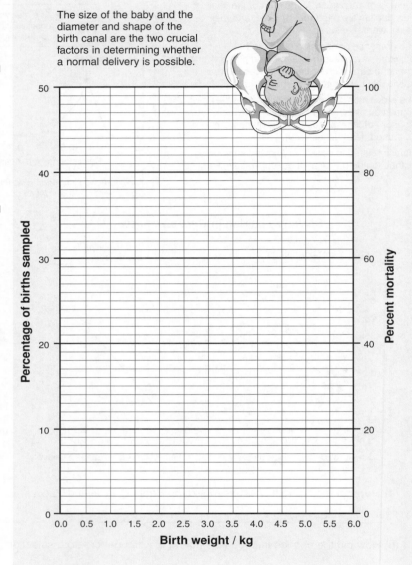

The size of the baby and the diameter and shape of the birth canal are the two crucial factors in determining whether a normal delivery is possible.

1. Describe the shape of the histogram for birth weights: _____

2. What is the optimum birth weight in terms of the lowest newborn mortality? _____

3. Describe the relationship between newborn mortality and birth weight: _____

   _____

4. Describe the selection pressures that are operating to control the range of birth weight: _____

   _____

   _____

5. How might have modern medical intervention during pregnancy and childbirth altered these selection pressures?

   _____

© 2015 **BIOZONE** International
ISBN: **978-1-927309-14-8**
Photocopying Prohibited

143 Natural Selection in Pocket Mice

Key Idea: The need to blend into their surroundings to avoid predation is an important selection pressure acting on the coat colour of rock pocket mice.

Rock pocket mice are found in the deserts of southwestern United States and northern Mexico. They are nocturnal, foraging at night for seeds, while avoiding owls (their main predator). During the day they shelter from the desert heat in their burrows. The coat colour of the mice varies from light brown to very dark brown. Throughout the desert environment in which the mice live there are outcrops of dark volcanic rock. The presence of these outcrops and the mice that live on them present an excellent study in directional selection.

▶ The coat colour of the Arizona rock pocket mice is controlled by the Mc1r gene (a gene that in mammals is commonly associated with the production of the pigment melanin).

There are variations for the gene that controls coat colour. These variations are called alleles. Homozygous dominant (**DD**) and heterozygous mice (**Dd**) have dark coats, while homozygous recessive mice (**dd**) have light coats. Coat colour of mice in New Mexico is not related to the Mc1r gene.

▶ 107 rock pocket mice from 14 sites were collected and their coat colour and the rock colour they were found on were recorded by measuring the percentage of light reflected from their coat (low percentage reflectance equals a dark coat). The data is presented right:

Site	Rock type (V volcanic)	Percent reflectance / %	
		Mice coat	Rock
KNZ	V	4	10.5
ARM	V	4	9
CAR	V	4	10
MEX	V	5	10.5
TUM	V	5	27
PIN	V	5.5	11
AFT		6	30
AVR		6.5	26
WHT		8	42
BLK	V	8.5	15
FRA		9	39
TIN		9	39
TUL		9.5	25
POR		12	34.5

1. (a) What are the genotypes of the dark coloured mice? _____

   (b) What is the genotype of the light coloured mice? _____

2. Using the data in the table above and the grids below and on the next page, draw column graphs of the percent reflectance of the mice coats and the rocks at each of the 14 collection sites.

WEB

143 DATA

3. (a) What do you notice about the reflectance of the rock pocket mice coat colour and the reflectance of the rocks they were found on?

_____

_____

(b) Suggest a cause for the pattern in 3(a). How do the phenotypes of the mice affect where the mice live?

_____

_____

_____

_____

(c) What are two exceptions to the pattern you have noticed in 3(a)? _____

_____

_____

_____

_____

(d) How might these exceptions have occurred? _____

_____

_____

_____

4. The rock pocket mice populations in Arizona use a different genetic mechanism to control coat colour than the New Mexico populations. What does this tell you about the evolution of the genetic mechanism for coat colour?

_____

_____

_____

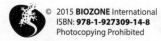
© 2015 **BIOZONE** International
ISBN: **978-1-927309-14-8**

144 Selection for Skin Colour in Humans

Key Idea: Skin colour is an evolutionary response to the need to synthesise vitamin D which requires sunlight, and to conserve folate which breaks down in sunlight.

Pigmented skin of varying tones is a feature of humans that evolved after early humans lost the majority of their body hair. However, the distribution of skin colour globally is not random; people native to equatorial regions have darker skin tones than people from higher latitudes. For many years, biologists postulated that this was because darker skins had evolved to protect against skin cancer. The problem with this explanation was that skin cancer is not tied to evolutionary fitness because it affects post-reproductive individuals and cannot therefore provide a mechanism for selection. More complex analyses of the physiological and epidemiological evidence has shown a more complex picture in which selection pressures on skin colour are finely balanced to produce a skin tone that regulates the effects of the sun's ultraviolet radiation on the nutrients vitamin D and folate, both of which are crucial to successful human reproduction, and therefore evolutionary fitness. The selection is stabilising within each latitudinal region.

Skin colour in humans: A product of natural selection

Adapted from Jablonski & Chaplin, Sci. Am. Oct. 2002

Human skin colour is the result of two opposing selection pressures. Skin pigmentation has evolved to protect against destruction of folate from ultraviolet light, but the skin must also be light enough to receive the light required to synthesise vitamin D. Vitamin D synthesis is a process that begins in the skin and is inhibited by dark pigment. Folate is needed for healthy neural development in humans and a deficiency is associated with fatal neural tube defects. Vitamin D is required for the absorption of calcium from the diet and therefore normal skeletal development.

Women also have a high requirement for calcium during pregnancy and lactation. Populations that live in the tropics receive enough ultraviolet (UV) radiation to synthesise vitamin D all year long. Those that live in northern or southern latitudes do not. In temperate zones, people lack sufficient UV light to make vitamin D for one month of the year. Those nearer the poles lack enough UV light for vitamin D synthesis most of the year (above). Their lighter skins reflect their need to maximise UV absorption (the photos show skin colour in people from different latitudes).

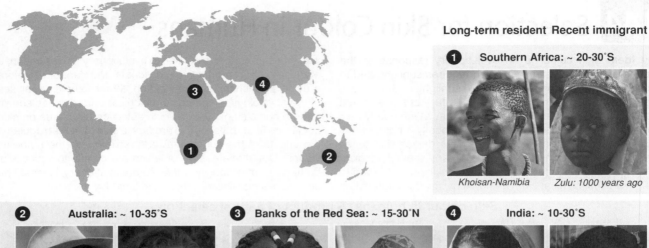

Long-term resident   Recent immigrant

1 Southern Africa: ~ 20-30°S

Khoisan-Namibia   Zulu: 1000 years ago

2 Australia: ~ 10-35°S

Aborigine   European: 300 years ago

3 Banks of the Red Sea: ~ 15-30°N

Nuba-Sudan   Arab: 2000 years ago

4 India: ~ 10-30°S

West Bengal   Tamil: ~100 years ago

The skin of people who have inhabited particular regions for millennia has adapted to allow sufficient vitamin D production while still protecting folate stores. In the photos above, some of these original inhabitants are illustrated to the left of each pair and compared with the skin tones of more recent immigrants (to the right of each pair, with the number of years since immigration). The numbered locations are on the map.

1. (a) Describe the role of folate in human physiology: _____

    (b) Describe the role of vitamin D in human physiology: _____

2. (a) Early hypotheses to explain skin colour linked pigmentation level only to the degree of protection it gave from UV-induced skin cancer. Explain why this hypothesis was inadequate in accounting for how skin colour evolved:

    _____

    _____

    (b) Explain how the new hypothesis for the evolution of skin colour overcomes these deficiencies:_____

    _____

    _____

    _____

    _____

3. Explain why, in any given geographical region, women tend to have lighter skins (by 3-4% on average) than men:

    _____

    _____

4. The Inuit people of Alaska and northern Canada have a diet rich in vitamin D and their skin colour is darker than predicted on the basis of UV intensity at their latitude. Explain this observation:

    _____

    _____

5. (a) What health problems might be expected for people of African origin now living in northern UK?_____

    _____

    (b) How could these people avoid these problems in their new higher latitude environment? _____

    _____

    _____

© 2015 **BIOZONE** International
ISBN: **978-1-927309-14-8**
Photocopying Prohibited

145 Gene Pool Exercise

The set of all the versions of all the genes in a population (it genetic make-up) is called the **gene pool**. Cut out the squares below and use them to model the events described in *Modeling Natural Selection*.

PRAC

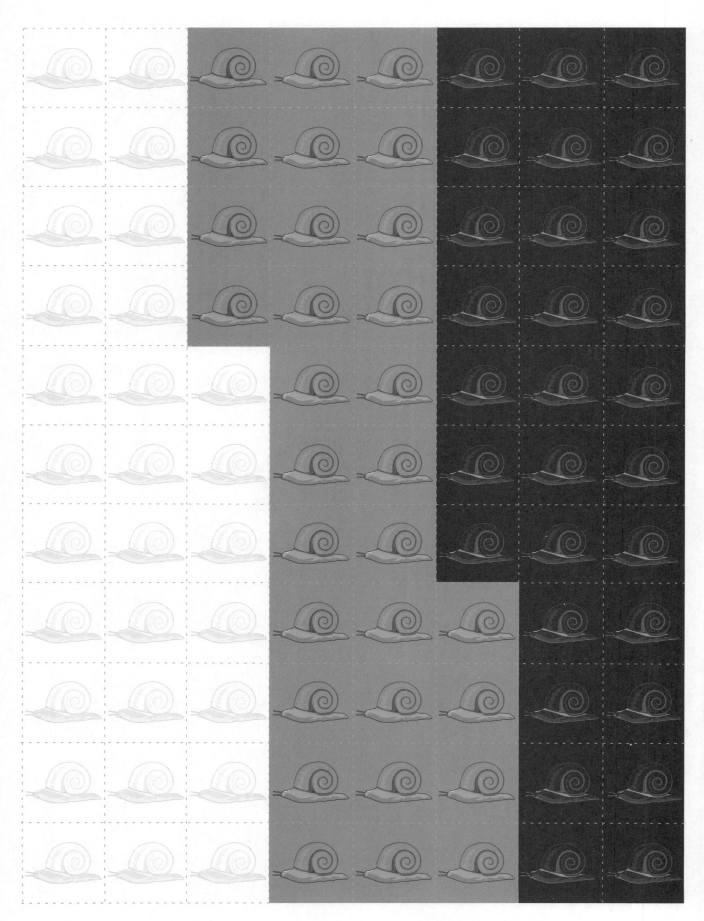

146 Modelling Natural Selection

Key Idea: The way that natural selection acts on phenotypes can be modelled for a hypothetical population in which individuals differ with respect to one phenotypic character.

Natural selection can be modelled in a simple activity based on predation. You can carry out the following activity by yourself, or work with a partner to increase the size of the population. The black, grey, and white squares on the preceding pages represent phenotypes of a population. Cut them out and follow the instructions below to model natural selection. You will also need a sheet of white paper and a sheet of black paper.

1. Cut out the squares on the preceding pages and record the number of black, grey, and white squares.

2. For the first half of the activity you will also need a black sheet of paper or material that will act as the environment (A3 is a good size). For the second half of the activity you will need a white sheet of paper.

3. Place 10 black, 10 white, and 22 grey squares in a bag and shake them up to mix them. Keep the other squares for making up population proportions later. Write the values in the numbers row of generation 1 below.

4. Work out the proportion of each phenotype in the population (e.g. 10/42 = 0.24) and place these values in the table below. This represents your starting population (you can combine populations with a partner to increase the population size for more reliable results).

5. Now take the squares out of the bag and randomly distribute them over the sheet of black paper (this works best if your partner does this while you aren't looking).

6. You will act the part of a predator on the snails. For 15 seconds, pick up the squares that stand out (are obvious) on the black paper using your thumb and forefinger. These squares represent animals in the population that have been preyed upon and killed. Place them to one side. The remaining squares represent the population that survived to reproduce.

7. Count the remaining phenotypes. In this population, black carries the alleles BB, grey the alleles Bb, and white the alleles bb. On a separate sheet, calculate the frequency of the B and b alleles in the remaining population (hint: if there are 5 black and 10 grey snails then there are 20 B alleles).

8. These frequencies are what is passed on to the next generation. To produce the next generation, the number of black, grey, and white snails must be calculated. This can be done using the original population number and Hardy - Weinberg equations ($p^2 + 2pq + q^2 = 1$ and $p + q = 1$).

9. For example. If there are 24 snails left with the numbers 5 black, 10 grey, and 9 white then the frequency of B (p) = (5 x 2 + 10) / (24 x 2) = 0.4167 and b (q) = 0.5833. The number of black snails in the next generation will therefore be p^2 x 42 = 0.4167^2 x 42 = 7.3 = 7 (you can't have 0.3 of a snail).

10. Record the number of black, grey, and white snails in the table below in generation 2, along with their phenotype frequencies.

11. Repeat steps 4 to 10 for generation 2, and 3 more generations (5 generations in total or more if you wish).

12. On separate graph paper, draw a line graph of the proportions of each colour over the five generations. Which colours have increased, which have decreased?

13. Now repeat the whole activity using a white sheet background instead of the black sheet. What do you notice about the proportions this time?

Generation		Black	Grey	White
1	Number			
	Proportion			
2	Number			
	Proportion			
3	Number			
	Proportion			
4	Number			
	Proportion			
5	Number			
	Proportion			

LINK
145 PRAC

147 Genetic Drift

Key Idea: Genetic drift is the term for the random changes in allele frequency that occur in all populations. It has a more pronounced effect in small populations.

Not all individuals, for various reasons, will be able to contribute their genes to the next generation. In a small population, the effect of a few individuals not contributing

their alleles to the next generation can have a great effect on allele frequencies. Alleles may even become **lost** from the gene pool altogether (frequency becomes 0%) or **fixed** as the only allele for the gene present (frequency becomes 100%). The random change in allele frequencies is called **genetic drift**.

The genetic makeup (allele frequencies) of the population changes randomly over a period of time

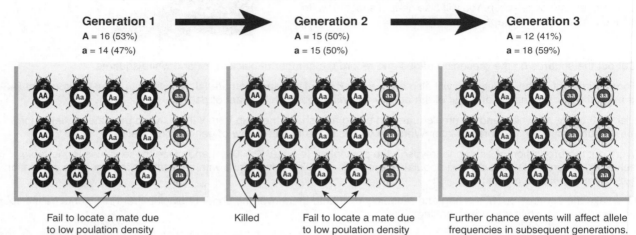

Generation 1
A = 16 (53%)
a = 14 (47%)

Generation 2
A = 15 (50%)
a = 15 (50%)

Generation 3
A = 12 (41%)
a = 18 (59%)

Fail to locate a mate due to low poulation density

Killed

Fail to locate a mate due to low poulation density

Further chance events will affect allele frequencies in subsequent generations.

This diagram shows the gene pool of a hypothetical small population over three generations. For various reasons, not all individuals contribute alleles to the next generation. With the random loss of the alleles carried by these individuals, the allele frequency changes from one generation to the next. The change in frequency is directionless as there is no selecting force. The allele combinations for each successive generation are determined by how many alleles of each type are passed on from the preceding one.

Computer simulation of genetic drift

Below are displayed the change in allele frequencies in a computer simulation showing random genetic drift. The breeding population progressively gets smaller from left to right. Each simulation was run for 140 generations.

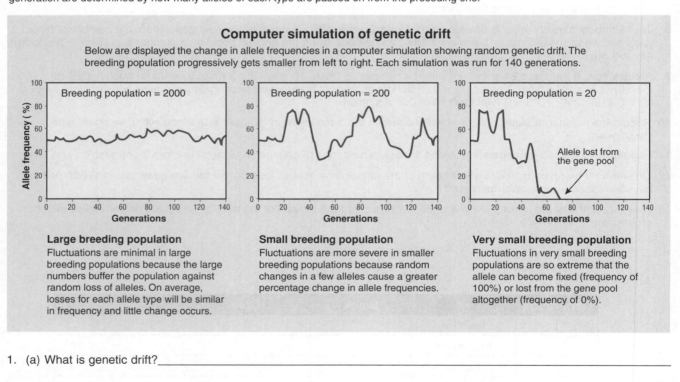

Large breeding population
Fluctuations are minimal in large breeding populations because the large numbers buffer the population against random loss of alleles. On average, losses for each allele type will be similar in frequency and little change occurs.

Small breeding population
Fluctuations are more severe in smaller breeding populations because random changes in a few alleles cause a greater percentage change in allele frequencies.

Very small breeding population
Fluctuations in very small breeding populations are so extreme that the allele can become fixed (frequency of 100%) or lost from the gene pool altogether (frequency of 0%).

1. (a) What is genetic drift?

   (b) Why is the effect of genetic drift more pronounced in small populations?

2. Suggest why genetic drift is an important process in the evolution of small populations:

© 2015 **BIOZONE** International
ISBN: **978-1-927309-14-8**
Photocopying Prohibited

148 The Founder Effect

Key Idea: The founder effect can result in differences in allele frequencies between a parent and founder populations.

If a small number of individuals from a large population becomes isolated from their original parent population, their sample of alleles is unlikely to represent the allele proportions of the parent population. This phenomenon is called the **founder effect** and it can result in the colonising (founder) population evolving in a different direction to the parent population. This is particularly the case if the founder population is subjected to different selection pressures in a new environment and if the population is missing alleles that are present in the parent population.

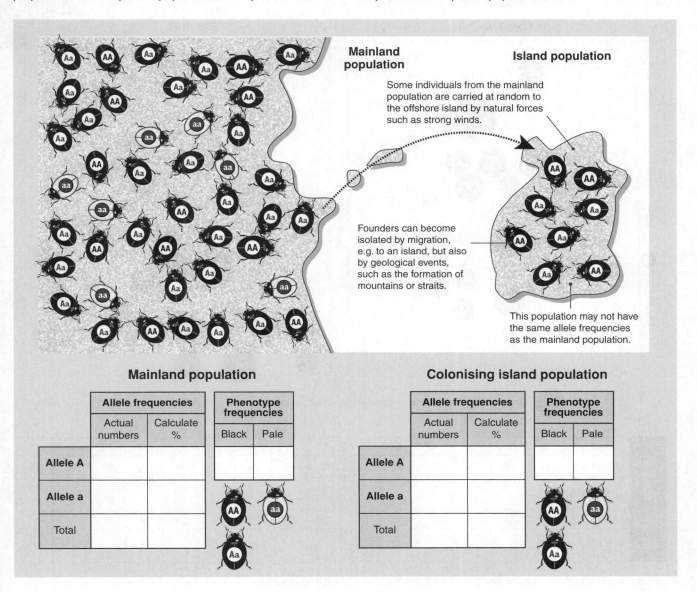

Mainland population

Some individuals from the mainland population are carried at random to the offshore island by natural forces such as strong winds.

Island population

Founders can become isolated by migration, e.g. to an island, but also by geological events, such as the formation of mountains or straits.

This population may not have the same allele frequencies as the mainland population.

Mainland population

| | Allele frequencies | | Phenotype frequencies | |
	Actual numbers	Calculate %	Black	Pale
Allele A				
Allele a				
Total				

Colonising island population

| | Allele frequencies | | Phenotype frequencies | |
	Actual numbers	Calculate %	Black	Pale
Allele A				
Allele a				
Total				

1. Compare the mainland population to the population which ended up on the island (use the spaces in the tables above):
   (a) Count the **phenotype** numbers for the two populations (i.e. the number of black and pale beetles).
   (b) Count the **allele** numbers for the two populations: the number of dominant alleles (A) and recessive alleles (a). Calculate these as a percentage of the total number of alleles for each population.

2. How are the allele frequencies of the two populations different? _____

   _____

   _____

3. Describe some possible ways in which various types of organism can be **carried** to an offshore island:

   (a) Plants: _____

   (b) Land animals: _____

   (c) Non-marine birds: _____

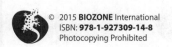
LINK 147 WEB 148 **DATA**

Microgeographic isolation in garden snails

The European garden snail (*Cornu aspersum*, formerly *Helix aspersa*) is widely distributed throughout the world, both naturally and by human introduction. However because of its relatively slow locomotion and need for moist environments it can be limited in its habitat and this can lead to regional variation. The study below illustrates an investigation carried out on two snail populations in the city of Bryan, Texas. The snail populations covered two adjacent city blocks surrounded by tarmac roads.

The snails were found in several colonies in each block. Allele frequencies for the gene *MDH-1* (alleles A and a) were obtained and compared. Statistical analysis of the allele frequencies of the two populations showed them to be significantly different ($P << 0.05$). Note: A Mann-Whitney U test was used in this instance. It is similar to a Student's t test, but does not assume a normal distribution of data (it is non-parametric).

Block A   **Block B**

Road (not to scale)

Source: Evolution, Vol 29, No. 3, 1975

● Snail colony (circle size is proportional to colony size).   ▢ Building

	Colony	1	2	3	4	5	6	7	8	9	10	11	12	13	14	15
Block A	*MDH-1* A %	39	39	36	42	39	47	32	42	44	42	44	50	50	58	75
	MDH-1 a %															
Block B	*MDH-1* A %	81	61	75	68	70	61	70	60	58	61	54	54	47		
	MDH-1 a %															

4. Complete the table above by filling in the frequencies of the *MDH-1* a allele:

5. Suggest why these snail populations are effectively geographically isolated: _____

_____

_____

6. Both the *MDH-1* alleles produce fully operative enzymes. Suggest why the frequencies of the alleles have become significantly different.

_____

_____

_____

_____

7. Identify the colony in block A that appears to be isolated from the rest of the block itself: _____

149 Genetic Bottlenecks

Key Idea: Genetic bottlenecks occur when population numbers and diversity fall dramatically. Although a population's numbers may recover, its genetic diversity often does not.

Populations may sometimes be reduced to low numbers by predation, disease, or periods of climatic change. These large scale reductions are called genetic (or population) bottlenecks. The sudden population decline is not necessarily selective and it may affect all phenotypes equally. Large scale catastrophic events, such as fire or volcanic eruptions, are examples of such non-selective events. Affected populations may later recover, having squeezed through a 'bottleneck' of low numbers. The diagram below illustrates how population numbers may be reduced as a result of a catastrophic event. Following such an event, the gene pool of the surviving remnant population may be markedly different to that of the original gene pool. Genetic drift may cause further changes to allele frequencies. The small population may return to previous levels but with a reduced genetic diversity.

Change in population numbers and diversity

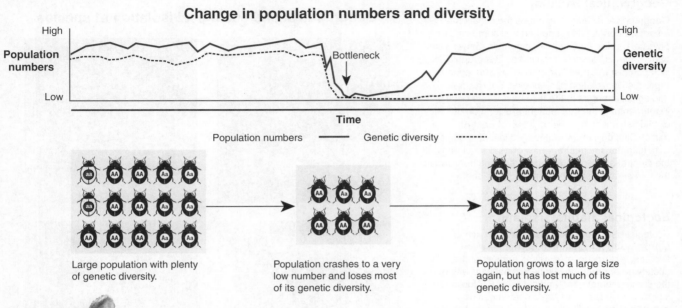

Population numbers ——— Genetic diversity ┈┈┈┈

Large population with plenty of genetic diversity.

Population crashes to a very low number and loses most of its genetic diversity.

Population grows to a large size again, but has lost much of its genetic diversity.

Modern examples of genetic bottlenecks

Cheetahs: The world population of cheetahs currently stands at fewer than 20 000. Recent genetic analysis has found that the entire population exhibits very little genetic diversity. It appears that cheetahs may have narrowly escaped extinction at the end of the last ice age, about 10-20 000 years ago. If all modern cheetahs arose from a very limited genetic stock, this would explain their present lack of genetic diversity. The lack of genetic variation has resulted in a number of problems that threaten cheetah survival, including sperm abnormalities, decreased fecundity, high cub mortality, and sensitivity to disease.

Illinois prairie chicken: When Europeans first arrived in North America, there were millions of prairie chickens. As a result of hunting and habitat loss, the Illinois population of prairie chickens fell from about 100 million in 1900 to fewer than 50 in the 1990s. A comparison of the DNA from birds collected in the mid-twentieth century and DNA from the surviving population indicated that most of the genetic diversity has been lost.

Photo: Dept. of Natural Resources, Illinois

1. Endangered species are often subjected to genetic bottlenecks. Explain how genetic bottlenecks affect the ability of a population of an endangered species to recover from its plight:

_____

_____

_____

2. Why has the lack of genetic diversity in cheetahs increased their sensitivity to disease?_____

_____

_____

3. Describe the effect of a genetic bottleneck on the potential of a species to adapt to changes (i.e. its ability to evolve):

_____

_____

LINK 147 WEB 149 **KNOW**

150 Isolation and Species Formation

Key Idea: Ecological and geographical isolation are important in separating populations prior to reproductive isolation. Isolating mechanisms are barriers to successful interbreeding between species. **Reproductive isolation** is fundamental to the biological species concept, which defines a species by its inability to breed with other species to produce fertile offspring. **Geographical barriers** are not regarded as reproductive isolating mechanisms because they are not part of the species' biology, although they are often a necessary precursor to reproductive isolation in sexually reproducing populations. Ecological isolating mechanisms are those that isolate gene pools on the basis of ecological preferences, e.g. habitat selection. Although ecological and geographical isolation are sometimes confused, they are quite distinct, as ecological isolation involves a component of the species biology.

Geographical isolation

Geographical isolation describes the isolation of a species population (gene pool) by some kind of physical barrier, for example, mountain range, water body, isthmus, desert, or ice sheet. Geographical isolation is a frequent first step in the subsequent reproductive isolation of a species. For example, geological changes to the lake basins has been instrumental in the subsequent proliferation of cichlid fish species in the rift lakes of East Africa (right). Similarly, many Galapagos Island species (e.g. iguanas, finches) are now quite distinct from the Central and South American species from which they arose after isolation from the mainland.

Ecological (habitat) isolation

Ecological isolation describes the existence of a **prezygotic reproductive barrier** between two species (or sub-species) as a result of them occupying or breeding in different habitats within the same general geographical area. Ecological isolation includes small scale differences (e.g. ground or tree dwelling) and broad differences (e.g. desert vs grasslands). The red-browed and brown **treecreepers** (*Climacteris* spp.) are sympatric in south-eastern Australia and both species feed largely on ants. However the brown spends most of its time foraging on the ground or on fallen logs while the red-browed forages almost entirely in the trees. Ecological isolation often follows geographical isolation, but in many cases the geographical barriers may remain in part. For example, five species of **antelope squirrels** occupy different habitat ranges throughout the southwestern United States and northern Mexico, a region divided in part by the Grand Canyon. The white tailed antelope squirrel is widely distributed in desert areas to the north and south of the canyon, while the smaller, more specialised Harris' antelope squirrel has a much more limited range only to the south in southern Arizona. The Grand Canyon still functions as a barrier to dispersal but the species are now ecologically isolated as well.

Geographical and ecological isolation of species

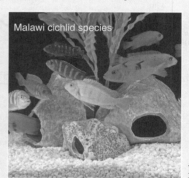
Malawi cichlid species

L. Victoria

L. Tanganyika

L. Malawi

Red-browed treecreeper

Brown treecreeper

White-tailed antelope squirrel

The Grand Canyon - a massive rift in the Colorado Plateau

Harris' antelope squirrel

1. Describe the role of isolating mechanisms in maintaining the integrity of a species: _____

_____

_____

2. (a) Why is geographical isolation not regarded as a reproductive isolating mechanism? _____

_____

(b) Explain why, despite this, it often precedes reproductive isolation: _____

_____

3. Distinguish between geographical and ecological isolation: _____

_____

LINK 151 LINK 152

KNOW

© 2015 **BIOZONE** International
ISBN: **978-1-927309-14-8**
Photocopying Prohibited

151 Reproductive Isolation

Key Idea: Reproductive isolating mechanisms acting before and after fertilisation, prevent interbreeding between species. Reproductive isolation is a defining feature of biological species. Any mechanism that prevents two species from producing viable, fertile hybrids contributes to reproductive isolation. Single barriers to gene flow (such as geographical barriers) are usually insufficient to isolate a gene pool, so most species commonly have more than one type of barrier. Most reproductive isolating mechanisms (RIMs) are prezygotic and operate before fertilisation. Postzyotic RIMs, which act after fertilisation, are important in maintaining the integrity of closely related species.

Prezygotic isolating mechanisms

Temporal Isolation

Individuals from different species do not mate because they are active during different times of the day or in different seasons. Plants flower at different times of the year or at different times of the day to avoid hybridisation (e.g. species of the orchid genus *Dendrobium* occupy the same location but flower on different days). Closely related animal species may have different breeding seasons or periods of emergence. Species of **periodical cicadas** (*Magicicada*) in a particular region are developmentally synchronised, despite very long life cycles. Once their underground period of development (13 or 17 years depending on the species) is over, the entire population emerges at much the same time to breed.

Gamete Isolation

The gametes from different species are often incompatible, so even if they meet they do not survive. Where fertilisation is internal, the sperm may not survive in the reproductive tract of another species. If the sperm does survive and reach the ovum, chemical differences in the gametes prevent fertilisation. Gamete isolation is particularly important in aquatic environments where the gametes are released into the water and fertilised externally, such as in reproduction in frogs. Chemical recognition is also used by flowering plants to recognise pollen from the same species.

Behavioural isolation

Behavioural isolation operates through differences in species courtship behaviours. Courtship is a necessary prelude to mating in many species and courtship behaviours are species specific. Mates of the same species are attracted with distinctive dances, vocalisations, and body language. Courtship behaviours are not easily misinterpreted and will be unrecognised and ignored by individuals of another species. Birds exhibit a remarkable range of courtship displays. The use of song is widespread but ritualised movements, including nest building, are also common. For example, the elaborate courtship bowers of bowerbirds are well known, and Galápagos frigatebirds have an elaborate display in which they inflate a bright red gular pouch (right). Amongst insects, empid flies have some of the most elaborate of courtship displays. They are aggressive hunters so ritualised behaviour involving presentation of a prey item facilitates mating. The sexual organs of the flies are also like a lock-and-key, providing mechanical reproductive isolation as well (see below).

Mechanical (morphological) isolation

Structural differences (incompatibility) in the anatomy of reproductive organs prevents sperm transfer between individuals of different species. This is an important isolating mechanism preventing breeding between closely related species of arthropods. Many flowering plants have coevolved with their animal pollinators and have flowers structures to allow only that insect access. Structural differences in the flowers and pollen of different plant species prevents cross breeding because pollen transfer is restricted to specific pollinators and the pollen itself must be species compatible.

Temporal isolation: periodical cicadas

Gamete isolation: amphibian ovary (*Rana*)

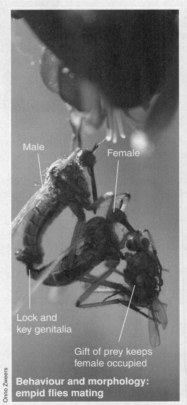

Male

Female

Lock and key genitalia

Gift of prey keeps female occupied

Behaviour and morphology: empid flies mating

Mechanical: Damselflies mating

Cicada emergence

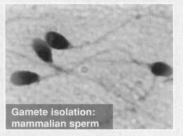

Gamete isolation: mammalian sperm

Behaviour: male frigatebird display

Behaviour: male tree frog calling

Behaviour: wing beating in male sage grouse

Mechanical: flower shape in orchids

LINK 153 LINK 152 **KNOW**

Postzygotic isolating mechanisms

Hybrid sterility

Even if two species mate and produce hybrid offspring that are vigorous, the species are still reproductively isolated if the hybrids are sterile (genes cannot flow from one species' gene pool to the other). Such cases are common among the horse family (such as the zebra and donkey shown on the right). One cause of this sterility is the failure of meiosis to produce normal gametes in the hybrid. This can occur if the chromosomes of the two parents are different in number or structure (see the **"zebronkey"** karyotype on the right). The **mule**, a cross between a donkey stallion and a horse mare, is also an example of **hybrid vigour** (they are robust) as well as **hybrid sterility**. Female mules sometimes produce viable eggs but males are infertile.

Hybrid inviability

Mating between individuals of two species may produce a zygote, but genetic incompatibility may stop development of the zygote. Fertilised eggs often fail to divide because of mis-matched chromosome numbers from each gamete. Very occasionally, the hybrid zygote will complete embryonic development but will not survive for long. For example, although sheep and goats seem similar and can be mated together, they belong to different genera. Any offspring of a sheep-goat pairing is generally stillborn.

Hybrid breakdown

Hybrid breakdown is common feature of some plant hybrids. The first generation (F_1) may be fertile, but the second generation (F_2) are infertile or inviable. Examples include hybrids between cotton species (near right), species within the genus *Populus*, and strains of the cultivated rice *Oryza* (far right)

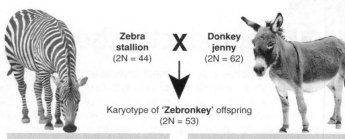

Zebra stallion (2N = 44) X Donkey jenny (2N = 62)

Karyotype of 'Zebronkey' offspring (2N = 53)

Chromosomes contributed by zebra stallion

Chromosomes contributed by donkey jenny

Sheep (*Ovis*) 54 chromosomes

Goat (*Capra*) 60 chromosomes

1. In the following examples, classify the reproductive isolating mechanism as either **prezygotic** or **postzygotic** and describe the mechanisms by which the isolation is achieved (e.g. structrual isolation, hybrid sterility etc.):

(a) Some different cotton species can produce fertile hybrids, but breakdown of the hybrid occurs in the next generation when the offspring of the hybrid die in their seeds or grow into defective plants:

Prezygotic / postzygotic (delete one)   Mechanism of isolation: _____

(b) Many plants have unique arrangements of their floral parts that stops transfer of pollen between plants:

Prezygotic / postzygotic (delete one)   Mechanism of isolation: _____

(c) Two skunk species do not mate despite having habitats that overlap because they mate at different times of the year:

Prezygotic / postzygotic (delete one)   Mechanism of isolation: _____

(d) Several species of the frog genus *Rana*, live in the same regions and habitats, where they may occasionally hybridise. The hybrids generally do not complete development, and those that do are weak and do not survive long:

Prezygotic / postzygotic (delete one)   Mechanism of isolation: _____

2. Postzygotic isolating mechanisms are said to reinforce prezygotic ones. Explain why this is the case:

_____

© 2015 **BIOZONE** International ISBN: **978-1-927309-14-8** Photocopying Prohibited

152 Allopatric Speciation

Key Idea: Allopatric speciation is the genetic divergence of a population after it becomes subdivided and isolated.

Allopatric speciation refers to the genetic divergence of a species after a population becomes split and then isolated geographically. It is probably the most common mechanism by which new species arise and has certainly been important in regions where there have been cycles of geographical fragmentation, e.g. as a result of ice expansion and retreat (and accompanying sea level changes) during glacial and interglacial periods.

Stage 1: Moving into new environments

There are times when the range of a species expands for a variety of different reasons. A single population in a relatively homogeneous environment will move into new regions of their environment when they are subjected to intense competition (whether it is interspecific or intraspecific). The most severe form of competition is between members of the same species since they are competing for identical resources in the habitat. In the diagram on the right there is a 'parent population' of a single species with a common gene pool with regular 'gene flow' (theoretically any individual has access to all members of the opposite sex for mating purposes).

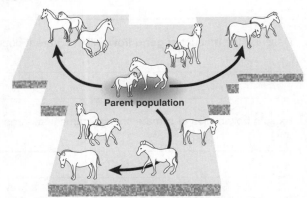

Parent population

Stage 2: Geographical isolation

Isolation of parts of the population may occur due to the formation of **physical barriers**, such as mountains, deserts, or stretches of water. These barriers may cut off those parts of the population that are at the extremes of the range and gene flow is prevented or rare. The rise and fall of the sea level has been particularly important in functioning as an isolating mechanism. Climatic change can leave 'islands' of habitat separated by large inhospitable zones that the species cannot traverse.

Example: In mountainous regions, alpine species can populate extensive areas of habitat during cool climatic periods. During warmer periods, they may become isolated because their habitat is reduced to 'islands' of high ground surrounded by inhospitable lowland habitat.

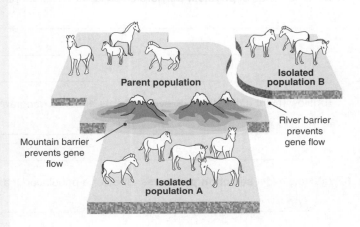

Parent population

Isolated population B

River barrier prevents gene flow

Mountain barrier prevents gene flow

Isolated population A

Stage 3: Different selection pressures

The isolated populations (A and B) may be subjected to quite different selection pressures. These will favour individuals with traits that suit each particular environment. For example, population A will be subjected to selection pressures that relate to drier conditions. This will favour those individuals with phenotypes (and therefore genotypes) that are better suited to dry conditions. They may for instance have a better ability to conserve water. This would result in improved health, allowing better disease resistance and greater reproductive performance (i.e. more of their offspring survive). Finally, as allele frequencies for certain genes change, the population takes on the status of a subspecies. Reproductive isolation is not yet established but the **subspecies** are significantly different genetically from other related populations.

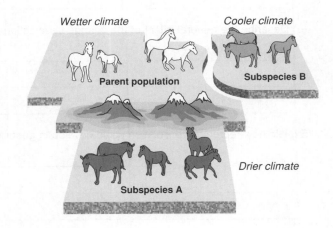

Wetter climate

Cooler climate

Parent population

Subspecies B

Drier climate

Subspecies A

Stage 4: Reproductive isolation

The separated populations (isolated subspecies) undergo genetic and behavioural changes. These ensure that the gene pool of each population remains isolated and 'undiluted' by genes from other populations, even if the two populations should be able to remix (due to the removal of the geographical barrier). Gene flow does not occur. The arrows (diagram, right) indicate the zone of overlap between two species after Species B has moved back into the range inhabited by the parent population. Closely-related species whose distribution overlaps are said to be **sympatric species**. Those that remain geographically isolated are called **allopatric species**.

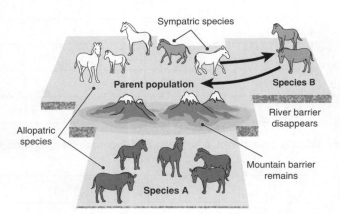

Sympatric species

Parent population

Species B

River barrier disappears

Allopatric species

Mountain barrier remains

Species A

LINK 154   LINK 153   WEB 152   **KNOW**

1. Why do some animals, given the opportunity, move into new environments? _____

_____

_____

2. Plants are unable to move. How might plants disperse to new environments? _____

_____

3. Describe the amount of **gene flow** within a parent population prior to and during the expansion of a species' range:

_____

_____

4. Explain how cycles of climate change can cause large changes in **sea level** (up to 200 m): _____

_____

_____

5. (a) What kinds of **physical barriers** could isolate different parts of the same population? _____

_____

_____

_____

   (b) How might emigration achieve the same effect as geographical isolation? _____

_____

_____

6. (a) How might **selection pressures** differ for a population that becomes isolated from the parent population?

_____

_____

   (b) Describe the general effect of the change in selection pressures on the **allele frequencies** of the isolated gene pool:

_____

_____

_____

7. Explain how reproductive isolation could develop in geographically separated populations (see previous pages):

_____

_____

_____

_____

_____

_____

_____

_____

8. What is the difference between an allopatric and sympatric species? _____

_____

_____

© 2015 **BIOZONE** International
ISBN: **978-1-927309-14-8**
Photocopying Prohibited
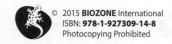

153 Stages in Species Formation

Key Idea: Speciation may occur in stages marked by increasing isolation of diverging gene pools. Physical separation is followed by increasing reproductive isolation. The diagram below shows a possible sequence of events in the origin of two new species from an ancestral population. Over time, the genetic differences between two populations increase and the populations become increasingly isolated from each other. The isolation of the two gene pools may begin with a geographical barrier. This may be followed by progressively greater reduction in gene flow between the populations until the two gene pools are isolated and they each attain species status.

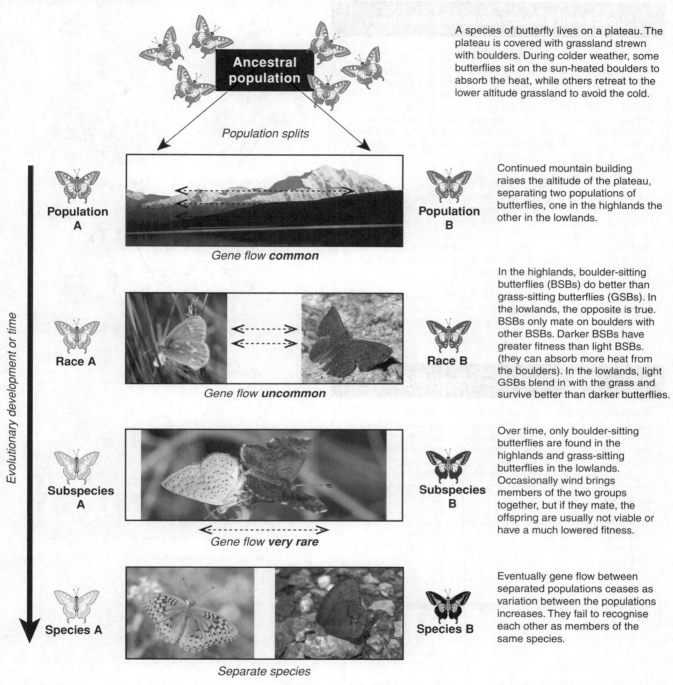

Ancestral population

Population splits

A species of butterfly lives on a plateau. The plateau is covered with grassland strewn with boulders. During colder weather, some butterflies sit on the sun-heated boulders to absorb the heat, while others retreat to the lower altitude grassland to avoid the cold.

Population A — **Population B**

Gene flow common

Continued mountain building raises the altitude of the plateau, separating two populations of butterflies, one in the highlands the other in the lowlands.

Race A — **Race B**

Gene flow uncommon

In the highlands, boulder-sitting butterflies (BSBs) do better than grass-sitting butterflies (GSBs). In the lowlands, the opposite is true. BSBs only mate on boulders with other BSBs. Darker BSBs have greater fitness than light BSBs. (they can absorb more heat from the boulders). In the lowlands, light GSBs blend in with the grass and survive better than darker butterflies.

Subspecies A — **Subspecies B**

Gene flow very rare

Over time, only boulder-sitting butterflies are found in the highlands and grass-sitting butterflies in the lowlands. Occasionally wind brings members of the two groups together, but if they mate, the offspring are usually not viable or have a much lowered fitness.

Species A — **Species B**

Separate species

Eventually gene flow between separated populations ceases as variation between the populations increases. They fail to recognise each other as members of the same species.

Evolutionary development or time

1. Identify the variation in behaviour in the original butterfly population: _____

_____

2. What were the selection pressures acting on BSBs in the highlands and GSBs in the lowlands respectively?

_____

_____

_____

KNOW

154 Sympatric Speciation

Key Idea: Sympatric speciation is speciation occurring in the absence of physical barriers between gene pools.

Sympatric speciation refers to the formation of new species within the same place (sympatry). Sympatric speciation is rarer than allopatric speciation because it is difficult to prevent gene flow. However, it is not uncommon in plants that form **polyploids** (organisms with extra complete sets of chromosomes). Sympatric speciation can occur through niche differentiation in areas of sympatry, or by instant speciation through polyploidy.

Speciation through niche differentiation

Niche isolation

In a heterogeneous environment (one that is not the same everywhere), a population exists within a diverse collection of **microhabitats**. Some organisms prefer to occupy one particular type of 'microhabitat' most of the time, only rarely coming in contact with fellow organisms that prefer other microhabitats. Some organisms become so dependent on the resources offered by their particular microhabitat that they never meet up with their counterparts in different microhabitats.

Reproductive isolation

Finally, the individual groups have remained genetically isolated for so long because of their microhabitat preferences, that they have become reproductively isolated. They have become new species that have developed subtle differences in behaviour, structure, or physiology. Gene flow (via sexual reproduction) is limited to organisms that share a similar microhabitat preference (as shown in the diagram on the right).

Example: Some beetles prefer to find plants identical to the species they grew up on, when it is time for them to lay eggs. Individual beetles of the same species have different preferences.

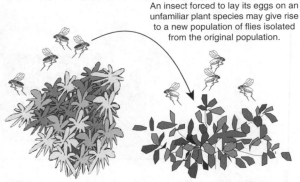

An insect forced to lay its eggs on an unfamiliar plant species may give rise to a new population of flies isolated from the original population.

Original host plant species   **New host plant species**

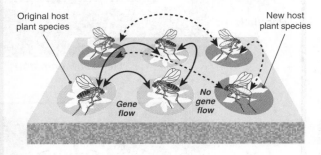

Original host plant species

New host plant species

Gene flow

No gene flow

Instant speciation by polyploidy

Polyploidy (duplication of chromosome sets) may result in the formation of a new species without physical isolation from the parent species. Polyploidy produces sudden reproductive isolation for the new group. Polyploids in animals are rarely viable. Many plants, on the other hand, are able to reproduce vegetatively, or carry out self pollination. This ability to reproduce on their own enables such polyploid plants to produce a breeding population.

Polyploidy in a hybrid between two different species can often make the hybrid fertile. This occurred in modern wheat. Swedes are also a polyploid species formed from a hybrid between a type of cabbage and a type of turnip.

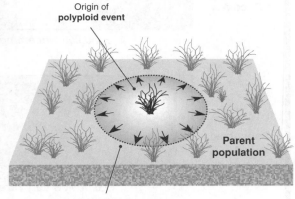

Origin of **polyploid event**

Parent population

New polyploid plant species spreads outwards through the existing parent population

1. Explain what is meant by **sympatric speciation** (do not confuse this with sympatric species):

_____

_____

2. Explain how **polyploidy** can result in the formation of a new species: _____

_____

_____

3. Identify an example of a species that has been formed by polyploidy: _____

4. Explain how **niche differentiation** can result in the formation of a new species: _____

_____

_____

© 2015 **BIOZONE** International
ISBN: **978-1-927309-14-8**
Photocopying Prohibited

155 Selective Breeding in Animals

Key Idea: Selective breeding is the process of breeding together organisms with desirable qualities (e.g. high milk yield) so the trait is reliably passed on to the next generation. **Selective breeding** (or artificial selection) is the process by which humans select organisms with desirable traits and breed them together so the trait appears in the next generation. The process is repeated over many generations until the characteristic becomes common. Selective breeding often uses reproductive technologies, such as artificial insemination, so that the desirable characteristics of one male can be passed onto many offspring. This increases the rate at which the desirable trait is passed to progeny. There are problems associated with selective breeding. The gene pool becomes more constrained and some alleles may be lost. A reduction in genetic diversity decreases the ability of a species to adapt to changes in the environment.

The origins of domestic dogs

All breeds of dog are members of the same species, **Canis familiaris** and provide an excellent example of selective breeding. The dog was the first domesticated species and, over centuries, humans have selected for desirable traits, so extensively that there are now more than 400 breeds of dogs. Until very recently, the grey wolf was considered to the ancestor of the domestic dog. However, recent (2015) genetic studies provide strong evidence that domestic dogs and grey wolves are sister groups and shared a now extinct wolf-like common ancestor, which gave rise to the dog before the agricultural revolution 12 000 years ago. Based on genetic analysis, four major clusters of ancient dog breeds are recognised. Through selective breeding, all other breeds are thought to have descended from these clusters.

1: Older lineages
The oldest lineages, including Chinese breeds, basenji, huskies, and malamutes.

2: Mastiff-type
An older lineage that includes the mastiffs, bull terriers, boxers, and rottweilers.

3: Herding
Includes German shepherd, St Bernard, borzoi, collie, corgi, pug, and greyhound

4: Hunting
Most arose in Europe. Includes terriers, spaniels, poodles, and modern hounds.

Modern dog breeds exhibit a huge variety of physical and behavioural phenotypes. Selective breeding has produced breeds to meet the specific requirements of humans.

Problems with selective breeding

Selection for a desirable phenotype can lead to a consequential emphasis of undesirable traits, often because genes for particular characteristics are linked and selection for one inadvertently selects for the other. For example, the German shepherd is a working dog, originally bred for its athleticism and ability to track targets. However in German shepherds bred to meet the specific appearance criteria of show dogs, some traits have been exaggerated so much that it causes health issues. The body shape of the show German shepherd has been selected for a flowing trot and has a pronounced sloping back. This has resulted in leg, hip, and spinal problems. In addition, selective breeding has increased the incidence of some genetic diseases such as epilepsy and blood disorders.

Straight-backed German shepherd

Sloped-backed German shepherd

1. (a) What is selective breeding? _____

_____

(b) What are the advantages of selective breeding? _____

_____

2. List the physical and behavioural traits that would be desirable (selected for) in the following uses of a dog:

(a) Hunting large game (e.g. boar and deer): _____

(b) Stock control (sheep/cattle dog): _____

(c) Family pet (house dog): _____

(d) Guard dog: _____

3. As a group, discuss the ethical considerations of using selective breeding to "improve" dog breeds. What would it take to change breed standards to avoid health issues? Summarise your arguments and attach the summary to this page.

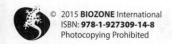
LINK **157** LINK **156** WEB **155** **KNOW**

156 Selection in Livestock

Key Idea: The performance of livestock can be improved by selective breeding based on measurable physical traits.

Most of the economically important traits in dairy cattle (below right) are expressed only in females, but the main opportunity for selection is in males. Selection of the best bulls, combined with their worldwide use through artificial insemination and frozen semen has seen a rapid genetic gain (i.e. the increase in performance as a result of genetic changes) in dairy cattle since the 1970s. Bulls are assigned breeding values based on the performance of their daughters and granddaughters. In this way, the bulls and cows with the best genetics can be selected to produce the next generation.

Beef breeds: Selection is for large breeds with a high proportion of lean muscle. **Desirable traits**: high muscle to bone ratio, rapid growth and weight gain, hardy, easy calving, docile temperament.

Dairy breeds: Selection is based primarily on high milk production, but good health and fertility are also selected for. **Desirable traits**: high milk yield with good protein and fat content, fast milking speed, docile temperament, good udder characteristics (e.g. good teat placement).

Special breeds: Some cattle are bred for their suitability to climate or terrain. Scottish highland cattle (above) are a hardy, long coated breed and produce well where other breeds cannot thrive.

The perfect dairy cow

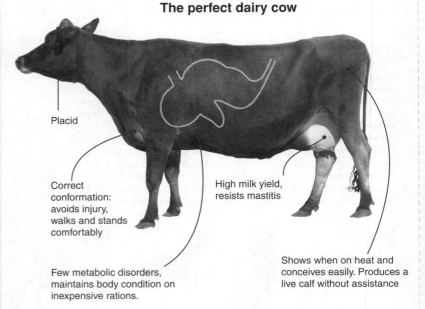

Placid

Correct conformation: avoids injury, walks and stands comfortably

Few metabolic disorders, maintains body condition on inexpensive rations.

High milk yield, resists mastitis

Shows when on heat and conceives easily. Produces a live calf without assistance

Breeding programs select not only for milk production, but also for fertility, udder characteristics, and good health. In addition, artificial selection can be based on milk composition, e.g. high butterfat content (a feature of the Jersey breed, above).

A2 milk, which contains the A2 form of the beta casein protein, has recently received worldwide attention for claims that its consumption lowers the risk of childhood diabetes and coronary heart disease. Selection for the A2 variant in **Holstein cattle** has increased the proportion of A2 milk produced in some regions. A2 milk commands a higher price than A1 milk, so there is a commercial incentive to farmers to produce it.

1. Why can artificial selection effect changes in phenotype much more rapidly than natural selection? _____

_____

_____

_____

2. Suggest why selective breeding has proceeded particularly rapidly in dairy cattle: _____

_____

_____

_____

157 Selection and Population Change

Key Idea: Selective breeding is able to produce rapid change in the phenotypic characteristics of a population.

Humans may create the selection pressure for evolutionary change by choosing and breeding together individuals with particular traits. The example of milk yield in Holstein cows (below) illustrates how humans have directly influenced the genetic makeup of Holstein cattle with respect to milk

production and fertility. Since the 1960s, the University of Minnesota has maintained a Holstein cattle herd that has not been subjected to any selection. They also maintain a herd that was subjected to selective breeding for increased milk production between 1965 and 1985. They compared the genetic merit of milk yield in these groups to that of the USA Holstein average.

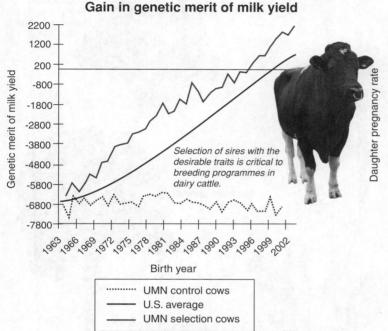

Gain in genetic merit of milk yield

Selection of sires with the desirable traits is critical to breeding programmes in dairy cattle.

.... UMN control cows
——— U.S. average
——— UMN selection cows

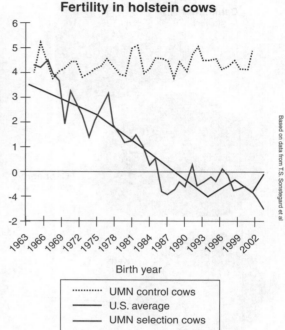

Fertility in holstein cows

Based on data from T.S. Sonstegard et al

.... UMN control cows
——— U.S. average
——— UMN selection cows

Milk production in the University of Minnesota (UMN) herd subjected to selective breeding increased in line with the U.S. average production. In real terms, milk production per cow per milking season increased by 3740 kg since 1964. The herd with no selection remained effectively constant for milk production.

Along with increased milk production there has been a distinct decrease in fertility. The fertility of the University of Minnesota (UMN) herd that was not subjected to selection remained constant while the fertility of the herd selected for milk production decreased with the U.S. fertility average.

1. (a) Describe the relationship between milk yield and fertility on Holstein cows: _____

_____

   (b) What does this suggest about where the genes for milk production and fertility are carried? _____

_____

_____

2. What limits might this place on maximum milk yield? _____

_____

3. Why is sire selection important in selective breeding, even if the characters involved are expressed only in the female?

_____

4. Natural selection is the mechanism by which organisms with favourable traits become proportionally more common in the population. How does selective breeding mimic natural selection? How does the example of the Holstein cattle show that reproductive success is a compromise between many competing traits?

_____

_____

_____

_____

LINK
156 KNOW

158 Selective Breeding in Crop Plants

Key Idea: The genetic diversity within crop varieties provides options to develop new crop plants through selective breeding. For thousands of years, farmers have used the variation in wild and cultivated plants to develop crops. *Brassica oleracea* is a good example of the variety that can be produced by selectively growing plants with desirable traits. Not only are there six varieties of *Brassica oleracea*, but each of those has a number of sub-varieties as well. Although brassicas have been cultivated for several thousand years, cauliflower, broccoli, and brussels sprouts appeared only in the last 500 years.

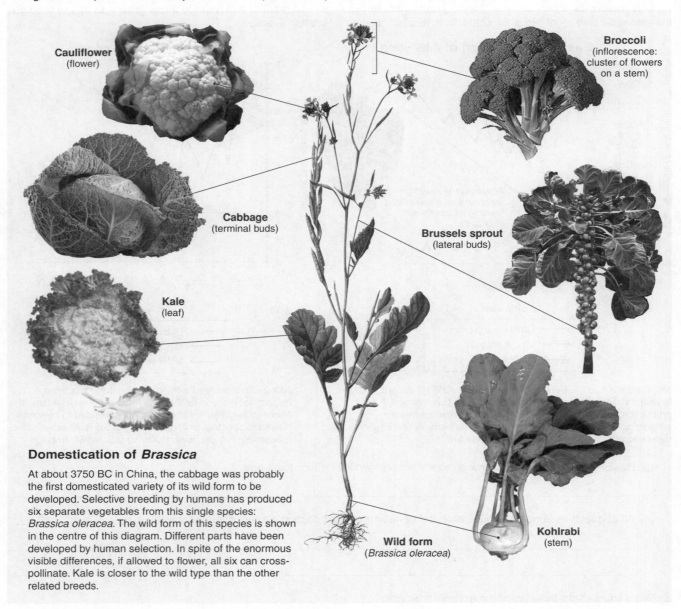

Cauliflower
(flower)

Broccoli
(inflorescence:
cluster of flowers
on a stem)

Cabbage
(terminal buds)

Brussels sprout
(lateral buds)

Kale
(leaf)

Kohlrabi
(stem)

Wild form
(*Brassica oleracea*)

Domestication of *Brassica*

At about 3750 BC in China, the cabbage was probably the first domesticated variety of its wild form to be developed. Selective breeding by humans has produced six separate vegetables from this single species: *Brassica oleracea*. The wild form of this species is shown in the centre of this diagram. Different parts have been developed by human selection. In spite of the enormous visible differences, if allowed to flower, all six can cross-pollinate. Kale is closer to the wild type than the other related breeds.

1. Study the diagram above and identify which part of the plant has been selected for to produce each of the vegetables:

   (a) Cauliflower: _____

   (b) Kale: _____

   (c) Broccoli: _____

   (d) Brussels sprout: _____

   (e) Cabbage: _____

   (f) Kohlrabi: _____

2. Describe the feature of these vegetables that suggests they are members of the same species: _____

   _____

3. What features of *Brassica oleracea* would humans have selected to produce broccoli? _____

   _____

   _____

The number of apple varieties available now is a fraction of the many hundreds grown a century ago. Apples are native to Kazakhstan and breeders are now looking back to this centre of diversity to develop apples resistant to the bacterial disease that causes fire blight.

In 18th-century Ireland, potatoes were the main source of food for about 30% of the population, and farmers relied almost entirely on one very fertile and productive variety. That variety proved susceptible to the potato blight fungus which resulted in a widespread famine.

Hybrid corn varieties have been bred to minimise damage by insect pests such as corn rootworm (above). Hybrids are important because they recombine the genetic characteristics of parental lines and show increased heterozygosity and hybrid vigour.

4. (a) Describe a phenotypic characteristic that might be desirable in an apple tree: _____

   (b) Outline how selective breeding could be used to establish this trait in the next generation: _____

   _____

   _____

   _____

5. (a) Explain why genetic diversity might decline during selective breeding for particular characteristics: _____

   _____

   _____

   _____

   (b) With reference to an example, discuss why retaining genetic diversity in crop plants is important for food security:

   _____

   _____

   _____

   _____

6. Cultivated American cotton plants have a total of 52 chromosomes (2N = 52). In each cell there are 26 large chromosomes and 26 small chromosomes. Old World cotton plants have 26 chromosomes (2N = 26), all large. Wild American cotton plants have 26 chromosomes, all small. How might cultivated American cotton have originated from Old World cotton and wild American cotton:

   _____

   _____

   _____

7. The Cavendish is the variety of banana most commonly sold in world supermarkets. It is seedless, sterile, and under threat of extinction by Panama disease Race 4. Explain why Cavendish banana crops are so endangered by this fungus:

   _____

   _____

   _____

8. Why is it important to maintain the biodiversity of wild plants and ancient farm breeds? _____

   _____

   _____

   _____

© 2015 BIOZONE International
ISBN: 978-1-927309-14-8

159 Breeding Modern Wheat

Key Idea: Modern wheat evolved as a result of two natural hybridisation events and the doubling of its chromosomes.

Wheat has been cultivated for more than 9000 years and has undergone many genetic changes during its domestication. The evolution of modern bread wheat from its wild ancestors (below) involved two natural **hybridisation** events, accompanied by **polyploidy**. Once wheat became domesticated, selective breeding emphasised characteristics such as high protein (gluten) content, high yield, and pest and disease resistance. Hybrid vigour (improved characteristics)

in wheat cultivars is produced by crossing inbred lines and selecting for desirable traits in the progeny, which can now be identified using genetic techniques such as marker assisted selection. This is an indirect selection process where a trait of interest is selected on the basis of a marker linked to it. Increasingly, research is focused on enhancing the genetic diversity of wheat to provide for future crop development. With this in mind, there is renewed interest in some of the lower yielding, ancient wheat varieties, which possess alleles no longer present in modern inbred varieties.

The evolution and domestication of wheat

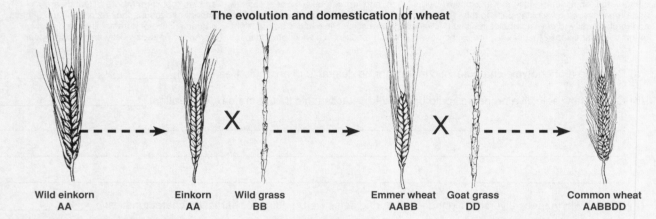

| Wild einkorn AA | Einkorn AA | Wild grass BB | Emmer wheat AABB | Goat grass DD | Common wheat AABBDD |

Wild einkorn becomes domesticated in the Middle East. There are slight changes to phenotype but not chromosome number.

A sterile hybrid between einkhorn and wild grass undergoes a chromosome doubling to create fertile emmer wheat.

A sterile hybrid between emmer wheat and goat grass undergoes a chromosome doubling to create fertile common wheat.

Ancient cereal grasses had heads which shattered easily so that the seeds were widely scattered. In this more primitive morphology, the wheat ear breaks into spikelets when threshed, and milling or pounding is needed to remove the hulls and obtain the grain. Cultivation and repeated harvesting and sowing of the grains of wild grasses led to domestic strains with larger seeds and sturdier heads. Modern selection methods incorporate genetic techniques to identify and isolate beneficial genes, e.g. the RHt dwarfing gene, which gave rise to shorter stemmed modern wheat varieties.

Modern bread wheat has been selected for its non-shattering heads, high yield, and high gluten (protein) content. The grains are larger and the seeds (spikelets) remain attached to the ear by a toughened rachis during harvesting. On threshing, the chaff breaks up, releasing the grains. Selection for these traits by farmers might not necessarily have been deliberate, but occurred because these traits made it easier to gather the seeds. Such **'incidental'** selection was an important part of crop domestication. **Hybrid vigour** in cultivars is generated by crossing inbred lines.

Durum wheat is a modern variety developed by selective breeding of the domesticated emmer wheat strains. Durum (also called hard wheat) has large firm kernels with a high protein content. These properties make it suitable for pasta production. As with all new wheat varieties, new cultivars are produced by crossing two lines using hand pollination, then selfing or **inbreeding** the progeny that combine the desirable traits of both parents. Progeny are evaluated for several years for the traits of interest, until they can be released as established varieties or cultivars.

1. Describe three phenotypic characteristics that would be desirable in a wheat plant:

   (a) _____

   (b) _____

   (c) _____

2. How have both natural events and selective breeding contributed to the high yielding modern wheat varieties?

   _____

   _____

160 Chapter Review

Summarise what you know about this topic under the headings and sub-headings provided. You can draw diagrams or mind maps, or write short notes to organise your thoughts. Use the images and hints to help you and refer back to the introduction to check the points covered:

Gene pools

HINT: How do gene pools change over time? What is the Hardy-Weinberg principle and how is it applied to the study of evolving populations.

Speciation

HINT: Describe speciation in allopatric and sympatric populations and explain the role of reproductive isolating mechanisms in the formation of species.

Natural selection

HINT: Define natural selection and include examples of types of natural selection.

Selective breeding

HINT: Explain the process of selective breeding. Why is it important to maintain genetic diversity?

REVISE

161 KEY TERMS: Did You Get?

1. Match each term to its definition, as identified by its preceding letter code.

allopatric speciation

founder effect

gene flow

gene pool

genetic bottleneck

genetic drift

Hardy-Weinberg principle

natural selection

polyploidy

reproductive isolation

selective breeding

speciation

sympatric speciation

A The process by which heritable traits become more or less common in a population through differential survival and reproduction.

B An evolutionary event in which a significant proportion of the alleles in a population are lost.

C The sum total of all genes of all breeding individuals in a population at any one time.

D The process by which particular phenotypes are favoured through human intervention.

E The division of one species, as a result of evolutionary processes, into two or more separate species.

F Speciation as a result of reproductive isolation without any physical separation of the populations, i.e. populations remain within the same range.

G The movement of alleles between populations as a result of migration.

H Speciation in which the populations are physically separated.

I The loss of genetic variation when a new colony is formed by a very small number of individuals from a larger population.

J The principle of genetic equilibrium that describes the constancy of population allele frequencies in the absence of evolutionary influences.

K The situation in which members of a group of organisms breed with each other but not with members of other groups

L The change in allele frequency in a population as a result of random sampling. The effect is proportionally larger in small populations.

M The heritable condition of having more than two complete chromosome sets. Rare in animals but important in the speciation events of many plants.

2. Using examples, contrast the characteristics of directional and stabilising selection and their effects:

_____

_____

_____

_____

3. Within a population of butterflies, brown colour (B) is dominant over white (b) and 40% of butterflies are white. Calculate:

(a) The percentage of butterflies that are heterozygous: _____

_____

(b) The frequency of homozygous dominant individuals: _____

_____

4. Blood samples of 1000 individuals were typed for the MN blood group, which can be detected because the alleles are codominant. Using the results (right) calculate the frequency of each allele in the population:

(a) Frequency of M: _____

_____

(b) Frequency of N: _____

_____

Blood type	Genotype	No. of individuals	Frequency
M	MM	490	0.49
MN	MN	420	0.42
N	NN	90	0.09

© 2015 **BIOZONE** International
ISBN: **978-1-927309-14-8**
Photocopying Prohibited

Manipulating Genomes

DNA sequencing, profiling, and analysis

Learning outcomes

		Activity number
☐	1 Appreciate the scope of genetic research and how the applications of genetic technologies have grown in recent decades.	162
☐	2 Explain the principles of DNA sequencing including the use of PCR and gel electrophoresis. Explain the role of automated (Next-Gen) sequencing in the feasibility of large scale genome analyses and outline its applications.	166 167
☐	3 Explain how gene sequencing is enabled genome-wide comparisons between individuals and species. Explain how bioinformatics and computational biology are contributing to our understanding of genetics, disease, and evolution.	167-171
☐	4 Explain how gene sequencing has enabled the sequences of amino acids in polypeptides to be predicted and how the technology has enabled the production of synthetic genes.	172
☐	5 Describe and explain the role of polymerase chain reaction (PCR) in DNA amplification, including the role of primers and DNA polymerase.	163
☐	6 Describe and explain DNA profiling using PCR. Describe the applications of DNA profiling in forensic analysis and in analysis of disease risk.	173-176
☐	7 **PAG6** ▶ Explain the principles and uses of gel electrophoresis for separating nucleic acid fragments or proteins. Explain how the fragments on a gel are made visible and how the different sized fragments are identified.	164 165

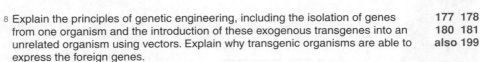

Genetic engineering

Learning outcomes

		Activity number
☐	8 Explain the principles of genetic engineering, including the isolation of genes from one organism and the introduction of these exogenous transgenes into an unrelated organism using vectors. Explain why transgenic organisms are able to express the foreign genes.	177 178 180 181 also 199
☐	9 Explain the techniques used in genetic engineering, including the use of restriction enzymes, plasmids, and DNA ligase to form recombinant DNA. Identify some of the vectors used in genetic engineering and explain methods for delivering them to recipient cells, e.g. gene guns and electroporation.	177-179
☐	10 Discuss the ethical issues relating to the use of genetically modified organisms (GMOs). Include reference to insect resistance in GM soy, GM pathogens for research, use of GM animals as biofactories to produce pharmaceuticals, and issues relating to patenting and technology transfer.	182
☐	11 Describe the principles of gene therapy and use examples to explain its potential uses in medicine. Explain the difference between somatic cell gene therapy and germ line cell gene therapy and its significance.	183 184

162 A Brief History of Human Genetic Research

Key Idea: Humans have been manipulating the transfer of genetic information between organisms ever since plants and animals were first domesticated over 10,000 years ago. Selective breeding, the breeding together of organisms with desirable traits, was the earliest form of genetic manipulation. In the last few decades, humans have developed sophisti-

cated methods to manipulate genetic information to produce organisms with beneficial traits. For example, the insertion of a gene from one species into another completely different species, is now common-place. The time-line below outlines some significant steps in the history of humans manipulating the transfer of genetic information.

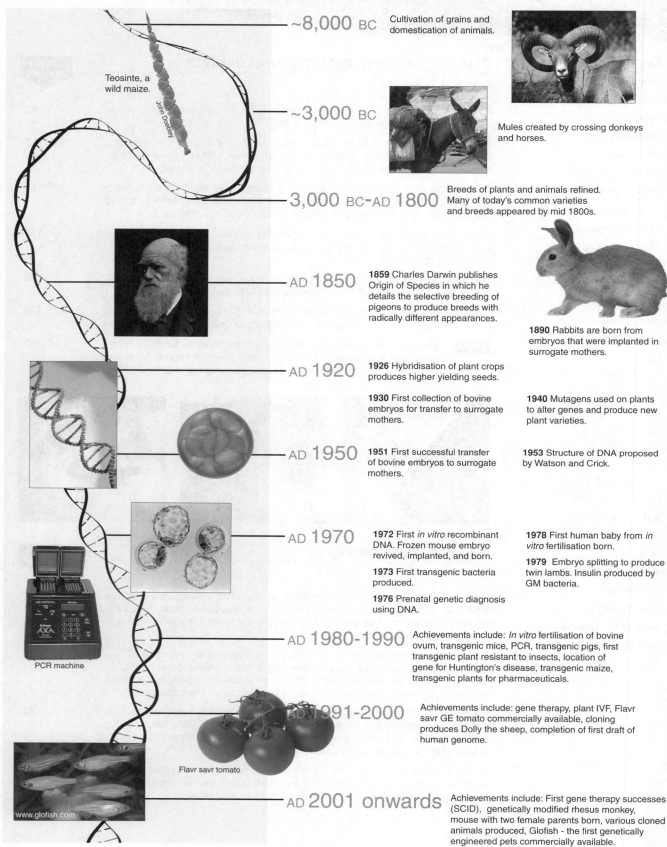

Teosinte, a wild maize.

John Doebley

~8,000 BC Cultivation of grains and domestication of animals.

~3,000 BC Mules created by crossing donkeys and horses.

3,000 BC–AD 1800 Breeds of plants and animals refined. Many of today's common varieties and breeds appeared by mid 1800s.

AD 1850 **1859** Charles Darwin publishes Origin of Species in which he details the selective breeding of pigeons to produce breeds with radically different appearances.

1890 Rabbits are born from embryos that were implanted in surrogate mothers.

AD 1920 **1926** Hybridisation of plant crops produces higher yielding seeds.

1930 First collection of bovine embryos for transfer to surrogate mothers.

1940 Mutagens used on plants to alter genes and produce new plant varieties.

AD 1950 **1951** First successful transfer of bovine embryos to surrogate mothers.

1953 Structure of DNA proposed by Watson and Crick.

AD 1970 **1972** First *in vitro* recombinant DNA. Frozen mouse embryo revived, implanted, and born.

1973 First transgenic bacteria produced.

1976 Prenatal genetic diagnosis using DNA.

1978 First human baby from *in vitro* fertilisation born.

1979 Embryo splitting to produce twin lambs. Insulin produced by GM bacteria.

PCR machine

AD 1980-1990 Achievements include: *In vitro* fertilisation of bovine ovum, transgenic mice, PCR, transgenic pigs, first transgenic plant resistant to insects, location of gene for Huntington's disease, transgenic maize, transgenic plants for pharmaceuticals.

AD 1991-2000 Achievements include: gene therapy, plant IVF, Flavr savr GE tomato commercially available, cloning produces Dolly the sheep, completion of first draft of human genome.

Flavr savr tomato

www.glofish.com

AD 2001 onwards Achievements include: First gene therapy successes (SCID), genetically modified rhesus monkey, mouse with two female parents born, various cloned animals produced, Glofish - the first genetically engineered pets commercially available.

© 2015 **BIOZONE** International
ISBN: **978-1-927309-14-8**
Photocopying Prohibited

163 DNA Amplification Using PCR

Key Idea: PCR uses a polymerase enzyme to copy a DNA sample, producing billions of copies in a few hours.

Many procedures in DNA technology, e.g. DNA sequencing and profiling, require substantial amounts of DNA yet, very often, only small amounts are obtainable (e.g. DNA from a crime scene or from an extinct organism). **PCR** (**polymerase**

chain reaction) is a technique for reproducing large quantities of DNA in the laboratory from an original sample. For this reason, it is often called **DNA amplification**. The technique is outlined below for a single cycle of replication. Subsequent cycles replicate DNA at an exponential rate, so PCR can produce billions of copies of DNA in only a few hours.

A single cycle of PCR

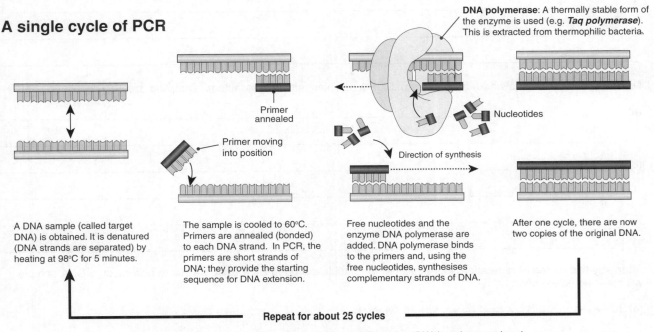

DNA polymerase: A thermally stable form of the enzyme is used (e.g. *Taq polymerase*). This is extracted from thermophilic bacteria.

Primer annealed

Primer moving into position

Nucleotides

Direction of synthesis

A DNA sample (called target DNA) is obtained. It is denatured (DNA strands are separated) by heating at 98°C for 5 minutes.

The sample is cooled to 60°C. Primers are annealed (bonded) to each DNA strand. In PCR, the primers are short strands of DNA; they provide the starting sequence for DNA extension.

Free nucleotides and the enzyme DNA polymerase are added. DNA polymerase binds to the primers and, using the free nucleotides, synthesises complementary strands of DNA.

After one cycle, there are now two copies of the original DNA.

Repeat for about 25 cycles

Repeat cycle of heating and cooling until enough copies of the target DNA have been produced

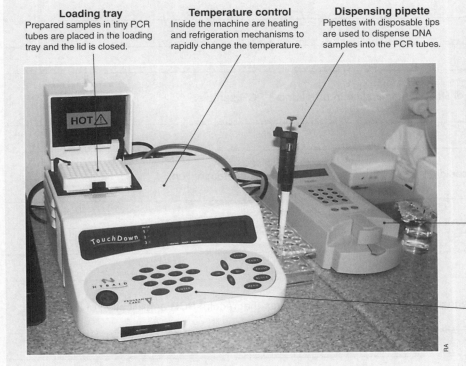

Loading tray
Prepared samples in tiny PCR tubes are placed in the loading tray and the lid is closed.

Temperature control
Inside the machine are heating and refrigeration mechanisms to rapidly change the temperature.

Dispensing pipette
Pipettes with disposable tips are used to dispense DNA samples into the PCR tubes.

Thermal cycler

Amplification of DNA can be carried out with simple-to-use machines called thermal cyclers. Once a DNA sample has been prepared, in just a few hours the amount of DNA can be increased billions of times. Thermal cyclers are in common use in the biology departments of universities, as well as other kinds of research and analytical laboratories. The one pictured on the left is typical of this modern piece of equipment.

DNA quantitation
The amount of DNA in a sample can be determined by placing a known volume in this quantitation machine. For many genetic engineering processes, a minimum amount of DNA is required.

Controls
The control panel allows a number of different PCR programmes to be stored in the machine's memory. Carrying out a PCR run usually just involves starting one of the stored programmes.

HOT ⚠

1. Explain the purpose of PCR: _____

_____

_____

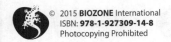
LINK LINK WEB
173 **169** **163** **KNOW**

2. Describe how the **polymerase chain reaction** works: _____

_____

_____

_____

_____

_____

_____

3. Describe three situations where only very small DNA samples may be available for sampling and PCR could be used:

(a) _____

_____

(b) _____

_____

(c) _____

_____

4. After only two cycles of replication, four copies of the double-stranded DNA exist. Calculate how much a DNA sample will have increased after:

(a) 10 cycles: _____ (b) 25 cycles: _____

5. The risk of contamination in the preparation for PCR is considerable.

(a) Describe the effect of having a single molecule of unwanted DNA in the sample prior to PCR:

_____

_____

_____

(b) Describe two possible sources of DNA contamination in preparing a PCR sample:

Source 1: _____

Source 2: _____

(c) Describe two precautions that could be taken to reduce the risk of DNA contamination:

Precaution 1: _____

_____

Precaution 2: _____

_____

6. Describe two other genetic engineering/genetic manipulation procedures that require PCR amplification of DNA:

(a) _____

_____

_____

(b) _____

_____

_____

164 Gel Electrophoresis

Key Idea: Gel electrophoresis is used to separate DNA fragments on the basis of size.

DNA can be loaded onto an electrophoresis gel and separated by size. DNA has an overall negative charge, so when an electrical current is run through a gel, the DNA moves towards the positive electrode. The rate at which the DNA molecules move through the gel depends primarily on their size and the strength of the electric field. The gel they move through is full of pores (holes). Smaller DNA molecules move through the pores more quickly than larger ones. At the end of the process, the DNA molecules can be stained and visualised as a series of bands. Each band contains DNA molecules of a particular size. The bands furthest from the start of the gel contain the smallest DNA fragments.

Analysing DNA using gel electrophoresis

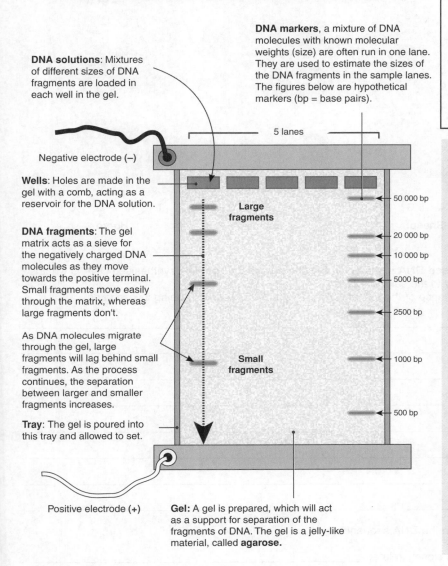

DNA solutions: Mixtures of different sizes of DNA fragments are loaded in each well in the gel.

DNA markers, a mixture of DNA molecules with known molecular weights (size) are often run in one lane. They are used to estimate the sizes of the DNA fragments in the sample lanes. The figures below are hypothetical markers (bp = base pairs).

5 lanes

Negative electrode (−)

Wells: Holes are made in the gel with a comb, acting as a reservoir for the DNA solution.

Large fragments

50 000 bp

DNA fragments: The gel matrix acts as a sieve for the negatively charged DNA molecules as they move towards the positive terminal. Small fragments move easily through the matrix, whereas large fragments don't.

20 000 bp

10 000 bp

5000 bp

As DNA molecules migrate through the gel, large fragments will lag behind small fragments. As the process continues, the separation between larger and smaller fragments increases.

2500 bp

Small fragments

1000 bp

Tray: The gel is poured into this tray and allowed to set.

500 bp

Positive electrode (+)

Gel: A gel is prepared, which will act as a support for separation of the fragments of DNA. The gel is a jelly-like material, called **agarose**.

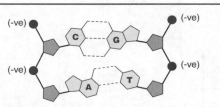

(−ve) C G (−ve)

(−ve) A T (−ve)

DNA is **negatively charged** because the phosphates (blue) that form part of the backbone of a DNA molecule have a negative charge.

Steps in the process of gel electrophoresis of DNA

1. A tray is prepared to hold the gel matrix.

2. A gel comb is used to create holes in the gel. The gel comb is placed in the tray.

3. Agarose gel powder is mixed with a buffer solution (this stabilises the DNA). The solution is heated until dissolved and poured into the tray and allowed to cool.

4. The gel tray is placed in an electrophoresis chamber and the chamber is filled with buffer, covering the gel. This allows the electric current from electrodes at either end of the gel to flow through the gel.

5. DNA samples are mixed with a "loading dye" to make the DNA sample visible. The dye also contains glycerol or sucrose to make the DNA sample heavy so that it will sink to the bottom of the well.

6. The gel is covered, electrodes are attached to a power supply and turned on.

7. When the dye marker has moved through the gel, the current is turned off and the gel is removed from the tray.

8. DNA molecules are made visible by staining the gel with **methylene blue** or ethidium bromide which binds to DNA and will fluoresce in UV light.

1. What is the purpose of gel electrophoresis? _____

_____

_____

2. Describe the two forces that control the speed at which fragments pass through the gel:

(a) _____

(b) _____

3. Why do the smallest fragments travel through the gel the fastest? _____

_____

_____

165 Interpreting Electrophoresis Gels

Key Idea: The banding pattern on an electrophoresis gel can give information about genetic variation and relationships.

Once made, an electrophoresis gel must be interpreted. If a specific DNA base sequence was being investigated, then the band pattern can be used to determine the DNA sequence and the protein that it encoded. Alternatively, depending on how the original DNA was treated, the banding pattern may be used as a profile for a species or individual. Commonly, the gene for cytochrome oxidase I (COXI), a mitochondrial protein, is used to distinguish animal species. The genetic information from this gene is both large enough to measure differences between species and small enough to have the differences make sense (i.e. the differences occur in small regions and aren't hugely varied).

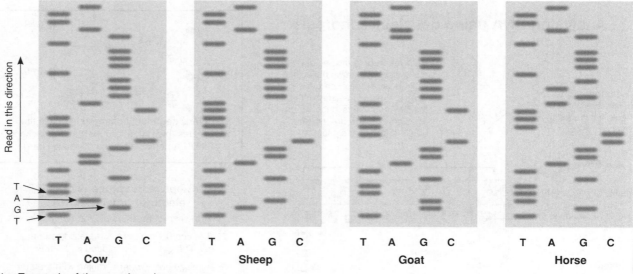

Read in this direction

Cow   T A G C

Sheep   T A G C

Goat   T A G C

Horse   T A G C

1. For each of the species above:

(a) Determine the sequence of **synthesised DNA** in the gel in the photographs above. The synthesised DNA is what is visible on the gel. It is complementary to the sample DNA.

(b) Convert it to the complementary sequence of the sample DNA. This is the DNA that is being investigated.

Cow: **synthesised DNA**: _____

        sample DNA: _____

Sheep: **synthesised DNA**: _____

        sample DNA: _____

Goat: **synthesised DNA**: _____

        sample DNA: _____

Horse: **synthesised DNA**: _____

        sample DNA: _____

Based on the number of differences in the DNA sequences:

(c) Identify the two species that are most closely related: _____

(d) Identify the two species that are the least closely related: _____

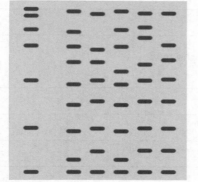

Calibration   A   B   C   D   E

2. Determine the relatedness of each individual (A-E) using each banding pattern on the set of DNA profiles (left). When you have done this, complete the phylogenetic tree by adding the letter of each individual.

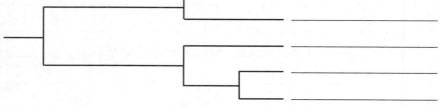

© 2015 **BIOZONE** International
ISBN: **978-1-927309-14-8**
Photocopying Prohibited

166 The Principles of DNA Sequencing

Key Idea: DNA sequencing techniques are used to determine the nucleotide (base) sequence of DNA.

The Sanger method (below) is a manual method for determining a DNA sequence. It uses modified nucleotides, which prematurely stop DNA replication when they are incorporated into the nucleotide sequence. Different lengths of DNA are produced and these can be put in order to reveal the original sequence. Four separate reactions are run, each containing a modified nucleotide mixed with

its normal counterpart, as well as the three other normal nucleotides. When a modified nucleotide is added to the growing complementary DNA, synthesis stops. The fragments of DNA produced from the four reactions are separated by electrophoresis and analysed by autoradiography to determine the DNA sequence. For large scale genome analyses, Sanger sequencing has largely been replaced by automated (so-called Next-Gen) sequencing methods, but it is still widely used for small scale projects.

1% modified T, C, G, or A nucleotides (dideoxyribonucleic acids) are added to each reaction vessel. Only one kind of modified nucleotide is added per reaction vessel to cause termination of replication at random T, C, G, or A sites.

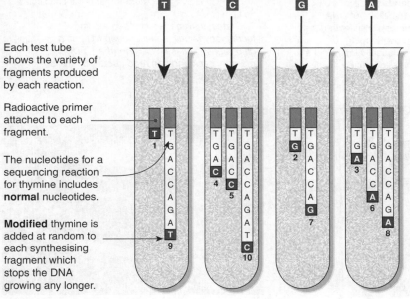

Each test tube shows the variety of fragments produced by each reaction.

Radioactive primer attached to each fragment.

The nucleotides for a sequencing reaction for thymine includes **normal** nucleotides.

Modified thymine is added at random to each synthesising fragment which stops the DNA growing any longer.

The fragments are placed on an electrophoresis gel to separate them so they can be read.

DNA fragments move in this direction

Gel is read in this direction

1. (a) In the Sanger method, what type of molecule is added to stop replication? _____

   (b) Analyse the gel diagram, above right, and write the sequence of the bands on the gel (shortest to largest).

   (c) On the diagram circle the shortest fragment:

   (d) Write the sequence of the copied DNA: _____

   (e) Write the sequence of the original DNA: _____

2. Why must this method of DNA sequencing use four separate reaction vessels? _____

   _____

   _____

   _____

   _____

3. Why is only 1% of the reaction mix modified DNA? _____

   _____

   _____

   _____

   _____

LINK
167

WEB
166

KNOW

167 Advancements in DNA Sequencing

Key Idea: DNA sequencing is many times faster than even a decade ago due to a new generation of DNA sequencers. The first DNA sequencing methods allowed scientists to determine the base sequence of relatively short DNA segments. The launch of the Human Genome Project in 1990 both required and initiated the development of fast and accurate DNA sequencing methods. The advancement of these methods has produced enormous amounts of information. The collection, storage, and analysis of this information using computers is called **bioinformatics**. Bioinformatics allows DNA sequence comparisons between species, a field called comparative genomics.

First generation and NextGen sequencing compared

Early DNA sequencing technologies, such as the Sanger method, required that the sample DNA sequence was copied using modified DNA, producing various lengths of DNA. These then had to be separated on a gel and read on a UV bed or as they passed by a laser.

High throughput, next generation (NextGen) sequencers read the DNA as it is being copied, a technique called **sequencing by synthesis**. As each nucleotide is added to the DNA a digital camera reads a fluorescent tag attached to the nucleotide. Thousands to millions of sequences can be read at once, allowing million to billions of DNA fragments to be sequenced at the same time. The resulting sequences are compared by computer and aligned based on overlapping sequences. Next generation sequencers have dramatically improved the feasibility and reduced the costs of whole genome sequencing.

Nanopore sequencer

Flow cell

The MinION, developed by Oxford Nanopore Technologies.

The latest third generation sequencing technology is now small enough to fit on a chip/reader that is little bigger than a USB memory stick and can read about 150 million base pairs per run.

NextGen sequencing technology

One synthesis cycle from a flow cell.

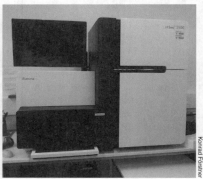

Illumina HiSeq 2500 sequencing machine

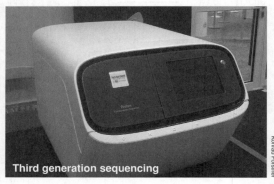

Third generation sequencing

Ion Proton semiconductor sequencer

Massively Parallel Signature Sequencing (MPSS)
The first MPSS methods, developed in the 1990s, were complicated and not widely used. One of the first methods, developed by Lynx Therapeutics, worked by using sample RNA to produce single stranded complementary DNA (cDNA). This was then tagged with a primer and coupled to microbeads. Each bead carried multiple copies of the cDNA, and each different bead carried different cDNA sequences. The beads were attached to a slide called a **flow cell** and exposed to nucleotides tagged by fluorescent dye. As the nucleotides attach to the cDNA, the fluorescent dye was read by a digital camera. Up to 1 million sequences could be read at once. MPSS has since been superseded by other methods.

One of the more commonly used and fastest methods currently available is the **Illumina sequencing** method. A DNA sequence is isolated by PCR and has short RNA adapters added to it. The DNA sequence is then denatured to produce a single strand and introduced to a flow cell with a "lawn" of complementary adapters to which the DNA sequence adapters attach. PCR then amplifies the DNA sequence multiple times resulting in a cluster of identical single stranded DNA molecules attached to the flow cell. The flow cell will have multiple clusters containing different DNA sequences. Primers are then added and the DNA is copied one base at a time with fluorescently tagged nucleotides. The fluorescent nucleotides are read by computer. Each DNA sequence can be up to 300 bases long and up to 6 billion sequences can be read at the same time. This allows the equivalent of the human genome to be read in just one run.

Third generation sequencers have the potential to vastly reduce the amount of DNA needed for a sequencing run. In general, they do not stop between read steps and the DNA molecule is read in a continuous sequence.

Ion semi-conducter sequencing uses a semiconductor to detect the hydrogen ions given off when nucleotides bind to a growing DNA molecule. The DNA template to be sampled is placed in a microwell on a slide (called a chip) and flooded with one particular modified nucleotide triphosphate (dNTP) corresponding to RNA bases A, U, C, G. If it is complementary to the next DNA base, it is incorporated into the growing strand, releasing hydrogen ions that are detected by a sensor, with different dNTPs giving different signals. A chip has many thousands of microwells so many sequences can be analysed at once.

In **nanopore sequencing** (top) DNA is passed through a pore less than 8 nm wide in a synthetic membrane. A voltage across the membrane produces a current through the nanopore. As each DNA base passes through the pore, it interrupts the current in a characteristic way.

1. (a) What is the major difference between first generation DNA sequencing and next generation DNA sequencing?

_____

_____

© 2015 **BIOZONE** International
ISBN: **978-1-927309-14-8**
Photocopying Prohibited

Using the sequence data

As genome sequencing has become faster and more genomes are sequenced there has been a corresponding growth in the use of **bioinformatics**, the storage, retrieval, and analysis of biological information. There are numerous online DNA databases which allow the comparison of DNA being studied to known DNA sequences. This can allow quick identification, of species especially bacteria or viruses.

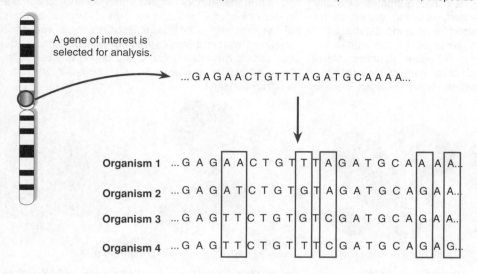

A gene of interest is selected for analysis.

...G A G A A C T G T T T A G A T G C A A A A...

High throughput next generation sequencing technologies allow the DNA sequence of the gene to be quickly determined.

Organism 1 ...G A G A A C T G T T T A G A T G C A A A A...

Organism 2 ...G A G A T C T G T G T A G A T G C A G A A...

Organism 3 ...G A G T T C T G T G T C G A T G C A G A A...

Organism 4 ...G A G T T C T G T T T C G A T G C A G A G...

Powerful computer software can quickly compare the DNA sequences of many organisms. Commonalities and differences in the DNA sequence can help to determine the organism and its evolutionary relationship to other organisms. The blue boxes indicate differences in the DNA sequences.

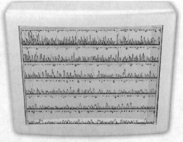

As faster and more reliable sequencing machines have become available and genome databases have become bigger, the cost of sequencing a genome has dropped dramatically, while the speed has increased. It is now possible to sequence the equivalent of a human genome within days.

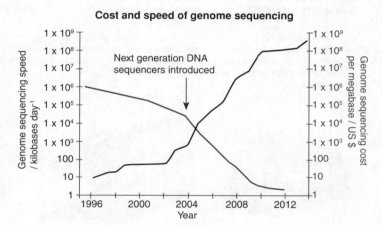

Cost and speed of genome sequencing

Next generation DNA sequencers introduced

(b) What is the difference between next generation DNA sequencers and so called third generation sequencers?

_____

_____

_____

(c) Generally speaking, what has physically happened over the last two decades to the devices used to sequence DNA?

_____

_____

2. (a) What is bioinformatics? _____

_____

_____

_____

(b) How has bioinformatics helped scientists determine the evolutionary relationship of organisms? _____

_____

_____

_____

168 Genome Projects

Key Idea: A genome is an organism's complete set of genetic material, including all of its genes. The genomes of many organisms have been sequenced, allowing genes to be compared. These can be searched for on gene databases. The aim of most genome projects is to determine the DNA sequence of the organism's entire genome. Many different species have now had their genomes sequenced including the honeybee, nematode worm, African clawed frog, pufferfish, zebra fish, rice, cow, dog, and rat. Genome sizes and the number of genes per genome vary, and are not necessarily correlated with the size and structural complexity of the organism. Once completed, genome sequences are analysed by computer to identify genes. Gene sequences and details are often entered into online databases that can be searched by anyone wishing to find out information about a particular gene.

*Mb = megabase pairs or 1,000,000 bp

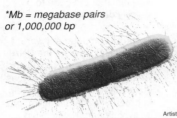   

Artist's impression

Bacterium
(*Escherichia coli*)

Genome size: 4.6 Mb*
Number of genes: 4403

E. coli has been used as a laboratory organism for over 70 years. Various strains of *E. coli* are responsible for several human diseases.

Yeast
(*Saccharomyces cerevisiae*)

Genome size: 13 Mb
Number of genes: 6000

The first eukaryotic genome to be completely sequenced. Yeast is used as a model organism to study human cancer.

Human
(*Homo sapiens*)

Genome size: 3000 Mb
Number of genes: < 22 500

The completion of the human genome has allowed advances in medical research, especially in cancer research.

Rice
(*Oryza sativa*)

Genome size: 466 Mb (indica) and 420 Mb (japonica)
Number of genes: 46 000

A food staple for much of the world's population. The importance of rice as a world food crop made sequencing it a high priority.

   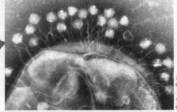

Mouse
(*Mus musculus*)

Genome size: 2500 Mb
Number of genes: 30 000

New drugs destined for human use are often tested on mice because more than 90% of their proteins show similarities to human proteins.

Fruit fly
(*Drosophila melanogaster*)

Genome size: 150 Mb
Number of genes: 14 000

Drosophila has been used extensively for genetic studies for many years. About 50% of all fly proteins show similarities to mammalian proteins.

Japanese canopy plant
(*Paris japonica*)

Genome size: 149 000 Mb

This rare native Japanese plant has the largest genome sequenced so far (15% larger than any previous estimate for a eukaryote). Plants with very large genomes reproduce and grow slowly.

T2 phage

Genome size: 160,000 bp
Number of genes: Approx. 300

T2 phage is one of a group of related T-even phages that infect bacteria. Analysis of these phages indicates a small core genome with variations being the result of genetic transfers during evolution.

1. For each organism below, calculate how much smaller or larger the genome is than the human genome:

   (a) Japanese canopy plant: _____

   (b) *E. coli*: _____

   (c) T2 phage: _____

2. Plants with very large genome sizes are at higher risk of extinction. Can you suggest why? _____

3. Why would geneticists want to sequence the genomes of plants such as wheat, rice, and maize?

© 2015 **BIOZONE** International
ISBN: **978-1-927309-14-8**
Photocopying Prohibited

169 Investigating Genetic Diversity

Key Idea: Genetic analysis of springtails in Taylor Valley has been able to separate morphologically cryptic species.

Genetic analysis is now widely used to investigate dispersal and divergence in all kinds of species. **Springtails** are tiny arthropods and have a limited capacity to move between locations. For this reason, they are good candidates for studying evolutionary phenomena. Researchers wanted to investigate the genetic relatedness of springtails in a Dry Valley in Antarctica. Results of a mtDNA study show two distinct genetic 'types' of springtail in Taylor Valley (see map, blue and white squares below). The two types have different DNA bases at a number of positions in a mitochondrial gene.

They also coexist in an area of **sympatry** in the middle of Taylor Valley. The results of the research are summarised on the following page. It shows an order of separation based on the genetic differences between the two types (TV1-14) compared with other populations of the same species (from Cape Evans, Cape Royds, and Beaufort Is). One other Antarctic species of springtail (*Biscoia sudpolaris*) is included on the diagram as an 'outgroup' (reference point). The genetic difference between populations is indicated by the distance to the 'branching point'. Groups that branch apart early in the tree are more different genetically than groups that branch later.

The springtail *Gomphiocephalus hodgsoni* (above) is a small arthropod, just over 1 mm long. It occupies the Dry Valleys region of Antarctica, particularly in Taylor Valley (below).

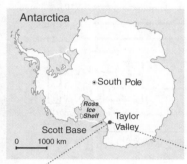

Sampling sites (below): A total of 14 sampling sites was used to build up a picture of the genetic diversity of springtails in an area of Taylor Valley. They were named TV1 through TV14 (TV = Taylor Valley). Bluesquares represent one genetic 'type' of springtail, while white squares represent another.

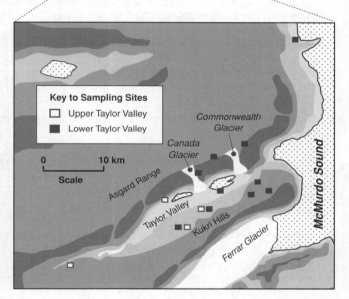

Key to Sampling Sites
- ☐ Upper Taylor Valley
- ■ Lower Taylor Valley

Taylor Valley (above) is one of the Dry Valleys in Antarctica, and is clear of snow virtually the whole year round. Any snow that falls in it soon melts as the dark rock surface heats up in the sun.

The process of DNA analysis of springtails:

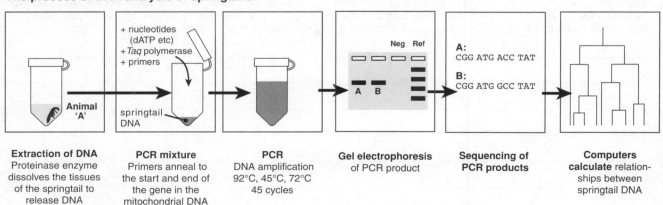

Extraction of DNA
Proteinase enzyme dissolves the tissues of the springtail to release DNA

PCR mixture
Primers anneal to the start and end of the gene in the mitochondrial DNA

PCR
DNA amplification 92°C, 45°C, 72°C 45 cycles

Gel electrophoresis of PCR product

Sequencing of PCR products

Computers calculate relationships between springtail DNA

Source: Many thanks to **Liam Nolan**, teacher at Tauranga Girls' College, for supplying the information for these pages. Liam studied with the Centre for Biodiversity and Ecology Research (University of Waikato, Hamilton, New Zealand), whilst the recipient of a study award from the NZ Ministry of Education.

LINK
167 KNOW

Genetic relationship between samples of springtail *Gomphiocephalus hodgsoni* in Taylor Valley, Antarctica

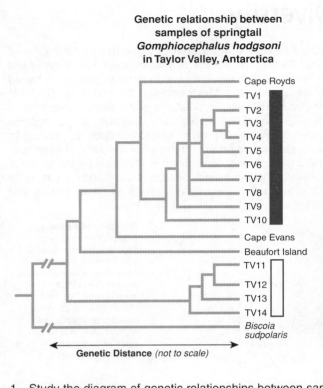

Cape Royds
TV1
TV2
TV3
TV4
TV5
TV6
TV7
TV8
TV9
TV10
Cape Evans
Beaufort Island
TV11
TV12
TV13
TV14
Biscoia sudpolaris

◄— **Genetic Distance** *(not to scale)* —►

Mosses (right) are the tallest plants in Antarctica. They provide ideal habitats for springtails. Although springtails have antifreeze (glycerol) in their blood, they are still vulnerable to freezing. Antarctic springtails do not possess the proteins that some Antarctic fish have to help them avoid freezing.

Burkhard Büdel

This photo taken in **Taylor Valley** (left) shows an ephemeral stream (it dries up at certain times of the year) emerging from one of the many "hanging glaciers" that line the margins of the valley. Such streams provide the moisture essential for springtails to survive amongst rocks, moss, lichen, and algae.

Leo Sanchez

1. Study the diagram of genetic relationships between samples of springtails (above). Describe what you notice about the branching point of the populations from the upper (TV11-14) and lower (TV1-10) Taylor Valley:

_____

_____

_____

2. Studies of the enzymes from the two 'types' of springtails indicate that the springtails do not interbreed. Explain why this is significant:

_____

_____

_____

3. Springtails cannot fly and in Antarctica quickly dry out and die if they are blown by the wind. Discuss the significance of these two features for gene flow between populations:

_____

_____

_____

4. Taylor Valley was once (thousands of years ago) covered in ice, with the only habitats available for springtails being the mountain tops lining both sides of the valley. Explain how this, together with low dispersal rates and small population size, could result in the formation of two species from one original species of springtail:

_____

_____

_____

_____

_____

_____

_____

170 The Human Genome Project

Key Idea: The Human Genome Project (HGP) was a publicly funded global venture to determine the sequence of bases in the human genome and identify and map the genes.

The HGP was completed in 2003, ahead of schedule, although analysis of it continues. Other large scale sequencing projects have arisen as a result of the initiative to sequence the human genome. In 2002, for example, the International HapMap Project was started with the aim of describing the common patterns of human genetic variation. The HGP has provided an immense amount of information, but it is not the whole story. The next task is to find out what the identified genes do. The identification and study of the protein products of genes (**proteomics**) is an important development of the HGP and will give a better understanding of the functioning of the genome. There is also increasing research in the area of the human **epigenome**, which is the record of chemical changes to the DNA and histone proteins that do not involve changes in the DNA base sequence itself. The epigenome is important in regulating genome function. Understanding how it works is important to understanding disease processes.

Gene mapping

This process involves determining the precise position of a gene on a chromosome. Once the position is known, it can be shown on a diagram.

One form of colour blindness

Production of a blood clotting factor

X Chromosome

Equipment used for DNA sequencing

Genesis Research and Development Corp, Auckland

Banks of PCR machines prepare the DNA for the sequencing gel stage. The DNA is amplified and chemically tagged (to make the DNA fluoresce and enable visualisation on a gel).

HGSI

Banks of DNA sequencing gels and powerful computers are used to determine the base order (the sequence) in DNA.

Count of mapped genes

The aim of the HGP was to produce a continuous block of sequence information for each chromosome. Initially the sequence information was obtained to draft quality, with an error rate of 1 in 1000 bases. The **Gold Standard** sequence, with an error rate of <1 per 100 000 bases, was completed in October 2004. This table shows the length and number of mapped genes for each chromosome.

Chromosome	Length (Mb)	No. of Mapped Genes
1	263	1873
2	255	1113
3	214	965
4	203	614
5	194	782
6	183	1217
7	171	995
8	155	591
9	145	804
10	144	872
11	144	1162
12	143	894
13	114	290
14	109	1013
15	106	510
16	98	658
17	92	1034
18	85	302
19	67	1129
20	72	599
21	50	386
22	56	501
X	164	1021
Y	59	122
Total:		**19 447**

Data to March 2008 from gdb.org (now offline)

Examples of mapped genes

The positions of an increasing number of genes have been mapped onto human chromosomes (see below). Sequence variations can cause or contribute to identifiable disorders. Note that chromosome 21 (the smallest human chromosome) has a relatively low gene density, while others are gene rich. This is possibly why trisomy 21 (Down syndrome) is one of the few viable human autosomal trisomies.

Key

Variable regions (heterochromatin)

Regions reflecting the unique patterns of light and dark bands seen on stained chromosomes

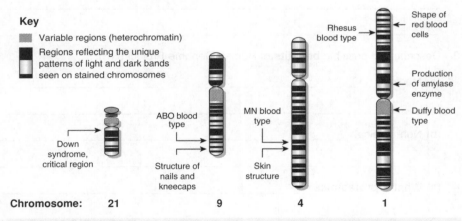

Down syndrome, critical region

ABO blood type

Structure of nails and kneecaps

MN blood type

Skin structure

Rhesus blood type

Shape of red blood cells

Production of amylase enzyme

Duffy blood type

Chromosome: 21   9   4   1

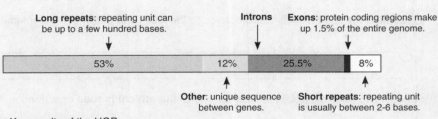

Long repeats: repeating unit can be up to a few hundred bases.

Introns

Exons: protein coding regions make up 1.5% of the entire genome.

| 53% | 12% | 25.5% | 8% |

Other: unique sequence between genes.

Short repeats: repeating unit is usually between 2-6 bases.

Key results of the HGP

- There are perhaps only 20 000-25 000 protein-coding genes in our human genome.
- It covers 99% of the gene containing parts of the genome and is 99.999% accurate.
- The new sequence correctly identifies almost all known genes (99.74%).
- Its accuracy and completeness allows systematic searches for causes of disease.

LINK 175   LINK 171   LINK 168   WEB 170   KNOW

Benefits and ethical issues arising from the Human Genome Project

Medical benefits	Non-medical benefits	Possible ethical issues
• Improved **diagnosis** of disease and predisposition to disease by genetic testing. • Better identification of disease carriers, through genetic testing. • Better **drugs** can be designed using knowledge of protein structure (from gene sequence information). • Greater possibility of successfully using **gene therapy** to correct genetic disorders.	• Greater knowledge of **family relationships** through genetic testing, e.g. paternity testing in family courts. • Advances **forensic science** through analysis of DNA at crime scenes. • Better knowledge of the evolutionary relationships between humans and other organisms, which will help to develop more accurate classification systems.	• Should third parties, e.g. health insurers, have rights to the results of genetic tests? • Knowing your genetic predisposition for a disease is of no use is there is no treatment. • Genetic tests are costly, and there is no easy answer as to who should pay for them. • Genetic information is hereditary so knowledge of an individual's own genome has implications for members of their family.

Couples can already have a limited range of genetic tests to determine the risk of having offspring with some genetic disorders.

Comparative analysis of the sequence data for humans and their ancestors may provide clues about human evolution.

Legislation is needed to prevent discrimination on the basis of genetic profile, e.g. at work or for health insurance.

1. Briefly describe the objectives of the Human Genome Project (HGP): _____

_____

_____

_____

2. Suggest a reason for developing a HapMap of the human genome: _____

_____

_____

3. Describe two possible **benefits** of Human Genome Project (HGP):

   (a) Medical: _____

   _____

   (b) Non-medical: _____

   _____

4. (a) What is **proteomics**? _____

   _____

   (b) Explain the significance of proteomics to the HGP and the ongoing benefits arising from it: _____

   _____

   _____

5. Suggest two possible points of view for one of the **ethical issues** described in the list above (top right):

   (a) _____

   _____

   (b) _____

   _____

© 2015 **BIOZONE** International
ISBN: **978-1-927309-14-8**
Photocopying Prohibited

171 Screening for Genes

Key Idea: DNA probes use attached markers (tags) to identify the presence and location of individual genes.

A DNA probe is a single stranded DNA sequence, with a base sequence that is complementary to a gene of interest. DNA probes target specific DNA sequences so they can be used to determine whether a person has a gene for a specific genetic disease, or to construct a gene map of a chromosome. DNA probes have either a radioactive label (e.g. ^{32}P) or a fluorescent dye so that they can be visualised on an electrophoresis gel or X-ray film.

Making and using a DNA probe

1

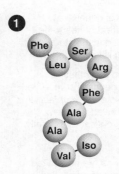

The protein product of a gene is isolated and its amino acid sequence is determined.

2 A tag is added. This can be one of two types:

Fluorescent dye: Shows up as a fluorescent band when exposed to ultraviolet light.

Radioactive tag: Shows up as a dark band when exposed to X-ray film.

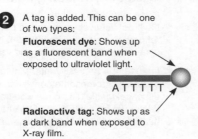

The DNA sequence for the protein product is identified from the amino acid sequence. The DNA sequence is artificially manufactured.

3

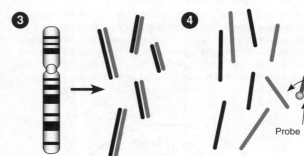

The DNA sequence being probed is cut into fragments using restriction enzymes.

4

The DNA fragments are denatured, forming single stranded DNA. The probe is added to the DNA fragments.

Probe

7

Probe identifies gene of interest

The gel is viewed by fluorescent light or on X-ray film (depending on the type of probe used). If the probe has bound to a gene, the tag makes it visible.

6

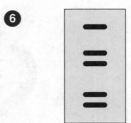

The DNA fragments are run on an electrophoresis gel. The fragments are separated by size.

5 If a complementary sequence is present, the probe will bind to it by base pairing.

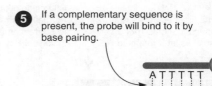

A T T T T T

C G T T T T G C T G A T A A A A A

Target DNA strand (contains the complementary sequence to that of the probe).

1. What is the purpose of a DNA probe? _____

_____

_____

2. Explain why a DNA probe can be used to identify a gene or DNA sequence: _____

_____

_____

3. Why does the DNA have to be denatured before adding the probe? _____

_____

_____

4. How is the presence of a specific DNA sequence or gene visualised? _____

_____

_____

_____

© 2015 **BIOZONE** International
ISBN: **978-1-927309-14-8**
Photocopying Prohibited

LINK 175 WEB 171 KNOW

172 Synthetic Genes

Key Idea: Synthetic genes are artificially produced DNA sequences made by piecing together nucleotides using conventional chemical processes.

The methods used to produce the DNA adapter sequences (oligonucleotides) for next generation DNA sequencing can also be used to produce synthetic genes. Today, if a gene has been sequenced, it can be produced artificially using a chemical process called solid-phase DNA synthesis. Unlike technologies such as PCR, no pre-existing DNA is needed as a template. Although there are currently some limitations, it is theoretically possible to produce any length of DNA in any base sequence. Already synthetic genes have been produced and transferred to yeasts and bacteria. The process is part of the wider field of **synthetic biology.**

Producing a synthetic gene

Short segments of DNA (oligonucleotides) can be produced using **solid-phase DNA synthesis** (below). Nucleotides are added in a stepwise fashion and are protected from incorrect reactions with blocking agents, which are removed at the end of the synthesis. Short fragments are joined together and *Taq* polymerase is used to complete the gene. The gene is then available for use, e.g. in recombinant DNA technology.

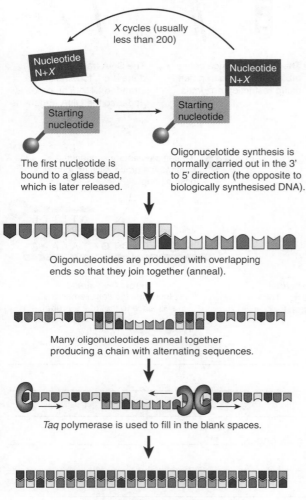

X cycles (usually less than 200)

Nucleotide N+*X*

Nucleotide N+*X*

Starting nucleotide

Starting nucleotide

The first nucleotide is bound to a glass bead, which is later released.

Oligonucelotide synthesis is normally carried out in the 3' to 5' direction (the opposite to biologically synthesised DNA).

Oligonucleotides are produced with overlapping ends so that they join together (anneal).

Many oligonucleotides anneal together producing a chain with alternating sequences.

Taq polymerase is used to fill in the blank spaces.

A complete gene is formed.

Uses of synthetic genes

Gene synthesis enables for production of novel genes that have not yet evolved in nature or it allows current genes to be refined and made more efficient. It can be used in the study and development of new drugs and vaccines, and in gene therapy.

In 2010, the J. Craig Venter Institute produced a synthetic bacterial chromosome consisting only of the genes shown to be essential for life. The gene was transplanted into a *Mycoplasma* bacterium from which the DNA had been removed. The new bacterium, called *Mycoplasma laboratorium*, replicated normally.

A new alphabet

The processes used to produce synthetic genes are not limited to the four bases normally found in DNA. Any type of nucleotide can be added providing it can be bound into the nucleotide chain in a stable way. Researchers have produced DNA with not four but six bases. The DNA was able to be replicated as a plasmid in *E. coli* until the new bases ran out, after which the bacterium replaced them with normal DNA bases.

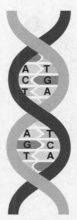
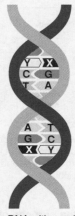

Natural DNA

DNA with new base pairs

The DNA triplets based on the four bases of DNA directly encode the 20 amino acids commonly found in proteins. If every triplet coded for a different amino acid there could be a maximum 64 amino acids (4^3) but code degeneracy means this is not achieved. A code with six DNA bases could encode 172 amino acids (6^3 - 44 with existing code degeneracy). Potentially, this could be useful in the manufacture of new proteins and materials for use in medicine or industry. Currently, DNA sequences containing the new bases do not code for anything, as there are no RNAs that recognise the new bases.

---

1. (a) How is the production of a synthetic gene different from natural DNA synthesis? _____

_____

(b) Why does the synthetic gene need to be built up of oligonucleotides? _____

_____

2. How might the production of synthetic genes be useful? _____

_____

WEB
172

LINK
179

LINK
183

LINK
197

KNOW

© 2015 **BIOZONE** International
ISBN: **978-1-927309-14-8**
Photocopying Prohibited

173 DNA Profiling Using PCR

Key Idea: Short units of DNA that repeat a different number of times in different people can be used to produce individual genetic profiles.

In chromosomes, some of the DNA contains simple, repetitive sequences. These non-coding nucleotide sequences repeat over and over again and are found scattered throughout the genome. Some repeating sequences, called **microsatellites** or **short tandem repeats** (STRs), are very short (2-6 base pairs) and can repeat up to 100 times. The human genome has many different microsatellites. Equivalent sequences in different people vary considerably in the numbers of the repeating unit. This phenomenon has been used to develop

DNA profiling, which identifies the natural variations found in every person's DNA. Identifying these DNA differences is a useful tool for forensic investigations. DNA testing in the UK is the Forensic Science Service (FSS). The FSS targets 10 STR sites; enough to guarantee that the odds of someone else sharing the same result are extremely unlikely; about one in a thousand million (a billion). DNA profiling has been used to help solve previously unsolved crimes and to assist in current or future investigations. DNA profiling can also be used to establish genetic relatedness (e.g. in paternity disputes or pedigree disputes), or when searching for a specific gene (e.g. screening for disease).

Microsatellites (short tandem repeats)

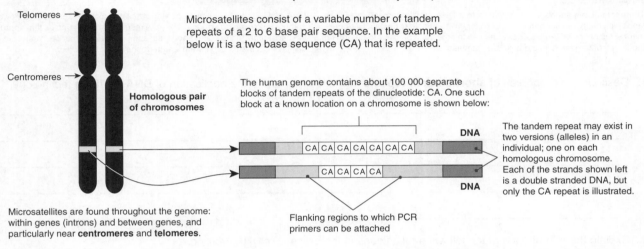

Microsatellites consist of a variable number of tandem repeats of a 2 to 6 base pair sequence. In the example below it is a two base sequence (CA) that is repeated.

Telomeres →

Centromeres →

Homologous pair of chromosomes

The human genome contains about 100 000 separate blocks of tandem repeats of the dinucleotide: CA. One such block at a known location on a chromosome is shown below:

DNA

DNA

The tandem repeat may exist in two versions (alleles) in an individual; one on each homologous chromosome. Each of the strands shown left is a double stranded DNA, but only the CA repeat is illustrated.

Microsatellites are found throughout the genome: within genes (introns) and between genes, and particularly near **centromeres** and **telomeres**.

Flanking regions to which PCR primers can be attached

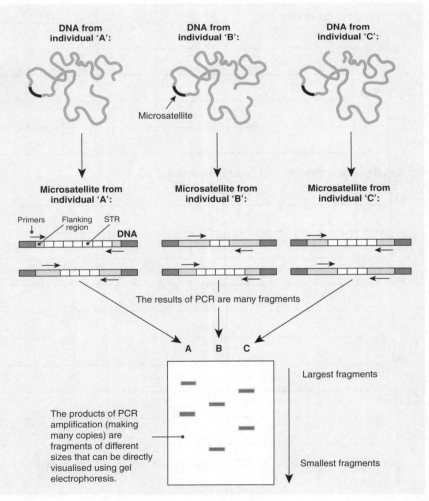

How short tandem repeats are used in DNA profiling

This diagram shows how three people can have quite different microsatellite arrangements at the same point (locus) in their DNA. Each will produce a different DNA profile using gel electrophoresis:

1 Extract DNA from sample

A sample collected from the tissue of a living or dead organism is treated with chemicals and enzymes to extract the DNA, which is separated and purified.

2 Amplify microsatellite using PCR

Specific primers (arrowed) that attach to the flanking regions (light grey) either side of the microsatellite are used to make large quantities of the micro-satellite and flanking regions sequence only (no other part of the DNA is amplified/replicated).

3 Visualise fragments on a gel

The fragments are separated by length, using **gel electrophoresis**. DNA, which is negatively charged, moves toward the positive terminal. The smaller fragments travel faster than larger ones.

DNA from individual 'A':

DNA from individual 'B':

DNA from individual 'C':

Microsatellite

Microsatellite from individual 'A':

Microsatellite from individual 'B':

Microsatellite from individual 'C':

Primers   Flanking region   STR   **DNA**

The results of PCR are many fragments

A   B   C

The products of PCR amplification (making many copies) are fragments of different sizes that can be directly visualised using gel electrophoresis.

Largest fragments

Smallest fragments

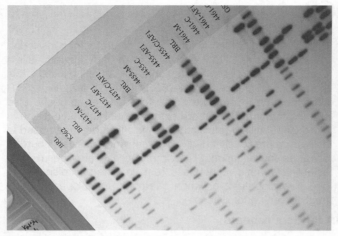

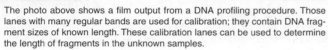

The photo above shows a film output from a DNA profiling procedure. Those lanes with many regular bands are used for calibration; they contain DNA fragment sizes of known length. These calibration lanes can be used to determine the length of fragments in the unknown samples.

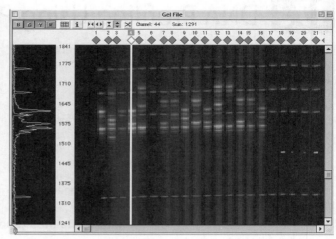

DNA profiling can be automated in the same way as DNA sequencing. Powerful computer software is able to display the results of many samples that are run at the same time. In the photo above, the sample in lane 4 has been selected and displays fragments of different length on the left of the screen.

1. Describe the properties of **short tandem repeats** that are important to the application of **DNA profiling** technology:

_____

_____

_____

_____

_____

2. Explain the role of each of the following techniques in the process of DNA profiling:

(a) Gel electrophoresis: _____

_____

_____

(b) PCR: _____

_____

_____

3. Describe the three main steps in DNA profiling using PCR:

(a) _____

_____

_____

(b) _____

_____

_____

(c) _____

_____

_____

_____

4. Explain why as many as 10 STR sites are used to gain a DNA profile for forensic evidence: _____

_____

174 Forensic Applications of DNA Profiling

Key Idea: DNA profiling has many forensic applications, from identifying criminal offenders to saving endangered species. The use of DNA as a tool for solving crimes such as homicide is well known, but it can also has several other applications.

DNA evidence has been used to identify body parts, solve cases of industrial sabotage and contamination, for paternity testing, and even in identifying animal products illegally made from endangered species.

Offender was wearing a cap but lost it when disturbed. DNA can be retrieved from flakes of skin and hair.

DNA left behind when offender drunk from a cup in the kitchen.

Bloodstain. DNA can be extracted from white blood cells in the sample

Hair. DNA can be recovered from cells at the base of the strand of hair.

During the initial investigation, samples of material that may contain DNA are taken for analysis. At a crime scene, this may include blood and body fluids as well as samples of clothing or objects that the offender might have touched. Samples from the victim are also taken to eliminate them as a possible source of contamination.

2 DNA is isolated and profiles are made from all samples and compared to known DNA profiles such as that of the victim.

Calibration   Profiles of collected DNA   Investigator (C)   Victim (D)

3 Unknown DNA samples are compared to DNA databases of convicted offenders and to the DNA of the alleged offender.

Alleged offender   Calibration   Profiles from DNA database

4 Although it does not make a complete case, DNA profiling, in conjunction with other evidence, is one of the most powerful tools in identifying offenders or unknown tissues.

The role of frequency and probability

Every person has two copies of each chromosome and therefore two copies (alleles) of every testable DNA marker. For example, the short tandem repeat (STR) known as CSF1PO contains between 7 and 15 repeats of GATA and has 9 possible alleles. Some alleles (and therefore genotypes) are more common in the population that others. For the CSF1PO STR, the frequency of the genotype 10,11 (allele 10 and allele 11) is 0.1270, i.e. it appears in 12.7% of the population. When DNA is tested, a number of STRs are sampled (the exact number varies between countries). When the data from all STRs is considered, levels of probability that the DNA came from a certain person can be calculated to 1 in 500 trillion.

Allele frequencies of the CSF1PO STR

Allele (number of repeats)	Frequency	Allele (number of repeats)	Frequency
7	0.0232	12	0.3446
8	0.0212	13	0.0656
9	0.0294	14	0.0092
10	0.2321	15	0.0010
11	0.2736		

1. Why are DNA profiles obtained for both the victim and investigator? _____

_____

_____

2. Use the evidence to decide if the alleged offender is innocent or guilty and explain your decision:

_____

_____

3. What is the frequency of the following CSF1PO alleles:

(a) 9: _____   (b) 12: _____

(c) The 9, 12 genotype (*hint, use the Hardy-Weinberg equation*): _____

LINK 176   LINK 136   WEB 174   KNOW

Paternity testing

DNA profiling can be used to determine paternity (and maternity) by looking for matches in alleles between parents and children. This can be used in cases such as child support or inheritance. DNA profiling can establish the certainty of paternity (and maternity) to a 99.99% probability of parentage.

Every STR allele is given the number of its repeats as its name, e.g. 8 or 9. In a paternity case, the mother may be 11, 12 and the father may be 8, 13 for a particular STR. The child will have a combination of these. The table below illustrates this:

DNA marker	Mother's alleles	Child's alleles	Father's alleles
CSF1PO	7, 8	8, 9	9, 12
D10S1248	14, 15	11, 14	10, 11
D12S391	16, 17	17, 17	17, 18
D13S317	10, 11	9, 10	8, 9

The frequency of the each allele occurring in the population is important when determining paternity (or maternity). For example, DNA marker CSF1PO allele 9 has a frequency of 0.0294 making the match between father and child very significant (whereas allele 12 has a frequency of 0.3446, making a match less significant). For each allele, a paternity index (PI) is calculated. These indicate the significance of the match. The PIs are combined to produce a probability of parentage. 10-13 different STRs are used to identify paternity. Mismatches of two STRs between the male and child is enough to exclude the male as the biological father.

Whale DNA: tracking illegal slaughter

Under International Whaling Commission regulations, some species of whales can be captured for scientific research and their meat sold legally. Most, including humpback and blue whales, are fully protected and to capture or kill them for any purpose is illegal. Between 1999 and 2003 Scott Baker and associates from Oregon State University's Marine Mammal Institute investigated whale meat sold in markets in Japan and South Korea. Using DNA profiling techniques, they found around 10% of the samples tested were from fully protected whales including western grey whales and humpbacks. They also found that many more whales were being killed than were being officially reported.

4. For the STR D10S1248 in the example above, what possible allele combinations could the child have?

_____

5. A paternity test was carried out and the abbreviated results are shown below:

DNA marker	Mother's alleles	Child's alleles	Man's alleles
CSF1PO	7, 8	8, 9	9, 12
D10S1248	14, 15	11, 14	10, 11
D19S433	9, 10	10,15	14, 16
D13S317	10, 11	9, 10	8, 9
D2S441	7, 15	7, 9	14, 17

(a) Could the man be the biological father? _____

(b) Explain your answer: _____

_____

_____

6. (a) How could DNA profiling be used to refute official claims of the **type** of whales captured and sold in fish markets?

_____

_____

_____

(b) How could DNA profiling be used to refute official claims of the **number** of whales captured and sold in fish markets?

_____

_____

_____

© 2015 **BIOZONE** International
ISBN: **978-1-927309-14-8**
Photocopying Prohibited

175 Hunting for a Gene

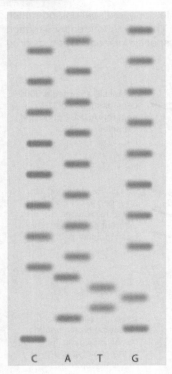

C   A   T   G

Key Idea: Huntington's disease is caused by a repeating section of DNA. The longer the repeating pattern, the earlier the disease tends to appear and the worse its symptoms.

Huntington's disease (HD) is a genetic neuro-degenerative disease that normally does not affect people until about the age of 40. Its symptoms usually appear first as a shaking of the hands and an awkward gait. Later manifestations of the disease include serious loss of muscle control and mental function, often ending in dementia and ultimately death.

All humans have the huntingtin (**HTT**) gene, which in its normal state produces a protein with roles in gene transcription, synaptic transmission, and brain cell survival. The mutant gene (**mHTT**) causes changes to and death of the cells of the cerebrum, the hippocampus, and cerebellum, resulting in the atrophy (reduction) of brain matter. The gene was discovered by Nancy Wexler in 1983 after ten years of research working with cell samples and family histories of more than 10 000 people from the town of San Luis in Venezuela, where around 1% of the population have the disease (compared to about 0.01% in the rest of the world). Ten years later the exact location of the gene on the chromosome 4 was discovered.

The identification of the HD gene began by looking for a gene probe that would bind to the DNA of people who had HD, and not to those who didn't. Eventually a marker for HD, called **G8**, was found. The next step was to find which chromosome carried the marker and where on the chromosome it was. The researchers hybridised human cells with those of mice so that each cell contained only one human chromosome, a different chromosome in each cell. The hybrid cell with chromosome 4 was the one with the G8 marker. They then found a marker that overlapped G8 and then another marker that overlapped that marker. By repeating this many times, they produced a map of the genes on chromosome 4. The researchers then sequenced the genes and found people who had HD had one gene that was considerably longer than people who did not have HD, and the increase in length was caused by the repetition of the base sequence CAG.

The HD mutation (mHTT) is called a trinucleotide repeat expansion. In the case of mHTT, the base sequence CAG is repeated multiple times on the short arm of chromosome 4. The normal number of CAG repeats is between 6 and 30. The mHTT gene causes the repeat number to be 35 or more and the size of the repeat often increases from generation to generation, with the severity of the disease increasing with the number of repeats. Individuals who have 27 to 35 CAG repeats in the HTT gene do not develop Huntington disease, but they are at risk of having children who will develop the disorder. The mutant allele, mHTT, is also dominant, so those who are homozygous or heterozygous for the allele are both at risk of developing HD.

New research has shown that the mHTT gene activates an enzyme called JNK3, which is expressed only in the neurones and causes a drop in nerve cell activity. While a person is young and still growing, the neurones can compensate for the accumulation of JNK3. However, when people get older and neurone growth stops, the effects of JNK3 become greater and the physical signs of HD become apparent. Because of mHTT's dominance, an affected person has a 50% chance of having offspring who are also affected. Genetic testing for the disease is relatively easy now that the genetic cause of the disease is known. While locating and counting the CAG repeats does not give a date for the occurrence of HD, it does provide some understanding of the chances of passing on the disease.

American singer-songwriter and folk musician Woody Guthrie died from complications of HD

1. Describe the physical effects of Huntington's disease: ⎯⎯⎯⎯⎯⎯⎯⎯⎯⎯⎯⎯⎯⎯⎯⎯⎯

⎯⎯⎯

2. Describe how the mHTT gene was discovered: ⎯⎯⎯⎯⎯⎯⎯⎯⎯⎯⎯⎯⎯⎯⎯⎯⎯⎯

⎯⎯⎯

⎯⎯⎯

3. Discuss the cause of Huntington's disease and its pattern of increasing severity with each generation: ⎯⎯⎯⎯⎯⎯⎯

176 Profiling for Analysis of Disease Risk

Key Idea: DNA profiling can be used to assess disease risk or to determine how well someone will respond to a treatment. DNA profiling relies on variations in the length of DNA fragments produced by PCR. This variation can be used to identify areas of DNA related to genetic diseases and match a person to a drug treatment. The key is to identify variation in the DNA that is related to specific disease types or drug susceptibility.

Identifying a relationship

To study the genetic component of a disease, researchers require two main study groups: people with the disease and people without the disease (known as phenotype first).

A genome wide association study (GWAS) is carried out on each individual in each group. The study looks for single nucleotide polymorphisms or **SNPs** (changes to single base pairs) to see there are differences between the control group and the afflicted group. There are over 100 million SNPs spread throughout the human genome and there are numerous ways to identify them, including DNA sequencing and using restriction enzymes.

Once the SNPs are identified, their frequencies are analysed to see if any are significantly different between the groups. SNPs found to be associated with a disease do not always just appear in people with the disease. Often they can be found in people without the disease. This lack of a definitive link makes linking a disease to a specific DNA profile a matter of probability and risks.

Using profiling to analyse disease risk

Using DNA profiling as a tool to analyse disease risk is a relatively new field. Although it promises a new way of diagnosing disease, to date it has produced inconsistent results because of the complexity of diseases involving large numbers of genes. One promising use of DNA profiling in disease analysis is the ability to determine response to albuterol in the treatment of asthma.

Albuterol is used to relieve the symptoms of asthma. It works well on some people but not on others. **1**

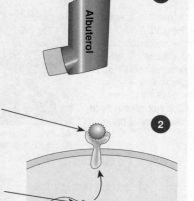

Albuterol binds to the beta2 adrenergic receptor in a cell's plasma membrane and causes the relaxation of smooth muscle in the airways.

The beta2 AR protein is encoded by the ADRB2 gene. Scientists wondered if genetic differences in or near this gene affected how well albuterol worked. **2**

3

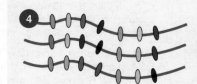

SNP

Scientists analysed a 3000 base pair piece of DNA near the ADRB2 gene and identified 13 SNPs.

4

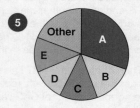

The SNPs are found arranged in combinations called haplotypes. 12 different haplotypes have been identified.

% haplotypes in population

5

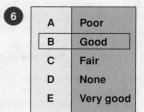

Other
A
E
D
C
B

Every person has a haplotype profile relating the ADRB2 gene. Five of the haplotypes are relatively common.

6

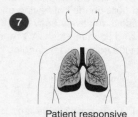

A	Poor
B	Good
C	Fair
D	None
E	Very good

Some of the haplotypes seem to be related to the effect of albuterol on people. Some haplotypes are found mainly in people who have a poor response to albuterol (D), while others are found in people who respond well to the drug (B, E).

7

This data may be able to be used by doctors when prescribing albuterol. In the future, other profiles could be used to determine the effect of other drugs on people.

Patient responsive to albuterol.

---

1. (a) Why is a set of SNPs (a haplotype) used when identifying a genetic disease, rather than just a single SNP?

_____

_____

(b) Why is the use of SNPs not a definitive way to assess the risk of a genetic disease?_____

_____

_____

2. How can personal genetic profiles be used to improve the treatment outcomes of patients? _____

_____

_____

© 2015 **BIOZONE** International
ISBN: **978-1-927309-14-8**
Photocopying Prohibited

177 Making Recombinant DNA

Key Idea: Recombinant DNA (rDNA) is produced by first isolating (or synthesising) a DNA sequence, then inserting it into the DNA of a different organism.

The production of rDNA is possible because the DNA of every organism is made of the same building blocks (**nucleotides**).

rDNA allows a gene from one organism to be moved into, and expressed in, a different organism. Two important tools used to create rDNA are restriction digestion (chopping up the DNA) using **restriction enzymes** and DNA ligation (joining of sections of DNA) using the enzyme **DNA ligase**.

Information about restriction enzymes

1. A **restriction enzyme** is an enzyme that cuts a double-stranded DNA molecule at a specific **recognition** site. There are many different types of restriction enzymes, each has a unique recognition site.

2. Some restriction enzymes produce DNA fragments with two **sticky ends** (right). A sticky end has exposed nucleotide bases at each end. DNA cut in such a way is able to be joined to other DNA with matching sticky ends. Such joins are specific to their recognition sites.

3. Some restriction enzymes produce a DNA fragment with two **blunt ends** (ends with no exposed nucleotide bases). The piece it is removed from is also left with blunt ends. DNA cut in such a way can be joined to any other blunt end fragment. Unlike sticky ends, blunt end joins are non-specific because there are no sticky ends to act as specific recognition sites.

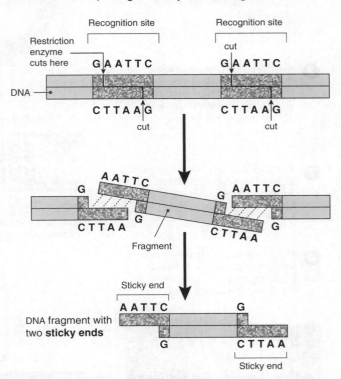

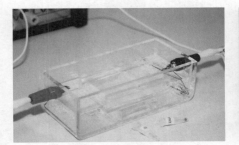

The fragments of DNA produced by the restriction enzymes are mixed with ethidium bromide, a molecule that fluoresces under UV light. The DNA fragments are then placed on an electrophoresis gel to separate the different lengths of DNA.

Once the DNA fragments are separated, the gel is placed on a UV viewing platform. The area of the gel containing the DNA fragments of the correct length is cut out and placed in a solution that dissolves the gel. This releases the DNA into the solution.

The solution containing the DNA is centrifuged at high speed to separate out the DNA. Centrifugation works by separating molecules of different densities. Once isolated, the DNA can be spliced into another DNA molecule.

1. What is the purpose of restriction enzymes in making recombinant DNA? _____

_____

_____

2. Describe the different uses of sticky ends and blunt ends: _____

_____

_____

_____

3. Why is it useful to have many different kinds of restriction enzymes? _____

_____

_____

LINK LINK WEB
179 178 177 KNOW

Creating a recombinant DNA plasmid

1 Two pieces of DNA are cut by the same restriction enzyme (they will produce fragments with matching **sticky ends**).

2 Fragments with matching sticky ends can be joined by base-pairing. This process is called **annealing.** This allows DNA fragments from different sources to be joined.

3 The fragments of DNA are joined together by the enzyme **DNA ligase**, producing a molecule of **recombinant DNA**.

4 The joined fragments will usually form either a linear or a circular molecule, as shown here (right) as recombinant **plasmid** DNA.

pGLO is a plasmid engineered to contain Green Fluorescent Protein (*gfp*). pGLO has been used to create fluorescent organisms, including the bacteria above (bright patches on agar plates).

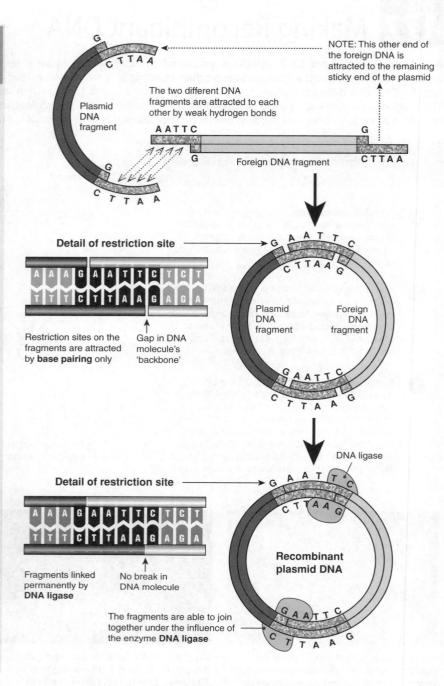

NOTE: This other end of the foreign DNA is attracted to the remaining sticky end of the plasmid

Plasmid DNA fragment

The two different DNA fragments are attracted to each other by weak hydrogen bonds

Foreign DNA fragment

Detail of restriction site

Restriction sites on the fragments are attracted by **base pairing** only

Gap in DNA molecule's 'backbone'

Plasmid DNA fragment

Foreign DNA fragment

Detail of restriction site

Fragments linked permanently by **DNA ligase**

No break in DNA molecule

DNA ligase

Recombinant plasmid DNA

The fragments are able to join together under the influence of the enzyme **DNA ligase**

4. Explain in your own words the two main steps in the process of joining two DNA fragments together:

   (a) Annealing: _____

   _____

   (b) DNA ligase: _____

   _____

5. Why can **ligation** be considered the reverse of the **restriction digestion** process? _____

   _____

6. Why can recombinant DNA be expressed in any kind of organism, even if it contains DNA from another species?

   _____

   _____

   _____

   _____

© 2015 **BIOZONE** International
ISBN: **978-1-927309-14-8**
Photocopying Prohibited

178 The Applications of Transgenesis

Key Idea: Transgenesis is the insertion of a gene from one species into another, so its protein product is expressed in the second species. Transgenesis has many applications including agriculture, and food and medical technologies. Transgenesis refers to the specific genetic engineering technique of inserting a gene from one species into another that does not normally contain the gene. It allows direct modification of a genome so that novel traits can be introduced to an organism. Organisms that have undergone transgenesis are called transgenic organisms. The genes are inserted using vectors or by direct insertion of the DNA. Applications of transgenesis include enhancing desirable features in livestock and crops, producing human proteins, and treating genetic defects with gene therapy. Cloning transgenics, or using them in selective breeding programmes, ensures the introduced gene is inherited in following generations.

Pronuclear injection

A gene that has been transferred into another organism is called a **transgene**. Genes can be introduced directly into an animal cell by microinjection. Multiple copies of the desired transgene are injected via a glass micropipette into a recently fertilised egg cell, which is then transferred to a surrogate mother. Transgenic mice and livestock are produced in this way. However, the process is inefficient: only 2-3% of eggs give rise to transgenic animals and only a proportion of these animals express the transgene adequately.

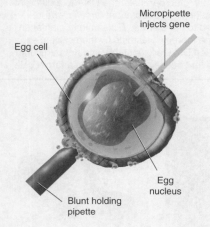

Egg cell

Micropipette injects gene

Egg nucleus

Blunt holding pipette

Creating transgenic mice using pronuclear injection

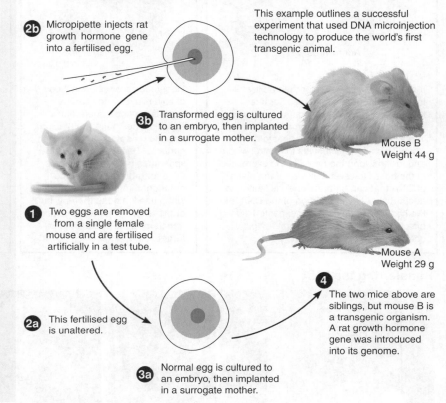

2b Micropipette injects rat growth hormone gene into a fertilised egg.

This example outlines a successful experiment that used DNA microinjection technology to produce the world's first transgenic animal.

3b Transformed egg is cultured to an embryo, then implanted in a surrogate mother.

Mouse B
Weight 44 g

1 Two eggs are removed from a single female mouse and are fertilised artificially in a test tube.

2a This fertilised egg is unaltered.

Mouse A
Weight 29 g

4 The two mice above are siblings, but mouse B is a transgenic organism. A rat growth hormone gene was introduced into its genome.

3a Normal egg is cultured to an embryo, then implanted in a surrogate mother.

Applications of transgenesis

USDA

Modifying crops

Transgenesis has been used to modify the genome of Bt cotton (above) to include genes that produce insecticides. Golden rice contains genes from a bacterium and a daffodil plant to improve its nutritional value.

Medical research

By inserting genes into model animals, the effect of a gene can be studied. Rhesus macaques have been engineered to provide models for the effects and potential treatments of diseases such as Huntington's and Parkinson's.

Livestock improvement

Transgenic sheep have been used to enhance wool production. The keratin protein of wool contains large amounts of the amino acid cysteine. Injecting developing sheep with the genes for the enzymes that generate cysteine produces woollier sheep.

Animals as biofactories

Transgenic animals can be used as biofactories to produce certain proteins. Transgenic sheep with the human α-1-antitrypsin gene produce the protein in their milk from which it can be extracted and used to treat hereditary emphysema.

1. What is transgenesis? _____

_____

2. Describe an application of transgenesis: _____

_____

_____

LINK   LINK   WEB
199 180 178 KNOW

179 Vectors for Transgenesis

Key Idea: Several different carriers, called vectors, can be used to introduce a gene into a cell. There are advantages and disadvantages associated with each type of vector.

Gene therapy usually requires a **vector** (carrier) to introduce the DNA to a cell. Viruses are often used as vectors because of their ability to integrate into the host's genome.

Viruses

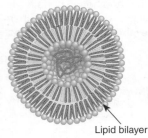

Retrovirus

Adenovirus

Viruses are well known for their ability to insert DNA into a host cell. For this reason they have become a favoured tool in transgenesis. Different types of viruses integrate their DNA into the host in different ways. This allows scientists to control where and for how long the new DNA is expressed in the host. However, the size of the piece of DNA that can be transferred is limited to about 8 kb. Also, integration of the DNA into the host DNA can cause unexpected side effects depending on where in the host's chromosome the DNA inserts itself.

Liposomes

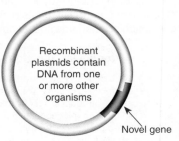

Lipid bilayer

Liposomes are spherical bodies of lipid bilayer. They can be quite large and targeted to specific types of cell by placing specific receptors on their surfaces. Because of their size, liposomes can carry plasmids 20 kb or more. They also do not trigger immune responses when used in gene therapy, but are less efficient than viruses at transferring the plasmid into a target cell.

Plasmids

Recombinant plasmids contain DNA from one or more other organisms

Novel gene

Plasmids are circular lengths of DNA that can be up to 1000 kb long (1 kb = 1000 bp). Recombinant plasmids are frequently used to produce transgenic organisms, especially bacteria. The bacteria maybe the final target for the recombinant DNA (e.g. transgenic *E. coli* producing insulin) or it can be used as a vector to transfer the DNA to a different host (e.g. *Agrobacterium tumefaciens* is used to transfer the *Ti* plasmid to plants). In gene therapy, plasmids by themselves, as naked DNA, are unstable and not particularly efficient at integrating DNA into a target cell.

Transferring the DNA

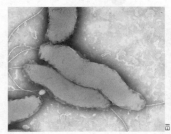

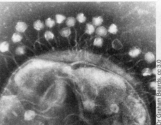

Electroporation cuvettes

Transformation is the direct uptake of foreign DNA and is common in bacteria. Recombinant DNA plasmids are mixed with bacteria and the bacteria that take up the DNA are used.

Transduction is the transfer of DNA into a bacterium by a virus. Bacteriophages (viruses that infect bacteria) are commonly used to integrate recombinant DNA into a target bacterium.

Transfection is the deliberate, often non-viral, introduction of foreign DNA into a cell. There are numerous methods including electroporation and the use of the gene gun (above).

Electroporation is a method in which an electric field is applied to cells, causing the plasma membrane to become more permeable. This allows DNA to cross the plasma membrane.

1. (a) Describe a feature of viruses that make them well suited as **vectors** for DNA transfer: _____

_____

_____

(b) Identify two problems with using viral vectors for DNA transfer: _____

_____

_____

_____

2. Describe two ways in which plasmids are used in genetic engineering: _____

_____

_____

_____

WEB LINK

© 2015 **BIOZONE** International
ISBN: **978-1-927309-14-8**
Photocopying Prohibited

180 Transgenic Plant: Golden Rice

Key Idea: The use of recombinant DNA to build a new metabolic pathway has greatly increased the nutritional value of a variety of rice.

The issue

▶ **Beta-carotene** (β-carotene) is a precursor to **vitamin A** which is involved in many functions including vision, immunity, foetal development, and skin health.

▶ Vitamin A deficiency is common in developing countries where up to 500 000 children suffer from night blindness, and death rates due to infections are high due to a lowered immune response.

▶ Providing enough food containing useful quantities of -carotene is difficult and expensive in many countries.

Concept 1

Rice is a staple food in many developing countries. It is grown in large quantities and is available to most of the population, but it lacks many of the essential nutrients required by the human body for healthy development. It is low in β-carotene.

Concept 2

Rice plants produce β-carotene but not in the edible rice endosperm. Engineering a new biosynthetic pathway would allow β-carotene to be produced in the endosperm. Genes expressing enzymes for carotene synthesis can be inserted into the rice genome.

Concept 3

The enzyme **carotene desaturase** (CRT1) in the soil bacterium *Erwinia uredovora*, catalyses multiple steps in carotenoid biosynthesis. **Phytoene synthase** (PSY) overexpresses a colourless carotene in the daffodil plant *Narcissus pseudonarcissus*.

Concept 4

DNA can be inserted into an organism's genome using a suitable vector. *Agrobacterium tumefaciens* is a tumour-forming bacterial plant pathogen that is commonly used to insert novel DNA into plants.

The development of golden rice

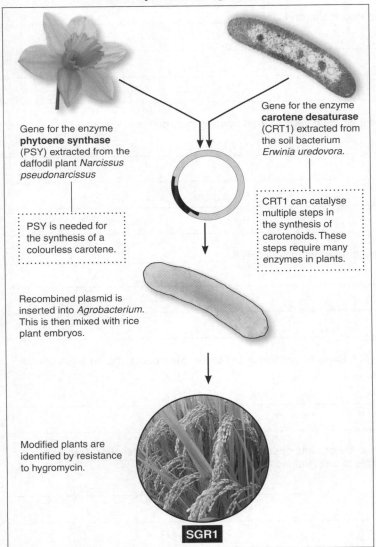

Gene for the enzyme **phytoene synthase** (PSY) extracted from the daffodil plant *Narcissus pseudonarcissus*

Gene for the enzyme **carotene desaturase** (CRT1) extracted from the soil bacterium *Erwinia uredovora*.

PSY is needed for the synthesis of a colourless carotene.

CRT1 can catalyse multiple steps in the synthesis of carotenoids. These steps require many enzymes in plants.

Recombined plasmid is inserted into *Agrobacterium*. This is then mixed with rice plant embryos.

Modified plants are identified by resistance to hygromycin.

SGR1

Techniques

The **PSY** gene from daffodils and the **CRT1** gene from *Erwinia uredovora* are sequenced.

DNA sequences are synthesised into packages containing the CRT1 or PSY gene, terminator sequences, and **endosperm specific promoters** (these ensure expression of the gene only in the edible portion of the rice).

The *Ti* **plasmid** from *Agrobacterium* is modified using restriction enzymes and DNA ligase to delete the tumour-forming gene and insert the synthesised DNA packages. A gene for resistance to the antibiotic **hygromycin** is also inserted so that transformed plants can be identified later. The parts of the *Ti* plasmid required for plant transformation are retained.

Modified *Ti* plasmid is inserted into the bacterium.

Agrobacterium is incubated with rice plant embryo. Transformed embryos are identified by their resistance to hygromycin.

Outcomes

The rice produced had endosperm with a distinctive yellow colour. Under greenhouse conditions golden rice (**SGR1**) contained 1.6 µg per g of carotenoids. Levels up to five times higher were produced in the field, probably due to improved growing conditions.

Further applications

Further research on the action of the PSY gene identified more efficient methods for the production of -carotene. The second generation of golden rice now contains up to 37 µg per g of carotenoids. Golden rice was the first instance where a complete biosynthetic pathway was engineered. The procedures could be applied to other food plants to increase their nutrient levels.

LINK 182 LINK 181 WEB 180 KNOW

The ability of *Agrobacterium* to transfer genes to plants is exploited for crop improvement. The tumour-inducing *Ti* plasmid is modified to delete the tumour-forming gene and insert a gene coding for a desirable trait. The parts of the *Ti* plasmid required for plant transformation are retained.

Soybeans are one of the many food crops that have been genetically modified for broad spectrum herbicide resistance. The first GM soybeans were planted in the US in 1996. By 2007, nearly 60% of the global soybean crop was genetically modified; the highest of any other crop plant.

GM cotton was produced by inserting the gene for the BT toxin into its genome. The bacterium *Bacillus thuringiensis* naturally produces BT toxin, which is harmful to a range of insects, including the larvae that eat cotton. The BT gene causes cotton to produce this insecticide in its tissues.

1. Describe the basic methodology used to create golden rice: _____

   _____

   _____

   _____

   _____

2. Explain how scientists ensured β-carotene was produced in the endosperm: _____

   _____

   _____

   _____

3. What property of *Agrobacterium tumefaciens* makes it an ideal vector for introducing new genes into plants?

   _____

   _____

   _____

   _____

4. (a) How could this new variety of rice reduce disease in developing countries? _____

   _____

   _____

   _____

   (b) Absorption of vitamin A requires sufficient dietary fat. Explain how this could be problematic for the targeted use of golden rice in developing countries:

   _____

   _____

5. As well as increasing nutrient content as in golden rice, other traits of crop plants are also desirable. For each of the following traits, suggest features that could be desirable in terms of increasing yield:

   (a) Grain size or number: _____

   (b) Maturation rate: _____

   (c) Pest resistance: _____

© 2015 **BIOZONE** International
ISBN: **978-1-927309-14-8**
Photocopying Prohibited

181 Food for the Masses

Key Idea: Genetic engineering has the potential to solve many of the world's food shortage problems by producing crops with greater yields than those currently grown.

Currently 1/6 of the world's population are undernourished. If trends continue, 1.5 billion people will be at risk of starvation by 2050 and, by 2100 (if global warming is taken into account), nearly half the world's population could be threatened with food shortages. The solution to the problem of food production is complicated. Most of the Earth's arable land has already been developed and currently uses 37% of

the Earth's land area, leaving little room to grow more crops or farm more animals. Development of new fast growing and high yield crops appears to be part of the solution, but many crops can only be grown under a narrow range of conditions or are susceptible to disease. Moreover, the farming and irrigation of some areas is difficult, costly, and can be environmentally damaging. Genetic modification of plants may help to solve some of these looming problems by producing plants that will require less intensive culture or that will grow in areas previously considered not arable.

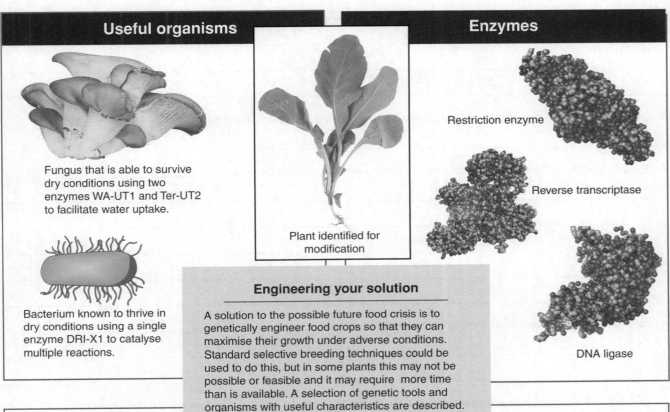

Useful organisms

Fungus that is able to survive dry conditions using two enzymes WA-UT1 and Ter-UT2 to facilitate water uptake.

Bacterium known to thrive in dry conditions using a single enzyme DRI-X1 to catalyse multiple reactions.

Plant identified for modification

Enzymes

Restriction enzyme

Reverse transcriptase

DNA ligase

Engineering your solution

A solution to the possible future food crisis is to genetically engineer food crops so that they can maximise their growth under adverse conditions. Standard selective breeding techniques could be used to do this, but in some plants this may not be possible or feasible and it may require more time than is available. A selection of genetic tools and organisms with useful characteristics are described. **Your task** is to use the items shown to devise a technique to successfully create a plant that could be successfully farmed in semi-desert environments such as sub-Saharan Africa. The following page will take you through the procedure. Not all the items will need to be used.

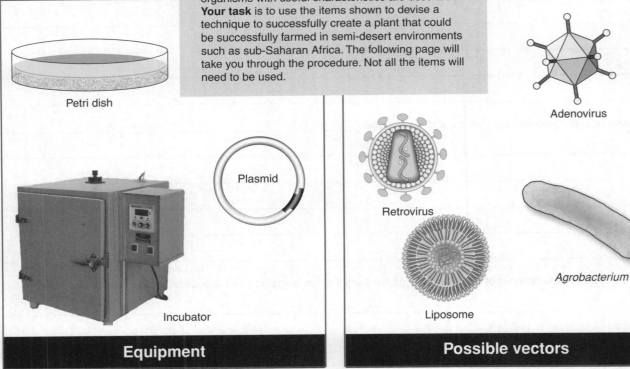

Petri dish

Plasmid

Incubator

Retrovirus

Liposome

Adenovirus

Agrobacterium

Equipment

Possible vectors

LINK   WEB

182 181 KNOW

1. Identify the organism you would chose as a 'donor' of drought survival genes and explain your choice:

   _____

   _____

2. Describe a process to identify and isolate the required gene(s) and identify the tools to be used: _____

   _____

   _____

   _____

   _____

   _____

   _____

3. Identify a vector for the transfer of the isolated gene(s) into the crop plant and explain your decision: _____

   _____

4. Explain how the isolated gene(s) would be integrated into the vector's genome: _____

   _____

   _____

   _____

   _____

   _____

5. (a) Explain how the vector will transform the identified plant: _____

   _____

   _____

   (b) Identify the stage of development at which the plant would most easily be transformed. Explain your choice:

   _____

   _____

   _____

   _____

6. Explain how the transformed plants could be identified: _____

   _____

   _____

   _____

   _____

7. Explain how a large number of plants can be grown from the few samples that have taken up the new DNA:

   _____

   _____

   _____

182 The Ethics of GMO Technology

Key Idea: There are many potential benefits, risks, and ethical questions in using genetically modified organisms. Genetically modified organisms (GMOs) have many potential benefits, but their use raises a number of biological and ethical concerns. Some of these include risk to human health, animal welfare issues, and environmental safety. Currently a matter of concern to consumers is the adequacy of government regulations for the labelling of food products with GMO content. In some countries GM products must be clearly labelled, while other countries have no requirements for GM labelling. This can take away consumer choice about the types of products they buy. The use of GM may also have trade implications for countries exporting and importing GMO produce.

Potential benefits of GMOs

1. Increase in crop yields, including crops with more nutritional value and that store for longer.
2. Decrease in use of pesticides, herbicides and animal remedies.
3. Production of crops that are drought tolerant or salt tolerant.
4. Improvement in the health of the human population and the medicines used to achieve it.
5. Development of animal factories for the production of proteins used in manufacturing, the food industry, and health.

Potential risks of GMOs

1. Possible (uncontrollable) spread of transgenes into other species of plants, or animals.
2. Concerns that the release of GMOs into the environment may be irreversible.
3. Animal welfare and ethical issues: GM animals may suffer poor health and reduced life span.
4. GMOs may cause the emergence of pest, insect, or microbial resistance to traditional control methods.
5. May create a monopoly and dependence of developing countries on companies who are seeking to control the world's commercial seed supply.

Issue: Genetically modified crops

Background: Soybeans are the world's largest agricultural crop. The United States produces 33% of the world's soybean crop, worth US$38.5 billion. Pests do a lot of damage to the crop so reducing pest damage would increase crop yields and value. Pesticide use is common and there has been a 130 fold increase in insecticide use in the US since 2001.

Genetic modification of crops to resist pests reduces the dependence on pesticides. This has already been successfully performed in corn (Bt corn) and soybeans (resistance against soybean cyst nematodes).

Problem: Plants that produce toxins may be toxic to humans.

Pests may become resistant to the pest-resistant properties of the engineered plant rendering it ineffective. The ultimate outcome of this is unknown.

Possible solution: Careful testing of the toxic properties of the plant under a variety of circumstances is required to ensure it is safe for human consumption.

Plans must be in place in the event that pests become resistant to the engineered plant.

Issue: Adding genes to organisms to produce pharmaceuticals for human use or study.

Background: Traditionally, producing protein-based drugs, e.g. insulin, has been costly and unreliable. Proteins are continuously made in living organisms and these living systems can be exploited to produce the products need by humans. Genetic modification of plants and animals to produce pharmaceutical proteins means the protein can be produced in large quantities relatively cheaply (once a stable GM organism is produced). This is already done with rennin (an enzyme used in cheese making) and human insulin (used to treat diabetes). Mammals can be genetically modified and induced to secrete useful proteins in their milk (e.g. transgenic goats produce antithrombin to prevent blood clots).

Problem: There are concerns with animal health. Many genetically modified mammals have congenital defects and reproductive difficulties (low conception to term rates).

There is also the question of animal rights and values. Is the genetic modification of an animal to produce proteins then valuing the protein over the animal?

Possible solution: Testing and monitoring animal health is important. Continued development of non-animal based methods for developing proteins.

Issue: Who owns the technology?

Background: Crop seed and animal breeders spend large amounts of money on development. The genetic modification of plants and animals requires Government approval to develop the technology, carry out testing, and bring the product to market. This is a lengthy process that can cost millions of dollars. Companies therefore wish to make a profit or at least recoup costs on their product. This leads to patents to protect the technology and increased costs to farmers.

Problem: Biotech companies may have some leverage over farmers. For example, a seed producing company produces GE seeds, which cost a lot to develop. To ensure sales and a profit, they sell only these seeds (at great cost) to the farmer, who has little choice.

GE crops may be sold to overseas markets with little regulation and little choice. These markets will carry the load of potential problems, increasing the divide between developed nations and developing ones.

Possible solution: Legislation must be in place to ensure intellectual property is protected while also ensuring farmers have access to all available seed and stock. There must be careful consideration of the effect of GE crops on the agriculture of developing countries.

LINK · LINK · WEB
199 **180** **182** KNOW

1. Describe an advantage and a problem with the use of plants genetically engineered to be resistant to crop pests:

   (a) Advantage: _____

   _____

   (b) Problem: _____

   _____

2. Describe an advantage and a problem with using plants and animals to produce pharmaceuticals:

   (a) Advantage: _____

   _____

   (b) Problem: _____

   _____

3. Describe two uses of transgenic animals within the livestock industry:

   (a) _____

   (b) _____

   (c) Describe the possible problems that may occur over the ownership of genetically modified organisms.

   _____

   _____

   _____

4. Some years ago, Britain banned the import of a GM, pest resistant corn variety containing marker genes for ampicillin antibiotic resistance. Suggest why the use of antibiotic-resistance genes as markers is no longer common practice:

   _____

   _____

5. Many agricultural applications of DNA technology make use of transgenic bacteria which infect plants and express a foreign gene. Explain one advantage of each of the following applications of genetic engineering to crop biology:

   (a) Development of nitrogen-fixing *Rhizobium* bacteria that can colonise non-legumes such as corn and wheat:

   _____

   _____

   (b) Addition of transgenic *Pseudomonas fluorescens* bacteria into seeds (bacterium produces a pathogen-killing toxin):

   _____

   _____

6. Some of the public's fears and concerns about genetically modified food stem from moral or religious convictions, while others have a biological basis and are related to the potential biological threat posed by GMOs.
   (a) Conduct a class discussion or debate to identify these fears and concerns, and list them below:

   _____

   _____

   _____

   (b) Identify which of those you have listed above pose a real biological threat: _____

   _____

   _____

   _____

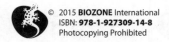 © 2015 **BIOZONE** International
ISBN: **978-1-927309-14-8**
Photocopying Prohibited

183 Gene Therapy

Key Idea: Gene therapy aims to correct a genetic fault by using a vector to insert a correctly functioning gene into a patient's DNA.

Gene therapy uses gene technology to treat disease by correcting or replacing faulty genes. Although the details vary, all gene therapies are based around the same technique. The correct non-faulty gene is inserted into a vector, which transfers the DNA into the patient's cells (transfection). The vector is introduced into a sample of the patient's cells, and

these are cultured to amplify the correct gene. The cells are then transferred back to the patient. The treatment of somatic cells or stem cells is therapeutic (provides a benefit) but the changes are not inherited. **Germline therapy** (modification of the gametes) would enable genetic changes to be passed on. Gene therapy has had limited success because transfection of targeted cells is inefficient, and the side effects can be severe or fatal. However, SCID, a genetic immune deficiency disease, has responded to gene therapy with some success.

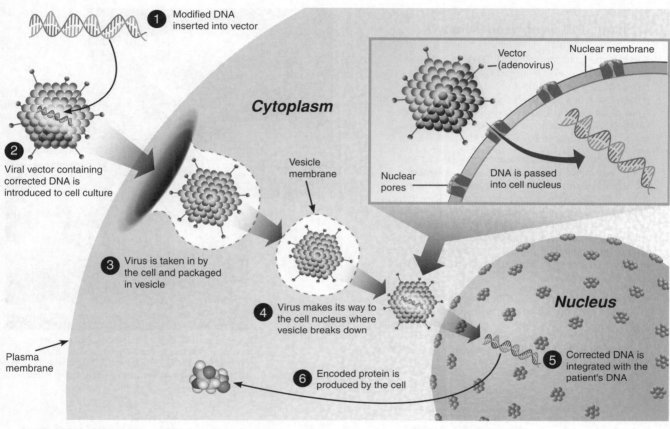

1. (a) Describe the general principle of gene therapy:

_____

_____

(b) Describe the medical areas where gene therapy might be used: _____

_____

_____

_____

2. Explain the significance of transfecting germline cells rather than somatic cells: _____

_____

_____

_____

3. What is the purpose of gene amplification in gene therapy? _____

_____

_____

LINK   WEB
184 183   KNOW

184 Using Gene Therapy to Treat Disease

Key Idea: The delivery of genes into target cells and then into patients has proved technically difficult, limiting the use of gene therapy.

It remains technically difficult to deliver genes successfully to a patient, limiting the success rate of gene therapy treatments. Any improvements have been mostly short-lived, or counteracted by adverse side effects. The inserted genes may reach only about 1% of target cells. Those that reach their target may work inefficiently and produce too little protein, too slowly to be of benefit. Many patients also have immune reactions to the vectors used in gene transfer. One of the first gene therapy trials was for cystic fibrosis (CF). CF was an obvious candidate for gene therapy because, in most cases, the disease is caused by a single, known gene mutation. However, despite its early promise, gene therapy for this disease has been disappointing (below right). Severe Combined Immune Deficiency (SCID) is another candidate for gene therapy, again because the disease is caused by single, known mutation (below left). Gene therapies for this disease have so far proved promising.

Treating SCID using gene therapy

The most common form of **SCID** (Severe Combined Immune Deficiency) is X-linked SCID, which results from mutations to a gene on the X chromosome encoding a protein that forms part of a receptor complex for numerous types of leukocytes. A less common form of the disease, (ADA-SCID) is caused by a defective gene that codes for the enzyme adenosine deaminase (ADA).

Both of these types of SCID lead to immune system failure. A common treatment for SCID is bone marrow transplant, but this is not always successful and runs the risks of infection from unscreened viruses. **Gene therapy** appears to hold the best chances of producing a cure for SCID because the mutation affects only one gene whose location is known. DNA containing the corrected gene is placed into a gutted retrovirus and introduced to a sample of the patient's bone marrow. The treated cells are then returned to the patient.

In some patients with ADA-SCID, treatment was so successful that supplementation with purified ADA was no longer required. The treatment carries risks though. In early trials, two of ten treated patients developed leukemia when the corrected gene was inserted next to a gene regulating cell growth.

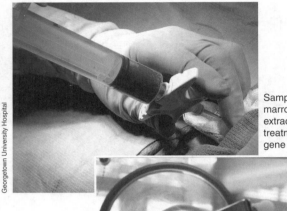

Samples of bone marrow being extracted prior to treatment with gene therapy.

Detection of SCID is difficult for the first months of an infant's life due to the mother's antibodies being present in the blood. Suspected SCID patients must be kept in sterile conditions at all times to avoid infection.

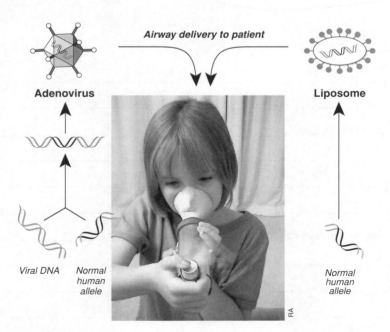

Airway delivery to patient

Adenovirus

Liposome

Viral DNA   *Normal human allele*

Normal human allele

An **adenovirus** that normally causes colds is genetically modified to make it safe and to carry the normal (unmutated) CFTR ('cystic fibrosis') gene.

Liposomes are tiny fat globules. Normal CF genes are enclosed in liposomes, which fuse with plasma membranes and deliver the genes into the cells.

Gene therapy - potential treatment for cystic fibrosis?

Cystic fibrosis (CF) is caused by a mutation to the gene coding for a chloride ion channel important in creating sweat, digestive juices, and mucus. The dysfunction results in abnormally thick, sticky mucus that accumulates in the lungs and intestines. The identification and isolation of the CF gene in 1989 meant that scientists could look for ways in which to correct the genetic defect rather than just treating the symptoms using traditional therapies.

The main target of CF gene therapy is the lung, because the progressive lung damage associated with the disease is eventually lethal. In trials, normal genes were isolated and inserted into patients using vectors such as adenoviruses and liposomes, delivered via the airways (left). The results of trials were disappointing: on average, there was only a 25% correction, the effects were short lived, and the benefits were quickly reversed. Alarmingly, the adenovirus used in one of the trials led to the death of one patient.

Source: Cystic Fibrosis Trust, UK.

© 2015 **BIOZONE** International
ISBN: **978-1-927309-14-8**
Photocopying Prohibited

1. A great deal of current research is being devoted to discovering a gene therapy solution to treat cystic fibrosis (CF):

    (a) Describe the symptoms of CF: _____

    _____

    _____

    (b) Explain why this genetic disease has been so eagerly targeted by gene therapy researchers: _____

    _____

    _____

    _____

    _____

    (c) Outline some of the problems so far encountered with gene therapy for CF: _____

    _____

    _____

    _____

    _____

    _____

    _____

2. Identify two vectors for introducing healthy CFTR genes into CF patients.

    (a) Vector 1: _____

    (b) Vector 2: _____

3. (a) Describe the difference between X-linked SCID and ADA-SCID: _____

    _____

    (b) Identify the vector used in the treatment of SCID: _____

    _____

4. Briefly outline the differences in the gene therapy treatment of CF and SCID: _____

    _____

    _____

    _____

    _____

5. Changes made to chromosomes as a result of gene therapy involving somatic cells are not inherited. Germ-line gene therapy has the potential to cure disease, but the risks and benefits are still not clear. For each of the points outlined below, evaluate the risk of germ-line gene therapy relative to somatic cell gene therapy and explain your answer:

    (a) Chance of interfering with an essential gene function: _____

    _____

    _____

    _____

    (b) Misuse of the therapy to selectively alter phenotype: _____

    _____

    _____

    _____

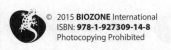

185 Chapter Review

Summarise what you know about this topic under the headings and sub-headings provided. You can draw diagrams or mind maps, or write short notes to organise your thoughts. Use the images and hints to help you and refer back to the introduction to check the points covered:

DNA amplification and sequencing
HINT: Explain PCR, gel electrophoresis, and DNA sequencing.

DNA profiling
HINT: Forensics and disease analysis

DNA technology
HINT: Describe techniques and applications of recombinant DNA technology and gene therapy.

REVISE

186 KEY TERMS: Did You Get It?

1. Test your vocabulary by matching each term to its definition, as identified by its preceding letter code.

annealing

DNA amplification

DNA ligation

DNA polymerase

gel electrophoresis

GMO

marker gene

microsatellite

PCR

primer

recognition site

recombinant DNA

restriction enzyme

sticky end

vector

A An organism or artificial vehicle that is capable of transferring a DNA sequence to another organism.

B The pairing (by hydrogen bonding) of complementary single-stranded nucleic acids to form a double-stranded polynucleotide. The term is applied to making recombinant DNA, to the binding of a DNA probe, or to the binding of a primer to a DNA strand during PCR.

C A cut in a length of DNA by a restriction enzyme that results in two strands of DNA being different lengths with one strand overhanging the other.

D A short length of DNA used to identify the starting sequence for PCR so that polymerase enzymes can begin amplification.

E An enzyme that is able to cut a length of DNA at a specific sequence or site.

F The site or sequence of DNA at which a restriction enzyme attaches and cuts.

G A gene, with an identifiable effect, used to determine if a piece of DNA has been successfully inserted into the host organism.

H A reaction that is used to amplify fragments of DNA using cycles of heating and cooling (abbreviation).

I A process that is used to separate different lengths of DNA by placing them in a gel matrix placed in a buffered solution through which an electric current is passed.

J The process of producing more copies of a length of DNA, normally using PCR.

K DNA that has had a new sequence added so that the original sequence has been changed.

L The repairing or attaching of fragmented DNA by ligase enzymes.

M A short (normally two base pairs) piece of DNA that repeats a variable number of times between people and so can be used to distinguish between individuals.

N An organism that has had part of its DNA sequence altered either by the removal or insertion of a piece of DNA.

O An enzyme that is able to replicate DNA and commonly used in PCR to amplify a length of DNA.

2. The electrophoresis gel (below, right) shows four profiles containing five STR sites: the mother (A) her daughter (B) and two possible fathers (C and D). Which of the possible fathers is the biological father?

(a) The biological father is: _____

(b) Why do profiles B and D only have 9 bands?

_____

_____

_____

_____

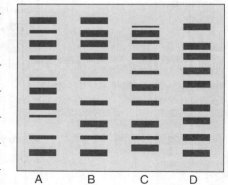

A   B   C   D

© 2015 **BIOZONE** International
ISBN: **978-1-927309-14-8**
Photocopying Prohibited

TEST

Cloning and Biotechnlogy

Key terms

artificial clone

aseptic technique

bacteria

batch culture

bioreactor

bioremediation

biotechnology

budding

clone

continuous culture

cutting

death phase

dilution plating

embryo splitting

enucleation

enzyme
immobilisation

fungi

grafting

lag phase

log phase

microorganism

micropropagation

optimum growth
conditions

serial dilution

somatic cell nuclear
transfer

stationary phase

strain isolation

tissue culture

twinning

vegetative
propagation

Cloning

Learning outcomes

Activity number

☐ 1 Describe examples of natural clones in plants and explain how natural clones are produced for use in agriculture. Include reference to simple methods of vegetative propagation such as cuttings and grafts.   187

☐ 2 **PAG2** ▶ Dissect plant material to produce cuttings.   187

☐ 3 Describe the production of artificial clones from plants using micropropagation (tissue culture) techniques. Identify arguments for and against this type of cloning.   188

☐ 4 Describe how natural clones in animal species arise, e.g. by budding, regeneration (as in planarians), and natural twinning by embryo splitting.   189

☐ 5 Describe the production of clones in animals using embryo twinning or by enucleation and somatic cell nuclear transfer (SCNT) techniques. Evaluate the uses of animal clones, e.g. in agriculture and medicine, and outline the arguments for and against the uses of animal clones.   190 191

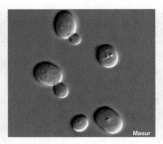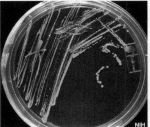

Microbiology and biotechnology

Learning outcomes

Activity number

☐ 6 Discuss the uses of microorganisms in biotechnology, including in brewing, baking, cheese and yoghurt production, bioremediation, and production of therapeutic medicines, such as penicillin and insulin. Explain why microorganisms are so well suited to biotechnological processes.   192-200

☐ 7 With reference to bacteria and fungi, explain the advantages and disadvantages of using microorganisms to produce food for human consumption.   197

☐ 8 Describe how microorganisms are cultured, including reference to the use of aseptic techniques and the importance of maintaining optimal growth conditions. Distinguish between batch and continuous culture systems and describe when and why each is used.   201-204

☐ 9 Describe the standard growth curve of a microorganism in a closed culture including reference to the different phases of growth.   205

☐ 10 **PAG2** ▶ Use appropriate microbiological techniques to investigate factors
     PAG7 ▶ affecting growth of microorganisms.   201-203

☐ 11 Describe and evaluate the use of immobilised enzymes in biotechnology, to include the different methods used for immobilisation. Examples include: 207-210

   ▶ glucose isomerase (converts glucose to fructose)

   ▶ penicillin acyclase to form semi-synthetic penicillins.

   ▶ lactase for hydrolysis of lactose to glucose and galactose

   ▶ amino acyclase to produce pure L-amino acids

   ▶ glucoamylase to convert dextrins to glucose

   ▶ nitrilase to covert acrylonitrile to acrylamide in the plastics industry

187 Natural Clones in Plants

Key Idea: The ability of plants to reproduce vegetatively can be exploited to produce large numbers of identical plants.

Clones are organisms that are genetically identical to the parent organism. Plants have the ability to produce clones via asexual reproduction. This allows them to spread rapidly and out compete other plants that must produce seeds to reproduce. Cloning includes the production of vegetative structures such as tubers (e.g. potatoes), rhizomes (e.g. ginger) and bulbs (e.g. garlic). They can also be propagated (reproduced) from cuttings. Many plants have the ability to develop roots wherever a part of the plant is touching the ground or where it may have been wounded. This comes from the plant's cells being able to de-differentiate (initiate new cell divisions and form new meristematic tissue containing totipotent cells) and thereby produce new roots or shoots. This property of plants can be exploited by humans to rapidly produce large numbers of clones from a single plant by taking multiple cuttings.

Propagating plants from cuttings

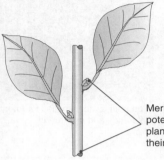

A cutting that includes a leaf bud is made. The plant hormone auxin travels down the stem and accumulates at the base of the stem triggering the formation of roots. Adding synthetic auxins to the end of the cutting promotes greater root development.

Meristems contain totipotent cells that can potentially differentiate into any cell in the plant. The application of auxin initiates their development into root cells.

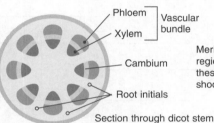

Phloem ⎤ Vascular
Xylem ⎦ bundle

Cambium

Root initials

Section through dicot stem

Meristems are the growing regions in plants. Normally these are the root meristem, shoot meristem, and cambium.

At the basal cut a plate of corky material seals the wound. Behind it cells begin to dedifferentiate and form root initials (areas of root meristems). In herbaceous plants the roots initials form from areas between the vascular bundles (above). In woody plants the root initials form from cells in the secondary phloem.

Kahuroa

By 1945 goats had eaten all but one of each of the Three Kings vine (above) and Three Kings kaikomako, found on the Three Kings islands of New Zealand. These plants were saved from extinction in part by taking cuttings to grow new plants.

The roots that form at the base of the cutting are called adventitious roots. Adventitious roots form from cells that would not normally develop into roots.

Natural vegetative structures in plants

Tubers are the swollen part of an underground stem or root, usually modified for storing food. Tubers can be cut into pieces that will grow into new plants provided a lateral bud is included in the piece.

Potato stem tuber

'Eye' (lateral bud)

A true **bulb** is simply a typical shoot compressed into a shortened form. They act as a storage organ for the plant. The bulbs can be sectioned to induce the production of new bulbs for propagation.

Garlic bulbs

In **rhizomes**, food is stored in the horizontal, underground stem. Rhizomes tend to be thick, fleshy or woody, and bear nodes with scale or foliage leaves and buds. Growth occurs at the buds on the ends of the rhizome or nearby nodes. Rhizomes can be cut into pieces to produce more plants.

Underground stem containing stored food

Iris rhizome

Corms also store food in stem tissue. Like bulbs they can divided to produce more identical plants Cyclamen, gladiolus, and crocus (above) are corms.

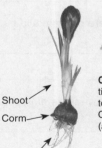

Shoot

Corm

Adventitious roots

Growth in crocus, a typical corm

1. What is meant by vegetative propagation? _____

_____

_____

2. Describe one major advantage (to the plant) of having a stem, tuber, or bulb filled with stored food:

_____

_____

LINK   WEB
188   187   KNOW

Grafting

Grafting involves joining structures from two or more plants. Typically a twig section (scion) from one plant is joined to the shoot of another (root stock). Grafting is used for many fruit and landscape trees (see photo series right).

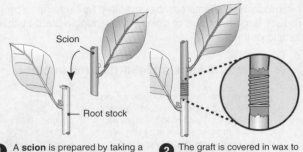

Scion

Root stock

1 A **scion** is prepared by taking a cutting. The scion is then grafted to another plant (root stock).

2 The graft is covered in wax to prevent infection and held together with twine or raffia.

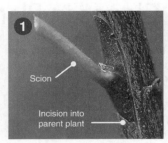

Scion

Incision into parent plant

A scion is removed from the parent plant prior to grafting.

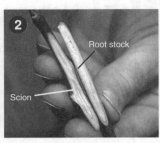

Root stock

Scion

Scion being grafted onto the stem of the root stock.

The graft is sealed and covered to prevent water loss and infection.

The graft is then labelled for future reference and monitoring.

3. How have humans benefited from the vegetative propagation of plants? _____

_____

_____

_____

4. Describe how plants benefit by reproducing vegetatively: _____

_____

_____

_____

5. (a) Explain how vegetative propagation of plant material can be used as a strategy in species conservation:

_____

_____

(b) Suggest why stocks of rare plants could be reproduced this way, rather than using seed: _____

_____

_____

(c) Describe a potential disadvantage of vegetative propagation of plants that are endangered by disease:

_____

_____

6. Distinguish between cutting and grafting, including reference to their applications: _____

_____

_____

_____

_____

_____

_____

188 Micropropagation of Plant Tissue

Key Idea: Micropropagation can produce large numbers of genetically identical plants in a short space of time.

Micropropagation (also called plant tissue culture) is a method used to clone plants. It is used widely for the rapid multiplication of commercially important plant species with superior genotypes, as well as in recovery programmes for endangered plant species. However, continued culture of a limited number of cloned varieties leads to a reduction in genetic diversity. As a result, plants may become susceptible to disease or changes in environmental conditions. New genetic stock may be introduced into cloned lines to prevent this reduction. Micropropagation is possible because totipotency (the ability to develop into any tissue type) can be induced in differentiated plant cells. It has considerable advantages over traditional methods of plant propagation, but it is very labour intensive. The success of tissue culture is affected by a variety of factors including selection of explant material, plant hormone levels, lighting, and temperature.

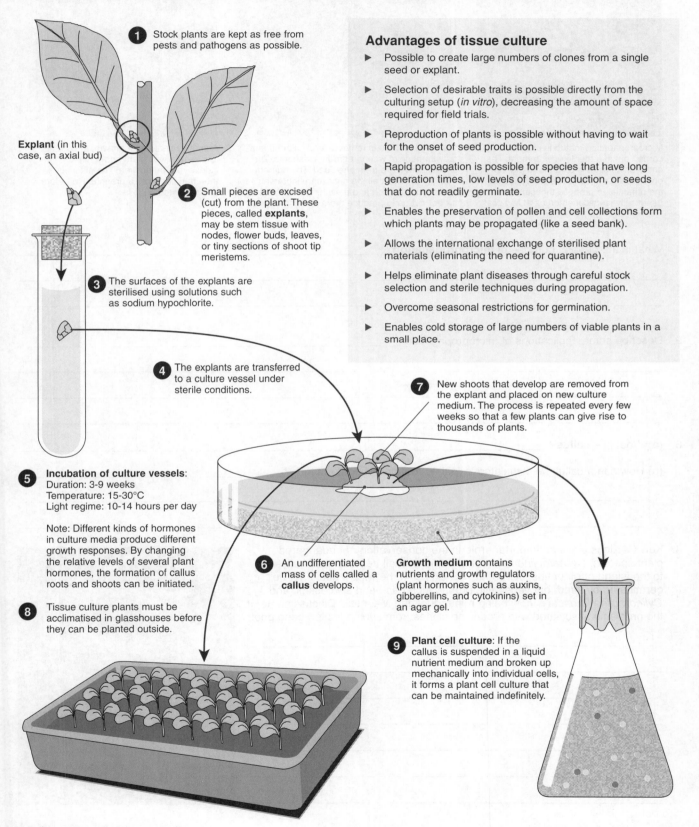

1 Stock plants are kept as free from pests and pathogens as possible.

Explant (in this case, an axial bud)

2 Small pieces are excised (cut) from the plant. These pieces, called **explants**, may be stem tissue with nodes, flower buds, leaves, or tiny sections of shoot tip meristems.

3 The surfaces of the explants are sterilised using solutions such as sodium hypochlorite.

4 The explants are transferred to a culture vessel under sterile conditions.

5 **Incubation of culture vessels**:
Duration: 3-9 weeks
Temperature: 15-30°C
Light regime: 10-14 hours per day

Note: Different kinds of hormones in culture media produce different growth responses. By changing the relative levels of several plant hormones, the formation of callus roots and shoots can be initiated.

6 An undifferentiated mass of cells called a **callus** develops.

7 New shoots that develop are removed from the explant and placed on new culture medium. The process is repeated every few weeks so that a few plants can give rise to thousands of plants.

8 Tissue culture plants must be acclimatised in glasshouses before they can be planted outside.

9 **Plant cell culture**: If the callus is suspended in a liquid nutrient medium and broken up mechanically into individual cells, it forms a plant cell culture that can be maintained indefinitely.

Growth medium contains nutrients and growth regulators (plant hormones such as auxins, gibberellins, and cytokinins) set in an agar gel.

Advantages of tissue culture

▶ Possible to create large numbers of clones from a single seed or explant.

▶ Selection of desirable traits is possible directly from the culturing setup (*in vitro*), decreasing the amount of space required for field trials.

▶ Reproduction of plants is possible without having to wait for the onset of seed production.

▶ Rapid propagation is possible for species that have long generation times, low levels of seed production, or seeds that do not readily germinate.

▶ Enables the preservation of pollen and cell collections form which plants may be propagated (like a seed bank).

▶ Allows the international exchange of sterilised plant materials (eliminating the need for quarantine).

▶ Helps eliminate plant diseases through careful stock selection and sterile techniques during propagation.

▶ Overcome seasonal restrictions for germination.

▶ Enables cold storage of large numbers of viable plants in a small place.

Micropropagation of *Pinus radiata*

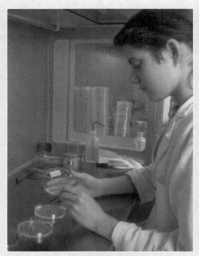

Micropropagation methods must be carried out in a sterile environment. The embryonic tissue is cut up and placed on a growth medium. The technique has the potential to produce thousands of genetically identical embryos at low cost.

The seed embryo is removed and cultured in a growth medium where it produces shoots. The shoots above are from one seed. The nutrient medium provides all the necessary ingredients for shoot multiplication and growth. These shoots are further cut up to produce more identical plants.

After sufficient shoot growth, the shoots are treated with plant hormones to induce root production. The plantlets are then transferred to a greenhouse before being planted outside.

1. What is the general purpose of **micropropagation**? _____

_____

_____

2. Describe some applications of micropropagation: _____

_____

_____

_____

3. (a) What is a **callus**? _____

(b) How can a callus be stimulated to initiate root and shoot formation? _____

_____

_____

4. Kew Gardens plays an important role in the conservation of endangered plant species. *Cylindrocline lorencei* (right) is a small tree that was native to the island of Mauritius. In 1990 it was extinct in the wild. It could not be germinated by seed, but vegetative propagation has been successful, and *Cylindrocline lorencei* is now being reintroduced to Mauritius. Discuss some of the problems associated with producing clones from such a limited gene pool:

_____

_____

_____

_____

_____

_____

_____

© 2015 **BIOZONE** International
ISBN: 978-1-927309-14-8
Photocopying Prohibited

189 Natural Clones in Animals

Key Idea: Some animals have the ability to produce clones naturally. Identical twins are an example of natural clones. Natural cloning in animals is less common than in plants. Animals which reproduce asexually are producing natural clones, the offspring all have genetic material identical to their parent. Natural cloning is more common in simple animals (planarians, starfish and *Hydra*), but the production of identical twins in mammals is also an example of natural cloning. Identical twins are clones of each other, but they are genetically different from their parents.

Planarians, a type of flatworm, are well known for their ability to form clones. The flatworm can be cut into three pieces, each of which will regenerate into a new individual. In nature, some species reproduce by pinching off a short section of tail which develops into a new organism.

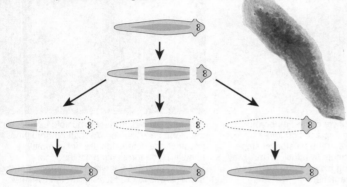

Identical twins are natural clones

Identical twins (also called monozygotic twins) are an example of natural clones in mammals. Identical twins occur when a single egg is fertilised to form one zygote. The zygote then divides into two separate embryos. Both individuals are genetically identical because they developed from the same fertilised egg. In humans, identical twins occur at a rate of three in every 1000 deliveries.

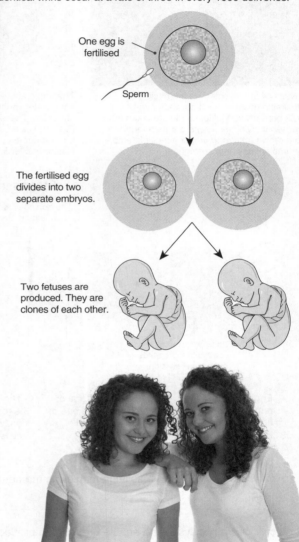

One egg is fertilised

Sperm

The fertilised egg divides into two separate embryos.

Two fetuses are produced. They are clones of each other.

Sponges and most cnidarians (e.g. *Hydra*, below) can reproduce by **budding**. A small part of the parent body separates from the rest and develops into a new individual. This new individual may remain attached as part of the colony, or the bud may constrict at its point of attachment and be released as an independent organism.

This photo shows *Hydra* budding. The new individuals are budding from the main body of the parent animal. The photograph shows the bulge and constriction where each new offspring will separate to form an independent individual.

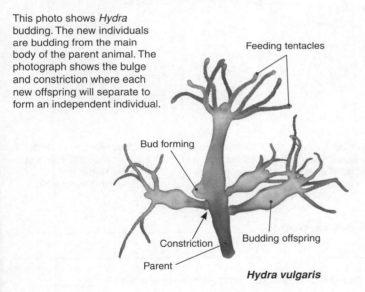

Feeding tentacles

Bud forming

Constriction

Budding offspring

Parent

Hydra vulgaris

1. (a) How do natural clones arise in animals? _____

_____

(b) Why does asexual reproduction produce clones? _____

_____

2. (a) How do identical twins arise? _____

_____

(b) In what way are identical twins different to other types of natural clones? _____

_____

LINK
187 KNOW

190 Cloning by Embryo Splitting

Key Idea: Cloning by embryo splitting replicates the natural twinning process, but enables multiple clones to be produced from just one high-value individual.

Livestock often produce only one or two offspring per year, so building a herd with desirable traits by selective breeding alone is a lengthy process. Cloning makes it possible to produce animals with desirable characteristics (e.g. high milk yield) more quickly. Embryo splitting, or artificial twinning, is the simplest way to create a clone. It replicates the natural twinning process *in-vitro*, and the genetically identical embryos are implanted into surrogates to complete development. The individuals produced by embryo splitting will have many of the same characteristics as the parents, although their exact phenotype is not known until after birth. Cloning provides genetically identical animals for studying disease processes. It can also be used (controversially) to produce embryos from which undifferentiated stem cells can be isolated for use in therapeutic medicine.

Livestock are selected on the basis of desirable qualities such as wool, meat, or milk production. Multiple eggs are taken from chosen individuals. These are then fertilised and grown *in-vitro* to produce multiple embryos for implantation into surrogates.

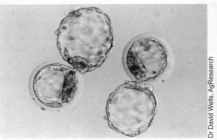

The photo above shows cloned embryos immediately prior to implantation into a surrogate. These are at the blastocyst stage (50 - 150 cells). A single livestock animal may provide numerous eggs and therefore many blastocysts for implantation.

Embryo splitting produces multiple clones, but the clones are derived from an embryo whose physical characteristics are not completely known. This represents a limitation for practical applications when the purpose of the procedure is to produce high value livestock.

Stages in embryo splitting

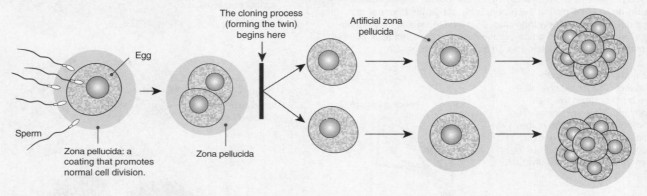

Egg cells are removed from an animal and fertilised in a petri dish.

At the first stage of development, one of these fertilised eggs divides in two.

The zona pellucida is removed with an enzyme and the two cells are separated.

An artificial zona is added, allowing development to proceed.

The cells continue to divide, forming genetically identical embryos. These are implanted into surrogates.

1. How is cloning by embryo splitting mimicking the natural twinning process? _____

_____

2. How does embryo splitting enable breeders to produce multiple clones from a single high value animal? _____

_____

_____

_____

3. Describe the benefits gained from cloning: _____

_____

_____

4. Why would it be undesirable to produce all livestock using embryo splitting? _____

_____

© 2015 **BIOZONE** International
ISBN: 978-1-927309-14-8
Photocopying Prohibited

191 Cloning by Somatic Cell Nuclear Transfer

Key Idea: Clones can be made by fusing the empty egg cell with a cell from the organism to be cloned.

Clones produced using traditional embryo-splitting must mature before their phenotype is known. Scientists wanted to speed up the selection process and produce clones directly from a proven phenotype. The technique developed to do this is called **somatic cell nuclear transfer**. It involves returning a somatic (body) cell (from an individual of known phenotype) to a dormant state and then fusing it with an egg cell in which the nucleus is removed. Embryonic development is triggered and the resulting embryo is implanted into a surrogate mother. The primary aim of the new cloning technologies is to provide an economically viable way to rapidly produce transgenic animals with very precise genetic modifications.

Concept 1
Somatic cells can be made to return to a dormant or embryonic state so that their genes will not be expressed.

Concept 2
The nucleus of a cell can be removed and replaced with the nucleus of an unrelated cell. Cells can be made to fuse together.

Concept 3
Fertilised egg cells produce embryos. Egg cells that contain the nucleus of a donor cell will produce embryos with DNA identical to the donor cell.

Concept 4
Embryos can be implanted into surrogate mothers and develop to full term with seemingly no ill effects.

Somatic cell nuclear transfer (SCNT)

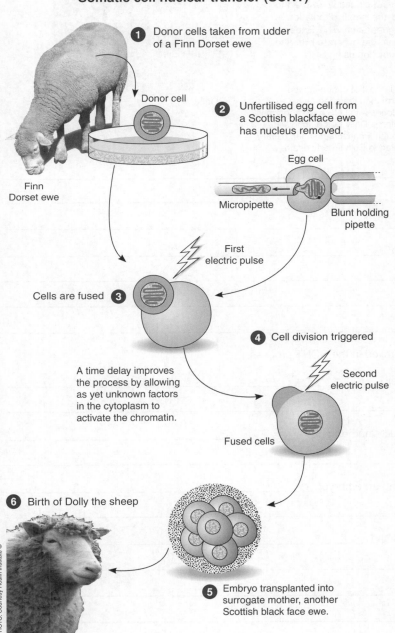

1. Donor cells taken from udder of a Finn Dorset ewe

Donor cell

Finn Dorset ewe

2. Unfertilised egg cell from a Scottish blackface ewe has nucleus removed.

Egg cell

Micropipette

Blunt holding pipette

First electric pulse

Cells are fused 3

A time delay improves the process by allowing as yet unknown factors in the cytoplasm to activate the chromatin.

4. Cell division triggered

Second electric pulse

Fused cells

6. Birth of Dolly the sheep

5. Embryo transplanted into surrogate mother, another Scottish black face ewe.

PHOTO: Courtesy Roslin Institute ©

Techniques

Donor cells from the udder of a Finn Dorset ewe are taken and cultured in a low nutrient media for a week. The nutrient deprived cells stop dividing and become dormant.

An unfertilised egg from a Scottish blackface ewe has the nucleus removed using a micropipette. The rest of the cell contents are left intact.

The dormant udder cell and the recipient denucleated egg cell are fused using a mild electric pulse.

A second electric pulse triggers cellular activity and cell division, jump starting the cell into development. This can also be triggered by chemical means.

After six days the embryo is transplanted into a surrogate mother, another Scottish blackface ewe.

After a 148 day gestation 'Dolly' is born. DNA profiling shows she is genetically identical to the original Finn Dorset cell donor.

Outcomes

Dolly, a Finn Dorset lamb, was born at the Roslin Institute (near Edinburgh) in July 1996. She was the first mammal to be cloned from non-embryonic cells, i.e. cells that had already differentiated into their final form. Dolly's birth showed that the process leading to cell specialisation is not irreversible and that cells can be 'reprogrammed' into an embryonic state. Although cloning seems relatively easy there are many problems that occur. Of the hundreds of eggs that were reconstructed only 29 formed embryos and only Dolly survived to birth.

Further Applications

In animal reproductive technology, cloning has facilitated the rapid production of genetically superior stock. These animals may then be dispersed among commercial herds. The primary focus of the new cloning technologies is to provide an economically viable way to rapidly produce transgenic animals with very precise genetic modifications.

LINK 190   WEB 191   KNOW

Uses of animal cloning

▶ Rapid production of animals with desirable qualities, e.g. high wool quality.

▶ Production of disease-resistant livestock.

▶ More rapid production of transgenic livestock with traits desirable to humans. Examples include human clotting factor IX secreted in the milk of transgenic cows and organs harvested from transgenic pigs which have been immunologically altered so the human body does not reject them in organ transplant situations.

▶ Clones can be produced to increase the numbers of endangered species. This has been achieved for Enderby Island cattle (below) and the grey wolf.

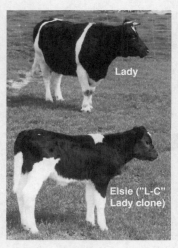

Lady

Elsie ("L-C" Lady clone)

Enderby Island is part of the Auckland Islands group, south of New Zealand. A distinct cattle breed arose there after 90 years of isolation following their abandonment on the island in the early 1900s. In attempts to restore the island ecology, most of the cattle were destroyed, but semen and egg cells were taken and stored. In 1992, it was discovered that two cattle remained on the island, a cow (later named Lady) and her calf (which later died). Lady produced a bull calf by *in vitro* fertilisation and implantation in a surrogate mother and Lady herself was cloned using SCNT. Two surviving clones were bred to the bull calf and the small population is now in its third generation. The Enderby Island cattle remain the only rare breed to be saved from extinction using SCNT.

Problems with clones: The life span of cloned animals is similar to that of non-cloned animals. However, many cloned animals are much bigger at birth than their natural counterparts. This is called large offspring syndrome (LOS). Clones with LOS have abnormally large organs, and can suffer from breathing or circulatory problems. Dolly was euthanised at six years of age suffering from arthritis and lung disease. Although Finn-Dorset sheep usually live to around 11 years, cloning is not thought to have contributed to Dolly's early death.

SCNT in humans?

SCNT could potentially be used to produce embryos as a source of human embryonic stem cells. The main ethical issue of this is that embryos would be destroyed in the process. To some, this is equal to the loss of a life. Another ethical issue is associated with the source of the eggs. Most commonly, they are spare eggs harvested from women undergoing IVF treatment. Harvesting of eggs is an invasive process and has some health risks associated with it. SCNT is a labour intensive and inefficient process (0.1-3% success rate). In the case of Dolly, only 29 viable embryos were produced from 227 eggs. Only three of these embryos survived until birth, and only one survived to adulthood.

In its favour, SCNT use in humans has the potential to treat many diseases including diabetes and Parkinson's disease. Cell rejection is minimised and immunosuppressant drugs (used to prevent tissue rejection) are not required.

Blackface ewe

Dolly

PHOTO: Courtesy Roslin Institute ©

1. (a) What is **SCNT**? _____

_____

_____

(b) How does SCNT differ from embryo splitting? _____

_____

_____

_____

2. Explain how each of the following events is controlled in the SCNT process:

(a) The switching off of all genes in the donor cell: _____

_____

(b) The fusion (combining) of donor cell with enucleated egg cell: _____

_____

(c) The activation of the cloned cell into producing an embryo: _____

_____

3. Discuss the advantages and disadvantages of SCNT: _____

_____

_____

_____

_____

© 2015 **BIOZONE** International
ISBN: 978-1-927309-14-8
Photocopying Prohibited

192 The Use of Microbes in Food Technology

Key Idea: Bacteria and fungi are used extensively in many aspects of food technology. They provide many advantages over other food technology techniques.

Bacteria and fungi have been used for thousands of years to preserve and produce a wide variety of foods (e.g. alcoholic beverages and bread). The microbes can play an important role in the food technology process (e.g. cheese production),

or they may be the final food (e.g. fungal mycoprotein). Features of microbial biology make microorganisms well suited to producing a range of products on an industrial scale. The industrial-scale culture of microbes is given the general name fermentation because it occurs in fermentation tanks (bioreactors). It can be aerobic or anaerobic and is not a reference to the metabolism of the organisms themselves.

Advantages of using microorganisms

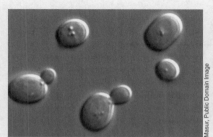
Masur, Public Domain Image

Starter culture for sourdough bread
Janus Sandsgaard cc 4.0

Jan Ainali cc3.0

Most microorganisms have short life cycles, and can reproduce rapidly to increase their numbers. Baker's yeast (*Saccharomyces cerevisiae*, above) is used in brewing and baking. Under optimal conditions, it can double its population every 100 minutes.

Microorganisms can be cost effective to produce as they can grow on a wide range of raw materials or even on waste products. Genetic modification of microorganisms can enhance the production of a naturally occurring substance or produce a novel desirable trait.

Sometimes the microbe itself is the food. Mycoprotein is a fungal protein and is an alternative to animal protein. The fungi are grown in reactors, which occupy very little space so, unlike livestock farming, mycoprotein can be produced anywhere, independent of climate.

Food production using microbes

Genetic engineering provides alternative sources for products that were once available only through expensive or wasteful means. The enzyme rennin is used in cheese making and was traditionally obtained from the stomachs of calves. It is now produced by GM microbes.

Sauerkraut production involves the fermentation of cabbage using lactic acid bacteria. Not only does this process change the characteristic of the cabbage, but it helps to preserve it. The low pH prevents food spoilage bacteria growing.

In the production of **soy sauce**, filamentous fungi (*Aspergillus soyae* and *A.oryzeae*) digest soy proteins. The culture is fermented in the presence of lactic acid bacteria (*Lactobacillus* spp.) and acid tolerant yeast to develop the characteristic soy flavours.

1. Discuss the advantages of using microorganisms in food technology: _____

_____

_____

_____

_____

_____

2. Describe one example of how genetic engineering has assisted a traditional biotechnology: _____

_____

_____

_____

3. How can fermentation help to increase the shelf-life of sauerkraut? _____

_____

_____

LINK 197 LINK 196 LINK 195 LINK 194 LINK 193 WEB 192 **KNOW**

193 Beer Brewing

Key Idea: Beer is an alcoholic drink produced by the fermentation of the sugars in barley by yeast. Ethanol and carbon dioxide are produced.

Using yeast to make foods and drinks is probably the oldest form of biotechnology. During beer production, yeast breaks down the sugar in barley to produce alcohol (ethanol) and carbon dioxide. Brewing is divisible into seven stages (below).

During the finishing stage, bacterial proteases are added to break down the yeast and prevent cloudiness. Amylase is added to break down sugars in the production of low calorie beers. Traditional beers are stored in barrels to develop their characteristic qualities. Beer is pasteurised, and standardised for colour and flavour before bottling. Pasteurisation also kills off any undesirable microbes.

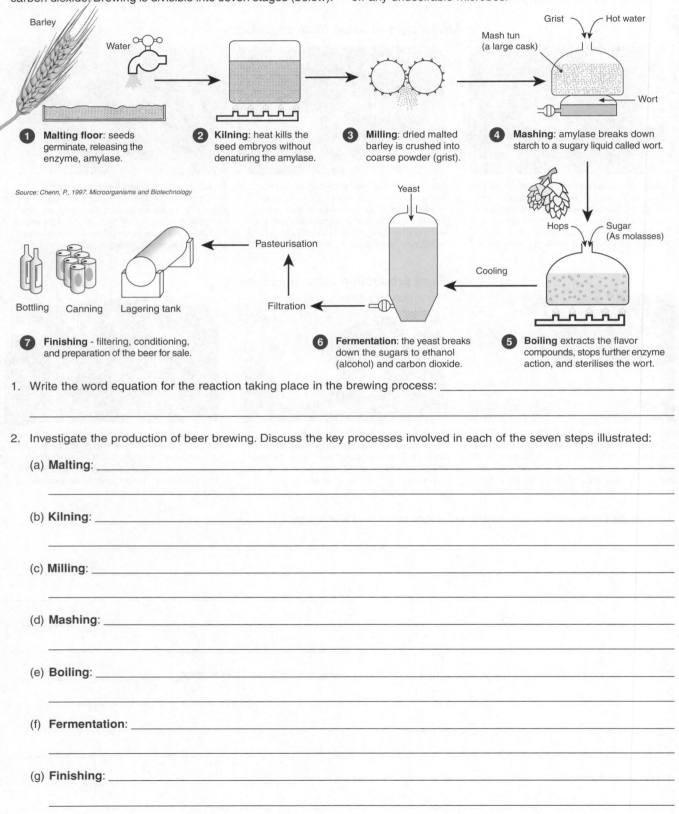

Barley

Water

1 **Malting floor**: seeds germinate, releasing the enzyme, amylase.

2 **Kilning**: heat kills the seed embryos without denaturing the amylase.

3 **Milling**: dried malted barley is crushed into coarse powder (grist).

Grist — Hot water

Mash tun (a large cask)

Wort

4 **Mashing**: amylase breaks down starch to a sugary liquid called wort.

Source: Chenn, P., 1997. Microorganisms and Biotechnology

Yeast

Pasteurisation

Filtration

Cooling

Hops — Sugar (As molasses)

Bottling   Canning   Lagering tank

7 **Finishing** - filtering, conditioning, and preparation of the beer for sale.

6 **Fermentation**: the yeast breaks down the sugars to ethanol (alcohol) and carbon dioxide.

5 **Boiling** extracts the flavor compounds, stops further enzyme action, and sterilises the wort.

1. Write the word equation for the reaction taking place in the brewing process: _____

    _____

2. Investigate the production of beer brewing. Discuss the key processes involved in each of the seven steps illustrated:

    (a) **Malting**: _____

    _____

    (b) **Kilning**: _____

    _____

    (c) **Milling**: _____

    _____

    (d) **Mashing**: _____

    _____

    (e) **Boiling**: _____

    _____

    (f) **Fermentation**: _____

    _____

    (g) **Finishing**: _____

    _____

© 2015 **BIOZONE** International
ISBN: 978-1-927309-14-8
Photocopying Prohibited

194 Bread Making

Key Idea: Bread is produced during a fermentation process using the yeast *Saccharomyces*. The carbon dioxide produced causes the bread to rise.

Leavened (risen) bread is produced using the yeast *Saccharomyces*. When the raw ingredients are mixed, the gluten (flour proteins) are hydrated and coalesce to form a sticky, elastic dough. Enzymes, having survived the milling process when grains are made into flour, act on the starch in the dough to make a mixture of sugars. Yeast uses the sugars (anaerobically) and produces ethanol and carbon dioxide gas which causes the bread to rise. *Lactobacilli* may grow during the early stages of proving, producing lactic acid which contributes to the final flavour and inhibits growth of other organisms. The commercial process is outlined below.

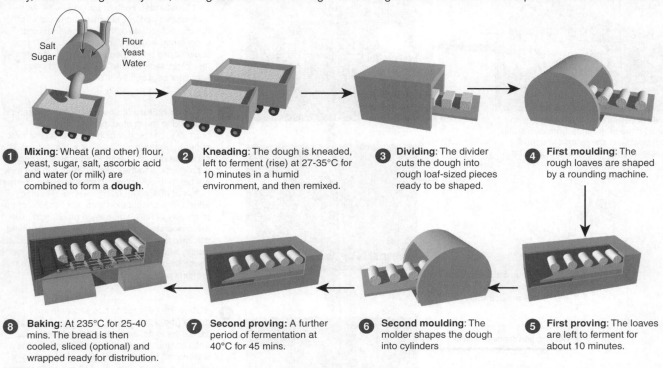

1. **Mixing**: Wheat (and other) flour, yeast, sugar, salt, ascorbic acid and water (or milk) are combined to form a **dough**.

2. **Kneading**: The dough is kneaded, left to ferment (rise) at 27-35°C for 10 minutes in a humid environment, and then remixed.

3. **Dividing**: The divider cuts the dough into rough loaf-sized pieces ready to be shaped.

4. **First moulding**: The rough loaves are shaped by a rounding machine.

8. **Baking**: At 235°C for 25-40 mins. The bread is then cooled, sliced (optional) and wrapped ready for distribution.

7. **Second proving**: A further period of fermentation at 40°C for 45 mins.

6. **Second moulding**: The molder shapes the dough into cylinders

5. **First proving**: The loaves are left to ferment for about 10 minutes.

Bread making is one of the oldest and simplest of biotechnologies, involving mixing wheat flour, water, and yeast to form a dough, which can be baked.

Kneading results in physical and chemical changes in the gluten, which give the dough its elastic and resilient texture and help it to rise.

During proving, the dough is left to ferment. The yeast metabolises sugars, producing ethanol and carbon dioxide. The carbon dioxide causes the dough to rise.

Baking kills the yeast, evaporates the ethanol, and cooks the flour. Vitamin C, whiteners, raising agents, stabilisers, and flavours may be added.

1. Explain the role of each of the following in the bread-making process:

   (a) Sugar: _____

   (b) Yeast: _____

   (c) Water (or milk): _____

2. (a) What happens to the dough during the fermentation (or proving) stages? _____

   _____

   (b) Why will bread not rise if it is baked too soon after adding the yeast? _____

   _____

3. Suggest why gluten free bread is flat and dense: _____

   _____

LINK
197
WEB
194
KNOW

195 Cheese Making

Key Idea: The coagulation of the milk protein casein by acid and/or rennin forms the basis for cheese production.

Cheese is produced when the milk protein casein is coagulated (curdled) to form an insoluble curd. The process varies depending on the type of cheese made. Some cheese (e.g. cottage cheese) is produced by acid coagulation only. The acid is produced by the bacterial starter culture which is added to the milk during the process. Ripened cheese is produced using a combination of acid and the enzyme rennin to form the curd.

Milk is delivered under refrigeration. Most cheese is made from cow's milk, but goat and sheep milk is used for some cheese varieties (such as feta).

Milk vats

Stirring rennet and starter

Ricotta - a low fat cheese resulting from processing of the drained whey

P
S
C

Cooking and draining remaining whey

1 The milk is often pasteurised (heated to 72°C for 15 seconds). Pasteurisation kills off any undesirable microorganisms that could alter the characteristics of the cheese and, most importantly, kills off dangerous microbes that could cause harm if eaten. The milk is pumped into large, temperature controlled vats and kept cool between 20-30°C.

2 A **starter culture** of specially selected bacteria is added to the cooled milk. Lactic acid producing bacteria, which metabolise the milk sugar to produce lactic acid are often used. The pH of the milk will begin to drop as lactic acid is produced and the casein proteins in the milk will begin to coagulate. In most cheeses, **rennet** (a mix of milk coagulating enzymes) is also added. The coagulation step is a function of the chemistry of milk. The casein proteins in milk are associated with other molecules, including calcium, to form stable structures called micelles. Acidity and hydrolysis by the proteases in rennet cause the micelles to destabilise, and the casein proteins precipitate out to form a gel.

3 Cutting the gel causes it to separate into **curds** (the solid portion consisting mainly of casein proteins) and **whey** (mainly water but does contain some whey proteins). The whey is removed from the curd by a combination of stirring, cooking, draining, salting, and pressing. The vigour with which the whey is removed has a profound effect on the final cheese product.

Key to finishing processes

P	Pressing	**C**	Cooking
R	Ripening	**T**	Turning
M	Internal mold	**W**	Washing curd
M	External mold	**B**	Brining**
CH	Cheddaring*	**S**	Salting

* Cheddaring involves the 'milling' (breaking up) of cooked curd and stirring

** Brining involves soaking in a salt solution

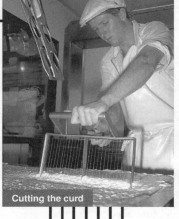

Cutting the curd

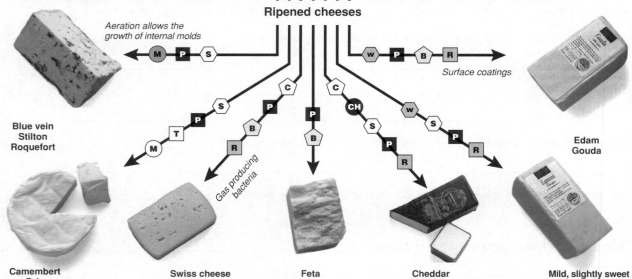

Appraising the final product.

All photos kindly supplied by Kapiti Cheeses Ltd

Ripened cheeses

Aeration allows the growth of internal molds

M — P — S

W — P — B — R

Surface coatings

**Blue vein
Stilton
Roquefort**

M — T — P — S — C

C — B — R

Gas producing bacteria

P — B

C — CH — S — W — P — R

P — R

**Edam
Gouda**

**Camembert
Brie**

**Swiss cheese
Gruyere**

Feta

**Cheddar
Cheshire**

**Mild, slightly sweet
cheddar style**

Microorganisms can alter cheese characteristics

Additional microorganisms are used to give specific characteristics to cheeses. *Propionibacterium freudenreichii* produces the carbon dioxide gas that produces the holes in swiss cheese (above) and creates the characteristic sweet nutty flavour.

Species of *Penicillium* produce the veining on blue cheese (above). The texture of the cheese is loose enough that oxygen can reach the aerobic moulds. Fungi in blue cheese use the lactic acids produced during the cheese-making process and release the odorous by-products associated with blue cheese.

Lactococcus lactis strains are used for most cheeses cultured at 30°C and 38°C. Thermophilic bacteria, which grow best at 42°C, are used for cheeses requiring higher cooking temperatures, such as Swiss and Parmesan (above). Unlike mesophilic bacteria, thermophilic strains will survive the cooking process.

1. Use an annotated diagram to summarise the general cheese making process:

2. Using examples from the flow opposite, explain how different actions during the ripening stage can influence the characteristics of a cheese:

   _____

   _____

   _____

3. (a) What could happen if milk was not pasteurised before the cheese-making process began? _____

   _____

   _____

   (b) Why is the milk cooled to 30°C before the starter culture is added? _____

   _____

   _____

4. Explain what is happening when the casein protein coagulates to form the curd: _____

   _____

   _____

5. Why are thermophilic bacterial varieties used for producing cheeses that require higher cooking temperatures?

   _____

   _____

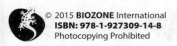

196 Yoghurt Making

Key Idea: Yoghurt is produced by the bacterial fermentation of milk. It is a way to preserve the nutritional qualities of milk. The biochemistry of yoghurt production is similar to that of cheese. Lactic acid bacteria are added into milk and the lactic acid they produce coagulates the milk proteins and thickens the yoghurt. The starter culture for yoghurt contains two symbiotic bacteria, *Lactobacillus bulgaricus* and *Streptococcus thermophilus*. *L. bulgaricus* metabolises lactose in the milk anaerobically to produce the lactic acid responsible for the formation of the yoghurt. *L. bulgaricus* also produces peptidases, which break down the milk proteins into peptides and amino acids. These stimulate the growth of the *Streptococcus* in the culture. *S. thermophilus* produces carbon dioxide and methanoic acid, which together lower the pH and, in turn, stimulate the growth and metabolism of the *Lactobacillus*.

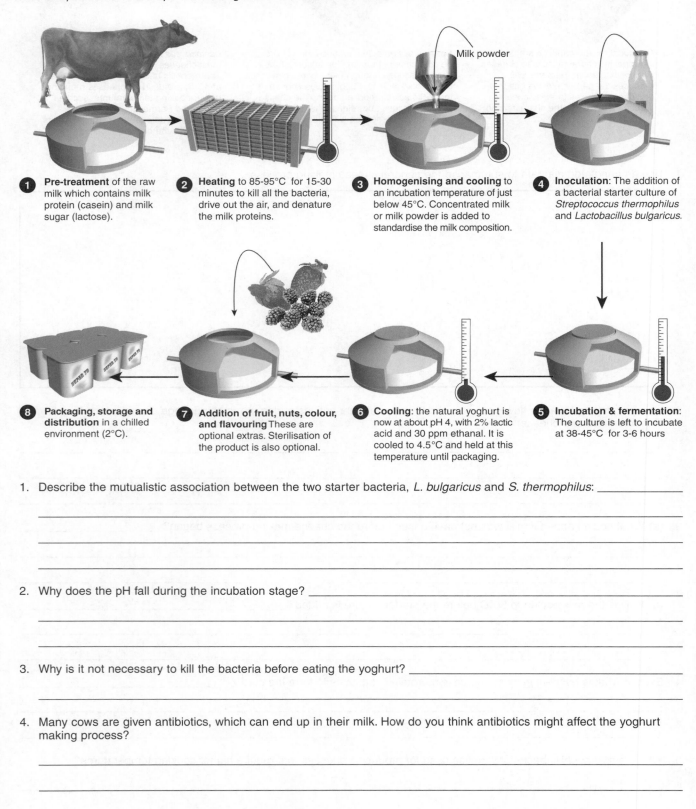

1. **Pre-treatment** of the raw milk which contains milk protein (casein) and milk sugar (lactose).

2. **Heating** to 85-95°C for 15-30 minutes to kill all the bacteria, drive out the air, and denature the milk proteins.

3. **Homogenising and cooling** to an incubation temperature of just below 45°C. Concentrated milk or milk powder is added to standardise the milk composition.

Milk powder

4. **Inoculation**: The addition of a bacterial starter culture of *Streptococcus thermophilus* and *Lactobacillus bulgaricus*.

8. **Packaging, storage and distribution** in a chilled environment (2°C).

7. **Addition of fruit, nuts, colour, and flavouring** These are optional extras. Sterilisation of the product is also optional.

6. **Cooling**: the natural yoghurt is now at about pH 4, with 2% lactic acid and 30 ppm ethanal. It is cooled to 4.5°C and held at this temperature until packaging.

5. **Incubation & fermentation**: The culture is left to incubate at 38-45°C for 3-6 hours

1. Describe the mutualistic association between the two starter bacteria, *L. bulgaricus* and *S. thermophilus*: _____

_____

_____

_____

2. Why does the pH fall during the incubation stage? _____

_____

_____

3. Why is it not necessary to kill the bacteria before eating the yoghurt? _____

_____

4. Many cows are given antibiotics, which can end up in their milk. How do you think antibiotics might affect the yoghurt making process?

_____

_____

_____

WEB LINK

KNOW 196 197

© 2015 **BIOZONE** International
ISBN: 978-1-927309-14-8
Photocopying Prohibited

197 Using Microbes To Make Food: Pros and Cons

Key Idea: There are many advantages to using microorganisms in food technology processes, but consumers have some concerns about their use.

Bacteria and fungi are used extensively in many food technology processes and also in the improvement of food crops. While traditional food safety issues (e.g. microbial contamination) are still valid, the use of genetically modified microorganisms has generated more debate about the safe use of microbes in food production. Some important aspects of this debate are described below.

The advantages of using microbes in food production

Many microorganisms used in food production are grown in bioreactors (above). The growth conditions (e.g. temperature and pH) can be easily adjusted to maintain maximum growth. This allows manufacturers to alter production to meet changes in demand. Often the microorganisms are grown on cheap waste products (e.g. whey) making their production cost efficient.

Microbes have been used to produce genetically modified crop plants. Genetic modification for pest resistance has improved crop yields in corn and rice, providing more food. Lactic acid producing bacteria have been genetically modified to improve the characteristics of the final product (e.g. nutritional value, flavour, or texture of cheese).

Many proteins are inaccessible to vegetarians because they are animal derived. However, single cell protein (SCP) is high quality protein derived from yeast, fungi, or bacteria. Quorn is an example of SCP. Historically, animal derived rennin was used to make cheese, but the use of recombinant rennin means many cheeses are now suitable for vegetarians.

The disadvantages of using microbes in food production

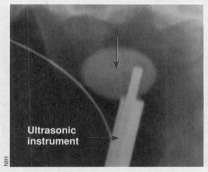

If bacteria are not removed from the finished food product, their high nucleic acid content can cause elevated uric acid levels in humans. This can result in a variety of painful diseases such as gout or kidney stones (above) which form when uric acid crystallises and precipitates out forming a "stone".

Many consumers have negative perceptions of food produced using microbes, especially those that have been genetically modified. The safety and ethics of GMO foods are often questioned and can sway consumer choice when it comes to purchasing food products. In the EU, GMO foods must be labelled.

Microbial rennin (a component of rennet) used in cheese making can sometimes produce bitter cheeses. Rennin produced using genetic engineering does not contain all of the enzymes found in natural calf rennin, so can require additional enzymes to be added to achieve a more realistic flavour profile.

1. Discuss the advantages and disadvantages of using bacteria and fungi to make food for human consumption:

_____

_____

_____

_____

_____

_____

_____

LINK
182 KNOW

198 Penicillin Production

Key Idea: Penicillin is an antibiotic derived from *Penicillium* fungi. It is produced commercially by fermentation using a fed-batch culture technique.

Penicillin is an antibiotic derived from the fungal genus *Penicillium*. Penicillins are widely used against many common bacterial infections. Penicillin is a secondary metabolite, i.e. a compound that is not immediately essential to the microbe's survival or reproduction, and is only produced in the stationary phase of growth. Industrial production of penicillin occurs by

fermentation under aerobic conditions in a fed-batch culture in which nutrients are added periodically, but the culture is not removed until the end of the process. Batch feeding optimises the conditions required for maximum penicillin production. If too many nutrients are supplied, the organism grows, but does not produce penicillin. The generalised process below describes the production of penicillin from *P. chrysogenum*, which yields high quantities of penicillin compared to other species of the genus.

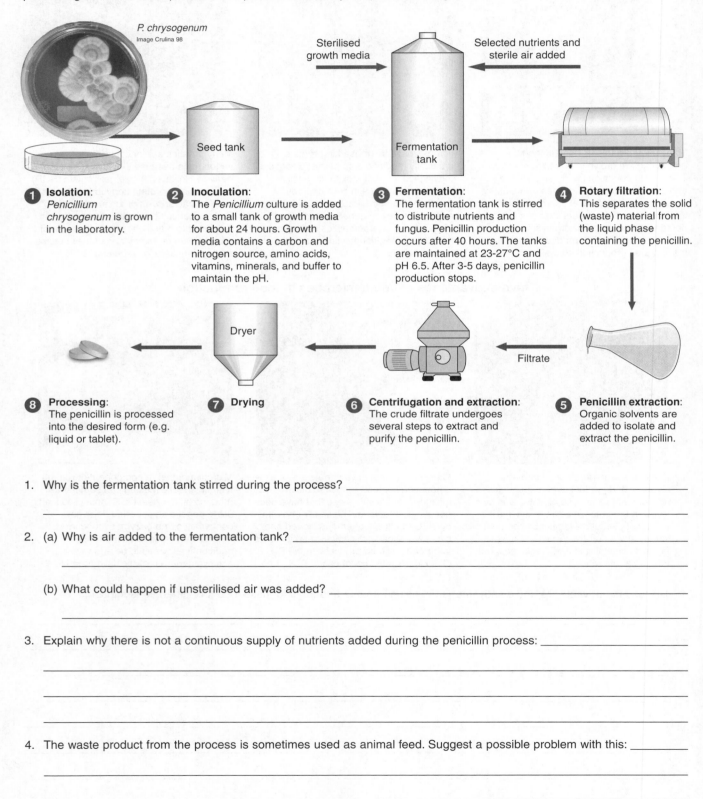

P. chrysogenum
Image Crulina 98

Sterilised growth media

Selected nutrients and sterile air added

Seed tank

Fermentation tank

1 Isolation:
Penicillium chrysogenum is grown in the laboratory.

2 Inoculation:
The *Penicillium* culture is added to a small tank of growth media for about 24 hours. Growth media contains a carbon and nitrogen source, amino acids, vitamins, minerals, and buffer to maintain the pH.

3 Fermentation:
The fermentation tank is stirred to distribute nutrients and fungus. Penicillin production occurs after 40 hours. The tanks are maintained at 23-27°C and pH 6.5. After 3-5 days, penicillin production stops.

4 Rotary filtration:
This separates the solid (waste) material from the liquid phase containing the penicillin.

Dryer

Filtrate

8 Processing:
The penicillin is processed into the desired form (e.g. liquid or tablet).

7 Drying

6 Centrifugation and extraction:
The crude filtrate undergoes several steps to extract and purify the penicillin.

5 Penicillin extraction:
Organic solvents are added to isolate and extract the penicillin.

1. Why is the fermentation tank stirred during the process? _____

_____

2. (a) Why is air added to the fermentation tank? _____

_____

 (b) What could happen if unsterilised air was added? _____

_____

3. Explain why there is not a continuous supply of nutrients added during the penicillin process: _____

_____

_____

_____

4. The waste product from the process is sometimes used as animal feed. Suggest a possible problem with this: _____

_____

_____

© 2015 **BIOZONE** International
ISBN: 978-1-927309-14-8
Photocopying Prohibited

199 Insulin Production

Key Idea: The microorganisms *E.coli* and *Saccharomyces* have been genetically modified to produce human insulin. This has solved the problems associated with traditional insulin sources such as high costs and allergic reactions.

Type 1 diabetes is a metabolic disease caused by a lack of insulin. Around 25 people in every 100 000 suffer from type 1 diabetes and currently the disease can only be treated with injections of insulin. In the past, insulin was obtained from the pancreatic tissue of cows and pigs and purified for human use. The method was expensive and some

patients had severe allergic reactions to the foreign insulin or its contaminants. The insulin used to treat type 1 diabetes patients today is produced by recombinant DNA technology. The human insulin gene is inserted into a plasmid vector, which is taken up by the bacterium *Escherichia coli* or the yeast *Saccharomyces*. These organisms then produce the human insulin in culture conditions. At the end of production the insulin is harvested and purified. Human insulin produced using recombinant DNA technology has fewer side effects than insulin sourced from non-human mammals.

Insulin production using the bacterium *E. coli*

Concept 1

DNA can be cut at specific sites using **restriction enzymes** and joined together using **DNA ligase**. New genes can be inserted into self-replicating bacterial **plasmids** at the point where the cuts are made.

Concept 2

Plasmids are small, circular pieces of DNA found in some bacteria. They usually carry genes useful to the bacterium. *E. coli* plasmids can carry promoters required for the transcription of genes.

Concept 3

Under certain conditions, Bacteria are able to lose or pick up plasmids from their environment. Bacteria can be readily grown in vat cultures at little expense.

Concept 4

The DNA sequences coding for the production of the two polypeptide chains (A and B) that form human insulin can be isolated from the human genome.

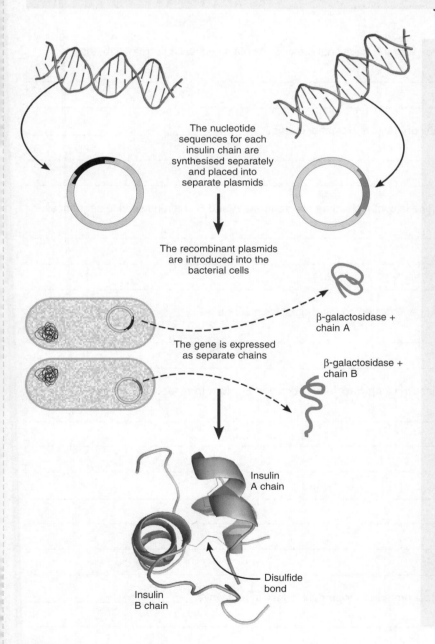

The nucleotide sequences for each insulin chain are synthesised separately and placed into separate plasmids

The recombinant plasmids are introduced into the bacterial cells

The gene is expressed as separate chains

β-galactosidase + chain A

β-galactosidase + chain B

Insulin A chain

Disulfide bond

Insulin B chain

Techniques

The **gene** is **chemically synthesised** as two nucleotide sequences, one for the **insulin A chain** and one for the **insulin B chain**. The two sequences are small enough to be inserted into a plasmid.

Plasmids are extracted from the bacteria *Escherichia coli*. The gene for the bacterial enzyme β-galactosidase is located on the plasmid. To make the bacteria produce insulin, the insulin gene must be linked to the β-galactosidase gene, which carries a promoter for transcription.

Restriction enzymes are used to cut plasmids at the appropriate site and the A and B insulin sequences are inserted. The sequences are joined with the plasmid DNA using **DNA ligase**.

The **recombinant plasmids** are inserted back into the bacteria by placing them together in a culture that favours plasmid uptake by bacteria.

The bacteria are then grown and multiplied in vats under carefully controlled growth conditions.

Outcomes

The product consists partly of β-galactosidase, joined with either the A or B chain of insulin. The chains are extracted, purified, and mixed together. The A and B insulin chains connect via **disulfide cross linkages** to form the functional insulin protein. The insulin can then be made ready for injection in various formulations.

Other Applications

The techniques involved in producing human insulin from genetically modified bacteria can be applied to a range of human proteins and hormones. Proteins currently being produced include human growth hormone, interferon, and factor VIII.

Insulin production using *Saccharomyces*

Yeast cells are **eukaryotic** and hence are much larger than bacterial cells. This enables them to accommodate much larger plasmids and proteins within them.

The gene for human insulin is inserted into a plasmid. The yeast plasmid is larger than that of *E. coli*, so the entire gene can be inserted in one piece rather than as two separate pieces.

The **proinsulin** protein that is produced folds into a specific shape and is cleaved by the yeast's own cellular enzymes, producing the completed insulin chain.

Cleavage site

Cleavage site

By producing insulin this way, the secondary step of combining the separate protein chains is eliminated, making the refining process much simpler.

1. (a) Describe some of the problems associated with the traditional method of obtaining insulin to treat diabetes: _____

_____

_____

(b) What are the advantages of using recombinant insulin to treat diabetes? _____

_____

_____

2. Explain why, when using *E. coli*, the insulin gene is synthesised as two separate A and B chain nucleotide sequences:

_____

_____

_____

3. Why are the synthetic nucleotide sequences ('genes') 'tied' to the β-galactosidase gene? _____

_____

_____

4. Discuss the differences in the production of insulin using *Saccharomyces* and *E. coli* with respect to:

(a) Insertion of the gene into the plasmid: _____

_____

_____

(b) Secretion and purification of the insulin: _____

_____

_____

_____

(c) Which organism do you think would be most preferred for producing insulin and why? _____

_____

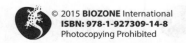

200 Bioremediation

Key Idea: Microorganisms can be used to remove or break down environmental contaminants such as oil and organic waste. This process is called bioremediation.

Bioremediation uses living organisms to remove or neutralise pollutants from a contaminated site. Microorganisms are often used in bioremediation processes where they break down the pollutant through a series of metabolic processes. Different microbes, but especially bacteria, naturally metabolise a range of different substrates, and this is one of the features which makes them useful in bioremediation. Some bacteria have been genetically modified to remove pollutants that no other organism naturally can (e.g. the bacterium *Deinococcus radiodurans* has been genetically engineered to digest ionic mercury produced from radioactive nuclear waste).

Ocean

Oil spill front

Oil spill from Deepwater Horizon

The oceans contain microbes that use the hydrocarbons found in oil as their energy source. The bacterium *Alcanivorax borkumensis* is one such organism. Its numbers quickly increase after an oil spill and it breaks down the oil into harmless compounds (H_2O and CO_2). Bioremediation was used in the *Deepwater Horizon* oil spill in the Gulf of Mexico in 2010.

In 2008, an oil spill occurred near Gujarat (Western India) due to a crude oil trunk line rupture. Crude oil contaminated a wide area of farm land. Oil soaked soil was excavated and transported off site for bioremediation. Oilzapper (a commercial product containing five different oil degrading bacteria) was applied to the soil.

The results are shown right. This is an example of *ex-situ* bioremdiation (treatment that occurs away from the initial site of pollution). According to the Energy and Resources Institute of India, 5000 hectares of oil contaminated cropland has been reclaimed in India and more than 26 000 tonnes of oily sludge has been successfully treated with Oilzapper.

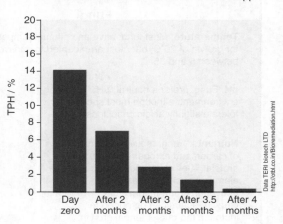

Total petroleum hydrocarbon (TPH) in contaminated soil after treatment with Oilzapper

Data TERI biotech LTD
http://dtbl.co.in/Bioremediation.html

Using bacteria to metabolise hydrocarbons

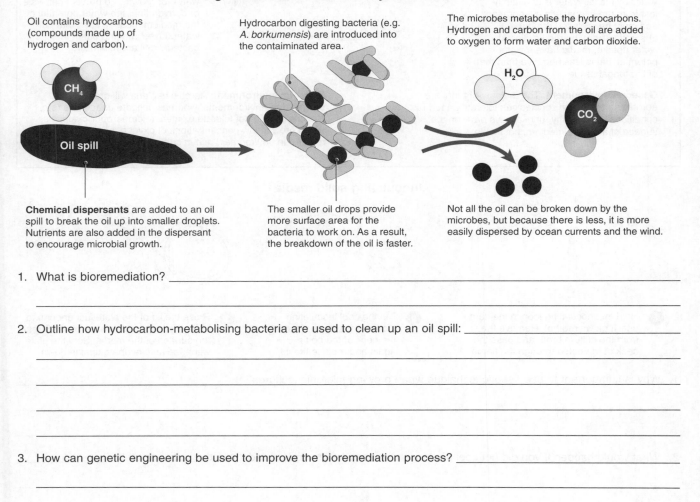

Oil contains hydrocarbons (compounds made up of hydrogen and carbon).

CH_4

Oil spill

Chemical dispersants are added to an oil spill to break the oil up into smaller droplets. Nutrients are also added in the dispersant to encourage microbial growth.

Hydrocarbon digesting bacteria (e.g. *A. borkumensis*) are introduced into the contaiminated area.

The smaller oil drops provide more surface area for the bacteria to work on. As a result, the breakdown of the oil is faster.

The microbes metabolise the hydrocarbons. Hydrogen and carbon from the oil are added to oxygen to form water and carbon dioxide.

H_2O

CO_2

Not all the oil can be broken down by the microbes, but because there is less, it is more easily dispersed by ocean currents and the wind.

1. What is bioremediation? _____

_____

2. Outline how hydrocarbon-metabolising bacteria are used to clean up an oil spill: _____

_____

_____

_____

_____

3. How can genetic engineering be used to improve the bioremediation process? _____

_____

_____

LINK 182 LINK 177 WEB 200 KNOW

201 Techniques in Microbial Culture

Key Idea: The conditions for optimal microbial growth vary depending on the species involved. Sterile techniques must be used when handling microbial cultures.

Bacteria and fungi are grown on agar growth media in the laboratory. Agar is a gelatinous extract of red algae, and can be used in solid or liquid form. It is used because of its two unique physical properties. Firstly, it melts at 100°C and remains liquid until cooled to 40°C, at which point it gels. Secondly, few microbes are capable of digesting agar, so the medium is not used up during culture. The addition of microbes to an agar plate, or to liquid agar, is called **inoculation** and must be carried out under aseptic conditions. **Aseptic techniques** involve the sterilisation of equipment and culture media (either by heat or by chemicals) to prevent cross contamination by unwanted microbes. Microbes and spores are destroyed during sterilisation.

Conditions for the culture of bacteria and fungi

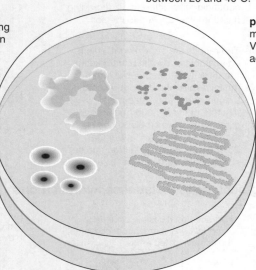

Fungi

Temperature: Most fungi have an optimum temperature for growth of 25°C, but most are adapted to survive between 5 and 35°C.

pH: Fungi prefer a neutral (pH 7) growing environment, although most species can tolerate slightly acidic conditions.

Nutrients: Fungi require a source of carbon and nitrogen to produce protein. They also require trace elements such as potassium, phosphorus and magnesium. Growth factors can be added to increase the rate of fungal growth.

Water potential: Fungi are 85-90% water by mass. Water is constantly lost from the hyphae via evaporation and must be replaced through absorption from the media. To aid water uptake, media have a water potential that is less negative than that of the fungal tissue.

Gaseous environment: The majority of fungi are aerobic and very few species can tolerate anaerobic conditions. This is why fungi always grow on the surface of a culture medium, not inside it.

Bacteria

Temperature: Most bacteria cultured in the school laboratory are classified as **mesophiles**. Mesophiles prefer temperatures between 20 and 40°C.

pH: Most bacteria grow optimally in media with a pH between 6 and 8. Very few bacteria can grow in very acidic conditions.

Nutrients: Bacteria need a source of carbon, nitrogen, and mineral salts as raw ingredients for cellular growth. Magnesium, zinc, copper, and iron are essential trace elements.

Water potential: All bacteria require water for growth. To prevent cell lysis or dehydration, the water potential of the medium must be such that net water fluxes into and out of the bacterial cell are minimised.

Gaseous environment: Aerobic bacteria will grow only in oxygenated environments, whereas obligate anaerobes (e.g. *Clostridium*) do not tolerate oxygen. Microaerophilic species, which grow in low concentrations of oxygen, sometimes require an environment rich in carbon dioxide.

Inoculating solid media

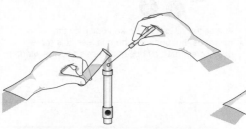

1. Hold the inoculating loop in the flame until it glows red hot. Remove the lid from the culture broth and pass the neck of the bottle through the flame.

2. Dip the cool inoculating loop into the broth. Flame the neck of the bottle again and replace the lid.

3. Raise the lid of the plate just enough to allow the loop to streak the plate. Streak the surface of the media. Seal the plate with tape and incubate upside down.

1. Why is it important to use aseptic technique when growing microbial cultures? _____

_____

_____

2. What would happen if you did not cool the inoculation loop before you dipped it into the culture broth? _____

_____

_____

© 2015 **BIOZONE** International
ISBN: 978-1-927309-14-8
Photocopying Prohibited

202 Strain Isolation

Key Idea: Streak plating is a simple method to separate individual species of bacteria from a mixed culture.

In nature, bacteria exist as mixed populations. To study them, they must exist as pure cultures (i.e. cultures in which all organisms are the same species). The most common way of separating bacterial cells on the agar surface is the **streak plate method**. This method dilutes the sample by mechanical means. After incubation, the area at the beginning of the streak pattern will show confluent growth (growth as a continuous sheet), while the area at the end of the streak will show discrete colonies. Isolated colonies can be removed using aseptic techniques, and transferred to a sterile medium. After incubation, all organisms in the new culture will be descendants of the same organism (i.e. a pure culture). The organism can then be identified and studied (e.g. for sensitivity to particular antibiotics).

The streaking starts here. Streaks are made in the order indicated by the numbers on the plate. The first streak is made from the initial bacterial mixture.

In each streak, the loop picks up bacteria from the previous series, diluting the number of cells each time.

Individual colonies (arising from one cell) should be obtained here. These can be removed and then cultured separately.

Latex gloves ensure no contamination from either bacteria or fungi on the hands.

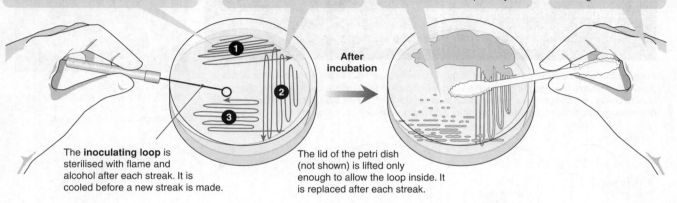

After incubation

The **inoculating loop** is sterilised with flame and alcohol after each streak. It is cooled before a new streak is made.

The lid of the petri dish (not shown) is lifted only enough to allow the loop inside. It is replaced after each streak.

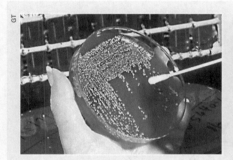

Colonies become visible when approximately 10 to 100 million bacterial cells are present. Note the well-isolated colonies in the photo above. A single colony may be removed for further investigation.

A swab containing a single strain of bacteria is used to inoculate additional nutrient plates to produce pure cultures of bacteria.

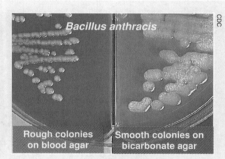

Bacillus anthracis

Rough colonies on blood agar   **Smooth colonies on bicarbonate agar**

To test purity, a sample of a culture can be grown on a selective medium that promotes the growth of a single species. A selective medium may contain a nutrient specific to a particular species.

1. What is the purpose of streak plating? _____

_____

2. Outline the process of streak plating: _____

_____

_____

_____

3. Why is the lid only partially removed during streaking? _____

_____

4. Why would you use **selective media** when culturing bacteria: _____

_____

_____

LINK   WEB
203 **202**   KNOW

203 Dilution Plating

Key idea: Dilution plating can be used to estimate culture density based on plate counts after a serial dilution.

The number of bacteria in a culture can be measured directly (e.g. by counting in a haemocytometer) or indirectly. Indirect methods include measuring culture dry weight or turbidity, both of which are directly proportional to cell density.

Microbial populations are often very large, so most counting methods rely on counting a very small sample of the culture. A commonly used indirect method is serial dilution followed by plate counts (dilution plating). If care is taken with the serial dilution, an accurate estimate of culture density can be obtained.

Measuring microbial growth using dilution plating

A **serial dilution** is the stepwise dilution of a substance into another solution. By making a series of dilutions and then counting the colonies that arise after plating, the density of the original inoculum (starting culture) can be calculated. To obtain good results, the colonies should be well separated and the number of colonies should not be too numerous to count.

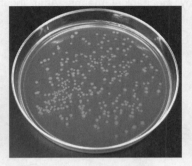

Madprime cc 3.0

CALCULATION: No. of colonies on plate X reciprocal of sample dilution = no. of bacteria per cm^3.

EXAMPLE: *28 colonies on a plate of 1/1000 dilution, then the original culture contained:*
28 x 1000 = 28 x 10^3 cm^{-3} bacterial cells

Plate counts are widely used in microbiology. It is a useful technique because only the viable (live) colonies are counted, but it requires some incubation time before colonies form. For quality control purposes in some food industries where the food product is perishable (e.g. milk processing) this time delay is unacceptable, and rapid detection methods are used.

When a culture has been sufficiently diluted, the colonies are discrete and can easily be counted or isolated. Each colony arises from a single cell.

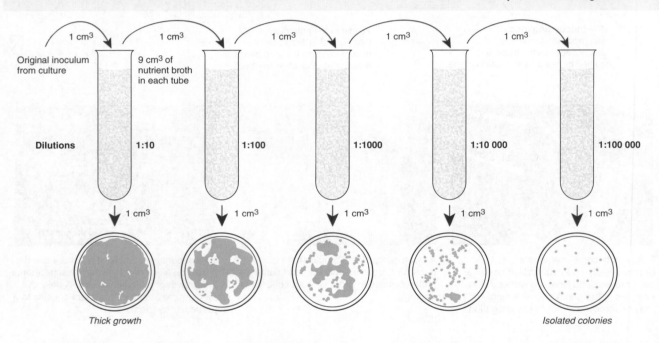

1 cm^3 1 cm^3 1 cm^3 1 cm^3 1 cm^3

Original inoculum from culture

9 cm^3 of nutrient broth in each tube

Dilutions   1:10   1:100   1:1000   1:10 000   1:100 000

1 cm^3 1 cm^3 1 cm^3 1 cm^3 1 cm^3

Thick growth   *Isolated colonies*

1. In the example of serial dilution above, use the equation provided to calculate the cell concentration in the original culture:

   _____

2. (a) Explain the term **viable count**: _____

   _____

   (b) Explain why dilution plating is a useful technique for obtaining a viable count: _____

   _____

   _____

   (c) Investigate an alternative technique, such as turbidimetry and identify how the technique differs from dilution plating:

   _____

   _____

   _____

204 Industrial Microbiology

Key Idea: The microbes used in industrial processes are grown in large bioreactors. The growth conditions must be monitored and maintained for optimal microbial growth.

The microbes used in many industrial processes are produced using large scale bioreactors (fermenters) to culture the organism. Note that the term fermentation, when used in reference to industrial microbiology, applies to both aerobic and anaerobic microbial growth in bioreactors. The microbes are first isolated and then cultured in an appropriate environment. The conditions within the bioreactors are constantly monitored and adjusted to maintain optimal growth conditions. The desired product is then extracted from the cells themselves (e.g. enzymes) or from the culture medium (e.g. antibiotics). Depending on the desired product, microbial culture may be carried out in batches (batch culture) or as a continuous culture.

Design of a continuously stirred bioreactor

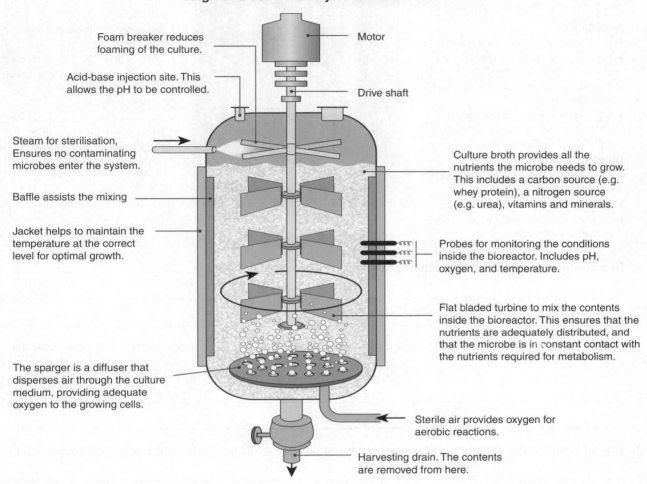

Foam breaker reduces foaming of the culture.

Motor

Acid-base injection site. This allows the pH to be controlled.

Drive shaft

Steam for sterilisation, Ensures no contaminating microbes enter the system.

Baffle assists the mixing

Jacket helps to maintain the temperature at the correct level for optimal growth.

The sparger is a diffuser that disperses air through the culture medium, providing adequate oxygen to the growing cells.

Culture broth provides all the nutrients the microbe needs to grow. This includes a carbon source (e.g. whey protein), a nitrogen source (e.g. urea), vitamins and minerals.

Probes for monitoring the conditions inside the bioreactor. Includes pH, oxygen, and temperature.

Flat bladed turbine to mix the contents inside the bioreactor. This ensures that the nutrients are adequately distributed, and that the microbe is in constant contact with the nutrients required for metabolism.

Sterile air provides oxygen for aerobic reactions.

Harvesting drain. The contents are removed from here.

The problems associated with scaling up

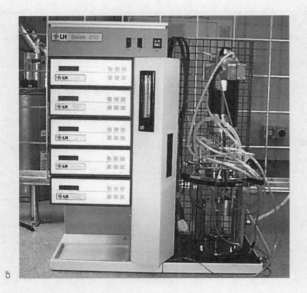

Industrial reactions are tested on a small scale (left) before being scaled up for an industrial sized production. Testing on a small scale identifies problems that need to be resolved before the process is scaled up. These include:

▶ All undesirable organisms must be prevented from entering the fermenter. The absence of undesirable microbes within a biotechnology process is called **asepsis**. Contamination can result in spoiled or low quality product, low product yield, and increased expense because of lost production time and extra clean-up costs.

▶ Aerobic microbes must be given an adequate supply of oxygen.

▶ Powerful motors are needed to mix the culture which has a porridge like consistency.

▶ Optimum nutrient levels must be maintained.

▶ The heat generated by microbial activity needs to dissipated. The entire culture must be keep at a constant temperature.

▶ Waste products need to be constantly removed.

▶ The build up of foam due to the production of carbon dioxide must be monitored and controlled.

LINK
210 KNOW

Continuous culture

Continuous culturing involves constant addition of fresh culture medium into the bioreactor and removal of material out of the bioreactor. The desired components are harvested from the material that is removed. Nutrient addition and product removal occurs at equal rates to maintain a constant volume. Continuous cultures are used when a culture of actively growing cells is needed (e.g. some antibiotics are only produced during active growth).

Advantages

▶ Continuous growth over long periods.

▶ Population can be kept in exponential growth for extended periods.

▶ Equipment is in constant use, so there is less down time.

▶ Nutrients are added and inhibitory metabolites are constantly removed to maintain optimum growth.

Disadvantages

▶ It can be difficult to maintain the optimum conditions for microbial growth.

▶ Contamination is more likely to occur.

▶ It can be difficult to maintain and control product consistency.

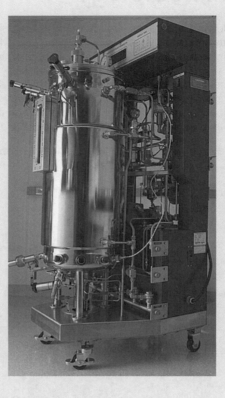

Batch culture

Batch culturing involves adding cells to a fixed volume of culture medium. The culture medium is harvested as a batch at the end of the process. The process is halted when all of the nutrients are used, or a threshold level of toxic metabolites is reached and further growth of the culture is inhibited. Most large scale production is carried out by batch cultures.

Advantages

▶ Bioreactor conditions are easier to manipulate.

▶ There is less risk of contamination.

▶ Product quality is easier to control.

Disadvantages

▶ More down time as equipment must be cleaned between each batch.

▶ Product output is determined by the limited nutrient supply, and build up of inhibitory metabolites.

1. Describe the main difference between a continuous and batch culture system: _____

_____

_____

2. Explain why continuous culture is often used when the harvested product is biomass (cells) or a primary metabolite:

_____

_____

_____

3. Explain when batch culture (with final harvest of the end-product) would be used in preference to continuous culture:

_____

_____

_____

4. Explain the importance of asepsis in industrial processes involving microbial cultures: _____

_____

_____

5. Outline how industrial bioreactors overcome the following problems associated with scaling up:

(a) Heat generated by microbial activity: _____

_____

(b) Microbial demand for oxygen: _____

_____

(c) Nutrient demand: _____

_____

205 Microbial Growth and Metabolites

Key Idea: Microbial growth in a closed culture consists of four phases (lag, log, stationary and death phases). Some metabolites produced during microbial growth are beneficial to humans, and are harvested.

Microbial growth follows a pattern consisting of four phases (lag, log, stationary, and death phases). During their growth, microbes produce **metabolites** (products) as part of their normal metabolism. These fall into two categories. **Primary metabolites** are compounds that are essential for the

microbe's normal metabolic activity. They are usually produced in small quantities and may be utilised by the organism. **Secondary metabolites** are not required for microbial metabolism, but may be beneficial to the microbe (e.g. by inhibiting competitors). They often accumulate in large quantities during the stationary phase. Bioreactor conditions can be manipulated to promote the production of specific metabolites. In general, it is more difficult to produce and harvest primary metabolites than it is secondary metabolites.

Microbial growth in a closed culture

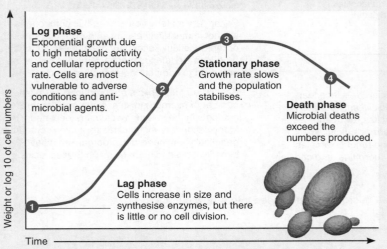

Log phase
Exponential growth due to high metabolic activity and cellular reproduction rate. Cells are most vulnerable to adverse conditions and anti-microbial agents.

Stationary phase
Growth rate slows and the population stabilises.

Death phase
Microbial deaths exceed the numbers produced.

Lag phase
Cells increase in size and synthesise enzymes, but there is little or no cell division.

(y-axis: Weight or log 10 of cell numbers; x-axis: Time)

① **Lag phase:** Cell numbers are relatively constant as the organisms adjust to the conditions and prepare for division.

② **Log phase:** The phase of **exponential growth**. In conditions optimal for microbial growth, the cells begin multiplying at an exponential rate, quickly increasing cell numbers. For yeast, the generation time is approximately 1 hour, but the doubling time of some bacteria can be as little as 15 minutes.

③ **Stationary phase:** In a closed culture system no new nutrients are added and waste products are not removed. Microbial growth slows as the nutrients become depleted and waste products build up. The growth rate equals the death rate, so there is no net growth in the microbial population, and numbers stabilise.

④ **Death phase:** Microbial numbers decrease as the death rate exceeds growth rate; a result of a lack of nutrients and build of toxic metabolites.

The graph above illustrates the growth curve for a yeast culture grown within a closed culture system. Bacteria show a similar growth curve. Growth curves of microbial cell numbers against time typically show these four phases.

Production of primary metabolites

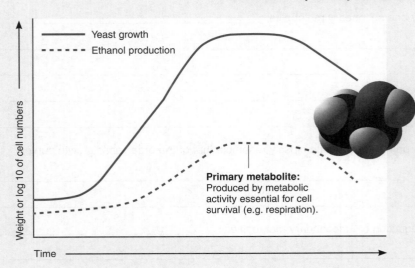

— Yeast growth
- - - Ethanol production

Primary metabolite:
Produced by metabolic activity essential for cell survival (e.g. respiration).

(y-axis: Weight or log 10 of cell numbers; x-axis: Time)

During the log phase of microbial growth (in culture), many intermediate metabolic products are produced, which are further required for growth or for energy-yielding catabolism. These **primary metabolites** are produced in excess of requirements and accumulate in the culture, from which they can be extracted and purified.

Primary metabolites form at the same time as the cells grow, so their production curves are very similar to the organism's growth curve. Microbial production of primary metabolites contributes significantly in modern biotechnology. Through fermentation, microorganisms growing on inexpensive carbon sources can produce valuable products such as amino acids, nucleotides, organic acids, and vitamins.

The graph (left) compares the production curve of the primary metabolite ethanol, with the growth curve for yeast.

Amino acids, nucleotides, proteins, carbohydrates, lipids, and vitamins are primary metabolites needed for culture growth. Acetone, ethanol, butanol, and organic acids are required for deriving energy. The quantity of some of these metabolites exceeds the requirements of the producers and accumulates in the culture.

LINK **210**   LINK **198**   WEB **205**   **KNOW**

Production of secondary metabolites

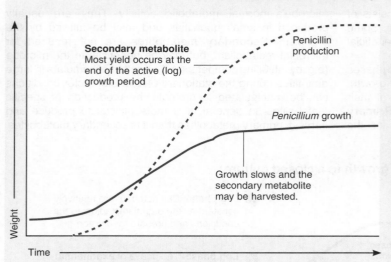

Secondary metabolite
Most yield occurs at the end of the active (log) growth period

Penicillin production

Penicillium growth

Growth slows and the secondary metabolite may be harvested.

Weight

Time

The graph (above) illustrates the production of penicillin, a secondary metabolite produced by species of the fungus, *Penicillium*. Penicillin is produced once the microbe has largely completed its growth and has entered the stationary phase. Many important pharmaceuticals are produced as secondary metabolites by bacteria and fungi. Examples include penicillin, quinine, atropine, erythromycin, morphine, and codeine.

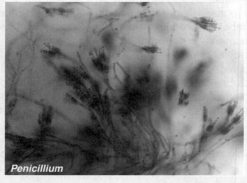

Penicillium

Peter Halasz

Secondary metabolites are organic compounds that are not immediately essential to microbial survival or reproduction. Secondary metabolites are often produced as defence mechanisms or to allow the organism to compete against other species.

Secondary metabolites are produced by a limited number of microorganisms, when one or more nutrients in the culture medium are depleted. Many secondary metabolites (including some from genetically engineered microorganisms) have beneficial uses to humans as pharmaceuticals.

1. (a) Why is there an initial lag in the growth of a microorganism placed into a new culture? _____

_____

_____

(b) Suggest how this time lag could be reduced when starting a new culture: _____

_____

2. Predict the effect on a microbial growth curve if fresh nutrients were added and toxic by-products removed continuously:

_____

_____

3. Explain the differences between a primary and secondary metabolite: _____

_____

_____

_____

_____

4. (a) Explain why the production curve for a primary metabolite closely resemble that of the organism's growth curve:

_____

_____

(b) Explain why this is not the case for production of a secondary metabolite: _____

_____

_____

5. Explain why a secondary metabolite might be produced after a microbe had completed most of its growth phase:

_____

_____

© 2015 **BIOZONE** International
ISBN: 978-1-927309-14-8
Photocopying Prohibited

206 Plotting Microbial Growth

Key Idea: Microbial growth can be plotted on a graph and used to predict microbial cell numbers at a set time.

Bacteria normally reproduce by a **binary fission**, a simple mitotic cell division that is preceded by cell elongation and involves one cell dividing in two. The time required for a cell to divide is the **generation time** and it varies between species

and with environmental conditions such as temperature. When actively growing bacteria are inoculated into a liquid growth medium and the population is counted at intervals, a line can be plotted to show the growth of the cell population over time. You can simulate this for a hypothetical bacterial population with a generation time of 20 minutes.

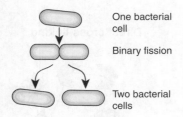

One bacterial cell

Binary fission

Two bacterial cells

Time / mins	Population size
0	1
20	2
40	4
60	8
80	
100	
120	
140	
160	
180	
200	
220	
240	
260	
280	
300	
320	
340	
360	

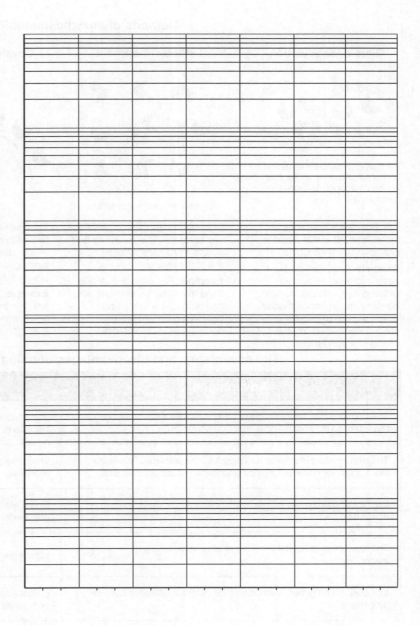

1. Complete the table above by doubling the number of bacteria for every 20 minute interval.

2. State how many bacteria were present after: 1 hour: _____   3 hours: _____   6 hours: _____

3. Graph the results on the grid above. Make sure that you choose suitable scales and labels for each axis.

4. (a) Predict the number of cells present after 380 minutes: _____

   (b) Plot this value on the graph above.

5. Why is a log graph used to plot microbial growth? _____

_____

DATA

207 Immobilised Enzymes

Key Idea: Immobilising enzymes on an inert support material enables them to be repeatedly used in industrial processes. Traditionally, enzymes have been added into solutions to catalyse a reaction. The disadvantage of this is that the enzyme cannot be recovered, and the end product will contain the enzyme. Immobilised enzymes are often used to catalyse industrial reactions. Immobilising enzymes involves physically or chemically attaching them to a solid support (see below). Once immobilised, the substrate is passed over the enzyme, and when the reaction is completed, the enzyme can be washed and is ready to be used again. Immobilised enzymes have a wide variety of applications including medical (antibiotic production), food (removing lactose from milk), and removing waste products from wastewater.

Methods of enzyme immobilisation

Micro-encapsulation	Lattice entrapment	Covalent attachment	Direct cross-linking

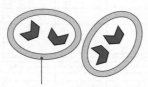

Partially-permeable membrane. Limits substrates to those that are small enough to cross the membrane.

Enzymes trapped in gel lattice

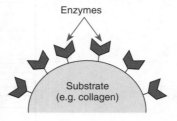

Enzymes

Substrate (e.g. collagen)

Glutaraldehyde

The enzyme is held within a membrane, or within alginate polyacrylamide capsules.

Example: Enzymes have been micro-encapsulated within cheeses to accelerate ripening and enhance flavour development. The enzymes are not inactivated by physical changes around them.

Enzyme is trapped in a gel lattice, e.g. silica gel. The substrate and reaction products diffuse in and out of the matrix.

Example: Penicillin acylase is used to produce semi-synthetic penicillins (to which some penicillin-resistant organisms have not yet evolved resistance).

Enzyme is covalently bonded to a solid surface (e.g. collagen or a synthetic polymer).The binding is very strong, so, there is very little leakage of enzyme.

Example: The protein digesting enzyme trypsin is used to pre-digest milk proteins used in infant formula.

Glutaraldehyde is used to cross-link the enzymes. They then precipitate out and are immobilised without support.

Example: Glucose isomerase converts glucose to fructose in the production of high-fructose syrup used in confectionery and soft drink.

The advantages and disadvantages of using immobilised enzymes

Advantages	Disadvantages
The enzyme can be easily cleaned and recovered, and used repeatedly. This reduces the cost of using them.	The immobilisation process may reduce enzyme activity because the active site may be unavailable.
The end product is not contaminated by the enzyme. This reduces the number of harvesting steps and improves product quality.	Immobilised enzymes can be less active because they do not mix freely with their substrate.
Immobilised enzymes are generally more stable (less likely to denature).	Some methods that offer high stability (e.g. covalent bonding) are harder to achieve.
The functional life of the enzyme is often extended by immobilisation.	Immobilisation can be expensive.
Immobilised enzymes are suitable for use in continuous culture processes.	Immobilisation offers no advantage when one or more of the substrates is insoluble.

1. (a) Describe two benefits of using immobilised enzymes (rather than enzymes in solution) for industrial processes:

_____

_____

_____

(b) Describe a disadvantage associated with the use of immobilised enzymes: _____

_____

2. Why would immobilisation reduce the activity of some enzymes? _____

_____

© 2015 **BIOZONE** International
ISBN: 978-1-927309-14-8
Photocopying Prohibited

208 Immobilisation of Lactase

Key Idea: Immobilised lactase is used to remove lactose from milk, making it suitable for people with lactose intolerance. Milk is a high quality food containing protein, fat, carbohydrate, minerals, and vitamins. Many people become lactose intolerant (cannot digest lactose) as they grow older. They avoid milk products, and lose out on the benefits of milk. Removing the lactose from milk allows lactose intolerant people to gain the nutritional benefits from milk.

Removing lactose from milk

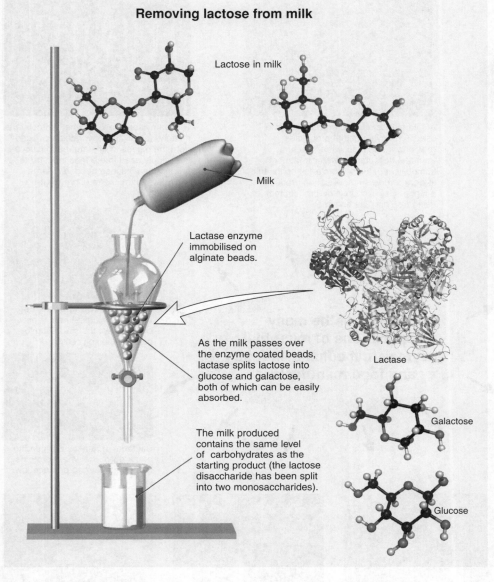

Lactose in milk

Milk

Lactase enzyme immobilised on alginate beads.

As the milk passes over the enzyme coated beads, lactase splits lactose into glucose and galactose, both of which can be easily absorbed.

The milk produced contains the same level of carbohydrates as the starting product (the lactose disaccharide has been split into two monosaccharides).

Lactase

Galactose

Glucose

Lactase and humans

Lactose is a disaccharide found in milk. It is less sweet than glucose. All infant humans produce the enzyme **lactase**, which hydrolyses lactose into glucose and galactose.

As humans become older, their production of lactase gradually declines and they lose their ability to hydrolyse lactose. As adults, they are **lactose intolerant**, and feel bloated after drinking milk.

In humans of mainly European, East African, or Indian descent, lactase production continues into adulthood. But people of mainly Asian descent cease production early in life and become lactose intolerant.

1. Explain why being able to continue to drink milk throughout life is of benefit to humans: _____

_____

_____

_____

2. How is lactase used to produce lactose-free milk? _____

_____

_____

_____

3. Why does lactose-free milk often has a slightly sweeter taste that ordinary milk? _____

_____

_____

LINK
209 **KNOW**

209 Applications of Enzymes

Key Idea: Microbes produce a wide range of different enzymes. The properties of these enzymes allows them to be used in a wide variety of industrial processes.

The metabolic diversity of microbes is enormous. As a result, the variety of microbial enzymes available to be used in industrial process is also very large (below). Genetic modification of microbes further increases the range and potential applications of microbial enzymes.

Immobilised aminoacyclase is used to produce **L-amino acids**. L-aspartic acid is manufactured in large quantities and used as an ingredient in many artificial sweeteners. Using immobilised aminoacyclase is more economical than the use of free enzyme.

Acrylamide is used to produce polymers used in many industrial processes (e.g. paper and plastic manufacture, and as a flocculant in water treatment). Immobilised nitrilase converts acrylonitrile to **acrylamide**. Immobilisation produces a higher yield and less by-product than using free nitrilase enzyme.

Glucoamylase is an enzyme that converts dextrins (small carbohydrates produced from the digestion of starch) into glucose. It is widely used in the food industry to produce the glucose needed in large scale fermentations (e.g. brewing).

Fungal ligninases are used in **pulp and paper industries** to remove lignin from wood pulp and treat wood waste.

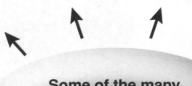

Some of the many applications of microbial enzymes in medicine, industry, and food manufacture.

In **soft centred chocolates**, invertase (sucrase) from yeast breaks down the solid filling to produce the soft centre.

Medical treatment of blood clots employs protease enzymes such as streptokinase from *Streptomyces* spp.

Bacterial proteases are used to break down the wheat proteins (gluten) in flour, to produce low gluten breads.

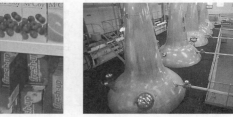

Cellulases and pectinases are used in the manufacture of packaged (as opposed to fresh) fruit juices to speed juice extraction and prevent cloudiness.

In **beer brewing**, proteases (from bacteria) are added to prevent cloudiness. Amyloglucosidases are used to produce low calorie beers.

Citric acid is used in **jam production** and is synthesised by a mutant strain of the fungus *Aspergillus niger*, which produces the enzyme citrate synthase.

Tanning industries now use proteases from *Bacillus subtilis* instead of toxic chemicals, such as sulfide pastes, to remove hairs and soften hides.

1. Research one of the following immobilised enzymes, and describe the reaction it catalyses and its application. Choose from aminoacyclase, glucoamylase, or nitrilase.

_____

_____

_____

_____

_____

_____

© 2015 **BIOZONE** International
ISBN: 978-1-927309-14-8
Photocopying Prohibited

210 Industrial Production of Enzymes

Key Idea: Microbial enzymes can be produced on an industrial scale by growing the microorganisms that produce them in large fermentation tanks. The processes involved depend on whether the enzymes are intracellular or extracellular.

Many industries rely on the large scale production of microbial enzymes to catalyse a range of reactions. In the absence of enzymes, these reactions sometimes require high temperatures or pressures to proceed. Enzyme technology involves the production, isolation, purification, and application of useful enzymes. Most enzymes used in industrial processes are microbial in origin and are produced in industrial-scale microbial fermentations. The production process depends on whether the enzymes are extracellular (secreted from a cell) or intracellular (contained within a cell).

1 Growth of the microorganisms:

A closed fermenter system is an enclosed, sterile system containing culture broth in which the microorganisms (bacteria or fungi) are grown until the extracellular products (or the cells themselves) have accumulated for harvesting. Conditions in the fermenter vessel are closely monitored and carefully regulated so that the conditions for maximal microbial growth are optimised.

The model (right) shows a cutaway section of a cylindrical fermentation chamber, typical of that used for continuous microbial cultures.

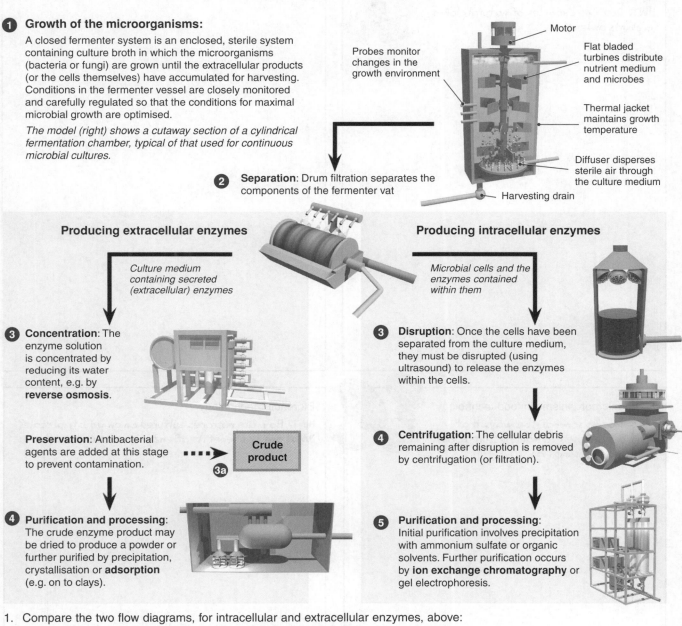

Probes monitor changes in the growth environment

Motor

Flat bladed turbines distribute nutrient medium and microbes

Thermal jacket maintains growth temperature

Diffuser disperses sterile air through the culture medium

Harvesting drain

2 Separation: Drum filtration separates the components of the fermenter vat

Producing extracellular enzymes

Culture medium containing secreted (extracellular) enzymes

3 Concentration: The enzyme solution is concentrated by reducing its water content, e.g. by **reverse osmosis**.

Preservation: Antibacterial agents are added at this stage to prevent contamination.

3a → **Crude product**

4 Purification and processing: The crude enzyme product may be dried to produce a powder or further purified by precipitation, crystallisation or **adsorption** (e.g. on to clays).

Producing intracellular enzymes

Microbial cells and the enzymes contained within them

3 Disruption: Once the cells have been separated from the culture medium, they must be disrupted (using ultrasound) to release the enzymes within the cells.

4 Centrifugation: The cellular debris remaining after disruption is removed by centrifugation (or filtration).

5 Purification and processing: Initial purification involves precipitation with ammonium sulfate or organic solvents. Further purification occurs by **ion exchange chromatography** or gel electrophoresis.

1. Compare the two flow diagrams, for intracellular and extracellular enzymes, above:

   (a) Explain the main way in which the two production methods differ: _____

   _____

   (b) Suggest the reason for this difference: _____

   _____

   _____

2. Enzyme solutions can be packaged and used as crude extracts without further purification (3a). State one benefit of this:

   _____

   _____

KNOW

211 Chapter Review

Summarise what you know about this topic under the headings and sub-headings provided. You can draw diagrams or mind maps, or write short notes to organise your thoughts. Use the images and hints to help you and refer back to the introduction to check the points covered:

Natural clones
HINT: Describe examples of natural clones in plants and animals.

Artificial clones
HINT: How are artificial clones made? What issues surround artificial cloning.

Using microorganisms in food technology
HINT: Discuss some of the ways that microbes are used to manufacture food for human consumption.

Bioreactor technology
HINT: How are microbes cultured on an industrial scale? What are the benefits of enzyme immobilisation?.

© 2015 **BIOZONE** International
ISBN: 978-1-927309-14-8
Photocopying Prohibited

REVISE

212 KEY TERMS: Did You Get It?

1. Test your vocabulary by matching each term to its definition, as identified by its preceding letter code.

aseptic technique

batch culture

bioreactor

bioremediation

biotechnology

clone

continuous culture

cutting

embryo splitting

enzyme immobilisation

lag phase

micropropagation

primary metabolite

secondary metabolite

somatic cell nuclear transfer

strain isolation

vegetative propagation

A The use of microorganisms to remove pollutants and contaminants from an environment.

B A compound produced by a microorganism and not required for its own metabolism, but often beneficial to it (e.g. by inhibiting competitor growth).

C The process of attaching or fixing an enzyme to an inert, insoluble material. The product can be removed from the enzyme allowing the enzyme to be used again..

D A compound produced by a microorganism that is essential to its own metabolic activity (e.g. normal growth, development, and reproduction).

E An organism that is genetically identical to the parent organism (or to its siblings in the case of identical twins).

F A method of cloning plants using explant tissue from the plant, and growing it in sterile conditions in a culture vessel.

G The transfer of the nucleus from a somatic cell into an egg from which the nucleus has been removed.

H A section of a parent plant which has been removed so that it can be grown as a new individual.

I Technique carried out under sterile conditions to minimise microbial contamination.

J A branch of science associated with the application of living organisms and biological processes in industry, medicine, food technology and other related fields.

K An industrial vessel used for the production of cultures.

L The phase of an idealised microbial growth curve where numbers are static as the cells increase in size and prepare to divide.

M The natural or artificial production of new plants without seed.

N Culture of microorganisms in a medium that is receiving a steady supply of nutrients. The end product is constantly harvested at a rate which equals nutrient addition so a constant volume is maintained.

O A simple form of cloning that replicates the natural twinning process.

P A closed system culture used to grow microorganisms. The cells are added to a fixed volume of culture medium. The end product is harvested at the end of the process.

Q Microbiology technique designed to isolate pure bacterial strains.

2. The figure below shows a typical bacterial growth curve for a closed system. The table below describes each of the steps (A-D) labelled on the diagram. Match the description with the correct letter on the diagram.

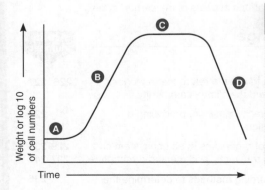

Description of stage	Letter
The number of cells dying exceeds the number being produced	
The rate of cell division equals that of cell death	
Cells increase in size and prepare for cell division	
Cell numbers increase at an exponential rate	

TEST

Ecosystems

Key terms

abiotic (=physical) factor

abundance

Azotobacter

belt transect

biomass

biotic factor

carbon cycle

climax community

community

consumer

decomposer

detritivore

distribution

ecological efficiency

ecological pyramid

ecological succession

ecosystem

environment

line transect

mark and recapture

Nitrobacter

nitrogen cycle

Nitrosomonas

nutrient cycle

physical (=abiotic) factor

pioneer species

plagioclimax

population

primary succession

producer

quadrat

realised niche

Rhizobium

sampling

species

transect

trophic level

Ecosystems and biomass transfers

Activity number

Learning outcomes

☐ 1 Define the terms ecosystem, community, population, species, and environment. With reference to specific examples, explain that ecosystems exist on different scales (from small to very large). Categorise the components of an ecosystem as biotic or abiotic factors and explain how these influence species distribution.

213-215

☐ 2 Explain how biomass (a store of chemical energy) is transferred through ecosystems. Describe the role of producers, consumers, detritivores, and decomposers in energy and biomass transfers and nutrient cycling.

216-218

☐ 3 Explain how biomass transfers between trophic levels can be measured. Interpret a biomass or energy flow diagram for a community or describe food chains quantitatively using ecological pyramids based on numbers, biomass, or energy at each trophic level. Describe and explain the efficiency of biomass transfers between trophic levels.

219-221

☐ 4 Describe and explain how human activities can manipulate the transfer of biomass though ecosystems. Compare and contrast the productivity of natural and agricultural ecosystems and explain the differences.

221

Nutrient cycling in ecosystems

Activity number

Learning outcomes

☐ 5 Describe the role of nutrient cycling in ecosystems, explaining how nutrients are exchanged within and between ecosystems, moving between the atmosphere, the Earth's crust, water, and organisms.

222

☐ 6 Describe the nitrogen cycle, using arrows to show the direction of nutrient flow and labels to identify the processes involved. Describe the role of microorganisms (including *Nitrosomonas*, *Nitrobacter*, *Azotobacter*, and *Rhizobium*) in recycling nitrogen and explain how humans may intervene in the cycle.

223

☐ 7 Describe the carbon cycle, using arrows to show the direction of nutrient flow and labels to identify the processes involved. Explain the importance of the carbon cycle, including the role of organisms in the processes that recycle carbon. Explain how human activity may intervene in various aspects of the carbon cycle.

224 225

Community patterns and change

Activity number

Learning outcomes

☐ 8 Describe primary succession in an ecosystem to include reference to pioneer species, changes in the abiotic environment, and the climax community.

226 227

☐ 9 Describe how humans can intervene in a natural succession, producing a plagioclimax as a result of a deflected succession.

228

☐ 10 Describe how the distribution and abundance of organisms in an ecosystem can be measured, including reference to quadrats, transects, and mark and recapture.

229-235 237-241

☐ 11 PAG3 Describe the use of sampling and recording methods to determine the distribution and abundance of organisms in a variety of ecosystems.

236

213 Components of an Ecosystem

Key idea: An ecosystem consists of all the organisms living in a particular area and their physical environment.

An **ecosystem** is a community of living organisms and the physical (non-living) components of their environment. The community (living component of the ecosystem) is in turn made up of a number of **populations**, these being organisms of the same species living in the same geographical area. The structure and function of an ecosystem is determined by the physical (abiotic) and the living (biotic) factors, which determine species distribution and survival.

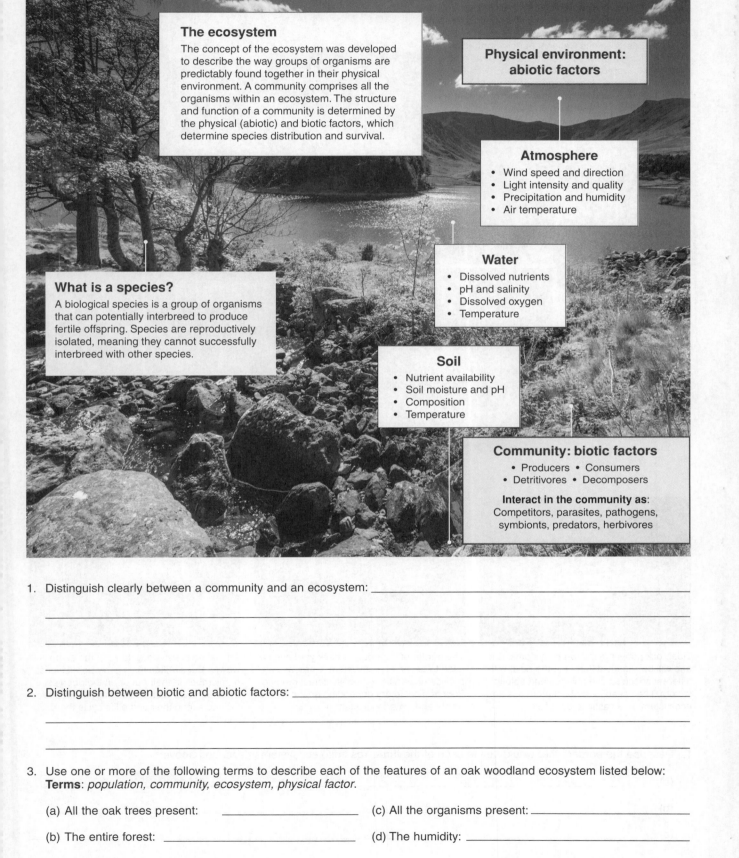

The ecosystem
The concept of the ecosystem was developed to describe the way groups of organisms are predictably found together in their physical environment. A community comprises all the organisms within an ecosystem. The structure and function of a community is determined by the physical (abiotic) and biotic factors, which determine species distribution and survival.

Physical environment: abiotic factors

Atmosphere
• Wind speed and direction
• Light intensity and quality
• Precipitation and humidity
• Air temperature

Water
• Dissolved nutrients
• pH and salinity
• Dissolved oxygen
• Temperature

What is a species?
A biological species is a group of organisms that can potentially interbreed to produce fertile offspring. Species are reproductively isolated, meaning they cannot successfully interbreed with other species.

Soil
• Nutrient availability
• Soil moisture and pH
• Composition
• Temperature

Community: biotic factors
• Producers • Consumers
• Detritivores • Decomposers

Interact in the community as:
Competitors, parasites, pathogens, symbionts, predators, herbivores

1. Distinguish clearly between a community and an ecosystem: _____
_____
_____
_____

2. Distinguish between biotic and abiotic factors: _____
_____
_____

3. Use one or more of the following terms to describe each of the features of an oak woodland ecosystem listed below:
   Terms: *population, community, ecosystem, physical factor.*

   (a) All the oak trees present: _____   (c) All the organisms present: _____

   (b) The entire forest: _____   (d) The humidity: _____

LINK 215   LINK 214   WEB 213

KNOW

214 Types of Ecosystems

Key Idea: Ecosystems have no fixed boundaries and so can vary in size.

Ecosystems can be of any size. The only limit is the size determined by the human observer. For example, a tree can be thought of as an ecosystem, if we ignore the individual comings and goings of animals and look at the system as a whole. But the tree may be part of a larger ecosystem, a forest, which again is part of a larger biome, and so on until we encompass the entire biosphere, that narrow belt around the Earth containing all the Earth's living organisms.

Ecosystems can be on vastly different scales. Yosemite National Park in northern California covers 3000 km². Large parts of it are covered in mixed coniferous forests. The forest ecosystem comprises various tree species (e.g. Douglas fir, giant sequoia, and black oak). There are over 250 species of vertebrates including deer, bear, mountain lion, and a variety of bird life.

Tuxyso / Wikimedia Commons / CC-BY-SA-3.0

The ecosystem of a tree can be quite varied. The tree provides energy and materials for insects and other invertebrates that live on or in it. Bacteria and fungi decompose leaves and dead material on the tree or in the soil. The tree provides roosts for birds and fruit or seeds as a food source.

Within the forested areas there are clearings that consist of grasses and scrub with the occasional isolated tree. These areas provide good grazing for deer and open hunting areas for owls.

Tidal rock pools are micro-ecosystems. Each one will be slightly different to the next, with different species assemblages and abiotic factors. The ocean in the background is an ecosystem on a vastly larger scale.

The border of a garden or back yard can be used to define an ecosystem. Gardens can provide quite different ecosystems, ranging from tropical to dry depending on the type of plants and watering system.

Animals can be ecosystems in the same way as trees. All animals carry populations of microbes in their gut or on their bodies. Invertebrates, such as lice, may live in the fur and spend their entire life cycle there.

1. Describe the borders that would define each of the three Yosemite ecosystems described above:

(a) _____

(b) _____

(c) _____

© 2015 **BIOZONE** International
ISBN: 978-1-927309-14-8
Photocopying Prohibited

215 Ecosystems Are Dynamic

Key Idea: Natural ecosystems are dynamic systems, responding to short-term and cyclical changes, but remaining relatively stable in the long term.
Ecosystems experience constant changes, from the daily light-dark cycle and seasonal changes, to the loss and gain of organisms. However, over the long term, a mature (or climax) ecosystem remains much the same, a situation known as a **dynamic equilibrium**.

The dynamic ecosystem

▶ Ecosystems are dynamic in that they are constantly changing. Temperature changes over the day, water enters as rain and leaves as water vapour, animals enter and leave. Many ecosystem changes are cyclical. Some cycles may be short term e.g. the seasons, others long term, e.g climatic cycles such as El Niño.

▶ Although ecosystems may change constantly over the short term, they may be relatively static over the middle to long term. For example, some tropical areas have wet and dry seasons, but over hundreds of years the ecosystem as a whole remains unchanged.

▶ However, over the long to very long term ecosystems change as the position of the continents and tilt of the Earth change, and as animals and plants evolve.

The type of ecosystem in a particular area is a result of the interactions between biological (biotic) and physical (abiotic) factors.

An ecosystem may remain stable for many hundreds or thousands of years provided that the components interacting within it remain stable.

Small scale changes usually have little effect on an ecosystem. Fire or flood may destroy some parts, but enough is left for the ecosystem to return to is original state relatively quickly.

Large scale disturbances such as volcanic eruptions, sea level rise, or large scale open cast mining remove all components of the ecosystem, changing it forever.

1. What is meant by the term dynamic ecosystem? _____

_____

2. (a) Describe two small scale events that an ecosystem may recover from: _____

_____

(b) Describe two large scale events that an ecosystem may not recover from: _____

_____

3. "Climax communities are ones that have reached an equilibrium." Explain what this means: _____

_____

_____

_____

© 2015 **BIOZONE** International
ISBN: 978-1-927309-14-8
Photocopying Prohibited

LINK 245   LINK 228   WEB 215   **KNOW**

216 Food Chains

Key Idea: A food chain is a model to illustrate the feeding relationships between organisms.

Organisms in ecosystems interact by way of their feeding (trophic) relationships. These interactions can be shown in a **food chain**, which is a simple model to illustrate how energy or biomass, in the form of food, passes from one organism to the next. Each organism in the chain is a source of energy for the next. The levels of a food chain are called **trophic**

levels. An organism is assigned to a trophic level based on its position in the food chain. Organisms may occupy different trophic levels in different food chains or during different stages of their life. Arrows link the organisms in a food chain and their direction shows the flow of energy and biomass through the trophic levels. Most food chains begin with a producer, which is eaten by a primary consumer (**herbivore**). Higher level consumers (e.g. **carnivores**) eat other consumers.

Millipede

Producers (autotrophs) e.g. plants, algae, and autotrophic bacteria, make their own food from simple inorganic substances, often by photosynthesis using energy from the sun. Inorganic nutrients are obtained from the abiotic environment, such as the soil and atmosphere.

Consumers (heterotrophs) e.g. animals, get their energy by eating other organisms. Consumers are ranked according to the trophic level they occupy, i.e. 1st order, 2nd order, and classified according to diet (e.g. carnivores eat animal tissue, omnivores eat plant and animal tissue).

Detritivores and **saprotrophs** both gain nutrients from digesting detritus (dead organic matter). Detritivores ingest (eat) and digest detritus inside their bodies. Saprotrophs break it down using enzymes, which are secreted and work externally to their bodies. Nutrients are then absorbed by the organism.

1. (a) Draw arrows on the diagram below to show how the energy flows through the organisms in the food chain. Label each arrow with the process involved in the energy transfer. Draw arrows to show how energy is lost by respiration.

   (b) What is the original energy source for this food chain? _____

   (c) How is this energy source converted to biomass? _____

2. Energy flows through food chains. In what form is it transferred between trophic levels: _____

   _____

3. Describe how the following obtain energy, and give an example of each:

   (a) Producers: _____

   (b) Consumers: _____

   (c) Detritivores: _____

   (d) Saprotrophs: _____

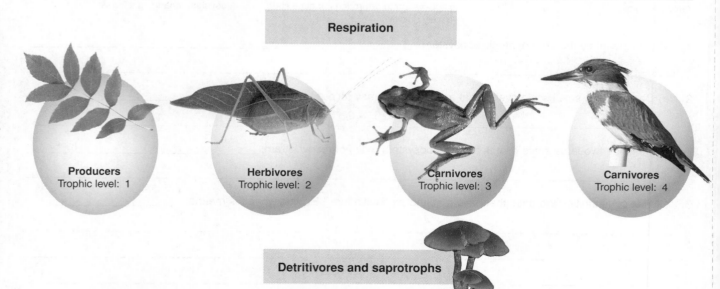

Respiration

| Producers
Trophic level: 1 | Herbivores
Trophic level: 2 | Carnivores
Trophic level: 3 | Carnivores
Trophic level: 4 |

Detritivores and saprotrophs

© 2015 **BIOZONE** International
ISBN: 978-1-927309-14-8
Photocopying Prohibited

217 Food Webs

Key Idea: A food web depicts all the interconnected food chains in an ecosystem. Sunlight is converted to biomass by plants and passed through subsequent trophic levels.

The different food chains in an ecosystem are interconnected to form a complex web of feeding interactions called a **food web.** Sunlight is the initial energy source for almost all ecosystems. Sunlight provides a continuous, but variable, energy supply, which is fixed in carbon compounds by photosynthesis, providing the building blocks and energy for biological materials. Energy stored in this biomass is passed through trophic levels. At each level, some of the energy is lost as heat to the environment so that progressively less is available at each level. This limits the number of links in most food chains to less than six.

▶ In any community, no species exists independently of others. All organisms, dead or alive, are potential sources of food for other organisms. Within a community, there are hundreds of feeding relationships, and most species participate in several food chains. The different food chains in an ecosystem tend to form food webs, a complex series of interactions showing the feeding relationships between organisms in an ecosystem.

▶ The complexity of feeding relationships in a community contributes to its structure and specific features. A simple community, like those that establish on bare soil after a landslide, will have a simpler web of feeding relationships than a mature forest. A food web model (below) can be used to show the trophic linkages between different organisms in a community and can be applied to any ecosystem.

Key to food web (below)

- - → Flow of nutrients from the living components to detritus or the nutrient pool.

→ Consumer–resource interactions.

⇒ Losses of each food web component from the system and external input of limiting nutrients.

A simple food web

(a) _____

Organisms whose food is obtained through the same number of links belong to the same trophic level.

Species interact in complex ways as competitors, predators, and symbionts.

Dragonfly larvae

Water beetle

(b) _____

Tadpoles

(e) _____

Only 5-20% of usable energy is transferred to the next trophic level. For this reason, food chains rarely have more than six links.

Photosynthetic protoctist

(c) _____

(d) _____

Energy flows through ecosystems in the high energy chemical bonds in organic matter.

Nutrients cycle between the atmosphere, the Earth's crust, water, and living organisms.

Nutrient pool

1. (a) - (e) Complete the food web above by adding the following labels: carnivore, herbivore, autotroph, detritus, detritivore:

2. Why do most food chains have fewer than six links? _____

_____

_____

_____

LINK **218** WEB **217** KNOW

218 Constructing a Food Web

Key Idea: Food chains can be put together to form food webs. The complexity of a food web depends on the number of food chains and trophic levels involved.

Species are assigned to trophic levels on the basis of their sources of nutrition, with the first trophic level (the producers), ultimately supporting all other (consumer) levels. Consumers are ranked according to the trophic level they occupy, although some consumers may feed at several different trophic levels. In the example of a lake ecosystem below, your task is to assemble the organisms into a food web in a way that illustrates their trophic status and their relative trophic position(s).

Feeding requirements of lake organisms

Autotrophic protists

Chlamydomonas (above), *Euglena* are two of the many genera that form the phytoplankton.

Macrophytes (various species)

Flowering aquatic plants are adapted for being submerged, free-floating, or growing at the lake margin.

Detritus

Decaying organic matter from within the lake itself or it may be washed in from the lake margins.

Asplanchna (planktonic rotifer)

A large, carnivorous rotifer that feeds on protozoa and young zooplankton (e.g. small *Daphnia*).

Daphnia

Small freshwater crustacean that forms part of the zooplankton. It feeds on planktonic algae by filtering them from the water with its limbs.

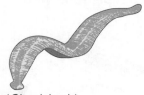

Leech (*Glossiphonia*)

Leeches are fluid feeding predators of smaller invertebrates, including rotifers, small pond snails and worms.

NYSDEC

Three-spined stickleback (*Gasterosteus*)

A common fish of freshwater ponds and lakes. It feeds mainly on small invertebrates such as *Daphnia* and insect larvae.

Diving beetle (*Dytiscus*)

Diving beetles feed on aquatic insect larvae and adult insects blown into the lake community. They will also eat organic detritus collected from the bottom mud.

Carp (*Cyprinus*)

A heavy bodied fish that feeds mainly on bottom living insect larvae and snails, but will also take some plant material (not algae).

Gina Mikel

Dragonfly larva

Large aquatic insect larvae that are predators of small invertebrates including *Hydra*, *Daphnia*, other insect larvae, and leeches.

Great pond snail (*Limnaea*)

Omnivorous pond snail, eating both plant and animal material, living or dead, although the main diet is aquatic macrophytes.

Herbivorous water beetles (e.g.*Hydrophilus*)

Feed on water plants, although the young beetle larvae are carnivorous, feeding primarily on small pond snails.

Protozan (e.g. *Paramecium*)

Ciliated protozoa such as *Paramecium* feed primarily on bacteria and microscopic green algae such as *Chlamydomonas*.

Pike (*Esox lucius*)

A top ambush predator of all smaller fish and amphibians. They are also opportunistic predators of rodents and small birds.

Mosquito larva (*Culex* spp.)

The larvae of most mosquito species, e.g. *Culex*, feed on planktonic algae and small protozoans before undergoing metamorphosis into adult mosquitoes.

Hydra

A small carnivorous cnidarian that captures small prey items, e.g. small *Daphnia* and insect larvae, using its stinging cells on the tentacles.

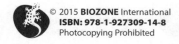
© 2015 **BIOZONE** International
ISBN: 978-1-927309-14-8
Photocopying Prohibited

1. From the information provided for the lake food web components on the previous page, construct **ten** different **food chains** to show the feeding relationships between the organisms. Some food chains may be shorter than others and most species will appear in more than one food chain. An example has been completed for you.

Example 1:   Macrophyte ⟶ Herbivorous water beetle ⟶ Carp ⟶ Pike

(a) _____

(b) _____

(c) _____

(d) _____

(e) _____

(f) _____

(g) _____

(h) _____

(i) _____

(j) _____

2. (a) Use the food chains created above to help you to draw up a **food web** for this community. Use the information supplied to draw arrows showing the flow of **energy** between species (only energy **from** the detritus is required).

   (b) Label each species to indicate its position in the food web, i.e. its trophic level (**T1, T2, T3, T4, T5**). Where a species occupies more than one trophic level, indicate this, e.g. **T2/3**:

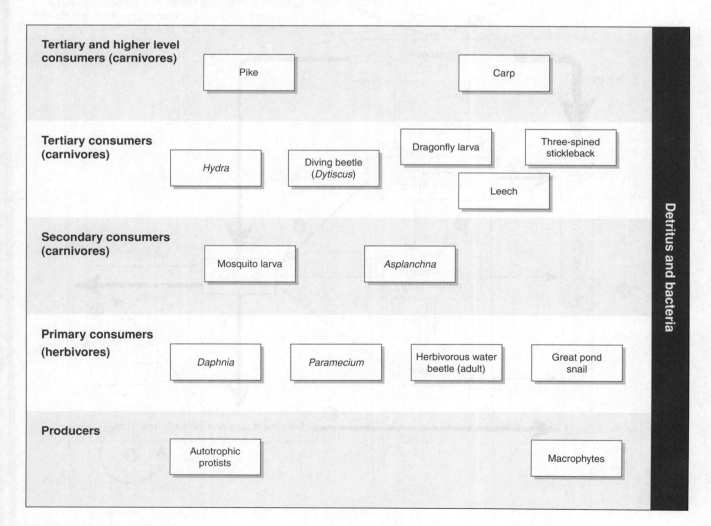

219 Energy Flow in an Ecosystem

Key Idea: Chemical energy in the bonds of molecules flows through an ecosystem between trophic levels. Only 5-20% of energy is transferred from one trophic level to the next.

Energy cannot be created or destroyed, only transformed from one form (e.g. light energy) to another (e.g. chemical energy in the bonds of molecules). This means that the flow of energy through an ecosystem can be measured. Each time energy is transferred from one trophic level to the next (by eating, defecation, etc.), some energy is given out as heat to the environment, usually during cellular respiration. Living

organisms cannot convert heat to other forms of energy, so the amount of energy available to one trophic level is always less than the amount at the previous level. Potentially, we can account for the transfer of energy from its input (as solar radiation) to its release as heat from organisms, because energy is conserved. The percentage of energy transferred from one trophic level to the next is the **trophic efficiency**. It varies between 5% and 20% and measures the efficiency of energy transfer. An average figure of 10% trophic efficiency is often used. This is called the **ten percent rule**.

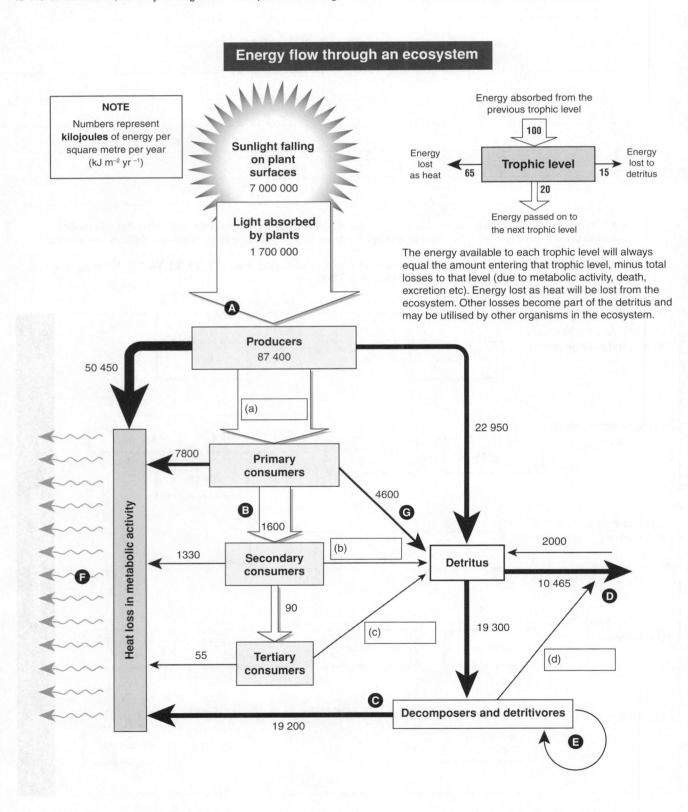

Energy flow through an ecosystem

NOTE

Numbers represent **kilojoules** of energy per square metre per year (kJ m⁻² yr⁻¹)

Sunlight falling on plant surfaces
7 000 000

Light absorbed by plants
1 700 000

Energy absorbed from the previous trophic level
100

Energy lost as heat 65 — Trophic level — 15 Energy lost to detritus

20

Energy passed on to the next trophic level

The energy available to each trophic level will always equal the amount entering that trophic level, minus total losses to that level (due to metabolic activity, death, excretion etc). Energy lost as heat will be lost from the ecosystem. Other losses become part of the detritus and may be utilised by other organisms in the ecosystem.

A

Producers
87 400

50 450

(a)

7800

Primary consumers

B

1600

22 950

4600

G

Secondary consumers

1330

(b)

Detritus

2000

10 465

D

90

(c)

19 300

Heat loss in metabolic activity

F

55

Tertiary consumers

(d)

C

Decomposers and detritivores

E

19 200

1. Study the diagram on the previous page illustrating energy flow through a hypothetical ecosystem. Use the example at the top of the page as a guide to calculate the missing values (a)–(d) in the diagram. Note that the sum of the energy inputs always equals the sum of the energy outputs. Place your answers in the spaces provided on the diagram.

2. What is the original source of energy for this ecosystem? _____

3. Identify the processes occurring at the points labelled **A – G** on the diagram:

   A. _____   E. _____

   B. _____   F. _____

   C. _____   G. _____

   D. _____

4. (a) Calculate the percentage of light energy falling on the plants that is absorbed at point **A**:

   Light absorbed by plants ÷ sunlight falling on plant surfaces x 100 = _____

   (b) What happens to the light energy that is not absorbed? _____

   _____

5. (a) Calculate the percentage of light energy absorbed that is actually converted (fixed) into producer energy:

   Producers ÷ light absorbed by plants x 100 = _____

   (b) How much light energy is absorbed but not fixed: _____

   (c) Account for the difference between the amount of energy absorbed and the amount actually fixed by producers:

   _____

   _____

6. Of the total amount of energy **fixed** by producers in this ecosystem (at point **A**) calculate:

   (a) The total amount that ended up as metabolic waste heat (in kJ): _____

   (b) The percentage of the energy fixed that ended up as waste heat: _____

7. (a) State the groups for which detritus is an energy source: _____

   (b) How could detritus be removed or added to an ecosystem? _____

   _____

8. Under certain conditions, decomposition rates can be very low or even zero, allowing detritus to accumulate:

   (a) From your knowledge of biological processes, what conditions might slow decomposition rates?

   _____

   (b) What are the consequences of this lack of decomposer activity to the energy flow? _____

   _____

   (c) Add an additional arrow to the diagram on the previous page to illustrate your answer. _____

   (d) Describe three examples of materials that have resulted from a lack of decomposer activity on detrital material:

   _____

   _____

9. The **ten percent rule** states that the total energy content of a trophic level in an ecosystem is only about one-tenth (or 10%) that of the preceding level. For each of the trophic levels in the diagram on the preceding page, determine the amount of energy passed on to the next trophic level as a percentage:

   (a) Producer to primary consumer: _____

   (b) Primary consumer to secondary consumer: _____

   (c) Secondary consumer to tertiary consumer: _____

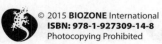

220 Ecological Pyramids

Key Idea: Ecological pyramids are used to illustrate the number of organisms, amount of energy, or amount of biomass at each trophic level in an ecosystem.

The energy, biomass, or numbers of organisms at each trophic level in any ecosystem can be represented by an ecological

pyramid. The first trophic level is placed at the bottom of the pyramid and subsequent trophic levels are stacked on top in their 'feeding sequence'. Ecological pyramids provide a convenient model to illustrate the relationship between different trophic levels in an ecosystem.

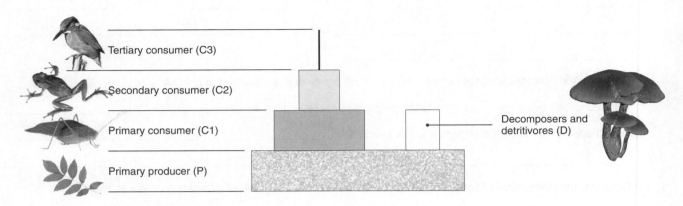

Tertiary consumer (C3)

Secondary consumer (C2)

Primary consumer (C1)

Primary producer (P)

Decomposers and detritivores (D)

The generalised ecological pyramid pictured above shows a conventional pyramid shape, with a large number (or biomass) of producers forming the base for an increasingly small number (or biomass) of consumers. Decomposers are placed at the level of the primary consumers and off to the side. They may obtain

energy from many different trophic levels and so do not fit into the conventional pyramid structure. For any particular ecosystem at any one time (e.g. the forest ecosystem below), the shape of this typical pyramid can vary greatly depending on whether the trophic relationships are expressed as numbers, biomass or energy

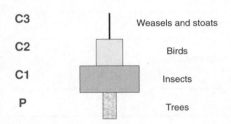

C3   Weasels and stoats

C2   Birds

C1   Insects

P   Trees

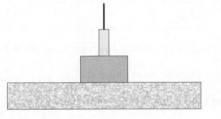

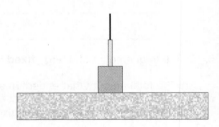

Numbers in a forest community

Pyramids of numbers display the number of individual organisms at each trophic level. The pyramid above has few producers, but they may be of a very large size (e.g. trees). This gives an 'inverted pyramid', although not all pyramids of numbers are like this.

Biomass in a forest community

Biomass pyramids measure the 'weight' of biological material at each trophic level. Water content of organisms varies, so 'dry weight' is often used. Organism size is taken into account, allowing meaningful comparisons of different trophic levels.

Energy in a forest community

Pyramids of energy are often very similar to biomass pyramids. The energy content at each trophic level is generally comparable to the biomass (i.e. similar amounts of dry biomass tend to have about the same energy content).

1. What do each of the following types of ecological pyramids measure?

   (a) Number pyramid: _____

   (b) Biomass pyramid: _____

   (c) Energy pyramid: _____

2. What is the advantage of using a biomass or energy pyramid rather than a pyramid of numbers to express the relationship between different trophic levels?

   _____

   _____

   _____

   _____

3. How can a forest community with relatively few producers (see next page) support a large number of consumers?

   _____

   _____

LINK
221

© 2015 **BIOZONE** International
ISBN: 978-1-927309-14-8
Photocopying Prohibited

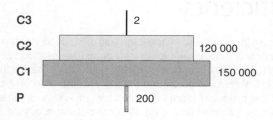

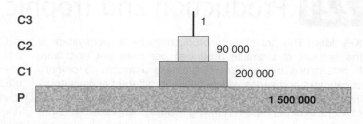

Pyramid of numbers: forest community

In a forest community, a few producers may support a large number of consumers. This is due to the large size of the producers; large trees can support many individual consumer organisms. The example above shows the numbers at each trophic level for an oak forest in England, in an area of 10 m^2.

Pyramid of numbers: grassland community

In a grassland community, a large number of (small) producers support a much smaller number of consumers. Grass plants can support only a few individual consumer organisms and take time to recover from grazing pressure. The example above shows the numbers at each trophic level for a derelict grassland area (10 m^2) in Michigan, United States.

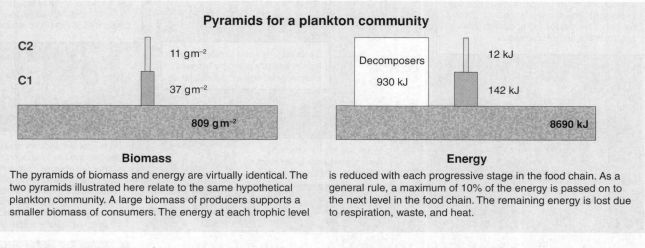

Pyramids for a plankton community

Biomass

The pyramids of biomass and energy are virtually identical. The two pyramids illustrated here relate to the same hypothetical plankton community. A large biomass of producers supports a smaller biomass of consumers. The energy at each trophic level

Energy

is reduced with each progressive stage in the food chain. As a general rule, a maximum of 10% of the energy is passed on to the next level in the food chain. The remaining energy is lost due to respiration, waste, and heat.

4. Determine the **energy transfer** between trophic levels in the plankton community example in the above diagram:

(a) Between producers and the primary consumers: _____

(b) Between the primary consumers and the secondary consumers: _____

(c) Why is the amount of energy transferred from the producer level to primary consumers considerably less than the expected 10% that occurs in many other communities?

_____

_____

(d) After the producers, which trophic group has the greatest energy content? _____

(e) Give a likely explanation why this is the case: _____

_____

_____

An unusual biomass pyramid

The biomass pyramids of some ecosystems appear rather unusual with an inverted shape. The first trophic level has a lower biomass than the second level. What this pyramid does not show is the rate at which the producers (algae) are reproducing in order to support the larger biomass of consumers.

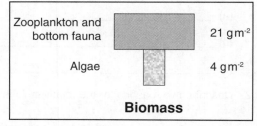

5. Give a possible explanation of how a small biomass of producers (algae) can support a larger biomass of consumers (zooplankton):

_____

_____

_____

© 2015 **BIOZONE** International
ISBN: 978-1-927309-14-8
Photocopying Prohibited

221 Production and Trophic Efficiency

Key Idea: The net primary productivity of an ecosystem is the amount of biomass produced per area per unit time. It determines the amount of biomass available to primary consumers and varies widely between different ecosystems. The energy entering ecosystems is fixed by producers at a rate that is dependent on limiting factors such as temperature and the availability of light, water, and nutrients. This energy is converted to biomass (the mass of biological material) by anabolic reactions. The rate of biomass production, or net primary productivity, is the biomass produced per area per unit time. Trophic efficiency refers to the efficiency of energy transfer from one trophic level to the next. The trophic efficiencies of herbivores can vary widely, depending on how much of the producer biomass is consumed and assimilated (incorporated into new biomass). In some natural ecosystems this can be surprisingly high. Humans intervene in natural energy flows by simplifying the system and reducing the number of transfers occurring between trophic levels.

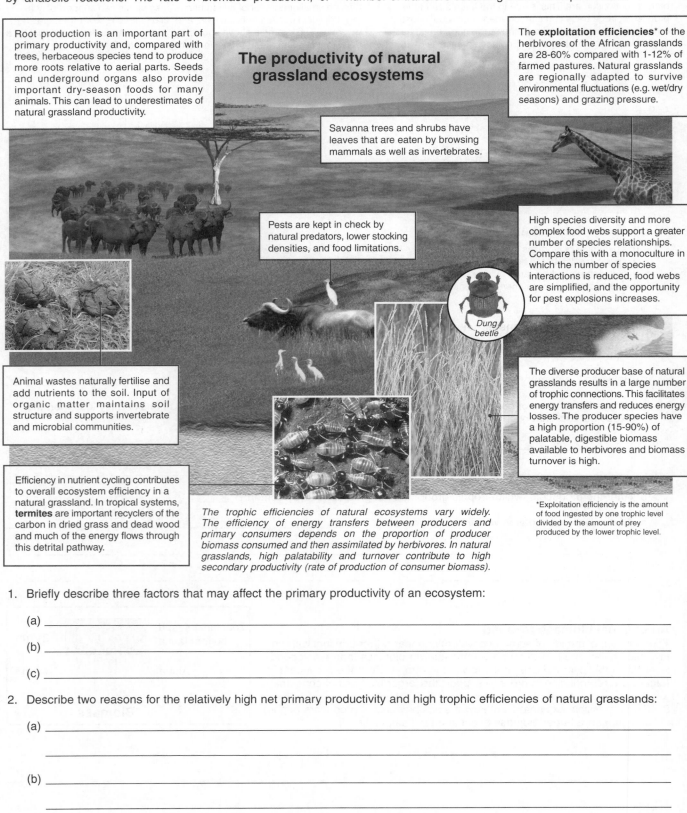

The productivity of natural grassland ecosystems

Root production is an important part of primary productivity and, compared with trees, herbaceous species tend to produce more roots relative to aerial parts. Seeds and underground organs also provide important dry-season foods for many animals. This can lead to underestimates of natural grassland productivity.

Savanna trees and shrubs have leaves that are eaten by browsing mammals as well as invertebrates.

The **exploitation efficiencies*** of the herbivores of the African grasslands are 28-60% compared with 1-12% of farmed pastures. Natural grasslands are regionally adapted to survive environmental fluctuations (e.g. wet/dry seasons) and grazing pressure.

Pests are kept in check by natural predators, lower stocking densities, and food limitations.

High species diversity and more complex food webs support a greater number of species relationships. Compare this with a monoculture in which the number of species interactions is reduced, food webs are simplified, and the opportunity for pest explosions increases.

Dung beetle

Animal wastes naturally fertilise and add nutrients to the soil. Input of organic matter maintains soil structure and supports invertebrate and microbial communities.

The diverse producer base of natural grasslands results in a large number of trophic connections. This facilitates energy transfers and reduces energy losses. The producer species have a high proportion (15-90%) of palatable, digestible biomass available to herbivores and biomass turnover is high.

Efficiency in nutrient cycling contributes to overall ecosystem efficiency in a natural grassland. In tropical systems, **termites** are important recyclers of the carbon in dried grass and dead wood and much of the energy flows through this detrital pathway.

The trophic efficiencies of natural ecosystems vary widely. The efficiency of energy transfers between producers and primary consumers depends on the proportion of producer biomass consumed and then assimilated by herbivores. In natural grasslands, high palatability and turnover contribute to high secondary productivity (rate of production of consumer biomass).

*Exploitation efficienciy is the amount of food ingested by one trophic level divided by the amount of prey produced by the lower trophic level.

1. Briefly describe three factors that may affect the primary productivity of an ecosystem:

   (a) _____

   (b) _____

   (c) _____

2. Describe two reasons for the relatively high net primary productivity and high trophic efficiencies of natural grasslands:

   (a) _____

   _____

   (b) _____

   _____

LINK
219

© 2015 **BIOZONE** International
ISBN: 978-1-927309-14-8
Photocopying Prohibited

Measuring productivity

The gross primary productivity of an ecosystem will depend on the capacity of the producers to capture and fix carbon in organic compounds. In most ecosystems, this is limited by constraints on photosynthesis (availability of light, nutrients, or water for example). The net primary productivity (NPP) is then determined by how much of this goes into plant biomass per unit time, after respiratory needs are met. This will be the amount available to the next trophic level. It is difficult to measure productivity, but it is often estimated from the harvestable dry biomass or standing crop (the net primary production).

| Estuaries |
| Swamps and marshes |
| Tropical rainforest |
| Temperate forest |
| Boreal forest |
| Savanna |
| Agricultural land |
| Woodland and shrubland |
| Temperate grassland |
| Lakes and streams |
| Continental shelf |
| Tundra |
| Open ocean |
| Desert scrub |
| Extreme desert |

Average net primary productivity (x 1000 kJ $m^{-2}y^{-1}$)
5 10 15 20 25 30 35 40 45 50

Globally, the least productive ecosystems are those that are limited by heat energy and water. The most productive are those with high temperatures, plenty of water, and non-limiting supplies of soil nitrogen. The primary productivity of oceans is lower overall than that of terrestrial ecosystems because the water reflects (or absorbs) much of the light energy before it reaches and is utilised by producers.

Agriculture and productivity

Increasing net productivity in agriculture (increasing yield) is a matter of manipulating and maximising energy flow through a reduced number of trophic levels. On a farm, the simplest way to increase the net primary productivity is to produce a monoculture. Monocultures reduce competition between the desirable crop and weed species, allowing crops to put more energy into biomass. Other agricultural practices designed to increase productivity in crops include pest (herbivore) control and spraying to reduce disease. Higher productivity in feed-crops also allows greater secondary productivity (e.g. in livestock). Here, similar agricultural practices make sure the energy from feed-crops is efficiently assimilated by livestock.

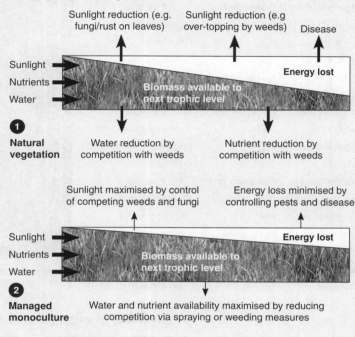

3. With reference to the bar graph above:

   (a) Suggest why tropical rainforests are among the most productive terrestrial ecosystems, while tundra and desert ecosystems are among the least productive:

   _____

   _____

   (b) Suggest why, amongst aquatic ecosystems, the NPP of the open ocean is low relative to that of coastal systems:

   _____

   _____

   _____

4. (a) How could a farmer maximise the net primary productivity of a particular crop? _____

   _____

   _____

   (b) How could a farmer maximise the productivity of their livestock?_____

   _____

   _____

5. Explain the contrasting net primary productivities of intensive agricultural land and extreme desert: _____

   _____

   _____

   _____

222 Nutrient Cycles

Key Idea: Matter cycles through the biotic and abiotic compartments of Earth's ecosystems in nutrient cycles.

Nutrient cycles move and transfer chemical elements (e.g. carbon, hydrogen, nitrogen, and oxygen) through the abiotic and biotic components of an ecosystem. Commonly, nutrients must be in an ionic (rather than elemental) form in order for plants and animals to have access to them. The supply of nutrients in an ecosystem is finite and limited. Macronutrients are required in large amounts by an organism, whereas micronutrients are needed in much smaller quantities.

Essential nutrients

Macronutrient	Common form	Function
Carbon (C)	CO_2	Organic molecules
Oxygen (O)	O_2	Respiration
Hydrogen (H)	H_2O	Cellular hydration
Nitrogen (N)	N_2, NO_3^-, NH_4^+	Proteins, nucleic acids
Potassium (K)	K^+	Principal ion in cells
Phosphorus (P)	$H_2PO_4^-$, HPO_4^{2-}	Nucleic acids, lipids
Calcium (Ca)	Ca^{2+}	Membrane permeability
Magnesium (Mg)	Mg^{2+}	Chlorophyll
Sulfur (S)	SO_4^{2-}	Proteins

Micronutrient	Common form	Function
Iron (Fe)	Fe^{2+}, Fe^{3+}	Chlorophyll, blood
Manganese (Mn)	Mn^{2+}	Enzyme activation
Molybdenum (Mo)	MoO_4^-	Nitrogen metabolism
Copper (Cu)	Cu^{2+}	Enzyme activation
Sodium (Na)	Na^+	Ion in cells
Silicon (Si)	$Si(OH)_4$	Support tissues

Tropical rainforest

Nutrients in plants and animals

High speed return of nutrients to plants and animals leaving soil nutrient deficient

Nutrients in soil

Temperate woodland

Nutrients in plants and animals

Slow return of nutrients allowing greater build up of nutrients in the soil

Nutrients in soil

The speed of nutrient cycling can vary markedly. Some nutrients are cycled slowly, others quickly. The environment and diversity of an ecosystem can also have a large effect on the speed at which nutrients are recycled.

The role of organisms in nutrient cycling

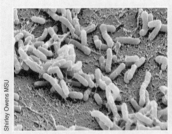

Bacteria
Bacteria play an essential role in nutrient cycles. They act as decomposers, but can also convert nutrients into forms accessible to plants and animals.

Fungi
Fungi are saprophytes and are important decomposers, returning nutrients to the soil or converting them into forms accessible to plants and animals.

Plants
Plants have a role in absorbing nutrients from the soil and making them directly available to browsing animals. They also add their own decaying matter to soils.

Animals
Animals utilise and break down materials from bacteria, plants and fungi and return the nutrients to soils and water via their wastes and when they die.

1. Describe the role of each of the following in nutrient cycling:

    (a) Bacteria: _____

    (b) Fungi: _____

    (c) Plants: _____

    (d) Animals: _____

2. Why are soils in tropical rainforests nutrient deficient relative to soils in temperate woodlands? _____
    _____
    _____

3. Distinguish between macronutrients and micronutrients: _____
    _____
    _____

© 2015 **BIOZONE** International
ISBN: 978-1-927309-14-8
Photocopying Prohibited

223 The Nitrogen Cycle

Key Idea: The nitrogen cycle describes how nitrogen is converted between its various chemical forms. Nitrogen gas is converted to nitrates which are taken up by plants. Heterotrophs obtain their nitrogen by eating other organisms. Nitrogen is an essential component of proteins and nucleic acids and required by all living things. The Earth's atmosphere is about 80% nitrogen gas (N_2), but molecular nitrogen is so stable that it is only rarely available directly to organisms and is often in short supply in biological systems. Bacteria transfer nitrogen between the biotic and abiotic environments. Some can fix atmospheric nitrogen, while others convert ammonia to nitrate, making it available to plants. Lightning discharges also cause the oxidation of nitrogen gas to nitrate. Nitrogen-fixing bacteria are found free in the soil (*Azotobacter*) and in symbioses with some plants in root nodules (*Rhizobium*). Denitrifying bacteria reverse this activity and return fixed nitrogen to the atmosphere. Humans intervene in the nitrogen cycle by applying nitrogen fertilisers to the land.

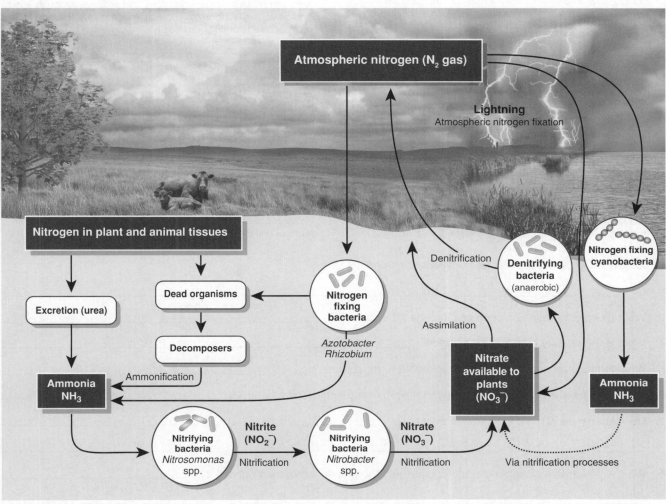

1. Describe five instances in the nitrogen cycle where **bacterial** action is important. Include the name of each of the processes and the changes to the form of nitrogen involved:

(a) _____

_____

(b) _____

_____

(c) _____

_____

(d) _____

_____

(e) _____

_____

LINK WEB

222 **223** KNOW

Nitrogen fixation in root nodules

Root nodules are a root **symbiosis** between a higher plant and a bacterium. The bacteria fix atmospheric nitrogen and are extremely important to the nutrition of many plants, including the economically important legume family. Root nodules are extensions of the root tissue caused by entry of a bacterium. In legumes, this bacterium is *Rhizobium*. Other bacterial genera are involved in the root nodule symbioses in non-legumes.

The bacteria in these symbioses live in the nodule where they fix atmospheric nitrogen and provide the plant with most, or all, of its nitrogen requirements. In return, they have access to a rich supply of carbohydrate. The fixation of atmospheric nitrogen to ammonia occurs within the nodule, using the enzyme **nitrogenase**. Nitrogenase is inhibited by oxygen and the nodule provides a low O_2 environment in which fixation can occur.

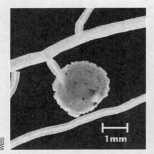 

Two examples of legume nodules caused by *Rhizobium*. The images above show the size of a single nodule (left), and the nodules forming clusters around the roots of *Acacia* (right).

Human intervention in the nitrogen cycle

The largest interventions in the nitrogen cycle by humans occur through farming and effluent discharges. Other interventions include burning, which releases nitrogen oxides into the atmosphere, and irrigation and land clearance, which leach nitrate ions from the soil.

Farmers apply organic nitrogen fertilisers to their land in the form of green crops and manures, replacing the nitrogen lost through cropping and harvest. Until the 1950s, atmospheric nitrogen could not be made available to plants except through microbial nitrogen fixation (left). However, during WW II, Fritz Haber developed the Haber process, combining nitrogen and hydrogen gas to form gaseous ammonia. The ammonia is converted into ammonium salts and sold as inorganic fertiliser. This process, although energy expensive, made inorganic nitrogen fertilisers readily available and revolutionised farming practices and crop yields.

Two examples of human intervention in the nitrogen cycle. The photographs above show the aerial application of a commercial fertiliser (left), and the harvesting of an agricultural crop (right).

2. Identify three processes that **fix** atmospheric nitrogen:

   (a) _____ (b) _____ (c) _____

3. What process releases nitrogen gas into the atmosphere? _____

4. What is the primary reservoir for nitrogen? _____

5. What form of nitrogen is most readily available to most plants? _____

6. Name one essential organic compound that plants need nitrogen for: _____

7. How do animals acquire the nitrogen they need? _____

   _____

8. Why might farmers plough a crop of legumes into the ground rather than harvest it? _____

   _____

9. Describe five ways in which humans may intervene in the nitrogen cycle and the effects of these interventions:

   (a) _____

   _____

   (b) _____

   _____

   (c) _____

   _____

   (d) _____

   _____

   (e) _____

   _____

224 The Carbon Cycle

Key Idea: The continued availability of carbon in ecosystems depends on carbon cycling through the abiotic and biotic components of an ecosystem.

Carbon is an essential element of life and is incorporated into the organic molecules that make up living organisms. Large quantities of carbon are stored in **sinks**, which include the atmosphere as carbon dioxide gas (CO_2), the ocean

as carbonate and bicarbonate, and rocks such as coal and limestone. Carbon moves between the biotic and abiotic environment. Autotrophs convert CO_2 into carbohydrates via photosynthesis and CO_2 is returned to the atmosphere through respiration. Some of the sinks and processes involved in the carbon cycle, together with the movement of carbon (carbon fluxes), are shown below.

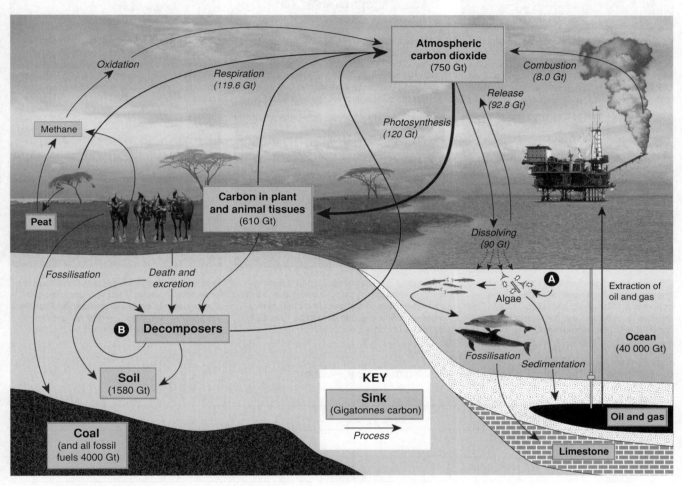

1. Add **arrows** and **labels** to the diagram above to show:

   (a) Dissolving of limestone by acid rain   (c) Mining and burning of coal

   (b) Release of carbon from the marine food chain   (d) Burning of plant material.

2. (a) Name the processes that release carbon into the atmosphere: _____

   _____

   (b) In what form is the carbon released? _____

3. Name the four geological reservoirs (sinks), in the diagram above, that can act as a source of carbon:

   (a) _____   (c) _____

   (b) _____   (d) _____

4. (a) Identify the process carried out by algae at point [**A**]: _____

   (b) Identify the process carried out by decomposers at [**B**]: _____

5. What would be the effect on carbon cycling if there were no decomposers present in an ecosystem? _____

   _____

   _____

LINK LINK WEB
225 222 224 **KNOW**

Bracket fungus on tree trunk

Coal mine in Wyoming

Carbon may be locked up in biotic or abiotic systems for long periods of time, e.g. in the wood of trees or in fossil fuels such as coal or oil. Human activity, e.g. extraction and combustion of fossil fuels, has disturbed the balance of the carbon cycle.

Organisms break down organic material to release carbon. Fungi and decomposing bacteria break down dead plant matter in the leaf litter of forests. Termites, with the aid of symbiotic protozoans and bacteria in their guts, digest the cellulose of woody tree tissue.

Coal is formed from the remains of terrestrial plant material buried in shallow swamps and subsequently compacted under sediments to form a hard black material. Coal is composed primarily of carbon and is a widely used fuel source.

Oil and natural gas formed in the past when dead algae and zooplankton settled to the bottom of shallow seas and lakes. These remains were buried and compressed under layers of non-porous sediment.

Limestone is a type of sedimentary rock composed mostly of calcium carbonate. It forms when the shells of molluscs and other marine organisms with calcium carbonate ($CaCO_3$) skeletons become fossilised.

Peat (partly decayed organic material) forms when plant material is not fully decomposed due to acidic or anaerobic conditions. Peatlands are a very efficient carbon sink but are easily lost through oxidation when land is drained.

6. Describe the **biological origin** of the following geological deposits:

   (a) Coal: _____

   _____

   (b) Oil: _____

   _____

   (c) Limestone: _____

   _____

   (d) Peat: _____

   _____

7. Describe the role of living organisms in the carbon cycle: _____

   _____

   _____

8. In natural circumstances, accumulated reserves of carbon such as peat, coal and oil represent a sink or natural diversion from the cycle. Eventually, the carbon in these sinks returns to the cycle through the action of geological processes which return deposits to the surface for oxidation.

   (a) What is the effect of human activity on the amount of carbon stored in sinks? _____

   _____

   (b) Describe the effect of human activity on atmospheric CO_2 levels: _____

   _____

225 Measuring Carbon Fluxes

Key Idea: Photosynthesis removes carbon from the atmosphere, and adds it to the biosphere. Respiration removes carbon from the biosphere and adds it the atmosphere. These fluxes of carbon can be measured.

The movement of carbon between the atmosphere and biosphere is called the **carbon flux**. Photosynthesis and respiration are important processes in the carbon cycle.

During photosynthesis CO_2 is fixed into carbohydrate, removing carbon from the atmosphere. Cellular respiration has the opposite effect, it breaks down glucose and releases CO_2 into the atmosphere. The movement of carbon between the biosphere and the atmosphere can be measured. The information enables scientists to assess the impact of human activity (e.g. burning fossil fuels) on the carbon cycle.

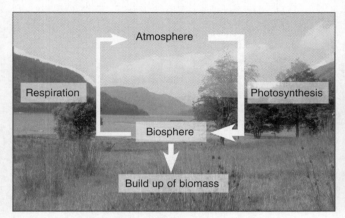

Photosynthesis and carbon

▶ Photosynthesis removes carbon from the atmosphere by fixing the carbon in CO_2 into carbohydrate molecules. Plants use the carbohydrates (e.g. glucose) to build structures such as wood.

▶ Some carbon may be returned to the atmosphere during respiration (either from the plant or from animals). If the amount or rate of carbon fixation is greater than that released during respiration then carbon will build up in the biosphere and be reduced in the atmosphere (diagram, above).

Respiration and carbon

▶ Cellular respiration releases carbon into the atmosphere as carbon dioxide as a result of the breakdown of glucose.

▶ If the rate of carbon release is greater than that fixed by photosynthesis then over time carbon may accumulate in the atmosphere (diagram above).

▶ Before the Industrial Revolution, many thousands of gigatonnes (Gt) of carbon were contained in the biosphere of in the Earth's crust (e.g. coal). Since the Industrial Revolution (1760-1840) more coal has been burned to power machinery.

▶ Human activities (e.g. deforestation and burning fossil fuels) have increased the amount of carbon in the atmosphere.

Carbon cycling simulation

Plants move about 120 Gt of carbon from the atmosphere to the biosphere a year. Respiration accounts for about 60 Gt of carbon a year. A simulation was carried out to study the effect of varying the rates of respiration and photosynthesis on carbon deposition in the biosphere or atmosphere. To keep the simulation simple, only the effects to the atmosphere and biosphere were simulated. Effects such as ocean deposition and deforestation were not studied. The results are shown in the tables right and below.

Table 1: Rate of photosynthesis equals the rate of cellular respiration.

Years	Gt carbon in biosphere	Gt carbon in atmosphere
0	610	600
20	608	600
40	608	600
60	609	598
80	612	598
100	610	596

Table 2: Rate of photosynthesis increases by 1 Gt per year.

Years	Gt carbon in biosphere	Gt carbon in atmosphere
0	610	600
20	632	580
40	651	558
60	671	538
80	691	518
100	710	498

Table 3: Rate of cellular respiration increases by 1 Gt per year.

Years	Gt carbon in biosphere	Gt carbon in atmosphere
0	610	600
20	590	619
40	570	641
60	548	664
80	528	686
100	509	703

LINK
224 **KNOW**

1. Plot the data for tables 1,2, and 3 on the grid provided (above). Include a key and appropriate titles and axes.

2. (a) What is the effect of increasing the rate of photosynthesis on atmospheric carbon? _____

   _____

   (b) i. What is the effect of increasing the rate of photosynthesis on biospheric carbon? _____

   _____

   ii. How does this effect occur? _____

   _____

   _____

3. What is the effect of increasing the rate of cellular respiration on atmospheric and biospheric carbon? _____

   _____

   _____

4. (a) Name two human activities that increase carbon dioxide production:_____

   _____

   (b) How did the Industrial Revolution alter the balance of carbon between the biosphere and atmosphere? _____

   _____

   _____

   _____

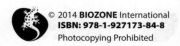

226 Primary Succession

Key Idea: Primary succession is a type of ecological succession occurring in a region where there is no pre-existing vegetation or soil.

Ecological succession is the process by which communities change over time. Succession occurs as a result of the interactions between biotic and abiotic factors. Earlier communities modify the physical environment, making it more favourable for species that make up the later communities. Over time, a succession results in a stable climax community.

Primary succession is a type of ecological succession describing the colonisation of a region where there is no pre-existing vegetation or soil.

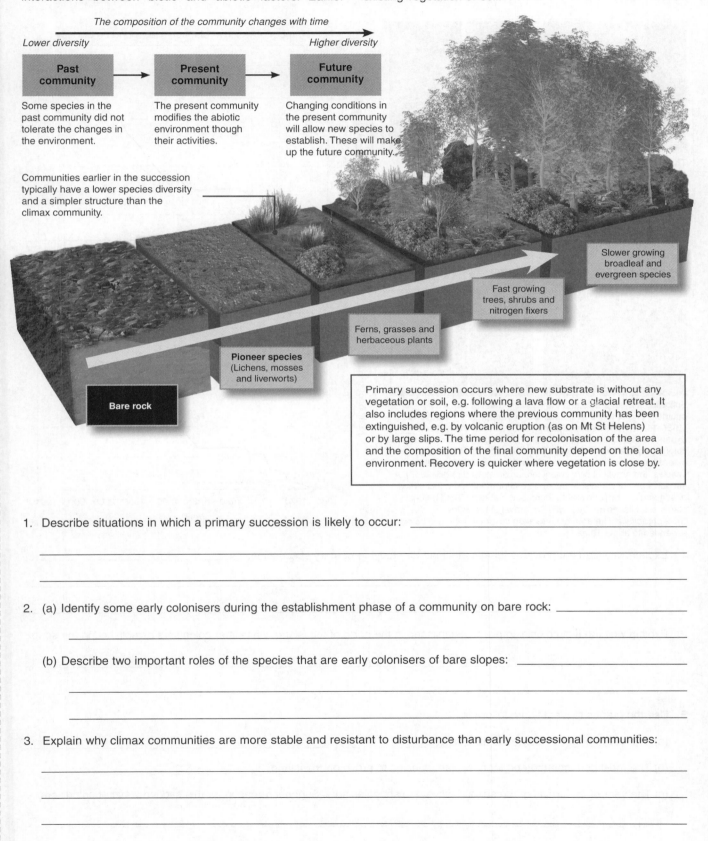

The composition of the community changes with time

Lower diversity → Higher diversity

Past community → **Present community** → **Future community**

Some species in the past community did not tolerate the changes in the environment.

The present community modifies the abiotic environment though their activities.

Changing conditions in the present community will allow new species to establish. These will make up the future community.

Communities earlier in the succession typically have a lower species diversity and a simpler structure than the climax community.

Slower growing broadleaf and evergreen species

Fast growing trees, shrubs and nitrogen fixers

Ferns, grasses and herbaceous plants

Pioneer species (Lichens, mosses and liverworts)

Bare rock

Primary succession occurs where new substrate is without any vegetation or soil, e.g. following a lava flow or a glacial retreat. It also includes regions where the previous community has been extinguished, e.g. by volcanic eruption (as on Mt St Helens) or by large slips. The time period for recolonisation of the area and the composition of the final community depend on the local environment. Recovery is quicker where vegetation is close by.

1. Describe situations in which a primary succession is likely to occur: _____

_____

_____

2. (a) Identify some early colonisers during the establishment phase of a community on bare rock: _____

_____

(b) Describe two important roles of the species that are early colonisers of bare slopes: _____

_____

_____

3. Explain why climax communities are more stable and resistant to disturbance than early successional communities:

_____

_____

_____

_____

LINK
227 WEB
226 KNOW

227 Succession on Surtsey Island

Key Idea: The successional events occurring on the island of Surtsey confirm that primary succession occurs in stages. Surtsey Island is a volcanic island, 33 km off Iceland. The island was formed over four years from 1963 to 1967 when a submerged volcano built up an island. The island is 150 m above sea level and 1.4 km². As an entirely new island,

Surtsey provided researchers with an ideal environment to study primary succession. Its colonisation by plants and animals has been recorded since its formation. The first vascular plant was discovered in 1965, two years before the eruptions ended. Since then, 69 plant species have colonised the island and there are several established seabird colonies.

Sea rocket

H. peploides

The first stage of colonisation of Surtsey (1965-1974) was dominated by shore plants colonising the northern shores of the island. The most successful coloniser was *Honckenya peploides* which established on tephra sand and gravel flats. It first set seed in 1971 and then spread across the island. Carbon and nitrogen levels in the soil were very low during this time. This initial colonisation by shore plants was followed by a lag phase (from 1975-1984). There was further establishment of shore plants but few new colonisers, which slowed the rate of succession.

P. annua

S. phylicifolia

Following the lag phase and the establishment of a gull colony on the southern end of the island, a number of new plant species arrived (1985-1994). Populations of plants inside or near the gull colony expanded rapidly covering about 3 ha, while populations outside the colony remained low but stable. Grasses such as *Poa annua* formed extensive patches of vegetation. After this rapid increase in plant species, the arrival of new colonisers again slowed (1995-2008). A second wave of colonisers began to establish following this slower phase and soil organic matter increased markedly. The first bushy plants established in 1998, with the arrival of the willow *Salix phylicifolia*. The area of vegetation cover near the gull colony expanded to about 10 ha.

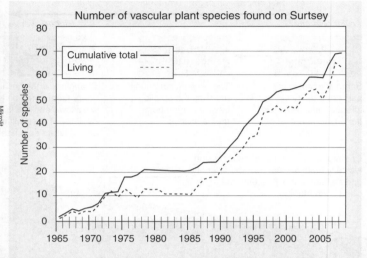
Number of vascular plant species found on Surtsey

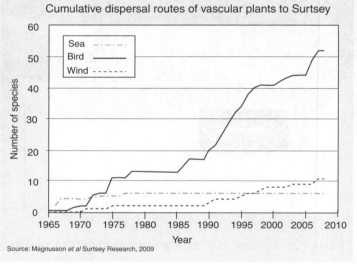
Cumulative dispersal routes of vascular plants to Surtsey

Source: Magnusson *et al* Surtsey Research, 2009

1. Explain why Surtsey provided ideal conditions for studying primary succession: _____

_____

_____

2. Explain why the first colonising plants established in the north of the island, while later colonisers established in the south.

_____

_____

3. Use the graphs to identify the following:

(a) The year the gull colony established: _____

(b) The most common method for new plant species to arrive on the island: _____

(c) The year of the arrival of the second wave of plant colonisers. Suggest a reason for this second wave of colonisers:

_____

_____

228 Deflected Succession

Key Idea: A plagioclimax community arises from human activity preventing any further ecosystem development.

The natural course of a succession can be deflected from its usual path by human interventions, such as mowing and burning. These activities produce (and maintain) a climax community that is different to the one that would naturally occur without human intervention. A climax community arising from a deflected succession is called a plagioclimax.

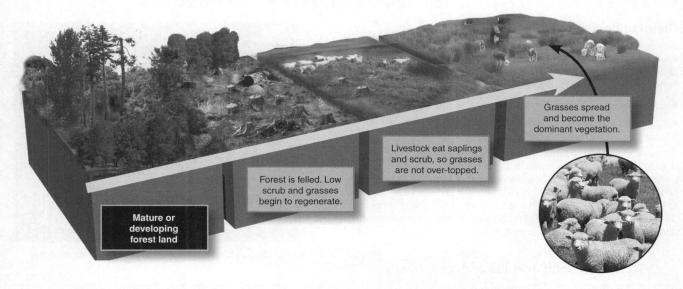

Mature or developing forest land

Forest is felled. Low scrub and grasses begin to regenerate.

Livestock eat saplings and scrub, so grasses are not over-topped.

Grasses spread and become the dominant vegetation.

In moorlands, burning is normally carried out around every twelve years (under strict controls). This is because after twelve years the vegetation's growth rate slows significantly and it is out-competed by larger trees. Burning maintains the heather's vigour and removes unwanted plants.

Brauton Burrows is a sand dune system on the North Devon coast in England. The system is ecologically important as it contains the complete successional range of dune plant communities. The dunes are maintained by managing the invasion of scrub plants and the advance to a climax community.

In the northern parts of the African rainforest, were the climate is relatively dry, frequent burning and cultivation have allowed the encroachment of fire resistant grasses and trees into what was rainforest. Experiments in 1974 showed that if the fires were prevented rainforest eventually returned.

1. What is deflected succession? _____

_____

_____

2. Using an example, explain how maintaining a deflected succession might help to maintain biodiversity: _____

_____

_____

_____

3. Large parts of England were once covered with woodland. During the Middle Ages, forests were cleared for timber and fuel. Sheep and cattle were then allowed to graze the cleared areas. Explain how this has affected the climax community in many English meadows:

_____

_____

_____

© 2015 **BIOZONE** International
ISBN: 978-1-927309-14-8
Photocopying Prohibited

LINK
253

KNOW

229 Measuring Distribution and Abundance

Key Idea: Random sampling using an appropriate technique provides unbiased information about the distribution and abundance of species in a community.

Most practical exercises in ecology involve collecting data about the distribution and abundance of one or more species in a community. Most studies also measure the physical factors in the environment as these may help to explain the patterns of distribution and abundance observed. The use of random sampling methods, in which every possible sample of a given size the same chance of selection, provides unbiased data. As long as the sample size is large enough and the sampling technique is appropriate to the community being studied, sample data enables us to make inferences about aspects of the whole population.

Distribution and abundance

Ecological sampling collects data about where organisms are found and how they are distributed in the environment. This information can be used to determine the health and viability of a population and its ecosystem. When investigating populations it is useful to monitor:

▶ Species **distribution** (where the species are located)

▶ Species **abundance** (how many of a species there are)

The methods used to sample communities and their constituent populations must be appropriate to the ecosystem being investigated. Communities in which the populations are at low density and have a random or clumped distribution will require a different sampling strategy to those where the populations are uniformly distributed and at higher density. There are many sampling options (below), each with advantages and drawbacks for particular communities.

Sampling designs and techniques

Random   Systematic (grid)

Point sampling
Individual points are chosen (using a grid reference or random numbers applied to a map grid) and the organisms are sampled at those points. Point sampling is most often used to collect data about vegetation distribution. It is time efficient and good for determining species abundance and community composition, however, organisms in low abundance may be missed.

Area sampling using quadrats
A quadrat is a sampling tool that provides a known unit area of sample (e.g. 0.5 m²). Quadrats are placed randomly or in a grid pattern on the sample area. The presence and abundance of organisms in these squares is noted. Quadrat sampling is appropriate for plants and slow moving animals and can be used to evaluate community composition.

Line transects
A tape or rope marks the line. The species occurring on the line are recorded (all along the line or at regular points). Lines can be chosen randomly (left) or may follow an environmental gradient. Line transects have little impact on the environment and are good for assessing the presence/absence of plant species. However, rare species may be missed.

Belt transects
A measured strip is located across the study area and quadrats are used to sample the plants or animals at regular intervals along the belt. Belt transects provide information on abundance and distribution as well as presence/absence. Depending on the width of the belt and length of the transect, they can be time consuming.

First sample: marked   Second sample: proportion recapture

Mark and recapture sampling
Animals are captured, marked, and released. After a suitable time, the population is resampled. The number of marked animals recaptured in a second sample is recorded as a proportion of the total. Mark and recapture is useful for highly mobile species which are otherwise difficult to record. However, it is time consuming to do well.

1. Distinguish between distribution and abundance:

_____

_____

_____

_____

2. Name a sampling technique that would be appropriate for determining:

(a) Percentage cover of a plant species in pasture:

_____

_____

(b) Change in community composition from low to high altitude on a mountain:

_____

_____

(c) Association of plant species with particular soil types in a nature reserve:

_____

_____

3. Why is it common practice to also collect information about the physical environment when sampling populations?

_____

_____

_____

_____

_____

230 Quadrat Sampling

Key Idea: Quadrat sampling involves a series of random placements of a frame of known size over an area of habitat to assess the abundance or diversity of organisms.

Quadrat sampling is a method by which organisms in a certain proportion (sample) of the habitat are counted directly. It is used when the organisms are too numerous to count in total. It can be used to estimate population **abundance** (number), **density, frequency of occurrence**, and **distribution**. Quadrats may be used without a transect when studying a relatively uniform habitat. In this case, the quadrat positions are chosen randomly using a random number table.

The general procedure is to count all the individuals (or estimate their percentage cover) in a number of quadrats of known size and to use this information to work out the abundance or percentage cover value for the whole area.

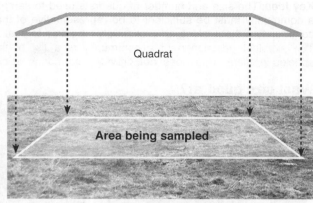

Quadrat

Area being sampled

$$\text{Estimated average density} = \frac{\text{Total number of individuals counted}}{\text{Number of quadrats X area of each quadrat}}$$

Guidelines for quadrat use:

1. The **area of each quadrat** must be known. Quadrats should be the same shape, but not necessarily square.

2. **Enough quadrat samples** must be taken to provide results that are representative of the total population.

3. The **population of each quadrat** must be known. Species must be distinguishable from each other, even if they have to be identified at a later date. It has to be decided beforehand what the count procedure will be and how organisms over the quadrat boundary will be counted.

4. The size of the quadrat should be appropriate to the organisms and habitat, e.g. a large size quadrat for trees.

5. The quadrats must be **representative of the whole area.** This is usually achieved by **random sampling** (right).

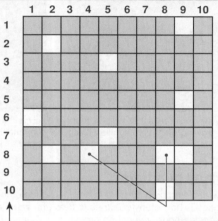

The area to be sampled is divided up into a grid pattern with indexed coordinates

Quadrats are applied to the predetermined grid on a random basis. This can be achieved by using a random number table.

Sampling a centipede population

A researcher by the name of Lloyd (1967) sampled centipedes in Wytham Woods, near Oxford in England. A total of 37 hexagon-shaped quadrats were used, each with a diameter of 30 cm (see diagram on right). These were arranged in a pattern so that they were all touching each other. Use the data in the diagram to answer the following questions.

1. Determine the average number of centipedes captured per quadrat:

_____

2. Calculate the estimated average density of centipedes per square metre (remember that each quadrat is 0.08 square metres in area):

_____

3. Looking at the data for individual quadrats, describe in general terms the distribution of the centipedes in the sample area:

_____

_____

4. Describe one factor that might account for the distribution pattern:

_____

_____

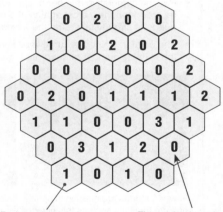

Each quadrat was a hexagon with a diameter of 30 cm and an area of 0.08 square meters.

The number in each hexagon indicates how many centipedes were caught in that quadrat.

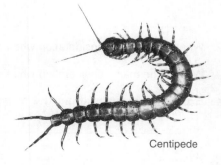

Centipede

LINK 236 LINK 232 LINK 231 WEB 230 DATA

231 Quadrat-Based Estimates

Key Idea: The size and number of quadrats used to sample a community must be sufficient to be representative of that community without taking an excessively long time to use.

The simplest description of a community is a list of the species present. This does not provide information about the relative abundance of the species, although this can be estimated using abundance scales (e.g. ACFOR). Quadrats can provide quantitative information about a community. The size of the quadrat and the number of samples taken must represent the community as fairly as possible.

What size quadrat?

Quadrats are usually square, and cover 0.25 m² (0.5 m x 0.5 m) or 1 m², but they can be of any size or shape, even a single point. The quadrats used to sample plant communities are often 0.25 m². This size is ideal for low-growing vegetation, but quadrat size needs to be adjusted to habitat type. The quadrat must be large enough to be representative of the community, but not so large as to take a very long time to use.

A quadrat covering an area of 0.25 m² is suitable for most low growing plant communities, such as this alpine meadow, fields, and grasslands.

Larger quadrats (e.g.1m²) are needed for communities with shrubs and trees. Quadrats as large as 4 m x 4 m may be needed in woodlands.

Small quadrats (0.01 m² or 100 mm x 100 mm) are appropriate for lichens and mosses on rock faces and tree trunks.

How many quadrats?

As well as deciding on a suitable quadrat size, the other consideration is how many quadrats to take (the sample size). In species-poor or very homogeneous habitats, a small number of quadrats will be sufficient. In species-rich or heterogeneous habitats, more quadrats will be needed to ensure that all species are represented adequately.

Determining the number of quadrats needed

- Plot the cumulative number of species recorded (on the y axis) against the number of quadrats already taken (on the x axis).

- The point at which the curve levels off indicates the suitable number of quadrats required.

Fewer quadrats are needed in species-poor or very uniform habitats, such as this bluebell woodland.

Describing vegetation

Density (number of individuals per unit area) is a useful measure of abundance for animal populations, but can be problematic in plant communities where it can be difficult to determine where one plant ends and another begins. For this reason, plant abundance is often assessed using **percentage cover**. Here, the percentage of each quadrat covered by each species is recorded, either as a numerical value or using an abundance scale such as the ACFOR scale.

The ACFOR Abundance Scale

A = Abundant (30% +)
C = Common (20-29%)
F = Frequent (10-19%)
O = Occasional (5-9%)
R = Rare (1-4%)

The ACFOR scale could be used to assess the abundance of species in this wildflower meadow. Abundance scales are subjective, but it is not difficult to determine which abundance category each species falls into.

---

1. Describe one difference between the methods used to assess species abundance in plant and in animal communities:

   _____

2. What is the main consideration when determining appropriate quadrat size? _____

3. What is the main consideration when determining number of quadrats? _____

4. Explain two main disadvantages of using the ACFOR abundance scale to record information about a plant community:

   (a) _____

   (b) _____

© 2015 **BIOZONE** International
ISBN: 978-1-927309-14-8
Photocopying Prohibited

232 Sampling a Rocky Shore Community

Key Idea: The estimates of a population gained from using quadrat sampling may vary depending on where the quadrats are placed. Larger samples can account for variation. The diagram (next page) represents an area of seashore with its resident organisms. The distribution of coralline algae and four animal species are shown. This exercise is designed to prepare you for planning and carrying out a similar procedure to practically investigate a natural community.

1. **Decide on the sampling method**
   For the purpose of this exercise, it has been decided that the populations to be investigated are too large to be counted directly and a quadrat sampling method is to be used to estimate the average density of the four animal species as well as that of the algae.

2. **Mark out a grid pattern**
   Use a ruler to mark out 3 cm intervals along each side of the sampling area (area of quadrat = 0.03 x 0.03 m). **Draw lines** between these marks to create a 6 x 6 grid pattern (total area = 0.18 x 0.18 m). This will provide a total of 36 quadrats that can be investigated.

3. **Number the axes of the grid**
   Only a small proportion of the possible quadrat positions will be sampled. It is necessary to select the quadrats in a random manner. It is not sufficient to simply guess or choose your own on a 'gut feeling'. The best way to choose the quadrats randomly is to create a numbering system for the grid pattern and then select the quadrats from a random number table. Starting at the *top left hand corner*, **number the columns** and **rows** from 1 to 6 on each axis.

4. **Choose quadrats randomly**
   To select the required number of quadrats randomly, use random numbers from a random number table. The random numbers are used as an index to the grid coordinates. Choose 6 quadrats from the total of 36 using table of random numbers provided for you at the bottom of the next page. Make a note of which column of random numbers you choose. Each member of your group should choose a different set of random numbers (i.e. different column: A–D) so that you can compare the effectiveness of the sampling method.

   Column of random numbers chosen: _____

   NOTE: Highlight the boundary of each selected quadrat with coloured pen/highlighter.

5. **Decide on the counting criteria**
   Before the counting of the individuals for each species is carried out, the criteria for counting need to be established.

There may be some problems here. You must decide before sampling begins as to what to do about individuals that are only partly inside the quadrat. Possible answers include:

(a) Only counting individuals that are completely inside the quadrat.
(b) Only counting individuals with a clearly defined part of their body inside the quadrat (such as the head).
(c) Allowing for 'half individuals' (e.g. 3.5 barnacles).
(d) Counting an individual that is inside the quadrat by half or more as one complete individual.

Discuss the merits and problems of the suggestions above with other members of the class (or group). You may even have counting criteria of your own. Think about other factors that could cause problems with your counting.

6. **Carry out the sampling**
   Carefully examine each selected quadrat and **count the number of individuals** of each species present. Record your data in the spaces provided on the next page.

7. **Calculate the population density**
   Use the combined data TOTALS for the sampled quadrats to estimate the average density for each species by using the formula:

$$\text{Density} = \frac{\text{Total number in all quadrats sampled}}{\text{Number of quadrats sampled} \times \text{area of a quadrat}}$$

Remember that a total of 6 quadrats are sampled and each has an area of 0.0009 m². The density should be expressed as the number of individuals *per square metre* (no. m^{-2}).

Plicate barnacle:	☐	Snakeskin chiton:	☐
Oyster borer:	☐	Coralline algae:	☐
Limpet:	☐		

8. (a) In this example the animals are not moving. Describe the problems associated with sampling moving organisms. Explain how you would cope with sampling these same animals if they were really alive and very active:

_____

_____

_____

(b) Carry out a direct count of all 4 animal species and the algae for the whole sample area (all 36 quadrats). Apply the data from your direct count to the equation given in (7) above to calculate the actual population density (remember that the number of quadrats in this case = 36):

Barnacle: ☐   Oyster borer: ☐   Chiton: ☐   Limpet: ☐   Algae: ☐

Compare your estimated population density to the actual population density for each species:

_____

_____

LINK 233 LINK 230 PRAC

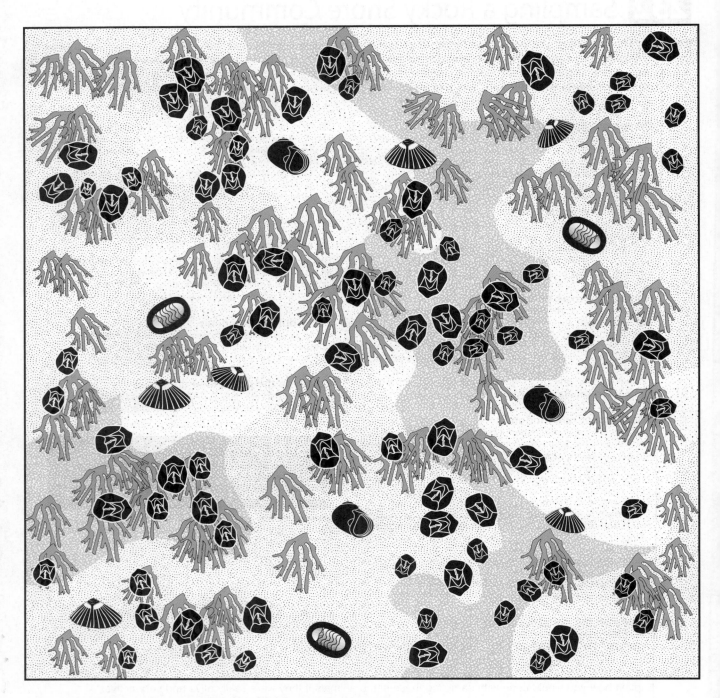

Coordinates for each quadrat	Plicate barnacle	Oyster borer	Snakeskin chiton	Limpet	Coralline algae
1:					
2:					
3:					
4:					
5:					
6:					
TOTAL					

Table of random numbers

A	B	C	D
2 2	3 1	6 2	2 2
3 2	1 5	6 3	4 3
3 1	5 6	3 6	6 4
4 6	3 6	1 3	4 5
4 3	4 2	4 5	3 5
5 6	1 4	3 1	1 4

The table above has been adapted from a table of random numbers from a statistics book. Use this table to select quadrats randomly from the grid above. Choose one of the columns (A to D) and use the numbers in that column as an index to the grid. The first digit refers to the row number and the second digit refers to the column number. To locate each of the 6 quadrats, find where the row and column intersect, as shown below:

Example: | 5 2 | refers to the 5th row and the 2nd column

233 Field Study of a Rocky Shore

Key Idea: Field studies collect physical and biological data that measure aspects of community structure or function. Many biological investigations require the collection of data from natural communities. Biotic data may include the density or distribution of organisms at a site. Recording physical (abiotic) data of the site allows the site to be compared with others. The investigation below looks at the populations of animals found on an exposed and a sheltered rocky shore.

Sample site A: Exposed rocky shore. Frequent heavy waves and high winds. Smooth rock face with few boulders and relatively steep slope towards the sea.

Coastline

Prevailing direction of wind and swell

1km

Sample site B: Sheltered rocky shore. Small, gentle waves and little wind. Jagged rock face with large boulders and shallower slope leading to the sea.

The aim

To investigate the differences in the abundance of intertidal animals on an exposed rocky shore and a sheltered rocky shore.

Background

The composition of rocky shore communities is strongly influenced by the shore's physical environment. Animals that cling to rocks must keep their hold on the substrate while being subjected to intense wave action and currents. However, the constant wave action brings high levels of nutrients and oxygen. Communities on sheltered rocky shores, although encountering less physical stress, may face lower nutrient and oxygen levels.

To investigate differences in the abundance of intertidal animals, students laid out 1 m² quadrats at regular intervals along one tidal zone at two separate but nearby sites: a rocky shore exposed to wind and heavy wave action and a rocky shore with very little heavy wave action. The animals were counted and their numbers in each quadrat recorded.

All photos: C. Pilditch except where indicated

Rocky shore animals

The oyster borer is carnivorous and preys on barnacles such as the brown barnacle and the plicate barnacle. Numbers of oyster borers may be lower when there are fewer barnacles as prey.

The columnar barnacle is found around the high to mid tide level but can extend lower in suitable areas. It is uncommon on soft substrates and prefers moderately exposed shore lines.

The plicate and brown barnacles can be found together on exposed rocky shores. On more sheltered shores, the columnar barnacle is more prevalent.

The rock oyster often grows on steeply sloped or vertical surfaces and tends to flourish in harbours, as settlement on rocks is inhibited by even moderate wave action.

Limpets are found throughout rocky shores, although the ornate limpet has a slight preference to exposed shores.

The black nerite (snail) is found throughout rocky shores and extends across most tidal zones. It is more common on exposed rocky shores.

Graham Bould

Photo: K Pryor

LINK
230 **DATA**

1. Underline an appropriate hypothesis for this field study from the four possible hypotheses below:

   (a) Rocky shore communities differ because of differences in wave action.

   (b) Rocky shore communities differ because of the topography of the coastline.

   (c) The physical conditions of exposed rocky shores and sheltered rocky shores are very different and so the intertidal communities will also be different.

   (d) Rocky shore communities differ because of differences in water temperature.

2. During the field study, students counted the number of animals in each quadrat and recorded them in a note book. Complete the table with the total number of each species at each site, the mean number of animals per quadrat, and the median and mode for each set of samples per species. Remember, in this case, there can be no 'part animals' so you will need to round your values to the nearest whole number:

Field data notebook
Count per quadrat. Quadrats 1 m²

Site A	1	2	3	4	5	6	7	8
Brown barnacle	39	38	37	21	40	56	36	41
Oyster borer	6	7	4	3	7	8	9	2
Columnar barnacle	6	8	14	10	9	12	8	11
Plicate barnacle	50	52	46	45	56	15	68	54
Ornate limpet	9	7	8	10	6	7	6	10
Radiate limpet	5	6	4	8	6	7	5	6
Black nerite	7	7	6	8	4	6	8	9
Site B								
Brown barnacle	7	6	7	5	8	5	7	7
Oyster borer	2	3	1	3	2	2	1	1
Columnar barnacle	56	57	58	55	60	47	58	36
Plicate barnacle	11	11	13	10	14	9	9	8
Rock oyster	7	8	8	6	2	4	8	6
Ornate limpet	7	8	5	6	5	7	9	3
Radiate limpet	13	14	11	10	14	12	9	13
Black nerite	6	5	3	1	4	5	2	3

		Brown barnacle	Oyster borer	Columnar barnacle	Plicate barnacle	Rock oyster	Ornate limpet	Radiate limpet	Black nerite
Site A	Total number of animals								
	Mean number of animals per m²								
	Median value								
	Modal value								
Site B	Total number of animals								
	Mean number of animals per m²								
	Median value								
	Modal value								

© 2015 **BIOZONE** International
ISBN: 978-1-927309-14-8
Photocopying Prohibited

3. Use the grid below to draw a column graph of the mean number of species per 1 m² at each sample site. Remember to include a title, correctly labelled axes, and a key.

----

4. (a) Compare the mean, median, and modal values obtained for the samples at each site: _____

_____

(b) What does this tell you about the distribution of the data: _____

_____

5. (a) Which species was entirely absent from site A? _____

(b) Suggest why this might be the case: _____

_____

6. (a) Explain why more brown barnacles and plicate barnacles were found at site A: _____

_____

_____

(b) Explain why more oyster borers were found at site A: _____

_____

_____

7. (a) Comment on the numbers of limpets at each site: _____

_____

(b) What does this suggest to you about their biology: _____

_____

234 Testing for Difference Using Chi-Squared

Key Idea: The chi-squared test for goodness of fit is used to compare sets of categorical data and evaluate if differences between them are statistically significant or due to chance.

The **chi-squared test** (χ^2), is used when you are working with frequencies (counts) rather than measurements. It is a simple test to perform but the data must meet the requirements of the test. Firstly, it can only be used for data that are raw counts (not measurements or transformed data such as percentages). Secondly, it is used to compare an experimental result with an expected theoretical outcome (e.g. an expected Mendelian ratio or a theoretical value indicating "no difference" between groups in a response such as habitat preference). Thirdly, it is not a valid test when sample sizes are small (<20). Like all statistical tests, it aims to test the null hypothesis. The following exercise is a worked example using the chi-squared test for difference to test habitat preference.

Using χ^2 in ecology

Pneumatophores

In an investigation of the ecological niche of the mangrove, *Avicennia marina var. resinifera*, the density of pneumatophores was measured in regions with different substrate. The mangrove trees were selected from four different areas: mostly sand, some sand, mostly mud, and some mud. Note that the variable, substrate type, is categorical in this case. Quadrats (1 m by 1 m) were placed around a large number of trees in each of these four areas and the numbers of pneumatophores were counted. Chi-squared was used to compare the observed results for pneumatophore density (as follows) to an expected outcome of no difference in density between substrates.

Mangrove pneumatophore density in different substrate areas			
Mostly sand	85	Mostly mud	130
Some sand	102	Some mud	123

Using χ^2, the probability of this result being consistent with the expected result could be tested. Worked example as follows:

Step 1: Calculate the expected value (E)

In this case, this is the sum of the observed values divided by the number of categories.

$$\frac{440}{4} = 110$$

Step 2: Calculate O – E

The difference between the observed and expected values is calculated as a measure of the deviation from a predicted result. Since some deviations are negative, they are all squared to give positive values. This step is usually performed as part of a tabulation (right, darker blue column).

Category	O	E	O - E	(O - E)²	$\frac{(O - E)^2}{E}$
Mostly sand	85	110	-25	625	5.68
Some sand	102	110	-8	64	0.58
Mostly mud	130	110	20	400	3.64
Some mud	123	110	13	169	1.54

Total = 440 $\chi^2 \rightarrow \Sigma = 11.44$

Step 3: Calculate the value of χ^2

$$\chi^2 = \sum \frac{(O - E)^2}{E}$$

Where:
O = the observed result
E = the expected result
Σ = sum of

The calculated χ^2 value is given at the bottom right of the last column in the tabulation.

Step 4: Calculating degrees of freedom

The probability that any particular χ^2 value could be exceeded by chance depends on the number of degrees of freedom. This is simply *one less than the total number of categories* (this is the number that could vary independently without affecting the last value). *In this case: 4–1 = 3.*

Step 5a: Using the χ^2 table

On the χ^2 table (part reproduced in Table 1 below) with 3 degrees of freedom, the calculated value for χ^2 of 11.44 corresponds to a probability of between 0.01 and 0.001 (see arrow). *This means that by chance alone a χ^2 value of 11.44 could be expected between 1% and 0.1% of the time.*

Step 5b: Using the χ^2 table

The probability of between 0.1 and 0.01 is lower than the 0.05 value which is generally regarded as significant. The null hypothesis can be rejected and we have reason to believe that the observed results differ significantly from the expected (at P = 0.05).

Table 1: Critical values of χ^2 at different levels of probability. By convention, the critical probability for rejecting the null hypothesis (H_0) is 5%. If the test statistic is less than the tabulated critical value for P = 0.05 we cannot reject H_0 and the result is not significant. If the test statistic is greater than the tabulated value for P = 0.05 we reject H_0 in favour of the alternative hypothesis.

Degrees of freedom	Level of probability (P)									
	0.98	0.95	0.80	0.50	0.20	0.10	0.05	0.02	0.01	0.001
1	0.001	0.004	0.064	0.455	1.64	2.71	3.84	5.41	6.64	10.83
2	0.040	0.103	0.466	1.386	3.22	4.61	5.99	7.82	9.21	13.82
3	0.185	0.352	1.005	2.366	4.64	6.25	7.82	9.84	11.35	16.27
4	0.429	0.711	1.649	3.357	5.99	7.78	9.49	11.67	13.28	18.47
5	0.752	0.145	2.343	4.351	7.29	9.24	11.07	13.39	15.09	20.52

χ^2 10.83 ↓ (for df 1, column 0.01)

← Do not reject H_0 Reject H_0 →

© 2015 **BIOZONE** International
ISBN: 978-1-927309-14-8
Photocopying Prohibited

235 Chi-Squared Exercise in Ecology

Key Idea: Chi-squared for goodness of fit can be used to study habitat preference using the counts of organisms.

This exercise illustrates the use of χ^2 for goodness of fit in ecological studies of habitat preference. In the first example, it is used for determining if the flat periwinkle *(Littorina littoralis)* shows significant preference for any of the four species of seaweeds with which it is found. Using quadrats, the numbers of periwinkles associated with each seaweed species were recorded. The data from this investigation are provided for you in Table 1. In the second example, the results of an investigation into habitat preference in woodlice (also called pillbugs, or slaters) are presented in Table 2.

1. (a) State your null hypothesis for this investigation (H_0):

_____

_____

_____

(b) State the alternative hypothesis (H_A): _____

_____

_____

Table 1: Number of periwinkles associated with different seaweed species

Seaweed species	Number of periwinkles
Spiral wrack	9
Bladder wrack	28
Toothed wrack	19
Knotted wrack	64

2. Use the chi-squared test to determine if the differences observed between the samples are significant or if they can be attributed to chance alone. The table of critical values of χ^2 is provided in "*The Chi-Squared Test*".

(a) Enter the observed values (no. of periwinkles) and complete the table to calculate the χ^2 value:

(b) Calculate χ^2 value using the equation:

$$\chi^2 = \sum \frac{(O - E)^2}{E} \qquad \chi^2 = _____$$

(c) Calculate the degrees of freedom: _____

(d) Using the χ^2, state the *P* value corresponding to your calculated χ^2 value:

_____

(e) State whether or not you reject your null hypothesis:

reject H_0 / do not reject H_0 (*circle one*)

Category	O	E	O - E	$(O - E)^2$	$\frac{(O - E)^2}{E}$
Spiral wrack					
Bladder wrack					
Toothed wrack					
Knotted wrack					
Σ					Σ

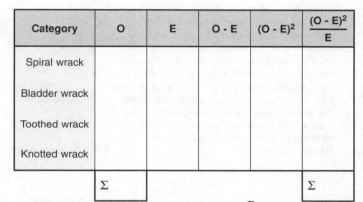

3. Students carried out an investigation into habitat preference in woodlice. In particular, they were wanting to know if the woodlice preferred a humid atmosphere to a dry one, as this may play a part in their choice of habitat. They designed a simple investigation to test this idea. The woodlice were randomly placed into a choice chamber for 5 minutes where they could choose between dry and humid conditions (atmosphere). The investigation consisted of five trials with ten woodlice used in each trial. Their results are shown on Table 2 (right):

(a) State the null and alternative hypotheses (H_0 and H_A) :

_____

_____

Table 2: Habitat preference in woodlice

Trial	Atmosphere	
	Dry	Humid
1	2	8
2	3	7
3	4	6
4	1	9
5	5	5

Use a separate piece of paper (or a spreadsheet) to calculate the chi-squared value and summarise your answers below:

(b) Calculate χ^2 value: _____

(c) Calculate the degrees of freedom and state the *P* value corresponding to your calculated χ^2 value: _____

(d) State whether or not you reject your null hypothesis: reject H_0 / do not reject H_0 (*circle one*)

LINK
234 DATA

236 Investigating Distribution and Abundance

Key Idea: Sampling populations *in-situ* can reveal patterns of distribution, which can be attributed to habitat preference. These investigations are common in ecological studies.

Use this activity to practise analysing data from a field study in which the aim was to identify and describe an existing pattern of species distribution.

The aim

To investigate the effect of fallen tree logs on millipede distribution in a forest.

Background

Millipedes consume decaying vegetation, and live in the moist conditions beneath logs and in the leaf litter of forest floors. The moist environment protects them from drying out as their cuticle is not a barrier to water loss.

Giant pill millipede
Procyliosoma tuberculata

Rudolph89 CC3.0

Experimental method

The distribution of millipede populations in relation to fallen tree logs was investigated in a small forest reserve. Six logs of similar size were chosen from similar but separate regions of the forest. Logs with the same or similar surrounding environment (e.g. leaf litter depth, moisture levels) were selected.

For each log, eight samples of leaf litter at varying distances from the fallen tree log were taken using 30 cm² quadrats. Samples were taken from two transects, one each side of the log. The sample distances were: directly below the log (0 m), 1.5 m, 2.5 m, and 3.5 m from the log. It was assumed that the conditions on each side of the log would be essentially the same. The leaf litter was placed in Tullgren funnels and the invertebrates extracted. The number of millipedes in each sample was counted. The raw data are shown below.

Experimental Setup

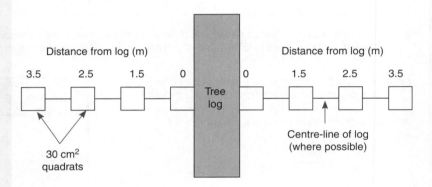

Environmental conditions on either side of the log were assumed to be equal.

Raw data for tree log and millipede investigation

Tree log	Transect	Distance from log (m)			
		0	1.5	2.5	3.5
1	1	12	11	3	2
	2	10	12	2	1
2	1	8	3	4	4
	2	9	5	2	1
3	1	14	6	3	3
	2	3	8	7	2

Tree log	Transect	Distance from log (m)			
		0	1.5	2.5	3.5
4	1	2	4	1	6
	2	4	5	2	2
5	1	12	10	16	10
	2	6	3	2	5
6	1	10	9	7	2
	2	11	11	8	1

LINK
DATA 234

1. Complete the table below using the raw data on the previous page:

Tree log	Distance from log / m			

2. Explain why a chi-squared test is the best statistical analysis of this data: _____

_____

_____

_____

3. State the null hypothesis and alternative hypothesis for the statistical test: _____

_____

_____

4. Carry out the chi-squared test on the data by completing the table below:

Distance / m	O	E	O-E	$(O-E)^2$	$\dfrac{(O-E)^2}{E}$
				$\Sigma \dfrac{(O-E)^2}{E}$	

5. Use the critical values table on page 316 to decide if the null hypothesis should be rejected or not rejected:

_____

_____

6. Discuss your findings in relation to how millipedes live. Include the validity of the findings and any biological ideas relevant to the findings in your discussion:

_____

_____

_____

_____

_____

_____

_____

_____

_____

_____

_____

237 Transect Sampling

Key Idea: Transect sampling is useful for providing information on species distribution along an environmental gradient.

A **transect** is a line placed across a community of organisms. Transects provide information on the distribution of species in the community. They are particularly valuable when the transect records community composition along an **environmental gradient** (e.g. up a mountain or across a seashore). The usual practice for small transects is to stretch a string between two markers. The string is marked off in measured distance intervals and the species at each marked point are noted. The sampling points along the transect may also be used for the siting of quadrats, so that changes in density and community composition can be recorded. Belt transects are essentially a form of continuous quadrat sampling. They provide more information on community composition but can be difficult to carry out. Some transects provide information on the vertical, as well as horizontal, distribution of species (e.g. tree canopies in a forest).

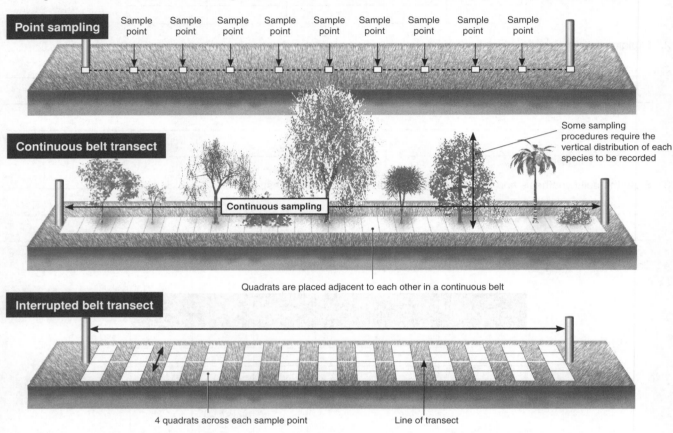

1. Belt transect sampling uses quadrats placed along a line at marked intervals. In contrast, point sampling transects record only the species that are touched or covered by the line at the marked points.

   (a) Describe one disadvantage of belt transects: _____

   _____

   (b) Why might line transects give an unrealistic sample of the community in question? _____

   _____

   _____

   (c) How do belt transects overcome this problem? _____

   _____

   (d) When would it not be appropriate to use transects to sample a community? _____

   _____

2. How could you test whether or not a transect sampling interval was sufficient to accurately sample a community?

   _____

   _____

   _____

A **kite graph** is a good way to show the distribution of organisms sampled using a belt transect. Data may be expressed as abundance or percentage cover along an environmental gradient. Several species can be shown together on the same plot so that the distributions can be easily compared.

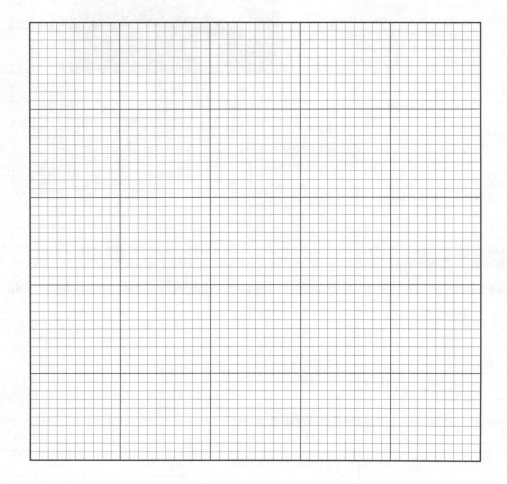

3. The data on the right were collected from a rocky shore field trip. Four common species of barnacle were sampled in a continuous belt transect from the low water mark, to a height of 10 m above that level. The number of each of the four species in a 1 m² quadrat was recorded.

Plot a **kite graph** of the data for all four species on the grid below. Be sure to choose a scale that takes account of the maximum number found at any one point and allows you to include all the species on the one plot. Include the scale on the diagram so that the number at each point on the kite can be calculated.

An example of a kite graph

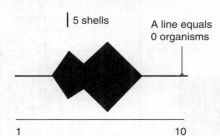

| 5 shells

A line equals 0 organisms

1 10
Distance above water line (m)

Field data notebook

Numbers of barnacles (4 common species) showing distribution on a rocky shore

Barnacle species

Height above low water (m)	Plicate barnacle	Columnar barnacle	Brown barnacle	Sheet barnacle
0	0	0	0	65
1	10	0	0	12
2	32	0	0	0
3	55	0	0	0
4	100	18	0	0
5	50	124	0	0
6	30	69	2	0
7	0	40	11	0
8	0	0	47	0
9	0	0	59	0
10	0	0	65	0

238 Qualitative Practical Work: Seaweed Zonation

Key Idea: Qualitative and quantitative data can be used to explain patterns of zonation in seashore communities.

Three species of brown algae (genus *Fucus*), together with the brown alga *Ascophyllum nodosum*, form the dominant seaweeds on rocky shores in Britain, where they form distinct zones along the shore. Zonation is a characteristic feature of many seashore communities where species' distribution is governed by tolerances to particular physical conditions (e.g. time of exposure to air). When collecting data on the distribution and abundance of *Fucus* species, it is useful to also make qualitative observations about the size, vigour, and degree of desiccation of specimens at different points on the shore. These observations provide biological information which can help to explain the observed patterns.

Spiral wrack (*Fucus spirallis*)

Andreas Trepte

Fucus is a genus of marine brown algae, commonly called wracks, which are found in the midlittoral zone of rocky seashores (i.e. the zone between the low and high levels). A group of students made a study of a rocky shore dominated by three species of *Fucus*: spiral wrack, bladder wrack, and serrated wrack. Their aim was to investigate the distribution of three *Fucus* species in the midlittoral zone and relate this to the size and vigour (V) of the seaweeds and the degree of desiccation (D) evident.

Bladder wrack (*F. vesiculosus*)

Thalli

Stemonitis

Serrated wrack (*F. serratus*)

Stemonitis

Procedure

Three 50 cm³ quadrats were positioned from the LTL to the HTL at two sites on the shore as shown in the diagram (far right). An estimate of **percentage cover (C)** of each species of *Fucus* was made for each sample. Information on vigour and degree of desiccation was collected at the same time.

Qualitative data were collected as simple scores:

+ = vigorous with large thalli
  no evidence of dessication

0 = less vigorous with smaller thalli
  some evidence of dessication

− = small, poorly grown thalli
  obvious signs of desiccation

Site 1   Site 2

Covered at high tide only

HTL   50 cm³   Upper midlittoral

Equally covered and exposed

MTL   Lower midlittoral

Exposed at low tide only

LTL   Lower littoral

1. (a) Describe the quantitative component of this study:

_____

_____

(b) Describe the qualitative component of this study:

	SITE 1									SITE 2								
	HTL			MTL			LTL			HTL			MTL			LTL		
Species	C	D	V	C	D	V	C	D	V	C	D	V	C	D	V	C	D	V
Spiral wrack	50	0	+	0	na	na	0	na	na	30	+	0	0	na	na	0	na	na
Bladder wrack	15	−	−	80	+	+	20	+	0	50	0	−	70	+	+	0	na	na
Serrated wrack	0	na	na	0	na	na	75	+	+	0	na	na	10	−	−	80	+	+

_____

2. The results of the quadrat survey are tabulated above. On a separate sheet, plot a column graph of the percentage coverage of each species at each position on the shore and at sites 1 and 2. Staple it to this page.

3. Relate the distribution pattern to the changes in degree of desiccation and in size and vigour of the seaweed thalli:

_____

_____

_____

_____

4. Suggest why the position of the quadrats was staggered for the two sites and describe a disadvantage of this design:

_____

_____

© 2015 **BIOZONE** International
ISBN: 978-1-927309-14-8
Photocopying Prohibited

239 Mark and Recapture Sampling

Key Idea: Mark and recapture sampling allows the population size of highly mobile organisms to be estimated.

The mark and recapture method of estimating population size is used in the study of animal populations in which the individuals are highly mobile. It is of no value where animals do not move or move very little. The number of animals caught in each sample must be large enough to be valid. The technique is outlined in the diagram below.

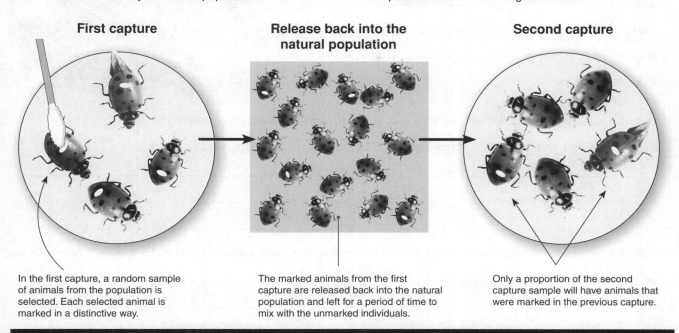

First capture

Release back into the natural population

Second capture

In the first capture, a random sample of animals from the population is selected. Each selected animal is marked in a distinctive way.

The marked animals from the first capture are released back into the natural population and left for a period of time to mix with the unmarked individuals.

Only a proportion of the second capture sample will have animals that were marked in the previous capture.

The Lincoln Index

$$\text{Total population} = \frac{\text{No. of animals in 1st sample (all marked)} \quad \text{X} \quad \text{Total no. of animals in 2nd sample}}{\text{Number of marked animals in the second sample (recaptured)}}$$

The mark and recapture technique comprises a number of simple steps:

1. The population is sampled by capturing as many of the individuals as possible and practical.

2. Each animal is marked in a way to distinguish it from unmarked animals (unique mark for each individual not required).

3. Return the animals to their habitat and leave them for a long enough period for complete mixing with the rest of the population to take place

4. Take another sample of the population (this does not need to be the same sample size as the first sample, but it does have to be large enough to be valid).

5. Determine the numbers of marked to unmarked animals in this second sample. Use the equation above to estimate the size of the overall population.

1. For this exercise you will need several boxes of matches and a pen. Work in a group of 2-3 students to 'sample' the population of matches in the full box by using the mark and recapture method. Each match will represent one animal.

   (a) Take out 10 matches from the box and mark them on 4 sides with a pen so that you will be able to recognise them from the other unmarked matches later.
   (b) Return the marked matches to the box and shake the box to mix the matches.
   (c) Take a sample of 20 matches from the same box and record the number of marked matches and unmarked matches.
   (d) Determine the total population size by using the equation above.
   (e) Repeat the sampling 4 more times (steps b–d above) and record your results:

	Sample 1	Sample 2	Sample 3	Sample 4	Sample 5
Estimated population					

   (f) Count the actual number of matches in the matchbox : _____

   (g) Compare the actual number to your estimates and state by how much it differs: _____

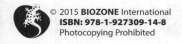

2. In 1919 a researcher by the name of Dahl wanted to estimate the number of trout in a Norwegian lake. The trout were subject to fishing so it was important to know how big the population was in order to manage the fish stock. He captured and marked 109 trout in his first sample. A few days later, he caught 177 trout in his second sample, of which 57 were marked. Use the **Lincoln index** (on the previous page) to estimate the total population size:

Size of 1st sample: _____

Size of 2nd sample: _____

No. marked in 2nd sample: _____

Estimated total population: _____

3. Describe some of the problems with the mark and recapture method if the second sampling is:

   (a) Left too long a time before being repeated: _____
   _____

   (b) Too soon after the first sampling: _____
   _____

4. Describe two important assumptions in this method of sampling that would cause the method to fail if they were not true:

   (a) _____
   _____
   _____

   (b) _____
   _____
   _____

5. Some types of animal would be unsuitable for this method of population estimation (i.e. would not work).

   (a) Name an animal for which this method of sampling would not be effective: _____

   (b) Explain your answer above: _____
   _____
   _____

6. Describe three methods for marking animals for mark and recapture sampling. Take into account the possibility of animals shedding their skin, or being difficult to get close to again:

   (a) _____

   (b) _____

   (c) _____

7. Scientists in the UK and Canada have, at various times since the 1950s, been involved in computerised tagging programs for Northern cod (a species once abundant in Northern Hemisphere waters but now severely depleted). Describe the type of information that could be obtained through such tagging programmes:

   _____
   _____
   _____
   _____
   _____
   _____

240 Indirect Sampling

Key Idea: Indirect sampling is a semi-quantitative way to determine the distribution and abundance of species that are difficult to sample by other means.

If populations are small and easily recognised they may be monitored directly quite easily. However, direct measurement of elusive, easily disturbed, or widely dispersed populations is not always feasible. In these cases, indirect methods can be used to assess population abundance, provide information on habitat use and range, and enable biologists to link habitat quality to species presence or absence. Indirect sampling methods provide less reliable measures of abundance than direct sampling methods, such as mark and recapture, but are widely used nevertheless. They rely on recording the signs of a species, e.g. scat, calls, tracks, and rubbings or markings on vegetation, and using these to assess population abundance. In the UK, surveys are often used to record the abundance and distribution of various animals. The Mammal Society uses volunteers to carry out surveys, including the National Hedgehog Survey (below). Volunteers use tracking tunnels to record hedgehog movements.

These hedgehog footprints were recorded in various tracking tunnels. These images are not to scale, but this paper was A4 in size, to give a relative indication of size.

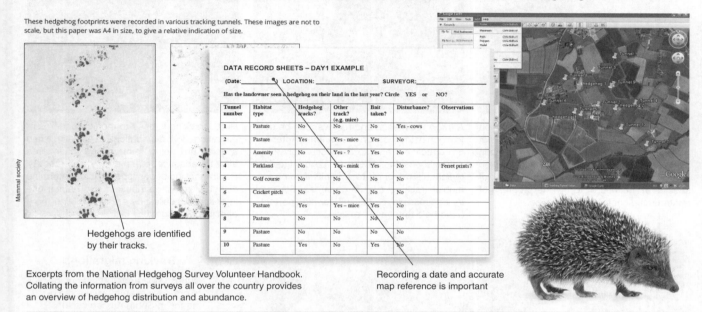

Hedgehogs are identified by their tracks.

DATA RECORD SHEETS – DAY1 EXAMPLE

(Date:_____ LOCATION:_____ SURVEYOR:_____

Has the landowner seen a hedgehog on their land in the last year? Circle YES or NO?

Tunnel number	Habitat type	Hedgehog tracks?	Other track? (e.g. mice)	Bait taken?	Disturbance?	Observations
1	Pasture	No	No	No	Yes - cows	
2	Pasture	Yes	Yes - mice	Yes	No	
3	Amenity	No	Yes - ?	Yes	No	
4	Parkland	No	Yes - mink	Yes	No	Ferret prints?
5	Golf course	No	No	No	No	
6	Cricket pitch	No	No	No	No	
7	Pasture	Yes	Yes – mice	Yes	No	
8	Pasture	No	No	No	No	
9	Pasture	No	No	No	No	
10	Pasture	Yes	No	Yes	No	

Recording a date and accurate map reference is important

Excerpts from the National Hedgehog Survey Volunteer Handbook. Collating the information from surveys all over the country provides an overview of hedgehog distribution and abundance.

Electronic devices, such as the bat detector above, can be used to estimate population density of nocturnal, highly mobile species, e.g. bats. In this case, the detector is tuned to the particular frequency of the hunting clicks emitted by specific species. The number of calls per unit time can be used to estimate numbers per area.

The analysis of tracks allows wildlife biologists to identify habitats in which animals live and to conduct population surveys. Interpreting tracks accurately requires considerable skill as tracks may vary in appearance even when from the same individual. Tracks are particularly useful as a way to determine habitat use and preference.

All animals leave scat (feces) which are species specific and readily identifiable. Scats can be a valuable tool by which to gather data from elusive, nocturnal, easily disturbed, or highly mobile species. Fecal analyses can provide information on diet, movements, population density, sex ratios, age structure, and even genetic diversity.

1. Describe two kinds of indirect signs that could be used to detect the presence an animal:

   (a) _____ (b) _____

2. (a) Describe the kind of information that would be gathered from the hedgehog data sheet: _____

   _____

   _____

   (b) Explain a use for this information: _____

   _____

WEB
240 KNOW

241 Sampling Using Radio-tracking

Key Idea: Radio-tracking makes it possible to monitor populations of highly mobile species.

Field work involving difficult terrain, aquatic environments, or highly mobile, secretive, or easily disturbed species, can be greatly assisted by the use of radio-transmitter technology. Radio-tracking can be used to quickly obtain accurate information about an animal's home range and can provide information about dispersal, distribution, habitat use, and competitive relationships. Radio-tracking is particularly suited to population studies of threatened species (because it is relatively non-invasive) and of pests (because their dispersal and habitat use can be monitored). The information can be used to manage an endangered species effectively or to plan more efficient pest control operations. Satellite transmitters can be used to study migratory movements of large animals and marine species, which are more difficult to follow.

Radio-tracking technology is widely used in conservation work to study animal movements and habitat use. The information allows conservation organisations to develop better strategies for the management of species in the wild or follow the progress of reintroduced captive-bred animals.

A tracking antenna and receiver can be used to pinpoint the location of an animal. Antennae are directional and so can accurately fix an animal's position. They can be mounted on to light aircraft or off-road vehicles to provide mobile tracking over large areas. For work in inaccessible or difficult terrain, portable, hand-held antennae are used.

Radio-tracking collar

Radio-tracking is used to monitor patterns of migration and distribution, especially when species are being reintroduced to an area after an absence, e.g. the grey wolf (above). Radio-tracking of pest species can determine dispersal rates, distribution, and habitat use in critical conservation areas, enabling more effective pest control.

From Bonfil et al 2005.

Tracking migrations

During 2002 and 2003, a number of great white sharks were radio-tagged in South African waters. The data recovered showed the first ever recorded intercontinental migration by a great white.

A female shark, known as P12, swam 11 000 km from South Africa to Australia in 99 days with a minimum speed just under 5 km h^{-1}. Within 9 months she had returned to South African waters, completing a round trip of more than 20 000 km.

1. Describe two applications of radio-tracking technology in endangered species management: _____

_____

_____

_____

2. Explain why radio-tracking might be used to monitor pest species: _____

_____

_____

_____

3. Explain how radio-tracking has increased our knowledge of the movement of marine animals: _____

_____

_____

_____

© 2015 **BIOZONE** International
ISBN: 978-1-927309-14-8
Photocopying Prohibited

242 Chapter Review

Summarise what you know about this topic under the headings and sub-headings provided. You can draw diagrams or mind maps, or write short notes to organise your thoughts. Use the images and hints to help you and refer back to the introduction to check the points covered:

Ecosystems and biomass transfers
HINT: Components and size of an ecosystem. Food chains and food webs.

Nutrient cycling
HINT: Describe the carbon and nitrogen cycles and the role of microorganisms in these.

Community patterns and change
HINT: Describe ecological succession and methods for measuring the distribution and abundance of organisms in ecosystems.

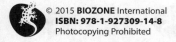
REVISE

243 KEY TERMS: Did You Get It?

1. Test your vocabulary by matching each term to its definition, as identified by its preceding letter code.

abundance

belt transect

carbon cycle

consumers

distribution

ecological pyramid

food chain

food web

line transect

mark and recapture

primary succession

quadrat

secondary succession

trophic level

A A line across a habitat along which organisms are sampled at set intervals to determine changes in community composition.

B The position an organism occupies on the food chain.

C A measured and marked region used to isolate a sample area for study.

D Organisms that obtain their energy from other living organisms or their dead remains.

E A complex series of interactions showing the feeding relationships between organisms in an ecosystem.

F A form of continuous quadrat sampling along a line.

G Biogeochemical cycle by which carbon is exchanged among the biotic and abiotic components of the Earth.

H The number of organisms in a population or area.

I A sequence of steps describing how an organism derives energy from the ones before it.

J A succession sequence that takes place after a land clearance event (e.g. forest fire or landslide). It does not involve the loss of seeds and root stock.

K The location of individuals of a population within an area.

L A succession sequence that occurs on land that has not had plants or soil in the past or has been cleared of its vegetation by volcanic eruption etc.

M Sampling method used to determine the size of a population in which individuals from a population are marked and released and then recapture after a set period of time.

N A graphical representation of the numbers, energy, or biomass at each trophic level in an ecosystem. Pyramidal in shape, but sometimes inversely so.

2. The schematic below shows the movement of energy and minerals from producers to consumers.

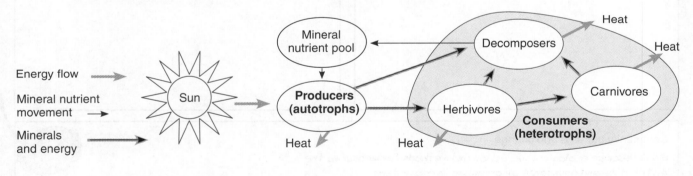

(a) How are the movements of minerals and energy different? _____

_____

(b) What process is responsible for losses of energy from the system? _____

3. A simple food chain for a cropland ecosystem is pictured below. Label the organisms with their trophic status (e.g. primary consumer).

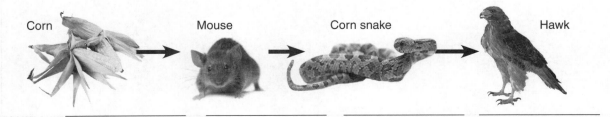

Corn   Mouse   Corn snake   Hawk

_____   _____   _____   _____

Module
6.3.2

Populations and Sustainability

Key terms

biodiversity

carrying capacity

competition

competitive exclusion principle

conservation

coppicing

distribution

interspecific competition

intraspecific competition

maximum sustainable yield

mortality

natality

population density

population size

predator

preservation

prey

resource

sustainable

Populations

Learning outcomes

Conservation and ecosystem management

Learning outcomes

244 Features of Populations

Key Idea: Populations exhibit attributes, such as density, age structure, and mortality, that are not shown by individuals.

A **population** refers to all the organisms of the same species in a particular area. Biologists are often interested in population size (abundance) and density, both of which reflect the carrying capacity of the environment, i.e. how many organisms the environment can support. Populations have structure, with particular ratios of different ages and sexes. Analysis of age structure can show if the population is declining or increasing in size. We can also look at the distribution of organisms in their environment and so determine what aspects of the habitat are favoured over others. One way to retrieve information about populations is to sample them. Sampling involves collecting data, directly or indirectly, about features of the population from samples (since populations are usually too large to examine in total).

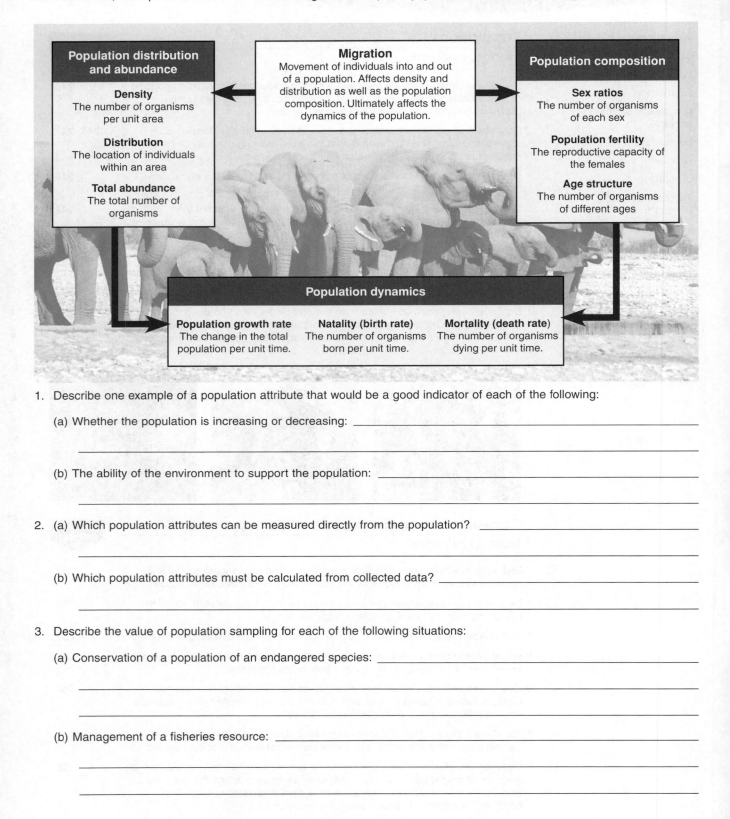

Population distribution and abundance

Density
The number of organisms per unit area

Distribution
The location of individuals within an area

Total abundance
The total number of organisms

Migration
Movement of individuals into and out of a population. Affects density and distribution as well as the population composition. Ultimately affects the dynamics of the population.

Population composition

Sex ratios
The number of organisms of each sex

Population fertility
The reproductive capacity of the females

Age structure
The number of organisms of different ages

Population dynamics

Population growth rate
The change in the total population per unit time.

Natality (birth rate)
The number of organisms born per unit time.

Mortality (death rate)
The number of organisms dying per unit time.

1. Describe one example of a population attribute that would be a good indicator of each of the following:

   (a) Whether the population is increasing or decreasing: _____

   _____

   (b) The ability of the environment to support the population: _____

   _____

2. (a) Which population attributes can be measured directly from the population? _____

   _____

   (b) Which population attributes must be calculated from collected data? _____

   _____

3. Describe the value of population sampling for each of the following situations:

   (a) Conservation of a population of an endangered species: _____

   _____

   _____

   (b) Management of a fisheries resource: _____

   _____

   _____

245 The Carrying Capacity of an Ecosystem

Key Idea: Carrying capacity is the maximum number of organisms a particular environment can support.

An ecosystem's carrying capacity, i.e. the maximum number of individuals of a given species that the resources can sustain indefinitely, is limited by the ecosystem's resources. Factors affecting carrying capacity of an ecosystem can be biotic (e.g. food supply) or abiotic (e.g. water, climate, and available space).The carrying capacity of an ecosystem is determined by the most limiting factor and can change over time (e.g. as a result of seasonal changes). Below carrying capacity, population size increases because resources are not limiting. As the population approaches carrying capacity (or exceeds it) resources become limiting and environmental resistance increases, decreasing population growth.

Limiting factors

The effect of limiting factors and the type of factor that is limiting may change over time. The graph, right, shows how the carrying capacity of a forest-dwelling species changes based on changes to the limiting factors:

1. A population moves into the forest and rapidly increases in numbers due to abundant resources.

2. The population overshoots the carrying capacity.

3. The environment is damaged due to large numbers and food becomes more limited, lowering the original carrying capacity.

4. The population becomes stable at the new carrying capacity.

5. The forest experiences a drought and the carrying capacity is reduced as a result.

6. The drought breaks and the carrying capacity rises but is less than before because of habitat damage during the drought.

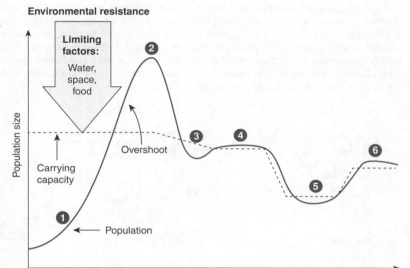

Factors affecting population size

Density dependent factors
The effect of these on population size is influenced by population density.

They include:

► Competition
► Predation
► Disease

Density dependent factors tend to be biotic and are less important when population density is low.

They regulate population size by decreasing birth rates and increasing death rates.

Density independent factors
The effect of these on population size does not depend on population density.

They include catastrophic events such as:

► Volcanic eruptions, fire
► Drought, flood, tsunamis
► Earthquakes

Density independent factors tend to be abiotic.

They regulate population size by increasing death rates.

1. What is carrying capacity? _____

_____

2. How does carrying capacity limit population numbers? _____

_____

_____

3. What limiting factors have changed at points 3, 5, and 6 in the graph above, and how have they changed?

(a) 3: _____

(b) 5: _____

(c) 6: _____

LINK LINK WEB
247 246 245 KNOW

246 A Case Study in Carrying Capacity

Key Idea: Environmental factors influence predator-prey interactions so the outcomes are not always predictable. Environmental carrying capacity can be studied when an organism is introduced to a new environment. One such study involves the introduction of wolves to Coronation Island in Alaska in an attempt to control deer numbers.

When wolves were introduced to Coronation Island

Coronation Island is a small, 116 km² island off the coast of Alaska. In 1960, the Alaska Department of Fish and Game released two breeding pairs of wolves to the island. Their aim was to control the black-tailed deer that had been overgrazing the land. The results (below) were not what they expected. Introduction of the wolves initially appeared to have the desired effect. The wolves fed off the deer and successfully bred, and deer numbers fell. However, within a few years the deer numbers crashed. The wolves ran out of food (deer) and began eating each other, causing a drop in wolf numbers. Within eight years, only one wolf inhabited the island, and the deer were abundant. By 1983, there were no wolves on the island, and the deer numbers were high.

Black-tailed deer

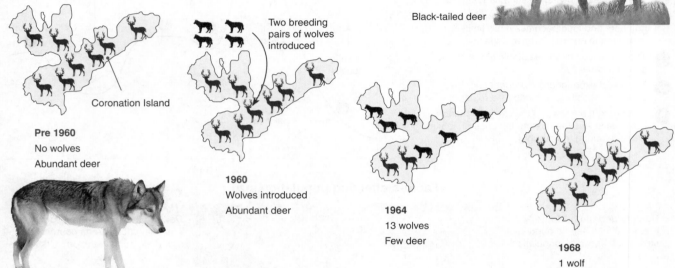

Pre 1960
No wolves
Abundant deer

Coronation Island

Two breeding pairs of wolves introduced

1960
Wolves introduced
Abundant deer

1964
13 wolves
Few deer

1968
1 wolf
Abundant deer

Grey wolf

What went wrong?

► The study showed Coronation Island was too small to sustain both the wolf and the deer populations.

► The deer could not easily find refuge from the wolves, so their numbers were quickly reduced.

► Reproductive rates in the deer may have been low because of poor quality forage following years of over-grazing. When wolves were introduced, predation and low reproductive rates caused deer numbers to fall.

► The deer were the only food source for the wolves. When deer became scarce the wolves ate each other because there was no other prey available.

1. Why were wolves introduced to Coronation Island? _____

_____

_____

2. (a) What were some of the factors that caused the unexpected result? _____

_____

_____

_____

(b) What do these results tell you about the carrying capacity of Coronation Island? _____

_____

_____

_____

© 2015 **BIOZONE** International
ISBN: **978-1-927309-14-8**
Photocopying Prohibited

247 The Rise and Fall of Human Populations

Key Idea: Human populations are subject to rises and collapses in the same way as natural animal populations.

Throughout history there have been a number of peaks of human civilisation followed by collapse. These collapses have been triggered by various events but can generally be attributed either to the spread of disease or to the collapse of a food source (normally agriculture). Examples can be traced right back to the origins of humans.

Mitochondrial DNA analyses show that the human population may have been on the brink of extinction with only around 10 000 individuals alive 150 000 years ago. The population remained low for virtually the whole of human prehistory. When the first towns and cities were being built, around 10 000 years ago, the human population had reached barely 15 million. By around 700 AD, the human population had reached 200 million. Throughout the world large cities had appeared. But these required resources to maintain. One such city was the Mayan city of Tikal

TIKAL: At its peak around 800 AD, Tikal and the surrounding area, was inhabited by over 400 000 people. Extensive fields were used to cultivate crops and the total area of the city and its satellite towns and fields may have reached over 250 km^2. Eventually the carrying capacity of the tropical, nutrient-poor land was overextended and people began to starve. By 900 AD the city had been deserted and the surrounding area abandoned.

EASTER ISLAND: Similar events happened elsewhere. Easter Island is located 3,500 km from South America and 2000 km from the nearest occupied land (the tiny, isolated Pitcairn Island). Easter Island has a mild climate and fertile volcanic soil, but when Europeans discovered it in the 1700s, it was covered in dry grassland, lacking trees or any vegetation above 1m high. Around 2000 people survived on the island by subsistence farming, yet all around stood huge stone statues, some 30 m tall and weighing over 200 tonnes. Clearly a much larger more advanced society had been living on the island at some time in the past. Archaeological studies have found that populations reached 20 000 people prior to 1500 AD. Exhaustion of the island's resources by the population was followed by war and civil unrest and the population fell to the subsistence levels found in the 1700s.

EUROPE: Despite isolated events, the world population continued to grow so that by 1350 AD it had reached around 450 million. As a result of the continued rise of urban populations, often living in squalid conditions, disease spread rapidly. The bubonic plague, which swept through Europe at this time, reduced its population almost by half, and reduced the world's population to 350 million. Despite further outbreaks of plague and the huge death tolls of various wars, the human population had reached 2.5 billion by 1950. By 1990 it was 5 billion and today it is more than 7 billion. In slightly less than 60 years the human population has grown almost twice as much as it did in the whole of human history up until 1950. Much of this growth can be attributed to major advances in agriculture and medicine. However, signs are appearing that the human population is approaching maximum sustainable levels. Annual crop yields have ceased increasing and many common illnesses are becoming more difficult to treat. The rapid spread of modern pandemics, such as H1N1 influenza in 2009 and Ebola in 2014, illustrates the vulnerability of modern human populations. Could it be, perhaps, another great reduction in the human population is imminent?

1. Describe the general trend of human population growth over the last 100 000 years: _____

_____

2. Explain why the human population has grown at such a increased rate in the last 60 years: _____

_____

_____

3. Discuss similarities between the events at Tikal and on the Easter Islands and how they can help us plan for the future:

_____

_____

_____

_____

_____

© 2015 **BIOZONE** International
ISBN: **978-1-927309-14-8**
Photocopying Prohibited

COMP

248 Species Interactions

Key Idea: All species interact with other species. These interactions frequently regulate population growth.

No organism exists in isolation. Each interacts with others of its own and other species. These interactions are often the result of coevolution, in which there is a reciprocal evolution of adaptations in both parties. When there is a very close association between the parties involved, the relationship is called a symbiosis, as occurs in mutualism and parasitism. If one party benefits at the expense of another, the relationship is an exploitation. In competitive interactions, resources are usually limited, so both parties are detrimentally affected. Interactions both within and between species serve to regulate population numbers, keeping population numbers within the carrying capacity of the environment.

Type of interaction between species				
Mutualism	**Exploitation**			**Competition**
	Predation	**Herbivory**	**Parasitism**	
A ⇄ B Benefits — Benefits	A → B Benefits — Harmed	A → B Benefits — Harmed	A → B Benefits — Harmed	A ⇄ B Harmed — Harmed
Both species benefit from the association. **Examples**: Flowering plants and their insect pollinators have a mututalistic relationship. Flowers are pollinated and the insect gains food (below). **Population effects**: Flower population spreads by producing seeds. Bees use pollen to make honey and feed larvae, ensuring the hive's survival.	Predator kills the prey outright and eats it. **Examples**: Lion preying on wildebeest or praying mantis (below) consuming insect prey. Predators have adaptations to capture prey and prey have adaptations to avoid capture. These relationships are often the result of coevolution. **Population effects**: Predator numbers lag behind prey numbers.	Herbivore eats parts of a plant and usually does not kill it. Plants often have defences to limit the impact of herbivory. **Example**: Giraffes browsing acacia trees. Browsing stimulates the acacia to produce toxic alkaloids, which cause the giraffe to move on to another plant. **Population effects**: Browser damage is self limiting, so the plant is able to recover.	The parasite lives in or on the host, taking (usually all) its nutrition from it. The host is harmed but usually not killed. **Examples**: Pork tapeworm in a pig's gut. **Population effects**: High parasite loads make the host susceptible to diseases that may kill it. Parasite numbers generally stay at a level that is tolerated by the host.	Species, or individuals, compete for the same resources, with both parties suffering, especially when resources are limited. **Examples**: Plants growing close to each other compete for light and soil nutrients. **Population effects**: Competition reduces the maximum number of any one species in an area as resources are limited.

Honeybee and flower — *Mantid eats cricket* (Luc Viatour www.Lucnix.be) — *Giraffe browses acacia* — *Pork tapeworm* — *Forest plants*

1. For the purposes of this exercise, assume that species A in the diagram represents humans. Briefly describe an example of our interaction with another species (B in the diagram above) that matches each of the following interaction types:

   (a) Mutualism: _____

   _____

   (b) Exploitation: _____

   _____

   (c) Competition: _____

   _____

2. Plants are not defenceless against herbivores. They have evolved physical and chemical defences to deter herbivores. In some cases (as in grasses) grazing stimulates growth in the plant.

   (a) What is the acacia's response to giraffe browsing? _____

   (b) How might this response prevent over-browsing? _____

   _____

© 2015 **BIOZONE** International
ISBN: **978-1-927309-14-8**
Photocopying Prohibited

249 Interpreting Predator-Prey Relationships

Key Idea: Predator and prey populations frequently show regular population cycles. The predator cycle is often based on the intrinsic population cycle of the prey species.

It was once thought that predators regulated the population numbers of their prey. However, we now know that this is not usually the case. Prey species are more likely to be regulated by other factors such as the availability of food. However, predator population cycles are often regulated by the availability of prey, especially when there is little opportunity for switching to alternative prey species.

A case study in predator-prey numbers

In some areas of Northeast India, a number of woolly aphid species colonise and feed off bamboo plants. The aphids can damage the bamboo so much that it is no longer able to be used by the local people for construction and the production of textiles.

Giant ladybird beetles (*Anisolemnia dilatata*) feed exclusively on the woolly aphids of bamboo plants. There is some interest in using them as biological control agents to reduce woolly aphid numbers, and limit the damage woolly aphids do to bamboo plants.

The graph below shows the relationship between the giant lady bird beetle and the woolly aphid when grown in controlled laboratory conditions.

Bamboo plants are home to many insect species, including ladybirds and aphids.

Aphids feed off the bamboo sap, and the ladybirds are predators of the aphids (below).

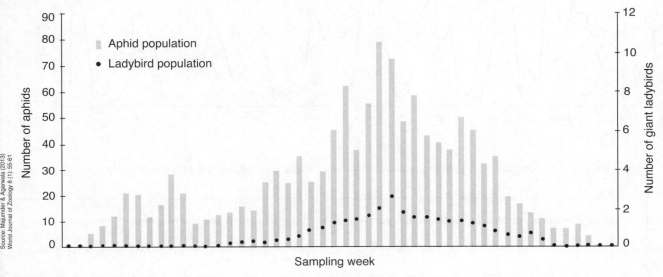

Source: Majumder & Agarwala (2013) World Journal of Zoology 8 (1): 55-61

1. (a) On the graph above, mark (using different coloured pens) where the peak numbers of woolly aphids and giant ladybirds occurs:

   (b) Do the peak numbers for both species occur at the same time? _____

   (c) Why do you think this is? _____

   _____

   _____

   _____

2. (a) Is the trend between the giant ladybirds woolly aphids positive or negative (circle one).

   (b) Explain your answer: _____

   _____

   _____

   _____

   _____

Snowshoe rabbits and Canadian lynx

Snowshoe hares in Canada exhibit cycles of population fluctuation that have a periodicity of 9–11 years. Populations of lynx in the area show a similar periodicity. There is little opportunity for prey switching in this system and the lynx are very dependent on the hares for food. Consequently, the oscillations in the two populations have a similar periodicity, with the lynx numbers lagging slightly behind those of the hare. This provides evidence that is contrary to early suggestions that the lynx controlled the size of the hare population. It is now known that the fluctuations in the hare population are governed by other factors, probably the availability of palatable grasses.

Oscillations in snowshoe hare and Canadian lynx populations

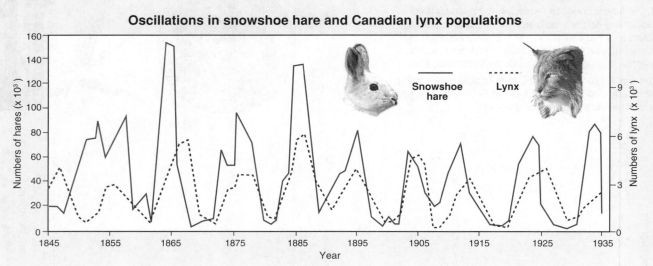

3. (a) From the graph above, determine the lag time between the population peaks of the hares and the lynx:

_____

(b) Explain why there is this time lag between the increase in the hare population and the response of the lynx:

_____

_____

4. Suggest why the lynx populations appear to be so dependent on the fluctuations on the hare:

_____

_____

5. (a) In terms of birth and death rates, explain how the availability of palatable food might regulate the numbers of hares:

_____

_____

(b) Explain how a decline in available palatable food might affect their ability to withstand predation pressure:

_____

_____

_____

6. Laboratory simulations involving predator-prey interactions almost always collapse after one cycle (the predators eat all the prey). Suggest why these systems collapse in laboratory settings but continue indefinitely in natural settings:

_____

_____

© 2015 **BIOZONE** International
ISBN: **978-1-927309-14-8**
Photocopying Prohibited

250 Intraspecific Competition

Key Idea: Intraspecific competition occurs when members of the same species compete for resources. It is usually intense as individuals are competing for exactly the same resources. As a population grows, the resources available to each individual become fewer and **intraspecific competition** (competition between members of the same species) increases. When the demand for a resource (e.g. food or light) exceeds supply, that resource becomes a limiting factor to the number of individuals the environment can support (the **carrying capacity**). Populations respond to resource limitation by reducing growth rate (e.g. lower birth rates or higher mortality). The response of individuals to limited resources varies. In many invertebrates and some vertebrates, individuals reduce their growth rate and mature at a smaller size. In many vertebrates, territories space individuals apart according to resource availability and only those individuals able to secure a territory will be able to breed.

Scramble competition in caterpillars

Direct competition for available food between members of the same species is called **scramble competition.** In some situations where scramble competition is intense, none of the competitors gets enough food to survive.

Contest competition in wolves

In some cases, competition is limited by hierarchies existing within a social group. Dominant individuals receive adequate food, but individuals low in the hierarchy must **contest** the remaining resources and may miss out.

Display of a male anole

Intraspecific competition may be for mates or breeding sites, or for food. In anole lizards (above), males have a bright red throat pouch and use much of their energy displaying to compete with other males for available mates.

Competition between tadpoles of *Rana tigrina*

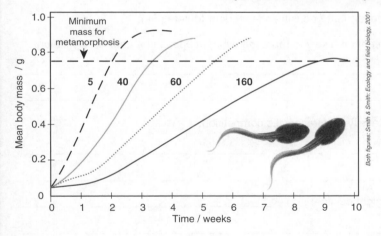

Both figures: Smith & Smith: Ecology and field biology, 2001

Food shortage reduces both individual growth rate and survival, and population growth. In some organisms, where there is a metamorphosis or a series of moults before adulthood (e.g. frogs, crustacean zooplankton, and butterflies), individuals may die before they mature. The graph (left) shows how the growth rate of tadpoles (*Rana tigrina*) declines as the density increases from 5 to 160 individuals (in the same sized space).

► At high densities, tadpoles grow more slowly, take longer to reach the minimum size for metamorphosis (0.75 g), and have less chance of metamorphosing into frogs.

► Tadpoles held at lower densities grow faster to a larger size, metamorphosing at an average size of 0.889 g.

► In some species, such as frogs and butterflies, the adults and juveniles reduce the intensity of intraspecific competition by exploiting different food resources.

1. Using an example, predict the likely effects of **intraspecific competition** on each of the following:

   (a) Individual growth rate: _____

   _____

   _____

   (b) Population growth rate: _____

   _____

   _____

   (c) Final population size: _____

   _____

   _____

LINK
248 WEB
250 **KNOW**

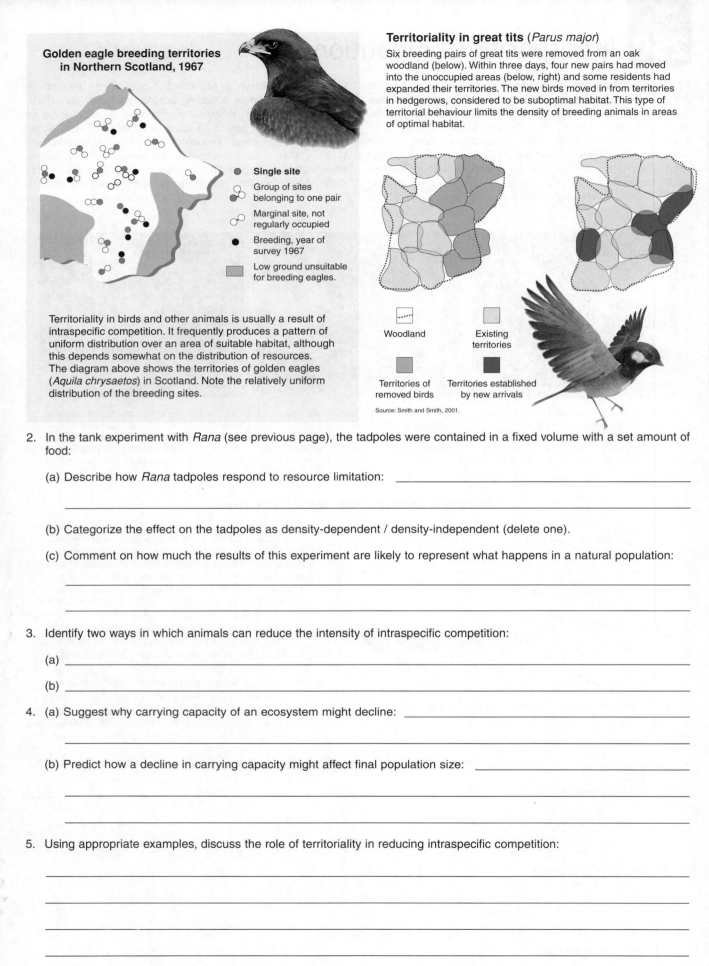

Golden eagle breeding territories in Northern Scotland, 1967

Single site

○ Group of sites belonging to one pair

○ Marginal site, not regularly occupied

● Breeding, year of survey 1967

▨ Low ground unsuitable for breeding eagles.

Territoriality in birds and other animals is usually a result of intraspecific competition. It frequently produces a pattern of uniform distribution over an area of suitable habitat, although this depends somewhat on the distribution of resources. The diagram above shows the territories of golden eagles (*Aquila chrysaetos*) in Scotland. Note the relatively uniform distribution of the breeding sites.

Territoriality in great tits (*Parus major*)

Six breeding pairs of great tits were removed from an oak woodland (below). Within three days, four new pairs had moved into the unoccupied areas (below, right) and some residents had expanded their territories. The new birds moved in from territories in hedgerows, considered to be suboptimal habitat. This type of territorial behaviour limits the density of breeding animals in areas of optimal habitat.

Woodland

Existing territories

Territories of removed birds

Territories established by new arrivals

Source: Smith and Smith, 2001.

2. In the tank experiment with *Rana* (see previous page), the tadpoles were contained in a fixed volume with a set amount of food:

(a) Describe how *Rana* tadpoles respond to resource limitation: _____

_____

(b) Categorize the effect on the tadpoles as density-dependent / density-independent (delete one).

(c) Comment on how much the results of this experiment are likely to represent what happens in a natural population:

_____

_____

3. Identify two ways in which animals can reduce the intensity of intraspecific competition:

(a) _____

(b) _____

4. (a) Suggest why carrying capacity of an ecosystem might decline: _____

_____

(b) Predict how a decline in carrying capacity might affect final population size: _____

_____

_____

5. Using appropriate examples, discuss the role of territoriality in reducing intraspecific competition:

_____

_____

_____

_____

_____

_____

© 2015 **BIOZONE** International
ISBN: **978-1-927309-14-8**
Photocopying Prohibited

251 Interspecific Competition

Key Idea: Interspecific competition occurs between individuals of different species for resources. It can affect the size and distribution of populations sharing the same environment.

Interspecific competition (competition between different species) is usually less intense than intraspecific (same species) competition because coexisting species have evolved slight differences in their realised niches. However, when two species with very similar niche requirements are brought into direct competition through the introduction of a foreign species, one usually benefits at the expense of

the other, which is excluded (the **competitive exclusion principle**). The introduction of alien species is implicated in the competitive displacement and decline of many native species. Displacement of native species by introduced ones is more likely if the introduced competitor is adaptable and hardy, with high fertility. In Britain, introduction of the larger, more aggressive, grey squirrel in 1876 has contributed to a contraction in range of the native red squirrel (below), and on the Scottish coast, this phenomenon has been well documented in barnacle species (see next page)

Range of red and grey squirrels

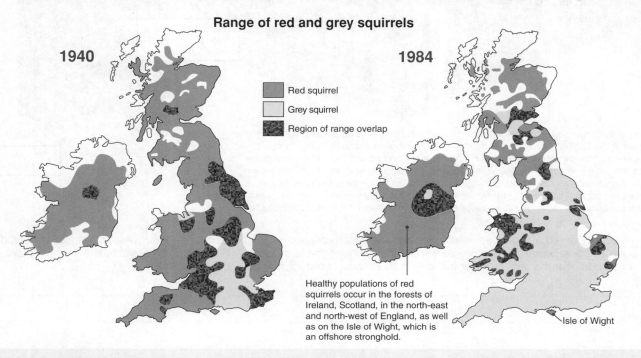

1940

1984

■ Red squirrel
□ Grey squirrel
▨ Region of range overlap

Healthy populations of red squirrels occur in the forests of Ireland, Scotland, in the north-east and north-west of England, as well as on the Isle of Wight, which is an offshore stronghold.

Isle of Wight

Red squirrel

The **European red squirrel**, *Sciurus vulgaris*, was the only squirrel species in Britain until the introduction of the **American grey squirrel**, *Sciurus carolinesis*, in 1876. In 44 years since the 1940 distribution survey (above left), the more adaptable grey squirrel has displaced populations of the native red squirrels over much of the British Isles, particularly in the south (above right). Whereas the red squirrels once occupied both coniferous and broad leafed woodland, they are now almost solely restricted to coniferous forest and are completely absent from much of their former range.

Gray squirrel

1. Outline the evidence to support the view that the red-grey squirrel distributions in Britain are an example of the competitive exclusion principle:

_____

_____

_____

2. Some biologists believe that competition with grey squirrels is only one of the factors contributing to the decline in the red squirrels in Britain. Explain the evidence from the 1984 distribution map that might support this view:

_____

_____

_____

_____

LINK   WEB

Competitive exclusion in barnacles

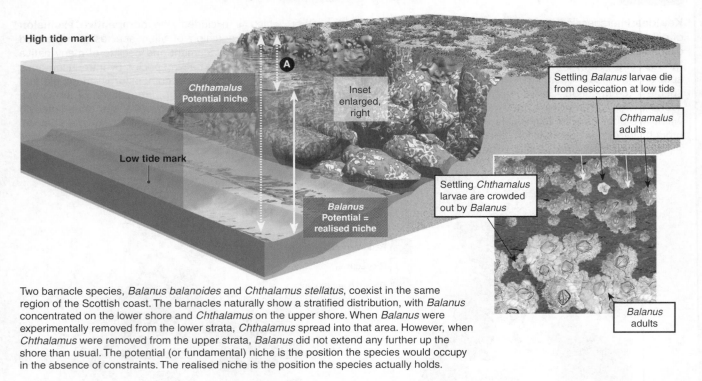

Two barnacle species, *Balanus balanoides* and *Chthalamus stellatus*, coexist in the same region of the Scottish coast. The barnacles naturally show a stratified distribution, with *Balanus* concentrated on the lower shore and *Chthalamus* on the upper shore. When *Balanus* were experimentally removed from the lower strata, *Chthalamus* spread into that area. However, when *Chthalamus* were removed from the upper strata, *Balanus* did not extend any further up the shore than usual. The potential (or fundamental) niche is the position the species would occupy in the absence of constraints. The realised niche is the position the species actually holds.

3. The ability of red and grey squirrels to coexist appears to depend on the diversity of habitat type and availability of food sources (reds appear to be more successful in regions of coniferous forest). Suggest why careful habitat management is thought to offer the best hope for the long term survival of red squirrel populations in Britain:

_____

_____

_____

_____

_____

_____

_____

4. Suggest other conservation methods that could possible aid the survival of viability of red squirrel populations:

_____

_____

_____

_____

5. (a) In the example of the barnacles (above), describe what is represented by the zone labeled with the arrow A:

_____

_____

_____

(b) Outline the evidence for the barnacle distribution being the result of competitive exclusion:

_____

_____

_____

_____

© 2015 **BIOZONE** International
ISBN: **978-1-927309-14-8**
Photocopying Prohibited

252 Conservation and Sustainability

Key Idea: Conservation and sustainability encompass the idea that resources should be managed so that they are replenished and available for future use.

Conservation is a term describing the management of a resource so that it is maintained into the future. It encompasses resources of all kinds, from plant and animal populations to mineral resources. Resource conservation has become an important theme in the twenty-first century as the rate of resource use by the expanding human population increases markedly. **Sustainability** refers to management so that the system or resource is replenished at least at same rate at which it is used. Sustainability is based on the idea of using resources within the capacity of the environment. As such, it allows for managed development and resource use.

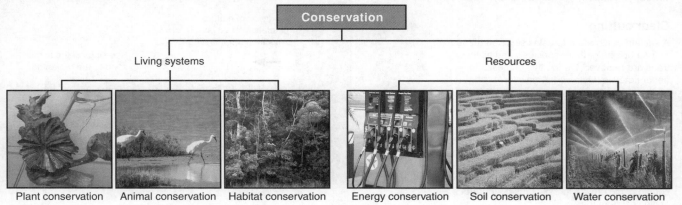

| Plant conservation | Animal conservation | Habitat conservation | Energy conservation | Soil conservation | Water conservation |

The conservation of living systems focuses heavily on the management of species so that their population numbers remain stable or increase over time. Many living systems have no directly measurable economic value but are important for global biodiversity. Many people also support the moral view that humans do not have the right to exterminate other organisms.

Conservation of resources focuses on the efficient use of resources so that remaining stocks are not wasted. Many of these resources are scarce or economically important so require prudent use. Others are damaging to the environment and it is better to use less of them. In recent decades, there has been a growing acknowledgement that humans cannot afford to continue to waste natural resources.

Sustainability

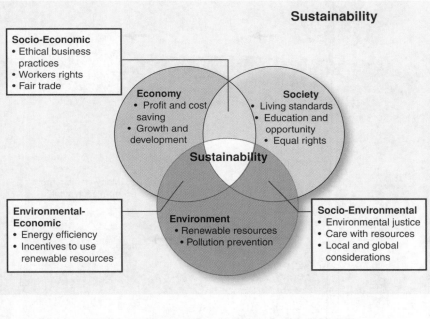

Socio-Economic
• Ethical business practices
• Workers rights
• Fair trade

Economy
• Profit and cost saving
• Growth and development

Society
• Living standards
• Education and opportunity
• Equal rights

Sustainability

Environmental-Economic
• Energy efficiency
• Incentives to use renewable resources

Environment
• Renewable resources
• Pollution prevention

Socio-Environmental
• Environmental justice
• Care with resources
• Local and global considerations

Sustainability can be represented conceptually as the intersection of the environment, society, and economics. Sustainable development must take into account all three of these concepts. Examples of cities that have used the concept of sustainability include Vancouver, San Francisco, Oslo, Curitaba, and Copenhagen. Curitaba, in Brazil, is a particularly good example of a city putting in sustainable plans that also enhance public well being. Started in the 1970s the Curitaba authorities redesigned the city to include new parks (producing 52 m^2 of green space per person), pedestrian only urban and business areas, strictly controlled urban planning, and a bus rapid transit system (essentially buses that act like trains).

1. Explain the relationship between conservation and sustainability: _____

_____

_____

2. Explain the concept of resource conservation: _____

_____

_____

3. What is the importance of society and economy on the conservation of living systems and resources?

_____

_____

© 2015 **BIOZONE** International
ISBN: **978-1-927309-14-8**
Photocopying Prohibited

KNOW

253 Sustainable Forestry

Key Idea: Sustainable forestry employs a variety of removal and replacement methods that provide timber while reducing the impact of timber removal on the environment.

For forestry to be sustainable, demand for timber must be balanced with the regrowth of seedlings. Sustainable forestry allows timber demands to be met without over-exploiting the timber-producing trees. Different methods for logging are used depending on the type of forest being logged. In the UK, afforestation programmes have increased the area of forest to 12%, totalling about 23 000 square kilometres. Careful management of these forests has allowed the forested area to double since 1947. Constant management is needed to ensure this resource continues to be used sustainably without damaging the ecosystems in each case.

Clear cutting

A section of a mature forest is selected (based on tree height, girth, or species), and all the trees are removed. During this process the understorey is destroyed. A new forest of economically desirable trees may be planted. In plantation forests, the trees are generally of a single species and may even be clones. Clear cutting is a very productive and economical method of managing a forest, however it is also the most damaging to the natural environment. In plantation forests, this may not be of concern and may not affect sustainability, but clear cutting of old growth forests causes enormous ecological damage.

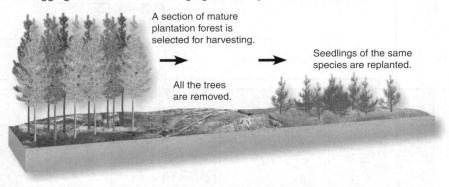

A section of mature plantation forest is selected for harvesting.

All the trees are removed.

Seedlings of the same species are replanted.

Selection logging

A mature forest is examined, and trees are selected for removal based on height, girth, or species. These trees are felled individually and directed to fall in such a way as to minimise the damage to the surrounding younger trees. The forest is managed in such a way as to ensure continual regeneration of young seedlings and provide a balance of tree ages that mirrors the natural age structure. This works well in forests with fast growing trees, but must be very carefully carried out in forests with slow growing trees so that the forest's age structure is not affected.

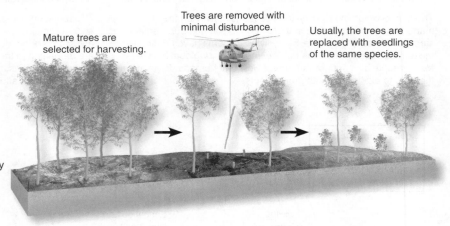

Mature trees are selected for harvesting.

Trees are removed with minimal disturbance.

Usually, the trees are replaced with seedlings of the same species.

Coppicing

Coppicing is the ancient practice of harvesting wood for weaving, thatching, firewood, or for making charcoal. A selection of deciduous trees is coppiced (cut close to the ground), leaving stumps known as stools. Instead of regrowing a single stem, multiple stems are produced. It is these stems that provide the wood for harvesting in the future. Well managed, coppiced woodlands are quite open with a diverse understorey that supports a wide range of species. If coppiced woodland is not well managed, the coppice stems grow tall forming a heavily shaded woodland with little ground vegetation. These **overstood** coppices are relatively low diversity because they no longer support open woodland species, but also lack the characteristics of old growth high forest (e.g. trees of different ages).

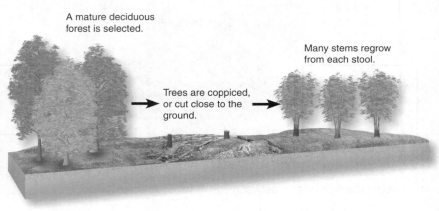

A mature deciduous forest is selected.

Trees are coppiced, or cut close to the ground.

Many stems regrow from each stool.

Strip Cutting

Strip cutting is a variation of clear cutting. Trees are clear cut out of a forest in strips. The strip is narrow enough that the forest on either side is able to reclaim the cleared land. As the cleared forest reestablishes (3-5 years) the next strip is cut. This allows the forest to be logged with minimal effort and damage to forest on either side of the cutting zone, while at the same time allowing the natural reestablishment of the original forest. Each strip is not cut again for around 30 years, depending on regeneration time.

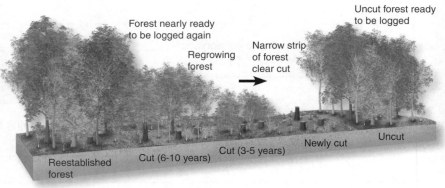

Forest nearly ready to be logged again

Regrowing forest

Narrow strip of forest clear cut

Uncut forest ready to be logged

Reestablished forest

Cut (6-10 years)

Cut (3-5 years)

Newly cut

Uncut

© 2015 **BIOZONE** International
ISBN: **978-1-927309-14-8**
Photocopying Prohibited

Old growth forests are climax communities. They have remained undisturbed by natural events and human interference for many hundreds of years. Old growth forests are ecologically significant because of their high biodiversity, and they are often home to endangered or endemic species. Larger forests also play a part in climate modification.

Second growth forests result from secondary ecological succession after a major forest disturbance such as fire or logging. At first, these forests may have quite different characteristics from the original community, especially if particular tree species were removed completely by logging. As the forest develops, the trees are often of the same age so that a single canopy develops.

Commercial plantations (tree farms) are specifically planted and grown for the production of timber or timber based products. These forests are virtual monocultures containing a specific timber tree, such as *Pinus radiata* (Monterey or radiata pine). These trees have often been selectively bred to produce straight-trunked, uniform trees that grow quickly and can be easily harvested and milled.

1. Describe the advantages and disadvantages of each of the following methods of logging:

   (a) Coppicing: _____

   _____

   _____

   (b) Strip cutting: _____

   _____

   _____

   (c) Clear cutting: _____

   _____

   _____

   (d) Selection logging: _____

   _____

   _____

2. With respect to sustainability, which of the four methods described on the previous page is best suited to:

   (a) Commercial plantations: _____

   (b) Traditional woodland of hardwood species such as hazel, ash, and oak: _____

   (c) Second growth forest: _____

3. Explain which logging method you think best suits the ideals of sustainability and explain your answer:

   _____

   _____

   _____

4. Discuss the role of coppicing as a method of sustainable forestry that also provides a means to conserve biodiversity:

   _____

   _____

   _____

   _____

254 Sustainable Fishing

Key Idea: Fisheries globally have a history of unsustainable management of stocks. The depletion of fish stocks has necessitated the need for careful management strategies. Stocks of commercially fished species must be managed carefully to ensure that the catch (take) does not undermine the long term sustainability of the fishery. This requires close attention to stock indicators, such as catch per unit of fishing effort, stock recruitment rates, population age structure, and spawning biomass. Many of the world's major fisheries, including North Sea cod, bluefin tuna, Atlantic halibut, and orange roughy have been severely over exploited and are in danger of complete collapse.

The sustainable harvesting of any food source requires that its rate of harvest is no more than its replacement rate. If the harvest rate is higher than the replacement rate then it follows that the food source will continually reduce at ever increasing percentages (assuming a constant harvest rate) and thus eventually be lost.

Sustainable yield (SY) refers to the number or weight of fish that can be removed by fishing without reducing the stock biomass from year to year. It assumes that the environmental conditions remain the same and do not contribute to fluctuations in biomass levels. The **maximum sustainable yield** (MSY) is the maximum amount of fish that can be taken without affecting the stock biomass and replacement rate. Calculating an MSY relies on obtaining precise data about a population's age structure, size, and growth rates. If the MSY is incorrectly established, unsustainable quotas may be set, and the fish stock may become depleted.

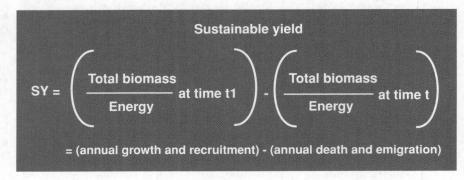

Sustainable yield

$$SY = \left(\frac{\text{Total biomass}}{\text{Energy}} \text{ at time t1} \right) - \left(\frac{\text{Total biomass}}{\text{Energy}} \text{ at time t} \right)$$

= (annual growth and recruitment) - (annual death and emigration)

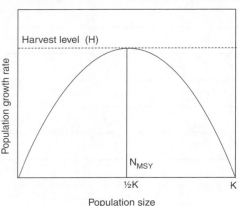

The theoretical maximum sustainable yield (N_{MSY}) occurs when a population is at half the carrying capacity (½K). At this point, the population growth rate will also be at its maximum. Under ideal conditions, harvesting at this rate (H) should be able to continue indefinitely. However, the growth rate of a population is likely to fluctuate from year to year. If a population has below-average growth for several years while the take remains the same, there is a high risk of population collapse because an ever-increasing proportion of the population will be taken with each harvest.

1. Explain why it is essential to have accurate estimates of population age structure, size and growth rate when determining a maximum sustainable yield:

_____

_____

_____

2. Explain the implications to the population of the following scenarios:

 a) The population size is overestimated: _____

 _____

 b) The population growth rate is overestimated: _____

 _____

 c) Initial studies of the age structure incorrectly show there is a greater proportion of mature fish than younger fish.

 _____

 _____

3. Discuss the statement "*Harvesting at the maximum sustainable yield puts the target population on a knife edge*.":

_____

_____

_____

© 2015 **BIOZONE** International
ISBN: **978-1-927309-14-8**
Photocopying Prohibited

North Sea cod

The stock of North Sea cod (*Gadus morhua*) is one of the world's six large populations of this economically important species. As one of the most intensively studied, monitored, and exploited fish stocks in the North Sea, it is considered a highly relevant indicator of how well sustainable fisheries policies are operating. Currently juvenile catch rates are much higher than adult catch rates. Recent figures show approximately 54 thousand tonnes are caught annually, vastly less than the 350 000 tonnes caught in the early 1970s.

The state of the fishery

► Fishing mortality (the chance of a fish being caught) reached its maximum in 2000 and has reduced sharply since then. However it has been above the theoretical maximum mortality rate (F_{MSY}) since at least the 1960s (right middle).

► Recruitment has been generally poor since 1987 (right bottom).

► The number of spawning adults has fallen to levels below those required to recruit new individuals into the stock (bottom right).

► ICES (the International Council for the Exploration of the Sea) advised that the spawning stock biomass (an indicator of the number of breeding adults) reached a new historic low in 2006, and that the risk of stock collapse is high.

What has been done?

► With the cod fishery at imminent collapse, measures were taken to try to save the fishery. Depending on the fishing gear being used, fishing vessels were restricted to between 9 and 25 days at sea per month.

► If stock levels do not rise on track with recovery plans, quotas and fishing days are automatically cut by 20% each year.

► ICES has recommended a zero catch limit until the stock reaches at least 70 000 tonnes.

► Net mesh sizes were increased to reduce juvenile mortality.

There has been staunch opposition by fishing companies to these measures. They argue that livelihoods will be affected and that stock has been recovering.

Throughout its range, cod has been heavily exploited. In Canada's Grand Banks, where *Gadus morhua* is known as the Atlantic cod, the fishery was closed in 1992 after the stock biomass fell to 1% of its historic levels. Nearly 22 000 jobs were lost.

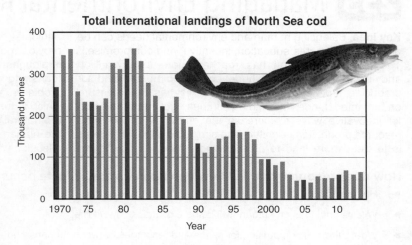

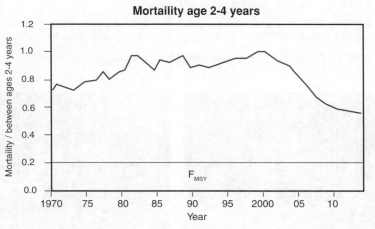

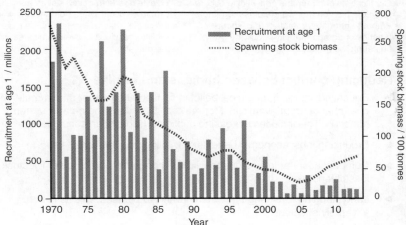

4. (a) Describe the trends in the North Sea cod fishery since 1970: _____

_____

_____

_____

_____

(b) The current recommended fisheries target for cod mortality is 0.4. What effect do you expect this will have on stock recovery?

_____

_____

255 Managing Environmental Resources

Key Idea: Balancing human and environmental needs can be difficult and requires education, incentive, and compromise. The human population has reached more than 7 billion and is still growing. This huge population needs land for producing food and resources and this has put pressure on untamed lands. In many countries, government funds for innovative ways to increase the efficiency of food and resource production is limited. The simple solution for farmers is to clear more land to produce more food, e.g. cut down rainforest or plough grassland. Rainforests in particular can provide money from the harvested wood before the ground is ploughed and sowed with crops. Ironically, in areas where tourism to natural areas has increased, it has caused similar problems as businesses move in and build tourist towns, which in turn bring more people and so encroach further into the natural areas. Finding the balance between the needs of the human population and the needs of the environment is difficult as they are often conflicting.

How does resource conflict between humans and wildlife occur?

► Human activity impinges on wildlife well being e.g. hunting.

► Wildlife impinges on human well being e.g. attacks by wildlife.

► Where there is competition for space and resources between humans and wildlife e.g. need for grazing and shelter.

► Where wildlife protection, legislation, or wildlife based industry (e.g. tourism) impinges on the rights of humans and access to resources.

► Where local population has negative attitudes to wildlife conservation.

Conflict between humans and wildlife occurs more often when the two are close together. Without adequate protection (e.g. secure hutches or compounds) livestock are likely to be caught by predators.

Wildlife needs to travel, just as humans do. Problems occur when humans and wildlife use the same routes. Many countries have installed wildlife crossings to avoid similar scenarios to the one above.

Resources under the ground are difficult to reach without some disruption to the landscape. Legislation requiring mines to return the land to its original state after mining ends is becoming more common.

Reducing conflict between humans and wildlife

► Education: instilling an ethical belief in conservation rather than a material one (change from "what's in it for me?" to "how does the greater system benefit?". This includes increasing public participation in conservation.

► Producing jobs: economic benefits of wildlife conservation.

► Compensation for losses due to wildlife infringement on crops or livestock or loss of land use.

► Land planning. Ensuring that where land is to be used, wildlife is not adversely affected.

1. Suggest why logging rainforests might appeal to neighbouring farmers needing to expand their land:

_____

_____

2. Suggest some situations in which locals might have a negative attitude towards wildlife: _____

_____

_____

3. Explain why public participation is particularly important in resource management: _____

_____

_____

© 2015 **BIOZONE** International
ISBN: **978-1-927309-14-8**
Photocopying Prohibited

Case study: The Maasai Mara

The Maasai Mara National Reserve is a region in south western Kenya covering 1500 km². It is part of the much larger Mara-Serengeti ecosystem, which covers around 25 000 km². Considerable change has occurred in the Maasai Mara region since the start of last century. Early in the 20th century, the region was much less populated and the land was used mainly for nomadic agriculture (raising cattle). The arrival of European settlers forced many of the Maasai off their traditional lands. In 1945, more land was turned into reserves and the Maasai land placed in Trust. As a result of changes in governments and ideals, Trust land was redesignated as group ranches. This encouraged the Maasai to subdivide the land to acquire individual titles in order to secure legal rights to lands, rather than risk losing them outright. Privatisation led to an increase in mechanised farming and a reduction in wildlife.

The changes to the land use has had a drastic affect on wildlife. Wildebeest numbers within the area dropped from approximately 150 000 in 1977 to 40 000 in 2010. Water buffalo numbers dropped from nearly 40 000 to approximately 5000. Livestock numbers increased, especially cattle, sheep, and goats.

Over time, it was realised that modern farming methods limited the range of wildlife and also grazing options for livestock. In 2005, many landowners in the northern Maasai Mara began consolidating their land into conservancies, aiming to generate income through tourism. This included establishing partnerships with tourism operators. The success of this approach has seen a rapid expansion of conservancies.

The development of conservancies has had benefits for the community. Payments by tour operators for use of the land are made directly to the land owners, reducing loss of income through bureaucratic handling and corruption. Today there are 8 conservancies representing 92 000 ha. Around $3.6 million is paid to the conservancies each year.

Although the formation of conservancies has benefited the wildlife and many people, those who do not own any land have been no better off. In addition, livestock are only allowed into the conservancies during certain times (e.g. drought) which has lead to higher stocking rates outside the park and conservancies.

Wildlife and livestock changes in the Maasai Mara

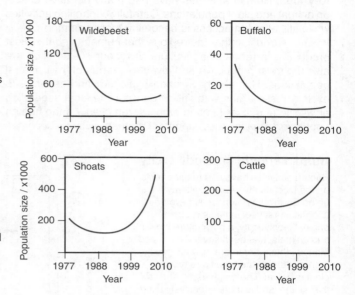

The Maasai Mara National Reserve and surrounding conservancies

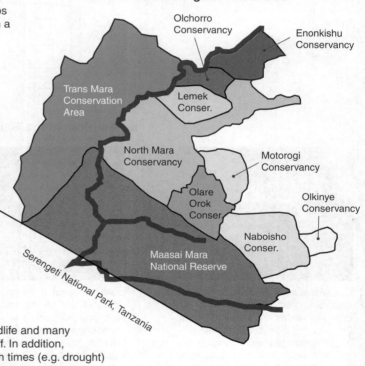

4. (a) What is the nature of the conservancies surrounding the Maasai Mara National Reserve?

_____

_____

_____

(b) In what way have these conservancies helped reduce conflict between humans are wildlife?

_____

_____

_____

256 Controlling Human Impact

Key Idea: Human activities have had many negative effects on animal and plant populations. Carefully controlling activities while still allowing access is becoming more common.

It is not surprising that the regions that humans find the most productive in terms of agriculture or resource extraction are also the most productive and diverse in terms of their natural populations. Humans have often exploited (and continue to exploit) these areas with little regard for the local vegetation or wildlife (e.g. over-hunting or forest removal). As the human population grows, the impact of human activity becomes

more of a problem, especially in countries with limited land. Pressure is often put on governments to open up land to provide housing or resources for the growing population. However, many countries are now beginning to realise that natural or wilderness areas can bring in money and provide jobs without development. This is especially true for environmentally sensitive regions. In these places, the impact of human activity can be managed by providing carefully regulated access, so that people may see or do as much as possible without damaging the landscape.

Human effects on biodiversity

Human activities have had major effects on the biodiversity of Earth. Nearly 40% of the Earth's land surface is devoted to agricultural use. In these areas, the original biodiversity, a polyculture of plants and animals, has been severely reduced. Many of these areas are now effectively monocultures, where just one type of plant is grown. The graph, right, shows that as the land is more intensively used, the populations and variety of plants and animals fall.

Average remaining % of population under each land use

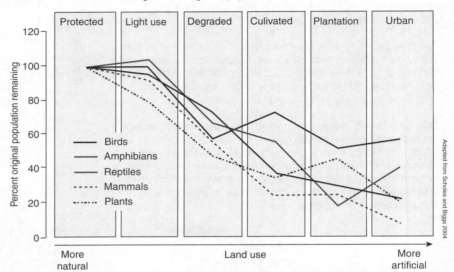

Adapted from Scholes and Biggs 2004

Ecotourism in the Galápagos Islands

One way to limit human activity in sensitive areas is to promote tourism as a viable economic alternative to development. Encouraging tourists to see unique unspoiled environments brings money and jobs to a region with minimal damage to the landscape. Access to the area can be controlled by permits. This **ecotourism** (the specific travelling to regions of ecological significance) has become a major contributor to the economies of many countries.

Ideally, ecotourism involves environmental education and has minimal impact to the environment around which it is based. Increasingly though, it involves large groups travelling to sensitive ecological areas with a guide. The impact of catering to the needs of these tourists can place heavy demands on pristine and fragile systems. The process requires careful planning and adequate infrastructure to cater for increased numbers of visitors.

The experience of the ecotourism industry in the Galápagos Islands, 97% of which are a National Park, illustrates this well. More than 180 000 people visit the islands each year, and ecotourism has brought costs and benefits to the islands, whose population has more than tripled in the last fifteen years. The industry has created greater local and international awareness of the importance of the islands' ecology but the high tourist traffic also puts that ecology at risk of damage.

1. Explain how ecotourism can help reduce human impact in environmentally sensitive areas:

_____

_____

_____

_____

_____

 © 2015 **BIOZONE** International
ISBN: **978-1-927309-14-8**
Photocopying Prohibited

Benefits

Economic

Greater development (upgrading of communications and infrastructure)

Larger population means more sustainable local economy

More jobs (in both tourism and infrastructure)

Environmental

Greater local understanding of the importance of the islands

Development of local wildlife services (National Park Service)

Greater global awareness of environmental issues to do with the islands

Costs

Economic

Restrictions placed on local fishing industry because of National Park

Mass immigration of people looking for jobs

Most tourist dollars do not go to the Galápagos economy

Environmental

Issues with rubbish disposal

Disturbance of plants and animals by tourists

Increased travel increases the risks of new species introductions

Despite the large impact of the tourist industry on the islands, there has been some progress in the reduction of introduced pests. The island of Santiago has had its population of feral pigs eradicated and the population of feral goats there has also been reduced.

The influx of humans to the Galápagos has had serious impacts on the islands outside the National Park. At least two ships bringing fuel for tourist boats have run aground, one spilling 3 million litres of fuel oil that killed 60% of the marine iguanas on the island of Santa Fe. Sea cucumber populations have also been devastated by more fishermen selling to overseas markets.

2. With reference to the Galápagos Islands, discuss some of the benefits and disadvantages of ecotourism:

_____

_____

_____

3. Describe the impact of human activity on the flora and fauna of the Galápagos with reference to each of the following:

(a) Increased tourist traffic: _____

_____

_____

(b) Higher local population: _____

_____

_____

(c) Support for National Park services: _____

_____

_____

(d) Greater environmental awareness: _____

_____

_____

 © 2015 BIOZONE International
ISBN: 978-1-927309-14-8
Photocopying Prohibited

257 Chapter Review

Summarise what you know about this topic under the headings provided. You can draw diagrams or mind maps, or write short notes to organise your thoughts. Use the images and hints included to help you:

Populations
HINT: Describe features of populations. Explain carrying capacity and factors regulating population size.

Species interactions
HINT: Include reference to both interspecific and intraspecific interactions

Conservation and sustainability
HINT: What are sustainable practices, why are they important, and how are they achieved in the management of a resource.

REVISE

258 KEY TERMS: Did You Get It?

1. Study the graph of population growth for a hypothetical population below and answer the following questions:

Population number (y-axis): 10 000, 7500, 5000, 2500, 0

Time (x-axis)

Points labelled **A** and **B** on the graph.

(a) Estimate the carrying capacity of the environment:

_____

(b) What happened at point **A** on the diagram?

_____

_____

_____

_____

(c) What happened at point **B** on the diagram?

_____

_____

_____

_____

(d) What factors might have caused this? _____

_____

_____

_____

2. Test your vocabulary by matching each term to its definition, as identified by its preceding letter code.

biodiversity

carrying capacity

competition

conservation

distribution

interspecific competition

intraspecific competition

maximum sustainable yield

mortality

natality

population size

predator

prey

sustainable

A The largest possible yield that can be obtained from a population which can then be replaced by the growth rate of that population.

B Organism that captures and kills prey for consumption.

C An interaction between organisms exploiting the same resource.

D The death rate of a population, (usually expressed as the number of deaths per 1000 individuals).

E The birth rate of a population, (usually expressed as the number of births per 1000 individuals).

F An organism that is killed and eaten by another.

G Competitive interactions that occur between members of the same species.

H The maximum number of a particular species that the environment can support indefinitely (without degradation).

I Competitive interactions that occur between different species.

J The location of individuals of a population within an area.

K A term describing the variation of life at all levels of biological organisation.

L The active management of natural populations in order to rebuild numbers and ensure species survival.

M Systems or resources that remain diverse and productive over time are called this.

N The total number of individuals of a species within a set habitat or area.

TEST

Image credits

The writing team would like to thank the following people and organisations who have kindly provided photographs or illustrations for this edition:

• D. Fankhauser, University of Cincinnati, Clermont College for the image of the Pacinian corpuscle • WMRCVM (Virginia-Maryland college of veterinary medicine for the image of the pancreas • UC Regents David campus • Wellington Harrier Athletic Club for the photo of the sprinters • Helen Hall for the photo of the marathon runner • Dartmouth college for the electron micrograph images of the chloroplast • Louisa Howard Dartmouth college for the electron micrograph of the mitochondria • Wintec for the sports testing image • Ed Uthman for the image of the human fetus • Marc King for the photos of the chicken combs • Aptychus for the photo of the Tamil girl • Rita Willaert for the photo of the Nuba woman • Dept. of Natural Resources, Illinois for the photo of the Illinois prairie chicken • Allan and Elaine Wilson for the photo of Harris' antelope squirrel • Dr David Wells, AgResearch • Roslin Institute for the images of Dolly • Kapiti Cheese LTD for the images of the cheese making process • Bioengineering AG (Switzerland) for the image of the bioreactor • C Gemmil for the transect sampling photo • Kent Pryor for the photo of the rocky shore • Conrad Pilditch for images of rocky shore organisms

We also acknowledge the photographers who have made images available through **Wikimedia Commons** under Creative Commons Licences 2.0, 2.5, or 3.0: • Ragesoss • RM Hunt • Ildar Sagdejev • Pöllö • Jfoldmei • Jpogi • Solimena Lab • Roadnottaken • Tangopaso • Ryan Somma • Kristian Peters • Woutergroen • Dan Ferber • Johnmaxmena • Piotr Kuczynski • Stem cell scientist • Matthias Zepper • it:Utente:Cits • NYWTS • Dr Graham Beards • Jpbarrass • Jim Conrad • Kamal Ratna Tuladhar • KTBN • Velela • Aviceda • UtahCamera • Bruce Marlin • Lorax • Onno Zweers • AKA • Dirk Beyer • Masur • Kahuroa • Citron • Janus Sandsgaard • Jan Ainali • Crulina 98 • Madprime • Peter Halasz • Sagt • Gina Mikel • Shirley Owens MSU • Wojsyl • Janke • Rasbak • Daderot • Mikrolit • Graham Bould • Rudolph89 • •Andreas Trepte • Stemonitis •

Contributors identified by coded credits:

BH: Brendan Hicks (Uni. of Waikato), **CDC:** Centers for Disease Control and Prevention, Atlanta, USA, **EII:** Education Interactive Imaging, **FRI:** Forest and Research Industry, **NASA:** National Aeronautics and Space Administration, **NIH:** National Institute of Health, **NYSDEC:** New York State Dept of Environmental Conservation, **RA:** Richard Allan, **RCN:** Ralph Cocklin, **TG:** Tracey Greenwood, **WBS:** Warwick Silvester (Uni. of Waikato), **WMU:** Waikato Microscope Unit, **USDA:** United States Department of Agriculture

Image libraries:

We also acknowledge our use of royalty-free images, purchased by BIOZONE International Ltd from the following sources: **Corel** Corporation from various titles in their Professional Photos CD-ROM collection; Dollar Photo Club, dollarphotoclub.com; istock photos, istockphoto.com; **IMSI** (International Microcomputer Software Inc.) images from IMSI's MasterClips® and MasterPhotosTM Collection, 1895 Francisco Blvd. East, San Rafael, CA 94901-5506, USA; ©1996 **Digital Stock**, Medicine and Health Care collection; ©**Hemera** Technologies Inc, 1997-2001; © 2005 JupiterImages Corporation www.clipart.com; ©1994., ©**Digital Vision**; Gazelle Technologies Inc.; ©1994-1996 **Education Interactive Imaging** (UK), **PhotoDisc®**, Inc. USA, www.photodisc.com. We also acknowledge the following clipart providers: TechPool Studios, for their clipart collection of human anatomy: Copyright ©1994, TechPool Studios Corp. USA (some of these images have been modified); Totem Graphics, for clipart; Corel Corporation, for vector art from the Corel MEGAGALLERY collection.

Index